Encyclopaedic Dictionary of

# BIOLOGICAL SCIENCES

# ENCYCLOPAEDIC DICTIONARY OF BIOLOGICAL SCIENCES

**Vol. 2**

K. NARANG
R. RANI
M. PRAKASH

**ANMOL PUBLICATIONS PVT LTD**
**New Delhi-110002**

**ANMOL PUBLICATIONS PVT LTD**
4374/4B, Ansari Road
Daryaganj, New Delhi-110 002

*Encyclopaedic Dictionary of Biological Sciences*



First Edition, 1991
ISBN 81-7041-462-8 (Set)
ISBN 81-7041-464-4 (Vol.2)
**Reprint 1994**
**Reprint ... 1998**

**PRINTED IN INDIA**
Published by J.L. Kumar for Anmol Publications Pvt. Ltd. New Delhi and Printed at Mehra Offset Press.

# Preface

The *Encyclopaedic Dictionary of Biological Sciences* (set of six volumes) has been carefully compiled and edited to meet the long felt needs of increasingly large number of, those who have to deal with the different aspects of biological sciences in colleges, universities, and research institutes. These volumes provide a speedy means of reference to easily interpreted definitions of the terms selected from botany, zoology, environmental science, ecology, genetics, biochemistry, forestry, agriculture geomorphology, cell biology, plant pathology, anatomy, evolution and ecology.

This set of dictionary is more or less encyclopaedic in its contents and style of representation which is evident from the comprehensiveness of its coverage and contextual relevance of explanations with illustrations and chemical formulae wherever necessary.

The entries in this dictionary have been written in a clear and explanatory style to provide both straight forward definitions and invaluable background information. The presentation throughout has been aimed at sustaining the interest of readers while enriching their vocabulary and comprehension of technical terms and expressions.

Throughout the process of compilation and editing these volumes our sincere effort was to make the dictionary as a ready reference for undergraduate and post graduate biological, agricultural, environmental, medical, marine and biochemistry students and also for those appearing for competitive examinations, research scholars, teachers and authors.

The editors express their thanks to their friends and colleagues whose continuous inspiration have initiated them to bring out these volumes.

**The Editors**

# Preface

[illegible]

[illegible]

[illegible]

[illegible]

[illegible]

[illegible]

# B

**B.** A class of flowers in which their nectar is fully concealed.

**B¹.** A class a flowers which are similar to B but having the flowers in heads.

**B-lymphocyte.** Kind of lymphocyte which is originating from bone marrow. It is the precursor of the plasma cells that secrete antibody.

**Babbler.** The name given to various unrelated birds with a loud and varied call. Most live in south-eastern Asia but there are babblers in Australia and one species, the wren-tit. lives in North America. Babblers live near the ground in the forests, searching for berries and insects in the undergrowth.

**Baboon.** A mainly ground-living primate of Africa which lives in highly organized family groups called troops. Baboons forage on a wide variety of food during the day and sleep in the safety of trees at night. Lions are their chief enemy.

**Bacca.** A berry which is formed from an inferior ovary. It means a berry to general.

**Baccate.** Shaped like a berry as, for example, the arils of yew (Taxus baccata).

**Baccaurea** (family Euphorbiaceae). Genus of small, dioecious trees in which the flowers are borne in clustered spikes or racemes, some cauliflorous. The fruit has a firm, fleshy pericarp which sometimes splits, and 1-6 large seeds, each with a juicy, sour jacket. Several species are edible, and some are cultivated. There are 80 species, occurring in lowland rain forest from Malesia to the Pacific islands.

**Bacciferous.** Producing berries.

**Bacciform.** Shaped like a berry.

**Baccivorous.** Feeding principally upon berries.

**Bacillaceae.** Fomily of bacteria in which the cells are mostly rod-shaped. Members are characterized by the formation of a type of differentiated resting cell, an endospore, which is highly resistant to adverse environmental conditions, *e.g.*, desiccation, or high temperatures. There are several genera, found in a wide range of habitats. Some can cause disease.

**Bacillariophyceae** (diatoms). Class of algae which are mostly unicellular, but which may be colonial or filamentous. The cell wall (frustule) is composed of silica and consists of two halves, one of which overlaps the other like the lid on a box. The frustule is commonly delicately ornamented. Most diatoms are photosynthetic, but there are also species which lack chlorophyll and live heterotrophically among decaying marine algae. Some species are capable of a gliding motility when in contact with a surface Cells with bilateral symmetry are said to be pennate, while those with radial symmetry are called centric. Pennate diatoms are found in both freshwater and marine habitats, either as plankton or attached to rocks, etc.; centric diatoms are predominantly marine.

**Bacillariophyta** (diatoms). A division of unicellular or colonial nonflagellate algae having delicately sculptured silica cell walls divided into two overlapping halves (frustule). Asexual reproduction is by fission and auxospore formation. There are two classes, the radially symmetrical or centric diatoms and the bilaterally symmetrical or pennate diatoms The cell walls are extremely resistant to decay and form deep deposits of diatomaceous earth or kieselguhr in lake and ocean beds. Diatoms are sometimes considered as a class, the Bacillariophyceae, of the divison Chrysophyta.

**Bacillary**

1. Rod-shaped; composed of rod-shaped structures.

2. Of, pertaining to, or caused by bacilli.

**Bacilliform**. Rod-shaped.

**Bacillus**. Any rod-shaped bacterium. Generally, bacilli are large, Gram-positive, spore-bearing, and have a tendency to form chains and produce a capsule. Some are motile, bearing flagella. They are ubiquitous in soil and air and many are responsible for food spoilage. The group also includes Bacillus anthracis, which causes anthrax.

**Bacitracin**. An antibiotic produced by Bacillus subtilis, effective especially against gram-positive bacteria.

**Backbone**. The spinal or verterbal column.

**Backcross**. A cross between an individual and one of its parents. If the organism is short lived this may not be a practical possibility, in which case the term refers to a cross between an individual and an organism genetically identical to one of its parents. A backcross performed to ascertain the genotype of an individual is termed a test cross.

**Back Cross** (test cross). A mating made to identify hidden recessive alleles. If an organism displays a dominant characteristic, it may possess two dominant alleles (*i.e.*, it is homozygous) or a dominant and a recessive allele for that characteristic (*i.e.*, it is heterozygous). To find out which is the case, the organism is crossed with one displaying the recessive characteristic. If all the offspring show the dominant characteristic then the organism is homozygous, but if half show the recessive characteristic, then the organism is heterozygous.

**Backcrossing.** A technique used in plant breeding to introduce a desirable gene into a cultivated variety. Unlike the pedigree method of plant breeding, the aim of a backcrossing programme is not to create entirely new varieties but to modify existing varieties.

The cultivated variety (the recurrent parent) is crossed with the donor parent, which may be quite useless agriculturally except for its possession of one particularly valued gene (*e.g.*, for disease resistance). The progeny from this cross, which contain 50% of the donor genetic material, are screened for the character and those possessing disease resistance are crossed back to the recurrent parent. The progeny of this cross—the first backcross generation ($B_1$)—now contain 25% of the genetic material of the donor. The plants are again screened, the resistant plants again backcrossed to the recurrent parent, and this process is repeated until about the seventh or eighth backcross generation, by which time less than 0.25% of the donor genetic material remains. At this stage the $B_7$ or $B_8$ generation plants are selfed (crossed with each other) to produce plants homozygous for disease resistance; these may be identified by a test cross.

The process described above assumes the allele for disease resistance is dominant. If it were recessive then it is necessary to alternate backcrossing with selfind of the backcross generations. Backcrossing is more efficient with self-pollinating species but the method is not necessarily limited to self pollinators.

**Back-scattered Electron Imaging.** In scanning electron microscopy, the use of a special detector to produce an image from the back-scattered electrons given off from below the surface of the specimen rather than the secondary electrons used in conventional imaging. The image obtained consequently includes subsurface information.

**Backswimmer.** A group of true bugs which swim upside down in ponds and streams, using their back legs as 'oars'. They eat tadpoles and other water animals and can give a painful bite. When diving, backswimmers trap a bubble of air against their abdomen. They are sometimes called water boatmen, though the true water boatmen form a separate group.

**Bacteria.** Minute, single-celled organisms, so small that they cannot be seen with the naked eye. The largest are only about 0.01 mm long. Many are essential to the processes of decay, helping to break down the dead remains of plants and animals and releasing materials that plants can absorb through their roots. Others have the ability to use atmospheric nitrogen in the building up of nitrates—mineral salts that are vital for healthy plant growth.

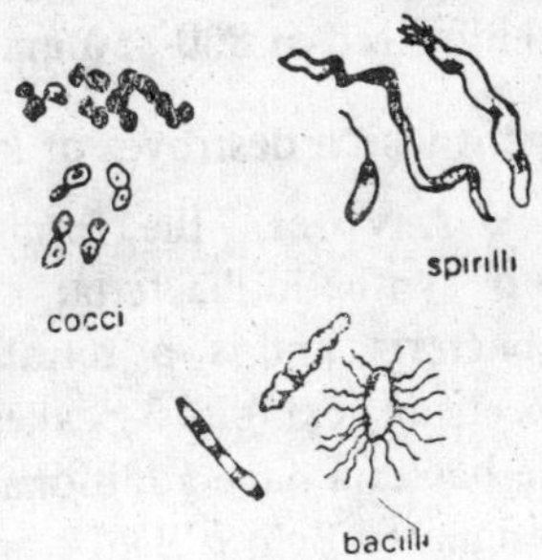


Bacteria

Many of the bacteria present in the gut of animals break down food materials and thus provide substances that the animal would otherwise be unable to obtain. The most obvious effect of bacterial activity, however, is disease. Only a small proportion of the species of bacteria are harmful, but even so the list of diseases that they cause is a lengthy one. Bacteria may be arranged into three groups according to their shape: rod-shaped forms (bacilli), spherical forms (cocci); and curved or spiral forms (spirilli).

**Bacterial Transformation.** The incorporation of genetic material into a bacterium from DNA in the surrounding medium. The phenomenon was discovered by F. Griffith (1928) who converted (transformed) rough-coated Diplococcus pneumoniae into a smooth-coated strain by mixing it with extracts from the latter under appropriate conditions. Later O. T. Avery, C.M. MacLeod, and M. MaCarty (1944) showed that the substance responsible for the transformation was DNA. The latter experiment is often quoted as one of the first pieces of evidence that DNA, not protein, is the genetic material.

**Bacteriochlorophyll.** Chlorophyll occurring in small vesicular bodies attached to the cell membrane in photosynthetic bacteria. It differs from the chlorophyll found in higher plants in that the double bond between $C_3$ and $C_4$ is replaced by a single bond and the vinyl group at $C_2$ is replaced by an acetyl group. As a result of this some of the major absorption bands of bacteriochlorophyll are displaced to the far-red at 800-850 nm.

**Bactericide.** An agent which destroyes or kills bacteria.

**Bacteriochlorophyll.** Any of the forms of chlorophylls found in photo synthetic bacteria. Bacteriochlorophyll occurs in all bacteria, and is a tetrahydroporphyrin. Its absorption spectrum exhibits 3 peakes at 365, 605 and 770 nm. Some bacteria have additional forms of bacteriochlorophyll designated Bchl *b* Bchl *c* and Bchl *d*.

**Bacteriocidal.** Capable of killing bacteria Common bacteriocides are some antibiotics, antiseptics, and disinfectants. Compare bacteriostatic.

**Bacterioclasis.** Disintegration of bacteria.

**Bacteriods.** Irregular, enlarged forms of rod-shaped bacteria especially of the root-nodule forming species. These are ultimately absorbed by the cells of the root-nodule.

**Bacteriods.** A Rhizobium bacterium present in a root nodule after it gets increased in size (about 40 times its original size) and changed in shape to a characteristic X-or Y-shaped cell. They lose the capacity of autonomous growth and become totally dependent on the host. In this metamorphosed state, bacteria bring about nitrogen fixation.

**Bacteriology.** The science which deals with bacteria.

**Bacteriolysin.** An antibody which, in the presence of the complement, causes the dissolution of the bacteria which are its antigen.

**Bacteriolysis.** The dissolution of bacteria.

**Bacteriophage** (phage). A virus that is parasitic within bacteria. Each phage is specific for only one type of bacterium. Phage infect, quickly multiply within, and destroy their host cells. They are used experimentally to identify bacteria, to control manufacturing processes (such as cheese production) that depend on bacteria, and, because they can alter the genetic make-up of bacterial cell, they are important tools in genetic engineering.

**Bacteriorhiza.** A symbiosis taking place between a root and bacteria.

**Bacteriostatic.** Capable of inhibiting or slowing down the growth and reproduction of bacteria. Some antibiotics are bacteriostatic. Compare bacteriocidal.

**Bacterium.** A single-celled organism usually classed as a plant and visible only through a microscope. Millions of bacteria are on everything we touch, including our own skin. They play an important part in breaking down dead matter in the soil, and are able to survive in places where no other living things can, for example, in hot springs. Bacteria multiply at an enormous rate by splitting into two every half hour or so. Some cause disease, while others are useful in medicine. Some bacteria are needed to make certain foods, including cheese.

**Bacteroid.** A Rhizobium bacterium in a legume root nodule after it has undergone a n increase in size (to about forty times its original size) and a change in shape to a characteristic X-or Y-shaped cell. Bacteroids lose their capacity for autonomous growth and are dependent on the host. It is in this metamorphosed state that the bacteria carry out nitrogen fixation.

**Bacteroides** (family Bacteroidaceae). Genus of Gram-negative bacteria which can grow only in the absence of air. They are found in the lower intestine of humans and other animals, in the rumen, and in sewage. Some species can act as 'opportunist' pathogens and have been isolated from various soft-tissue infections. There are many species.

**Baculum**. The penis bone (os penis, os priapi) a heterotopic bone present in the penis of various male mammals (insectivores, bats, rodents, carnivores, and primates, except man).

**Badger**. A stout-bodied, burrowing carnivore of the family Mustelidae. A common American species is Taxidea taxus, European species is Meles.

**Badlands**. Term originally applied to the intricately eroded plateau country of S. Dakota, Nebraska, and N. Dakota, USA, but now widened to refer to any barren terrain that has been similarly dissected. It is most common in areas of infrequent but intense rainfall and little vegetation cover.

**Bagridae** (bagrid catfish; class Osteichthyes, subclass Actinopterygii, order Siluriformes). Large family of freshwater catfish which are recognizable by a large, adipose dorsal fin, small eyes, and four pairs of barbels around the mouth. Many of the smaller species are of interest to aquarium hobbyists. Some (*e.g.* Bagrus docmac from Africa) may reach a length of up to 1 m. The family is distributed widely in tropical Africa and Asia.

**Bagworm**. The name given to various moths whose caterpillars make little cases from silk and plant fragments. Most of them feed on trees, and some are considerable pests. When ready to pupate, the bagworm larva fixes its case to a twing and pupates inside it. The female adult is wingless and usually remains inside the case. The male is fully winged and active,

**Bagworm Moth**. A moth so named because its larva makes a 'bag' of silk interwoven with leaf and twig fragments, and carries this around. When the larva or bagworm is ready to pupate it attaches the case to a twig and pupates inside it. Female bagworm moths have neither wings nor legs, and they remain permanently inside the larval case. The males do have wings and emerge in the early summer to fly by day.

**Bajada** (bahada). Extensive, gently sloping plain of unconsolidated rock debris resting against the foot of a mountain front in a semi-arid environment. Typically it is made of a number of coalescing alluvial fans laid down by ephemeral streams as their gradients lessen on leaving the mountain zone. Material is also supplied by the weathering of the mountain front. Alternatively, it may comprise the alluvial accumulation on the lower part of a pediment.

**Bakanae Disease** (foolish seedling disease). Important disease of rice in which early symptoms include excessive growth of the stem. The disease is caused by the fungus Gibberlla fujikuroi.

**Balaenicipitidae** (shoe-bill; order Ciconiiformes). Monotypic genus, comprising Balaeniceps rex, a grey, stork-like bird with a huge, broad, flattened bill. It is found in swamps feeding on fish, and it nests on the ground. It occurs in tropical E. Africa.

**Balaenidal** (order Cetacea, suborder Mysticeti). Family comprising the right and bowhead whales. The body is robust, the snout blunt, the throat ungrooved. A dorsal fin is present in some species. The flippers are broad and short. The posterior margin of the tail is notched as the midline.

The cervical vertebrae are fused. The baleen plates are long and narrow, and left and right rows are separated anteriorly. The animals are dark grey or black and feed on plankton. Balaena mysticetus (bowhead whale) is confined to northern waters, Caperea (pygmy right whale) to the southern hemisphere, and B. glacialis (right whale) occurs in both hemispheres. They grow to about 6 m (Caperea) or 20 m (Balaena). There are two genera, and three species.

**Balaenopteridae** (Order Cetacea, suborder Mysticeti). Family that includes the fin, humpback, and blue whales. The body is streamlined, the shout pointed, the throat and chest grooved. The dorsal fin is hooked and set far back on the body. The tail is slightly notched at the midline, and scalloped along the posterior edge. The cervical vertebrae are not fused. The baleen plates are broad and short, the left and right rows being joined anteriorly. The animals are typically grey on the dorsal surface, with some white on the ventral surface; but Megaptera (*e.g.* M. novaengliae, humpback) may be black above and below, with white flippers. They feed on krill and small fish, and occur in both hemispheres. They grow to 7-30 m depending on species. There are six species, in two genera : Balaenoptera (*e.g.* B. acutorostrata, minke or lesser rorqual; B. borealis, sei; B. physalus, fin; B. musculus, blue; B. edeni, Bryde's) and Megaptera.

**Balance.** The adjustment of the genetic material of an individual to permit for the healthy growth and development of the individual.

**Balanced Carrier.** An individual whose karyotype is abnormal but who nevertheless is having a normal chromosomal complement. Usually the result of translocation.

**Balanced Polymorphism.** Genetic polymorphism that is stable, and is maintained in a population by natural selection, because the heterozygotes for particular alleles have a higher adaptive value (fitness) than either homozygote.

This condition is also referred to as overdominance, as opposed to underdominance where the homozygote has a lower fitness, giving rise to unstable equilibrium.

**Balancer**

1. A halter.
2. One of a pair of lateral appendages extending from the angle of the mouth in certain immature salamanders.

**Balancing Organ.** A receptor which functions in the maintenance of posture and equilibrium.

**Balanidae** (acron barnacles; order Thoracica, suborder Balanomorpha). Family of radially symmetrical, balanomorph barnacles in which the third pair of cerci resemble the second rather than the fourth, and in which there are no caudal appendages. The family includes the familiar barnacles exposed at low tide, of the genus **Balanus**, which has been divided into 10 subgenera.

**Balanophoraceae.** Family of plants which are obligate parasites attached to roots. A tuberous, subterranean, knobbly rhizome with no chlorophyll bears stout aerial spikes on which are borne minute male and female flowers and then tiny nuts, or drupes. There are 18 genera, and 120 species, occurring in rain forests throughout the tropics.

**Balanopsidaceae** (Balanopaceae; order Fagales). Small family of dicotyledonous trees and shrubs. The leaves are alternate or whorled. Tne flowers are simple; male flowers are borne in catkins on separate trees from the female flowers, which are solitary with scale-like perianths. The fruit is an acorn-like drupe. The family comprises one genus, with 12 species, native to Queensland and the SW Pacific.

**Balausta.** The fruit of the pomenanate, a many-seeded, indehiscent fruit with a thick, toughouned.

**Balbiani Ring** (chromosome puff). A swollen region of polytene chromosome which corresponds to a site where mRNA synthesis is taking place actively. Although polytene chromosomes are occurring in dipterous insects, formation of such ring (puffing phenommenon) is assumed to have wider genetic significance.

**Bald Eagle**. This striking bird used to be found all over North America and it was adopted as the emblem of the United States. Today it is extremely rare. It is not really bald; it gets its name from the pure white feathers on its head and neck, which contrast vividly with the brown feathers on the rest of the body. The bald eagle feeds mainly on fish.

**Baleen.** Horny plates of the protein keratin which hang down from the upper jaw of toothless whales. Also known as whalebone. The whales filter water through the plates to catch the tiny crustaceans on which they feed.

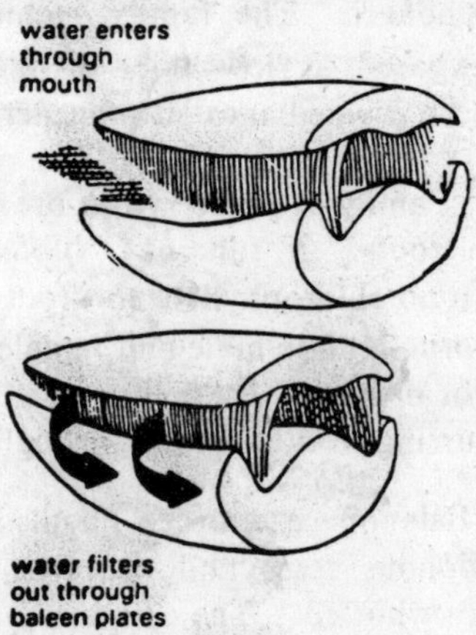


**Baleen**

**Ballistospore.** A spore that is violently projected, *e.g.* the basidiospores of the Hymenomycetes.

**Ballooning.** A method of transport employed by young spiderlings in which secreted strands of silk are caught by air currents and the young are carried considerable distances.

**Balm**. A white-flowered, lemon-scented herb used for cooking and often for medicine. It is of medium height with whorls of pointed oval leaves.

**Balsam**. A family of hairless plants with fleshy stems, easily recognized by their spurred, two-lipped flowers. One species is often called touch-me-not as the fruit bursts at the slightest touch. It has bright yellow flowers. The more common Himalayan or Indian balsam was introduced from Asia. It has large pink flowers and grows by fresh water.

**Balsaminaceae**. Family of herbs with brittle, translucent stems, and simple leaves. The flowers have 3-5 sepals and five petals, usually all coloured and strongly zygomorphic, the lowest sepal being large, spurred, and petal-like. The fruits are capsules, exploding if touched when ripe. Several are cultivated for their showy flowers. There are two genera, one (Hydrocera) monotypic, occurring only in SE Asia, the other (Impatiens) (balsams, or touch-me-nots) of more than 200 species, mostly of tropical Asia and Africa, but with a few in northern temperate America and Eurasia, and in S. Africa.

**Bamboo**. Any of a number of woody, arborescent grasses of the family Gramineae, which grow in most tropical countries. Their hollow, woody stems are used extensively in furniture making and in various types of construction. An example is Dendrocalamus, the giant bamboo.

**Bamboo Worm**. Axiothella, a tube-dwelling polychaete worm, whose tube resembles the stem of a bamboo plant.

**Bambusaceae** (bamboos). Family closely related to the grasses (Gramineae) and sometimes considered to be a subfamily (Bambusoideae) of them. Nearly all have woody stems, a few are herbs. The tallest grow to 40 m, the stoutest to 90 cm girth. Usually they are clump-forming, with a big underground rhizome. They fruit annually, or at long intervals, and then die. The fruit is dry, or occasionally fleshy. Many are of major economic importance for building, scaffolding, or paper making, or for the edible young shoot tip. Some whole cultures in Asia are based on bamboos. There are about 45 genera, mainly tropical and subtropical, and most diverse in S. America.

**Banana**. A tropical plant producing large clusters of long yellow fruit. Its leaf-stalks grow together to resemble a woody trunk. There are many varieties, whose fruits vary in sweetness. Some particularly starchy forms are called plantains. Cultivated varieties generally have no seeds and are grown from cuttings.

**Band**. Vertical stripe on a polytene chromosome resulting from the specific association of a large number of chromomeres (small band-like structures visible on a chromosome during prophase of meiosis and mitosis). The most commonly examined polytene chromosomes are in the salivary-gland nuclei of insects, and recent studies of Drosophila suggest that each band contains the genetic material of a single gene. However, the significance of the bands in human and other chromosomes is not known.

**Bandar**. Macaque.

**Bandicoot**

1. A small insectivorous and vegetarian marsupial of the genera Perameles and Thylacomys found in Australia.

2. A large rat of southern Asia of the genus Nesokia.

**Bangiales** (class Rhodophyceae). Order of red algae which are fairly simple in their structural organization. Two common genera are Bangia and Porphyra; Bangia is filamentous and can live in freshwater and marine habitats, while Porphyra is membranaceous and is found in intertidal regions on temperate coasts.

**Bangioidcae** (Banglophycidae). Rhodophyta.

**Banjosidae** (class Osteichthyes, subclass Actinopterygii, order Perciformes). Monospecific family of marine fish which have a deep, compressed body, and fairly large eyes, the head showing a steep profile. The first dorsal fin, with 10 spiny rays, is separated by a deep notch from the second dorsal fin, consisting of 12 soft rays. The second of the three anal spines is much larger than the other two. Greenish along the back and silvery along the sides, Banjos banjos (30 cm) is of some commercial importance to local fisheries along the coasts of China and Japan.

**Bankfull Discharge.** Maximum amount of discharge (usually measured in $m^3/s$) that a stream channel can carry without overflowing. Its frequency varies between streams, from a few times each year to once every few years. The water height at bankfull discharge is referred to as the 'bankfull stage'.

**Banner.** The broad uppermost petal in an irregular flower, as that of members of the pea family. Also called standard, vexillum.

**Banteng**. Bibos sondaicus, a large ox of Southest Asia occurring both wild and domesticated.

**Banyan.** An Indian fig tree whose branches send out roots which descend to the ground and form trunks. A large banyan can look like a small forest because it has so many trunks. The banyan often starts life on the branch of another tree, from a seed dropped there by a bird.

**Baobab.** An African tree with a very thick trunk, up to 15 metres in diameter. It has gourd-like fruit, called monkey bread.

**BAP** (6-benzylaminopurine, benzyl-adenine). A synthetic cytokinin.

**Baptornis Advenus.** Grebe like, fish-eating bird from the Upper Cretaceous. Baptornis is recordad from N. America. Like modern divers, it had rather poorly developed wings. Described by Marsh in 1877, Baptornis is known only from disarticulated bones.

**Bar**

1. Unit of pressure, equal to one million dynes per square centimetre. The pressure of the atmosphere at sea-level on average is very approximately one bar, or about 1013 millibars (the bar commonly being divided into one thousand millibars).

2. Geomorphological term: (a) Low ridge of sand or shingle laid down by marine aggradation in shallow water adjacent to a coastline. There are several varieties; a bay bar joins the two flanks of a bay and may enclose a lagoon; an offshore or barrier bar runs parallel to a coastline and up to 40 km distant. (b) Rocky obstruction across a glaciated valley. Glacial stairway. (c) Lobate river bedform, typically constructed of gravel, often regularly spaced, and forming a riffle or shallow section. (d) Point bar : a low crescentic shoal on the convex side (inside) of a

river bend, consisting of material that has been eroded from the outside bend either opposite or upstream. Point-bar deposits consist of gravel, pebbles, and boulders, often showing an upstream dip ('imbricate structure').

**Barb**

1. (in zoology). Any one of the stiff filaments forming a row on each side of the longitudinal shaft of a feather. Together the barbs form the expanded part (vane) of the feather.

2. (in botany) A hooked hair.

**Barbary Ape.** This is not an ape at all, but a monkey of the macaque family. It is about 60 cm long and has an extremely short tail. Barbary apes live in North Africa and a small colony lives in Gibraltar.

**Barbary Sheep.** Found in the mountains of north-western Africa, this sheep has a long mane, particularly in the male : it grows on the underside of the neck and reaches down the front legs.

**Barbed.** Having a barb or barbs; with short, pointed, and usually reflexed awns or bristles.

**Barbel**

1. A freshwater fish belonging to the carp family, that gets its name from the four barbels on its upper lip. It lives in clear, fast-flowing stretches of rivers during the summer, and spends the winter hibernating in large shoals in deeper water.

2. A fleshy filament hanging from a fish's mouth.

**Barbellate.** Finely barbed.

**Barber Fish**. These fishes come from a wide range of families and are also called cleaner fishes. They feed on the parasites attached to other fishes. While this takes place, the fish being cleaned co-operates with the barber, even allowing it to enter the mouth and gill cavities.

**Barberry.** A low spiny shrub with yellow flowers in drooping spikes. It produces bright red berries and is found in hedgerows and scrubland.

**Barbet.** A group of colourful birds related to woodpeckers. They live in the tropical forests of America, Africa and Asia, feeding mainly on fruit.

**Barbula** (order Pottiales). Large genus of mosses, species of which are not always easy to distinguish. The plants are mostly small, forming tufts, cushions, or short turfs. Leaves may be blunt or pointed, but lack the hair-point typical of the related genus Tortula. Capsules are cylindrical and erect, with an oblique, beaked lid; the peristome has short, straight teeth in some species (*e.g.*, B. tophacea and B. recurvirostra) and long, twisted teeth in others (*e.g.*, B. fallax, B. unguiculata, and B. convoluta). There are about 500 species, occurring mainly in temperate regions, and found on the ground, on walls, on garden paths, etc.

**Barbule.** Any of the minute filaments forming a row on each side of the barb of a feather. In a contour feather adjacent barbules interlock by means of hooks (barbicels) and grooves, forming a firm vane. Down feathers have no barbicels.

**Barchan.** Crescent-shaped mobile dune in a sand desert in which the wind blows predominantly from one direction. It moves by erosion of sand from the windward slope, and accumulation on the steeper lee or slip slope which stands at about 32°. Average velocities of dune movement are 10-20 m/yr.

**Barclaya** (family Nymphaeaceae). Genus of water lilies which produce large, solitary flowers, with an inferior ovary. There are three or four species, found in damp places on the floor or Indo-Malaysian tropical rain forests.

**Barfoed's Test.** A biochemical test to detect monosaccharide (reducing) sugars in solution, devised by the Swedish physician C. T. Barfoed (1815-99). Barfoed's reagent, a mixture of ethanoic (acetic) acid and copper(II) acetate, is added to the test solution and boiled. If any reducing sugars are present a red precipitate of copper(II) oxide is formed. The reaction will be negative in the presence of disaccharide sugars as they are weaker reducing agents.

**Barite** (barytes). Mineral, specific gravity 4.3-4.6, hardness 3.0-3.5, chemical composition $BaSO_4$, whose name is derived from the Greek for 'heavy'. In occurs as a vein filling, and also as a gangue mineral with ores of lead, copper, zinc, silver, iron, and nickel, associated with calcite, quartz, fluorite, dolomite, and siderite. It is a low-temperature mineral which also occurs as a replacement for limestone, and as a cement in sandstone. It is distinguished by its high specific gravity, cleavage, and insolubility in acid. It is colourless to white, often tinged yellow, brown, blue, green, and red with a white streak and a vitreous lustre. It crystallizes in the orthorhombic system. The crystals are commonly tabular, prismatic, fibrous, and lamellar, and often granular. It is used as a weighting agent in drilling muds; in the chemical industry; in the manufacture of rubber, paper, and high-quality paints; and as an X-ray absorbant.

**Bark.** All the tissues, collectively, lying outside the vascular cambium in the stems and roots of plants showing secondary growth, *i.e.*, the primary and secondary phloem, the cortex, and the periderm. The term is also used in a more restricted sense to mean the tissue arising to the outside of the phellogen, *i.e.*, the phellem, when this is exposed by the sloughing off of the epidermis. The bark of different trees can be very distinctive and its characteristics are used to aid identification. In some species the same phellogen is active each year and a thick layer consisting solely of phellem is formed (*e.g.*, oak, beech), but in most species a new phellogen arises annually in the cortex below : the bark thus consists of both phellem and dead cortex and is termed rhytidome. As the thickness of the bark increases the outer layers may either become fissured (*e.g.*, elm) or be shed as scales (*e.g.*, plane) or rings (*e.g.*, birch).

**Bark Beetle.** These insects include a variety of small species whose larvae live by tunnelling just under the bark of trees. The tunnelling activity may separate the bark completely from the wood and, if larvae are very numerous, they can kill the trees. But many species merely make small tunnel systems, doing little real harm. The elm-bark beetle carries Dutch elm disease.

**Bark Lice.** Psocids, winged insects of the order Psocoptera.

**Barley.** An important Cereal grain grown in all temperate countries. It is used as human and animal food, and to make malt. It is shallow-rooted, hardy and grows quickly. Barley is one of the oldest plants cultivated by man, being grown probably 8000 years ago in the Nile valley. Barley resembles wheat in appearance, its seeds growing in long clusters along a central spike.

**Barnacle.** A group of crustaceans related to the crabs and lobsters. Barnacle larvae swim freely but the adults usually attach themselves by the head to rocks, ships' bottoms, and sometimes other animals. They are

Acorn barnacles

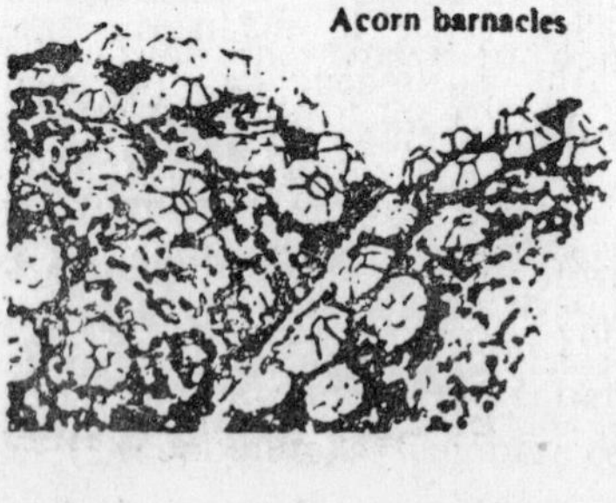

protected by chalky plates which close over the body when the animal is out of water. When under water, the plates open out and the barnacle stretches out its feathery legs which act as combs to trap food. The acorn barnacle, whose white cones are found all over rocks on the shore, is the commonest species.

**Barnacle Goose.** This bird was so named because it was once thought to hatch from the goose barnacle (a small crustacean of the seashore). It is a mostly grey goose, with a black neck and white face. It breeds in the Arctic and flies south to winter in warmer regions, where it lives in saltmarshes and estuaries.

**Barn Owl.** A family of owls with heart-shaped faces. There are 10 species, of which only one is commonly found in Europe. Those living in the British Isles and south-western Europe have white breasts, while those further east are darker-breasted. They nest in barns, church towers and similar buildings and can sometimes be seen flying by day. They are also called white owls, or screech owls after their long, strangled cry.

**Baroceptor.** A pressure receptor as that in the wall of certain blood vessels. Also called pressoreceptor or baroreceptor.

**Barometer.** Instrument for the measurement of atmospheric pressure. The usual type is a mercury barometer, in which the atmosphere's pressure on a small reservoir of mercury supports a column of mercury in a vacuum tube the open end of which is below the surface of the mercury in the reservoir. The column is on average about 76 cm (30 inches) high. Readings must be corrected to compensate for pressure variation due to gravitational anomalies and for thermal expansion or contraction of the mercury, therefore correction to a standard temperature is necessary.

**Baroreceptor.** A receptor that responds to changes in pressure. The carotid sinus in the carotid artery contains baroreceptors that respond to changes in arterial pressure and are therefore involved in the regulation of blood pressure and heart beat.

**Barracuda.** A large, carnivorous marine fish of the family Sphyraenidae, order Percomorpha, as Sphyraena barracuda, the giant barracuda.

**Barr Body.** The condensed single X-chromosome, appearing as a densely-staining mass, found in the nuclei of somatic cells of female mammals. It is named after its discoverer, Murray Barr. It is derived from one of the two X-chromosomes, which becomes inactivated. The number of Barr bodies is thus one less than the number of X-chromosomes. Barr bodies are commonly referred to as sex chromatin. The human abnormalities called Kleinefelter's syndrome and Turner's syndrome both result from an unnatural presence or absence of a Barr body. In the case of the former, the male possesses a Barr body that he would normally not have, and in the latter case the Barr body is absent.

**Barrier**

1. An obstacle or obstruction.
2. *biol.* That which prevents the spread or distribution of animals or plants.

**Barrier Island.** Segmented barrier-bar complex found between two tidal inlets. Barrier-island systems have a lagoonal area on their landward side, and often have dunes and vegetation on the exposed barrier. There are three main hypotheses to explain the origin of barrier islands : (a) the building up of submarine bars; (b) spit progradation parallel to the coast and segmentation by inlets; and (c) submergence of subaerial coastal beach ridges by a rise in sea-level. Barrier islands are most common in areas of low tidal range.

**Barrier Reef.** Reef trending parallel to, but separated by a lagoon from, a shore. The reef-building organisms build up the structure to approximately the low-tide level. One of the finest examples is the Great Barrier Reef which lies off the NW coast of Australia; it extends for about 1900 km and is 30-160 km in width.

**Barringtonia** (family Lecythidaceae). Genus of mostly small tropical trees whose flowers are nocturnal, sweet-scented, borne in spikes, and often cauliflorous. They have many stamens, and the ovary is inferior. The fruits are indehiscent, with one seed. B, asiatico is a widespread species found along sandy coasts. There are 40 species, occurring in Africa, Madagascar, and from Indo-Malaysia to the Pacific.

**Barrow.** A castrated male hog.

**Bartsia.** A short plant with spikes of two-lipped flowers. The most common species, the red bartsia, is often tinged purple with purple flowers. It is found on waste ground.

**Basal**

1. Basic, fundamental.
2. Located at or near the base of a structure.

**Basal Body** (Blepharoplast Kinetosome). A body which is found at the base of all cilia and flagella. It is identical in structure to the centriole. It is essential for formation of cilia and flagella.

**Basal Cell**

1. Used for the lewest cell which is cut off from the antheridial initial of the Filicales and Hepaticae.
2. Used for the lower cell which is cut off from the antheridial initial of the Heparicae. It remains sterile.
3. Used for one of the pair of cells formed by the initial division of a germinating spore of the Lycopodinae, in the early stages of the development of the gametophyte. It gives rise to a rudimentary rhizoidal cell.

4. A uninucleate cell which may be the oogonium in the Uredinales.

**Basal Disc.** The flattened, adhesive disc of various coelenterate polyps or other sessile animals.

**Basal Ganglia.** Small masses of nervous tissue within the brain that connect the cerebrum with other parts of the nervous system. They are involved with the subconscious regulation of voluntary movements.

**Basal Granule.** A kinetosome.

**Basalia.** One of three basal cartilages in the fins of elasmobranh fishes, designated pro-, meso-, and metapterygium.

**Basal Lamina.** Thin layer of collagen-like protein which is secreted by epithelial and some other cells. It is visible by electron microscopy close to the cell surface on the basal side of epithelia. It is 500-1000 Å units thick.

**Basal Metabolic Rate** (BMR). The rate of energy metabolism required to maintain an animal at rest. BMR is measured in terms of heat production per unit time: it indicates the energy consumed in order to sustain such vital functions as heartbeat, breathing, nervous activity, active transport, and secretion. Different tissues have different metabolic rates (*e.g.*, the BMR of brain tissue is much greater than that of bone tissue) and therefore the tissue composition of an animal determines its overall BMR. For any comparable group of animals (such as mammals) BMR is proportional to body weight according to the allometric equation (allometric growth); small animals tend to have a higher metabolic rate per unit weight than large ones.

**Basal Placentation.** A form of placentation, found in ovaries containing only one ovule, in which the placenta develops at the base of the ovary. It is seen in bistorts (Polygonum).

**Basapophyses.** The ventrolateral processes of oustrum, remnants of a haemal arch.

**Base**

1. *biot.* *a.* The lowest part of a body or structure; *b.* The portion upon which a structure rests; *c.* The broadest portion of a cone-shaped structure.

2. *chem.* *a.* A substance which neutralizes an acid and turns litmus blue. *b.* A substance which furnishes hydroxyl (OH) ions and a positive ion, usually a metal. *c.* An ion or molecule which will combine with a proton. *d.* An alkali.

**Base Analogue.** Purine or pyrimidine base that differs slightly in structure from the normal base, but that because of its similarity to that base may act as a mutagen when incorporated into DNA. Once in place, these bases, which have pairing properties unlike those of the bases they replace, can produce mutations by causing insertions of incorrect nucleotides opposite them during replication. Though the original base analogue exists only in a single strand, it can cause a nucleotide-pair substitution that is replicated in all DNA copies descended from that original strand. An example is 5-bromouracil (5BU), an analogue of thymine that has bromine at the $C_5$ position in place of the $CH_3$ group found in thymine.

**Basement Membrane.** Delicate intercellular membrane. It becomes visible in light microscope. It underlies most animal epithelia. Besides the basal lamina, it consists of mucopolysaccharide and very fine (reticulin) fibres.

**Base Number** (Basic number). The number of chromosomes present in the characteristic genome of an organism, generally between 6 and 13 and represented by symbol X.

**Base Pair.** One of the pairs of bases forming the cross-links in the DNA molecule. They are always paired in the following manner : Adenine and Thymine, Guanine and Cytosine or 5-methyl cytosine.

**Base Pairing.** The chemical linking of two complementary nitrogenous bases in DNA and in certain types of RNA molecules. the four such bases in DNA, adenine pairs with thymine and cytosine with guanine. In RNA, thymine is replaced by uracil. Base pairing is responsible for holding together the two strands of a DNA molecule to form a double helix and for faithful reproduction and reading of the genetic code. The links between bases take the form of hydrogen bonds.

**Base Ratio.** A comparison of the molar quantities of one base to another base in DNA, or of one base pair with another base pair. The observation that the amount of adenine (A) always equals the amount ot thymine (T) and similarly the amount of guanine (G) equals that of cytosine (C) provided one of the first indications that adenine always pairs with thymine and guanine with cytosine in the complementary polynucleotide chains. A comparison of base pair ratios, A+T : G+C, or percentage G+C of the total, shows a constant figure within a species but differences between species.

**Base Triplet Hypothesis.** According to this hypothesis, the shortest sequence of any four bases that could specify all the types of amino acids found in proteins is three.

**Basic Grassland.** Vegetation pattern that occurs on soils with an alkaline reaction, particularly those developed in chalk or limestone. In Britain, and NW Europe generally, basic grasslands include some of the oldest areas of rough grazing, dating from Neolithic times. Floristically they are comparatively diverse and there are numerous characteristic herbs other than grasses.

**Basic Number.** Genome.

**Basic Stain.** Staining.

**Basidiocarp.** The reproductive organ of all basidiomycete fungi (except the Ustilaginales and Uredinales), which bears the basidia (basidium). It may be mushroom shaped, bracket shaped, club shaped, or a hollow sphere or cylinder. Much of the basidiocarp is composed of sterile pseudoparenchymatous tissue. The basidia are borne in a fertile layer, the hymenium.

**Basidiomycete.** The basidiomycetes form one of the major groups of fungi. The fruiting bodies form spores on the

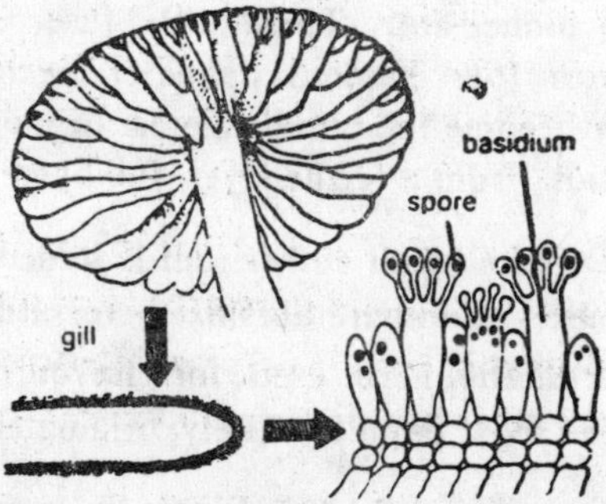


Basidiomycete

outside of club-shaped cells called basidia. All the umbrella-shaped toadstools are basidiomycetes, as are puffballs, bracket fungi, parasitic rusts and many others.

**Basidiomycotina**. A subdivision containing the most advanced fungi of the Eumycota, which are characterized by the production of basidia. The mycelium, which may be uninucleate or dikaryotic, is typically divided by inflated septa with a central pore (dolipore septum). In dikaryotic, mycelia, characteristic clamp connection are seen. The Basidiomycotina contains over 12 000 species in some 900 genera and is divided into the theree classes Teliomycetes, Hymenomycetes, and Gasteromycetes. In some classifications these fungi are grouped in the class Basidiomycetes, which is then divided into the subclasses Heterobasidiomycetidae, in which the basidium in deeply divided or septate (*e.g.*, rusts and smuts), and Homobasidiomycetidae, in which the basidium is a single large cell.

**Basidiospore.** A haploid spore, four of which are characteristically borne on the outer surface of a basidium.

**Basidium.** The spore-bearing structure of fungi in the Basidiomycotina. Each basidium usually bears four basidiospores on its outer surface, often on projections called sterigmata. The basidium is usually a single cell but in some basidiomycetes (*e.g.* Ustilaginales and Uredinales) it is segmented. The basidium is initially binucleate. These nuclei fuse, undergo meiosis, and form four haploid daughter nuclei, which subsequently become the basidiospores. In most basidiomyeetes the basidia from a fertile layer, the hymenium.

**Basifixed.** Describing an anther that is joined to the filament as its base. Compare dorsifixed, versatile.

**Basil.** An aromatic herb used for flavouring food. Sweet basil, the most popular variety, originated in India.

**Basilar Artery.** Blood flow to brain in human beings takes place via 2 vertebral and 2 internal carotids. The vertebral arteries get united to form basilar artery and also part of circle of Willis.

**Basilar Membrane.** A membrane which is forming the base of organ of Corti and suppoi ting the sensory cells in the cochlea of the mammalian ear. It separates the scala tympani from the scale media.

**Basileuterus** (wool-warblers; family Parulidae). Genus of small warblers, brown above and yellow below, most with coloured head stripes. They inhabit forest undergrowth, are insectivorous, and build a domed nest with a side entrance on or near the ground. There are 21 species, found in C. and S. America.

**Basiliscus** (basilisks; order Squamata, suborder Sauria (Lacertilia), family Iguanidae). Genus of arboreal, iguanid lizards which are fast, bipedal runners on land, and also over the surface of water! They are excellent swimmers. Adults develop a casque on the head, which is larger in males. They feed on fruit and small animals. They occur in Mexico and Ecuador.

**Basilisk.** A group of lizards living in tropical America. They are up to 60 cm long, and the males have a crest on the head and back. The animals always live near water and they can actually skim across the surface using only their back legs. They will also run on land in this semi-erect position. Basilisks eat small animals and insects.

**Basil, Wild.** A faintly aromatic plant, found in dry grassland or among rocks, with whorls of pink flowers.

**Basilosaurus.** Whales first appeared in the Eocene. They most likely arose from a group of carnivores during the Palaeocene, and the earliest forms possessed large saw-edged teeth. These were called archaeocetes, and Basilosaurus is one of the best-known forms. It grew to approximately 20 m in length and lived during the Upper Eocene.

**Basil-thyme.** A low, sprawling, hairy plant with violet-blue flowers. The flowers have a small white patch on the lower lip which guides bees to the nectar. Basil-thyme is usually found in fields and meadows.

**Basin.** The concave, inner portion of the sternum in birds.

**Basin-and-range Province**

1. Specifically, the structural subdivision of the western USA between the Colorado Plateau to the west and the Sierra Nevada to the east. It is dominated by a series of block-faulted ranges and troughs which dissect it, rising above bajadas and alluvial plains which mask down-faulted units. Frequently the ranges are tilted blocks approximately 30-40 km across. Movement occurred initially in Miocene times, and then during the late Pliocene to Recent.

2. Generally, applied to landscapes having a series of tilted fault blocks that form long, asymmetric ranges separated by broad basins.

**Basinerved.** Having veins extending from the base, said of leaves.

**Basipetal.** Describing movement, differentiation, etc., occurring from apex to base. For example, the direction of proto- and metaxylem formation is from the apex or nodes downwards, while the transport of auxin in the stem is generally towards the base. Compare acropetal.

**Basipodite.** The second segment of a crustacean appendage.

**Basis**

1. The attached undersurface of a sessile barnacle.

2. A basipodite.

**Basket.** A type of phylactocarp.

**Basket Star.** An echinoderm of the class Ophiuroidea, with arms which branch repeatedly and terminate in small flexible tendrils as Gorgonocephalus.

**Basking Shark.** At 15 metres this is the world's second biggest shark. It feeds by filtering plankton from water passed over a series of hormy rakers situated in the gill chambers. The sharks live singly or in shoals of up to 250 individuals. They live mostly south of Iceland but visit European waters during the summer.

**Basophil or Basophile**

1. A leukocyte with large cytoplasmic granules which stain readily with basic stains.
2. A basophilic cell of the anterior lobe of the pituitary.

**Basophilic.** Having an affinity for or staining readily with basic stains.

**Bass.** A name given to several types of fishes, both marine and freshwater. The common sea-bass is a predatory fish which lives in small shoals off rocky shores. It grows up to 80 cm long. The freshwater large-mouthed black bass Is a member of the sunperch family, that has been introduced into European rivers from North America.

**Bassarisk.** The ring-tàiled cat (Bassariscus astutus) of the family Procyonidae; cacomistle.

**Basswood.** Any of a number of species of the genus Tilla of the linden family (Tiliaceae). Also called whitewood.

**Bast.** Sometimes used to mean 'phloem' and sometimes to mean 'bast-fibre'. A very vague term which, should not be used.

**Bastard Wing.** Alula.

**Bat** The only mammal capable of flight, although several other mammals can glide. The wings are formed by large folds of skin stretched across the animal's long fingers and attached to its limbs and body. Bats are nocturnal creatures and all the European species eat insects such as moths. They have extremely poor vision, though they are not blind, and navigate in the dark by sending out high-pitched sounds which bounce off nearby objects. The bats detect these echoes with their highly sensitive ears, using the information to determine where

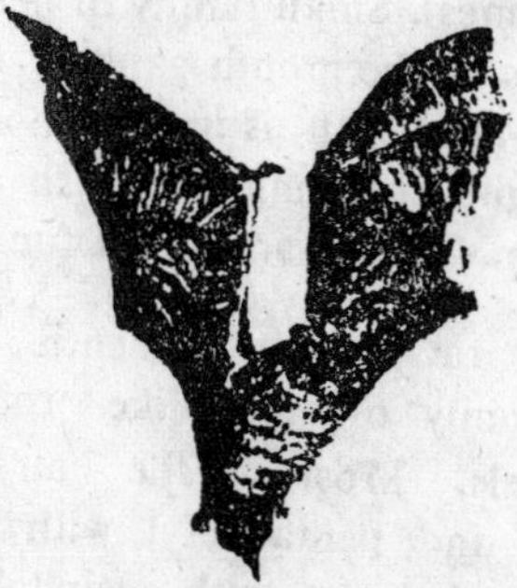

Serotine bat

the object are. In this way they can locate something as small as a moth. Bats in temperate climates hibernate during the winter, generally hanging upside-down in a dark, sheltered place.

**Bat-eared Fox.** A small fox of southern and eastern Africa with a jackal-like face and long ears measuring up to 11 cm.

**Bath Sponge.** The horny skeletons of several species of Sponge are familar in their role of the traditional bathroom sponge. These simple animals are found in warm seas, particularly the Mediterranean, down to 200 metres. Today nearly all bath 'sponges' are made of synthetic materials.

**Bathyal Zone.** Oceanic zone at depths of 200-200 m, lying to the seaward of the shallower neritic zone, and landward of the deeper abyssal zone. The upper limit of the bathyal zone is marked by the edge of the continental shelf. In marine ecology, it is the region of the continental slope and rise. It may be geologically active, and include trenches and canyons, with underwater erosion producing avalanches.

**Batfish.** One of a number of grotesque, marine fishes, as Aetobatus, the California batfish; Dactylopterus, the flying gurnard; Ogcocephalus, the longnose seabat of the batfish family, Ogcocephalidae.

**Bathyclupeidae** (class Osteichthyes, subclass Actinopterygii, order Perciformes). Small family of deep-sea fish found in tropical waters. The mouth gape of these silvery, deep-bodied, large-eyed fish is in an almost vertical position. Physically fragile, these midwater fish are found at depths of about 500 m. There are about four species.

**Bathyergidae** (mole rats; order Rodentia, suborder Hystricomorpha). Family of mole-like rodents that live in shallow tunnels. Most of the hair is lost, the legs are short, strong, and pentadactyl, with strong claws. The skull is short and strong, with occipital and sagittal crests prominent, and paroccipital processes short. The check teeth are hypsodont, and rooted. The teeth are reduced in number. The animals are distributed throughout Africa south of the Sahara. There are about 22 species, in five genera.

**Bathymetric.** Vertical or altitudinal, with reference to distribution of organisms.

**Bathypteroidae** (class Osteichthyes, subclass Actinoaterygii, order Myctophiformes). Small family of mainly deep-water, bottom-living fish. They are distinguishable by a flattened head, minute eyes, slender body, and very long first pectoral and pelvic fins, the latter being used occasionally to 'walk' over the sea bottom. There are about eight species, including Bathypterois longipes.

**Batrachian.** A frog or toad.

**Batrachoididae** (toadfish; class Osteichthyes, subclass Actinopterygii, order Batrachoidiformes). Fairly large family of bottom-dwelling, inshore marine fish of tropical and subtropical waters. THey have a wide (toad-lihe) mouth; a large head with dorsally-positioned eyes, a short, stout body; and small gill openings. Some species, *e.g.* Opsanus tau, can produce underwater sounds by means of special muscles acting on the wall of the swim-bladder.

**Batrachostomus** (frogmouths; family Podargidae). Genus of grey-brown, cryptically-coloured, nocturnal birds, with large, wide bills. They are arboreal and insectivorous, picking insects off branches and the ground. Their nest is a pad of down secured to a horizontal branch. There are 10 species, found in India, SE Asia, Indonesia, and Malaysia.

**Battery.** In coelenterates, a cluster of nematocysts.

**Bauhinia** (family Leguminosae, subfamily Caesalpinadeae). Genus of plants, most of which are woody climbers with curiously flattened, or corrugated, stems. A few are small trees. The flowers are very showy. The leaves are simple, mare or less split into two lobes, with many main veins. Because of the bilobed leaves, the genus is named in honour of the Bauhin brothers, Jean (1541-1623) and Gaspard (1550-1624), French botanists who were also physicians and who were among the earliest workers to attempt a comprehensive taxonomic classification of plants. There are 300 species of Bauhinia, distributed through the tropics and subtropics.

**Baumgrneze.** A line, through the last of the stunted trees, marking the limit of a zone of stunted tree growth (such as is often found near the upper limits of tree growth, above the elevations at which trees grow uniformly erect and in forest densities). The individual trees are sparsely scattered, and prostrate, or almost so.

**Bay Tree.** The name of several different trees. The bay of southern Europe is an evergreen of the laurel family. It has aromatic leaves used for flavouring, and by the ancient Greeks to crown heroes. Sweet bay is an American species of magnolia.

**B-chromosome** (accessory chromosome, supernumerary chromosome). Any of a number of small chromosomes present in some organisms in addition to the fixed number of stable chromosomes characteristic of the species (the A-chromosomes). They are of widespread occurrence and have been reported in over 80 genera and 20 families of plants. The numbers found may differ between members of a species and even within a single individual, with gametic nuclei often having larger numbers. B-chromosomes are composed largely of hetero-chromatin and in many cases appear to have little effect. However when present in large numbers they may be deleterious.

**Bdellovibrio**. Genus of Gram-negative bacteria which is not assigned to any taxonomic family. The cells are small, curved rods, usually motile with a single flagellum at one end. They are aerobic. They parasitize other bacteria by penetrating them, and then growing and dividing within them. They are found in soil, in freshwater and marine habitats, and in sewage, etc.

**Beach.** Accumulation of sand and gravel found at the landward margin of the sea or a lake. Upper and lower limits approximate to the position of highest and lowest tidal water levels. The angle of slope and the sedimentary structures of a beach are related to the grain size of the beach materials, and to the nature of wave activity and other sedimentary processes active in the area.

**Beach Cusp.** One of a series of regularly-spaced crescent-shaped structures forming local relief along a beach face. The horns or 'headlands' of the cusp are composed of coarse sand or gravel, and point seaward down the beach. The intervening troughs or 'bays' are made up of finer sand. The height of beach cusps is usually in the order of several centimetres, although larger examples have been described. The size and spacing of cusps appears to be related to the nature of waves breaking on the beach.

**Beach Flea.** Any of a number of small, terrestrial amphipods of the family Talitridae, as Talitrus, Orchestria.

**Beach Rock.** Cemented beach sand deposit that develops within the intertidal zone by the precipitation of needle-like crystals of aragonite in the pore space between the grains. The cementation process is relatively rapid, taking as little as 10 years for a lithified rock to develop. The precipitation of the cement is favoured by a warm climate, and may be aided by algal or bacterial action.

**Beaded.** Used of the gill of an agaric which is having a row of small droplets of liquid along its edge.

**Beak**

1. A projecting structure ending in a point.
2. *zool. a.* The nib or bill of a bird or turtle. *b.* The projecting mouth parts of certain insects. *c.* The

horny jaws of an octopus. *d.* The earliest part of the shell of a bivalve. *e.* The apex of the ventral valve of a brachiopod.

3. *bot.* A prolongation of certain fruits or carpels.

**Beaked.** Having a long, pointed prolongation.

**Beaked Whale.** A family of toothed whales with a distinct dolphin-like beak. The most common and largest are the bottle-nosed whales.

**Beaker Cell.** A unicellular gland in the integument of a cyclostome.

**Bean**

1. The large, edible, kidney-shaped seed borne by various leguminous plants, especially those of the genus Phaseolus, as the kidney, lima, string, and soy bean.
2. The plants producing these seeds or the pods containing them.
3. Various other bean-like seeds or the plants producing them, as the castor bean or coffee bean.

**Bean Gall.** Red or pink, kidney-bean-shaped gall, found on the leaves of Salix species (willow) and caused by the small sawfly, Pontania proxima (family Tenthredinidae). A second brood laid in the early autumn by the adults that emerged in summer may overwinter in the gall. Sometimes the term 'bean gall' is used more generally to describe any red or brown gall caused by any Pontania species. Many galls may occur on a single leaf and, like other gall-causing species, the insects support a large community of parasities and hyperparasites.

**Bear.** A large mammal belonging to the family Ursidae. Bears are plantigrade animals, *i.e.* they walk (like man) on the soles of their feet. They have powerful limbs with strong claws, small round ears and a short tail almost completely hidden in the fur. Bears are found in most parts of the world with the exception of Africa and Australia. They include the Black Bear, Brown Bear, Polar Bear, Sloth Bear and Sun Bear.

**Bear Animalcule** A tardigrade.

**Beard**

1. The hair that grows on the face of a man.
2. Any structure which resembles a man's beard, as *a.* the long hairs on the chain of a goat; *b.* hairlike feathers under the bill of a bird.
3. *bot.* A cluster of bristlelike hairs or awns.

**Bearded**

1. Having many awns as for example, the ears of the bearded fescue (Festuca ambigua).
2. Having any other kind of stiff hairs as, for example, the collection of hairs on the lower petals of the flag iris (Iris pseudacorus).

**Beaufort Scale.** Scale of values, from 0 to 12, for describing wind strength, as defined by Admiral Beaufort in the nineteenth century. Each wind force is recognized by its common effects on objects in the landscape (dust, flags, trees, etc.) and on people in the open, or on the state of the sea surface.

**Beaumont Period.** Forty-eight hours during which the minimum temperature is 10°C and the relative humidity is 75% or more. These periods are the basis of the system used in England to forecast an outbreak of late blight of potatoes (Phytophthora infestans).

Sporulation of the potato blight fungus and subsequent invasion of potato leaves is favoured by moist weather. By examining meteorological data A Beaumont worked out that blight could be expected ten days after a 'Beaumont period'. Careful monitoring of local meteorological data enables the advisory services to record Beaumont periods and give farmers accurate advice on when to spray their potato crops.

**Beaver**. An aquatic rodent of the genus Castor, with chisel-like teeth, webbed hind feet, and a flat scaly tail; valued for its fur.

**Beaver**. The second largest rodent in the world, the beaver is up to 1.4 metres long, including the tail. It weighs up to 35 kg. There are two species, very much alike. One lives in northern Europe and the other in North America. Beavers always live near water and they make their homes in river banks or in 'lodges' built of branches in the middle of a pond. Even the pond is made by beavers. They use their chisel-like front teeth to cut down small trees which they then use to build a dam across a stream. The beavers feed on bark, which they strip from trees. The front feet are clawed, for digging, and the hind feet are webbed. Beavers are excellent swimmers and they use their broad tails as rudders.

**Bear**. A large carnivore with powerful limbs, large strong claws and a very short tail. The brown bear is Europe's only resident species. It is about 2 metres long and has a thick brown coat. It eats a wide variety of both plant and animal food. Brown bears used to live all over Europe but now survive in only a few forested, mountainous areas.

**Becquerel** Symbol Bq. The SI unit of activity. The unit is named after the discoverer of radioactivity, A. H. Becquerel (1852—1908).

**Bedbug**. A small wingless insect which feeds by sucking blood from humans and animals. Bedbugs come out at night to feed. They give off an unpleasant, oily smell and their bite irritates the skin. Though bedbugs were once common, they are now becoming scarce.

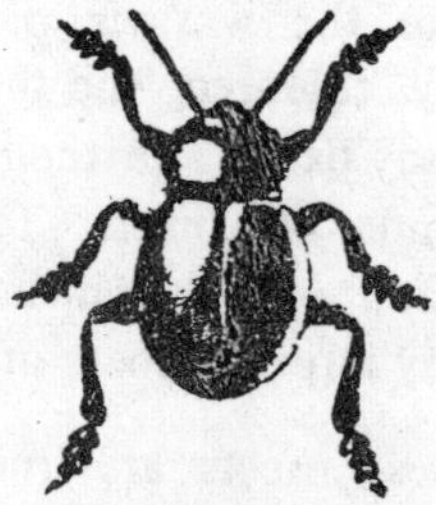

Bedbug

**Bedstraw.** A group of herbs with weak stems supporting whorls of narrow leaves and small, usually white flowers. The name comes from the day when they were used to stuff pillows and mattresses.

**Bee.** A group of insects related to ants and wasps. Some bees, such as the familiar Honey Bee, are social insects, living in colonies. The queen lays eggs, most of which produce infertile females called workers who tend the nest and new young; others produce males (drones) and new queens. Bumble Bees are also social bees, though they are not so highly organized as honey bees and have smaller nests which last for only one summer. Solitary bees, such as the Mining Bee, nest in burrows in the ground. Bees can sting, but are not normally aggressive. They feed on nectar and pollen from flowers, the honey bee using much of the nectar to make honey. A 'language' of body movements is used by bees to tell one another where to find flowers.

**Beebread.** Pollen stored by bees in the honeycomb and used for food by larvae and newly-emerged workers.

**Beech.** A large, strong deciduous tree growing up to 30 metres tall. The fruit, known as beechmast, consists of a hairy green husk which dries and splits open to release one or two shiny brown triangular nuts. Some beeches have purple leaves and are called copper beeches. All have smooth grey bark, oval leaves and slender pointed buds.

**Bee-eater.** The bee-eaters are very spctacular birds distributed over most of the warmer parts of the Old World. They are brightly coloured and they have curved beaks. They nest in sandy banks and their nesting colonies may contain thousands of birds. They feed on insects, including bees and wasps, which they catch in flight. They also destroy large numbers of locusts.

**Bee-fly.** Although these insects are true flies, most look like bees. They have hairy bodies and long mouth parts with which to suck nectar from flowers. The larvae of some bee-flies live as parasites on solitary bees, beetles or grasshoppers.

**Beefsteak Fungus.** Common name for the fruit body of Fistulina hepatica. The flesh is red-brown with a gelatinous upper surface, and yields a reddish juice; spores are formed within tubes which open via pores on the pale underside of the fruit body. It is parasitic on trees, particularly oak. It is fairly common in late summer and autumn.

**Bee Louse.** A minute, dipterous insect of the genus Braula, parasitic on bees.

**Bee Moth.** Wax Moth.

**Bees.** Hymenoptera.

**Beeswax.** A wax produced by worker bees and used in the construction of the honeycomb. It is produced by glands on ventral surface of the abdomen.

**Beet.** A plant with large roots used as food. Red beetroots are cooked as a vegetable; white sugar-beets yield sugar; mangel-wurzels or mangolds are grown as cattle-feed.

**Beetle.** One of the most widespread groups of insects, recognized by their hard wing-covers, or elytra, which are modified forewings. They protect the delicate hind wings. Beetles look similar to bugs, but have biting jaws rather than sucking mouth parts, as bugs have. Although they can fly, most beetles are ground-dwellers, and many are burrowers. They eat almost anything, including other insects, plants, carrion and dung. Many beetle larvae are pests, damaging plants and trees. Like butterflies, beetles have a four-stage life cycle. From the egg hatches a larva or grub, which grows by shedding its skin. The larva eventually turns into a pupa, from which the adult beetle emerges. There are about 330,000 species of beetle, making up the insect group Coleoptera. The name Coleoptera comes from two Greek words meaning 'sheath-wing'.

**Beet Sugar**. Sucrose.

**Beggar's Lice**. The fruit of the stickseed (Hackelia) or the plant that produces it.

**Beggar Tick**. A sticktight, the fruit or achene of Bidens, the burmarigold, or the plant which produces it, with recurved or hispid awns or bristles.

**Beggiatoaceae** (order Cytophagales). Family of gliding bacteria which form colourless, flexible, sheathed filaments. The sheath may enclose a single filament (*e.g.*, in Beggiatoa), or bunches of filaments (in Thioploca). They are aerobes or micro-aerophiles. Some genera form granules of sulphur inside their cells when grown in the presence of hydrogen sulphide. They are found in marine or fresh-water habitats.

**Beggiatoales**. An order of filamentous or unicellular bacteria that move by gliding over the substrate, hence their common name gliding bacteria. Many of its members (the filamentous sulphur bacteria) grow by oxidizing sulphides. The genus Beggiatoa has certain features in common with the blue-green alga Oscillatoria. It has been suggested that some of the Beggiatoaceae are colourless blue-green algae.

**Begonia**. Any of 900 species of plants grown for their showy flowers. The waxy flowers range from white to red. The leaves are sometimes tinted pink or red and the stems are rather succulent.

**Begoniaceae.** Family of mostly succulent herbs or undershrubs, which are almost entirely tropical. The stems are pointed, with alternate simple, often unequal-sided leaves. They are monoecious, and the flowers are usually irregular, borne in cymes, and showy. There are two (to five) free sepals and petals, and many stamens in the male flower; and the ovary is usually inferior. The fruit is a capsule, or berry. Begonia is much cultivated, but is not hardy in climates with frosty winters.

**Behaviour, Animal** A general term applicable to any observable activity of a whole animal. Behaviour incorporates all the processes by which an animal senses its external surroundings and the internal state of its body and responds to any changes it perceives. An animal behaves continuously so as to survive—to feed, drink, reproduce, and avoid being eaten.

**Behavioural Genetics.** The branch of genetics concerned with determining the relative importance of the genetic constitution of animals as compared to environmental factors in influencing animal behaviour.

**Belemnite.** A fossil cephalopod with a straight, slender, pointed shell.

**Belemnoidea** (belemnites; class Cephalopoda, subclass Coleoidea). Order of extinct cephalopods which had an internal shell composed of phragmacone, a rostrum, and a proostracum. There are five families. They appear in Upper Carboniferous rocks and persist generally until the end of the Cretaceous, and in one area into the Eocene.

**Bell**

1. The medusa form of a coelenterate; an umbrella.
2. The corolla of certain flowers.

**Bell Animalcule.** A group of protozoans with a cup-shaped body attached to a stem. Some are anchored to underwater objects. Others join together in large, jelly-like colonies.

**Bell Bird.** The name given to several unrelated species of bird living in the southern hemisphere whose voices have a metallic ring.

**Bellflower.** A family of plants with generally blue, bell-shaped flowers. Most, like the Harebell, grow upright with pointed leaves; the creeping ivy-leaved bellflower is an exception.

**Bell-magendie Law.** This law states that the dorsal root of spinal cord has only sensory axons while the ventral root has only motor axons.

**Bell Toad.** One of two genera of small frogs of the family Liopelmidae, Liopelma of New Zealand and Ascaphus of the northwestern United States.

**Belly**

1. The abdomen or abdominal cavity.
2. The central, fleshy portion of a skeletal muscle.
3. The underneath or ventral side of an animal.

**Bellying.** Protruding on one side, said of the corolla of certain flowers.

**Belonidae** (garfish, long tom, needlefish; class Osteichthyes, subclass Actinopterygii, order Atheriniformes). Family of mainly marine, tropical and subtropical fish with very long, slender bodies, beak-like jaws, and dorsal and anal fins placed close to the tail-fin. Often swimming in schools, they are known to leap out of the water when frightened. Tylosurus crocodilus (houndfish) is probably the largest of the 26 or so species.

**Belontiidae** (gourami, labyrinth fish, class Osteichthyes, subclass Actinopterygii, order Perciformes). Family of small, freshwater fish, characterized by a protrúsible upper jaw, vestigial lateral line, ten or fewer soft rays in the dorsal fin, and often an elongate pelvic ray in the jugular pelvic fins. Labyrinth-like accessory breathing organs can be found in the gill chambers. Prior to spawning, males often make a foamy bubble nest at the surface of the water. The many species popular with aquarium hobbyists include the Siamese fighting fish (Betta splendens), the paradise fish (Macropodus opercularis) and the thicklip gourami (Colisa labiosa). They are indigenous to Africa and S. Asia.

**Belostomatidae** (order Hemiptera, suborder Heteroptera). Family of large, aquatic bugs, which are ferocious predators of small fish and frogs as well as of invertebrates, seizing their prey with the front pair of legs. The family includes some of the largest aquatic insects. They are often attracted to artificial light. They occur mainly in the tropics.

**Belt Transect.** A narrow strip of land which is a taken as a sample of an area in studying the vegetation.

**Beluga.** The belugas or white whales are related to the dolphins and porpoises. The young animals are grey, but the skin gradually becomes white by reduction of the black pigment. Belugas usually grow to about 4 metres in length. They live in and around the Arctic Ocean.

**Benedict's Reagent.** A mixture of copper(II) sulphate in solution together with a filtered mixture of sodium citrate and sodium carbonate. The reagent is used to detect the presence of reducing sugars in solution. After boiling, a high concentration of reducing sugars in the test solution causes the formation of a red precipitate, while a lower concentration results in the formation of a yellow precipitate. It is a more sensitive test than Fehling's solution.

**Benedict's Test.** A biochemical test to detect reducing sugars in solution, devised by the US chemist S. R. Benedict (1884-1936). Benedict's reagent—a mixture of copper(II) sulphate and a filtered mixture of hydrated sodium citrate and hydrated sodium carbonate—is added to the test solution and boiled. A high concentration of reducing sugars induces the formation of a red precipitate; a lower concentration produces a yellow precipitate. Benedict's test is a more sensitive alternative to Fehling's test.

**Bennettitales** (Cycadeoidales). An extinct order of gymnosperms known from fossils extending throughout the Mesozoic era. They resembled cycads in habit and in leaf structure but can be distinguished from fossil cycads by certain features of the leaf epidermis, notably the possession of a syndetocheilic stomatal complex as compared to the haplocheilic stomata of the cycads. Like the cycads, they may have originated from the Pteridospermales.

**Benson-calvin-bassham Cycle.** The cycle in photosynthetic carbon dioxide fixation that regenerates the primary carbon dioxide acceptor. It is named after the three discoverers but is commonly abbreviated to Calvin cycle.

**Benthic.** Of or pertaining to the benthos.

**Benthic Fish.** Fish that live on or near the sea-bottom : the term is used irrespective of whether the sea is shallow or deep. Many species (*e g* , gurnard) possess modified fins, enabling them to crawl over the bottom; others (*e.g.*, flounder and ray) have flattened bodies and can lie on the sand. Weed beds, rocky outcrops, and coral reefs provide living space for another group of benthic fish, including damselfish, moray eels, and triggerfish.

**Benthoic.** Bottom-dwelling.

**Benthos.** The organisms that live on a lake or sea bed. The plants (phytobenthos) that grow below low-tide mark include members of the flowering plant family Zosteraceae, such as eelgrasses (Zostera), and certain red algae, such as dulse (Rhodymenia palmata). A variety of plants grow rooted in the littoral zone of lakes and ponds, including water lilies (Nuphar, Nymphaea), pondweeds (Potamogeton), and water milfoils (Myriophyllum).

**Bentinckia** (family Palmae). Genus of palms in which the trunk is solitary, and hoop-marked. The leaves are pinnate, with a long crown-shaft, below which appear the much-branched inflorescences. B. nicobarica is widely cultivated. There are two species, one native to India, and the other to the Nicobar Islands.

**Benzyladenine.** BAP.

**6-benzylaminopurine.** BAP.

**Berberidaceae.** Family of herbs and shrubs, in whose flowers the perianth is regular, tri- or dimerous, and composed of free parts in 2-7 whorls, the whorls being either alike or different. The ovary consists of a single carpel, forming a berry or capsule. There are ten genera, and some 300 species, mainly confined to the northern temperate zone (but Berberis is almost cosmopolitan).

**Berberis** (barberry; family Berberidaceae). Genus of spiny, simple-leaved shrubs producing flowers which are trimerous, with spines in threes, the perianth usually consisting of five yellow or orange whorls. The fruit is an edible berry. They are much cultivated for ornament, and formerly were grown for their edible fruits. They are a secondary host of wheat rust, so are often eliminated in wheat-growing areas. There are more than 200 species, of cosmopolitan distribution in temperate zones and in the mountains of tropical Africa.

**Bergen School.** Name used to distinguish the group of meteorologists (V. Bjerknes, J. Bjerknes, H. Solberg, and T. Bergeron) who, working in Norway between 1917 and 1920, established the existence and role of fronts and air masses in the atmosphere.

**Bergeron Theory** (Bergeron-Findeisen theory). A theory, proposed around 1930 by T. Bergeron, and subsequently developed by W. Findeisen, that provides a mechanism for the growth of raindrops in ice/water cloud. It is based on the differential values for saturation vapour pressure over ice and supercooled-water surfaces. At cloud temperatures of −12 to 30 °C air can be saturated over ice but not over water particles, so evaporation can take place from the water drops, and ice particles can grow by sublimation at the expense of water droplets. When they are large enough, the ice particles can fall from the cloud. The process depends on there being a mixture of ice and water, and so may operate in mid- and high-latitude cloud, but not in all clouds, *e.g.*, not in tropical clouds which are at temperatures above freezing.

**Bergmann's Rule.** The idea that the size of homoiothermic animals in a single, closely-related, evolutionary line increases along a gradient from warm to cold temperatures—*i.e.*, that races of species from cold climates tend to be composed of individuals physically larger than those of races from warm climates. This is because the surface-area : body-weight ratio decreases as body weight increases. Thus a large body loses proportionately less heat than a small one. This is advantageous in a cold climate but disadvantageous in a warm one.

**Berg Wind.** Local wind, generically of the fohn type, which blows offshore in S. Africa.

**Beringia.** Area comprising the Bering Strait and adjacent Siberia and Alaska. At various times in the late Mesozoic and Cenozoic, the Strait was dry land and so provided for plants and animals an important migration route between the Palaearctic and Nearctic biogeographical regions.

**Beri-beri.** A form of polyneuritis (degeneration of the peripheral nerves causing paralysis) which is caused in mammals, birds and possibly other animals by a deficiency of vitamin $B_1$ (thiamin).

**Berry**

1. Any small juicy fruit.
2. A simple fruit in which the inner portion of the ovary wall and the partitions between the locules are thick and juicy, as the grape, pepper, tomato, orange.

**Bertholletia** (family Lecythidaceae). Genus of two species of big, locally common, rainforest trees of tropical America. B. excelsa is the brazil-nut. The fruit is a hard, spherical, woody capsule opening by a terminal plug and containing numerous very hard, woody seeds with copious, oily endosperm.

**Beryciformes** (class Osteichthyes, subclass Actinopterygii). Order of bony fish, most with short, deep bodies, rough scales, sharp spines on the head, and usually more than five soft rays in the ventral fins. With more than 140 species, this order is divided into several suborders, *e.g.*, Berycidae (alfonsinos), Holocentridae (squirrel-fish), Anomalopidae (lantern-eye fish).

**Beta.** The second letter of the Greek alphabet ($\beta$) used to designate the second of a series, as beta cell, beta carbon, beta oxidation.

**Beta-blocker.** Animal cells are having two kinds of catecholamine receptors such as the beta-receptors which are stimulated more by adrenaline than by noradrenaline, and operate by activating adenyl cyclase (Cyclic AMP) and the alpha-receptors which are stimulated more by noradrenaline than by adrenaline and operate probably through increasing the calcium intake of the cell. A drug, propranolol inhibits beta-receptors and finds use medically as a 'beta-blocker'.

**Beta-cells** ($\beta$-cells). One of the cells found in islets of Langerhans constituting about 75% of its part; having granules which stain purple (bluish-purple) with Mallory's stain; secreting insulin which is able to control excess of blood sugar by converting it into glycogen.

**Betaceous.** Beetlike.

**Betacyanin.** Any of nitrogen-having red pigments, *e.g.*, betanidin, which replace and perfrom the function of floral pigment anthocyanin in certain plants.

**Beta-keratin.** Refers to the insoluable sulphur-rich scleroprotein; constituent of epidermis, horns, nails, feathers and tooth enamel. Beta pertains to protein's secondary structure which is in pleated sheets (*e.g.*, silk produced by caterpillers).

**Betalain.** A class of nitrogen-containing pigments containing the red betacyanins (*e.g.*, betanidin, the beetroot pigment) and the yellow betaxanthins (*e.g.*, indicaxanthin from the fruits of Opuntia ficus-indica). They replace and perform the functions of the floral pigment anthocyanin in certain plants. The possession of betalains has been used as a taxonomic character. Its occurrence into stricted to a group of families (nine or ten depending on the classification system used) which, with the exception of the Cactaceae, have all traditionally been placed in the order Centrospermae (or Caryophyllales). The Cactaceae are sometimes included in the Centrospermae on the basis of their resemblance to members of the Aizoaceae (mesems bryanthemum family) but others have placed them in the monotypic order Cactales (or Opuntiales). The occurrence of betalains in cacti is strong evidence for their inclusion in the Centrospermae. Interestingly one family, the Caryophyllaceae, normally included in the Centrospermae, lacks betalains.

**Beta-oxidation.** Pertains to oxidation at beta-position, a pathway in which there occurs removal of two carbon atoms at a time from carboxyl group (end) of molecule. Knoop postulated such oxidation for fatty acids. β-oxidation of fatty acids gives rise to the formation of two molecules of acetyl Coenzyme-A.

**Beta Pleated Sheet.** A type of protein structure in which polypeptide chains are running close or each other and are held together by hydrogen bonds at right angles to the main chain. The structure is folded in regular 'pleats'.

**Betaxanthin.** Any of nitrogen-containing yellow pigments which belong to group of pigments betalain and replace and function such as anthocyanin floral pigment in certain families.

**Betel Nut.** The fruit of the Asian betel palm. Many people of southern Asia chew the betel nut as a narcotic stimulant.

**Bethylidae** (suborder Apocrita, superfamily Bethyloidea). Family of small to medium-sized wasps (usually less than 8 mm long), which are usually black, with an elongate head, and slightly elbowed, 12- or 13-segmented antennae. The wing venation is reduced, and the hindwing has a jugal lobe. The females of many species are apterous and ant-like, and a few will sting. The habits of the family are very diverse, but in most cases no true nest is made; rather the host larva (a small lepidopteran or coleopteran) is dragged to a sheltered location where more than one egg may be laid. The larvae are external parasites, and having matured will spin a silken cocoon. Adults may be collected from tree trunks or leaf litter, but these wasps are seldom encountered. The Bethylidae is often considered to represent an intermediate condition between true parasitoid and fossorial (burrowing) families.

**Betony.** A small flowering plant that produces reddish-purple flowers, arranged in tight oblong spikes, and has heart-shaped leaves. Betony is often used in herbal medicine.

**Betulaceae.** Family of deciduous shrubs and trees in which the leaves are simple, with stipules. The flowers are unisexual, the males borne in catkins, with 2-12 stamens; the females clustered, the ovary inferior and composed of two fused carpels. They are wind-pollinated in early spring. The fruit is a one-seeded nut, often winged. The family includes the birches (Betula), alders (Alnus), hornbeams (Carpinus), and hazels (Corylus). There are six genera and 170 species occurring in the northern hemisphere, extending to the Himalayas and Andes.

**Between Race.** A race of plants intermediate in character between the typical species and one of its well-marked sub-species or varieties.

**Bezoar.** A concretion consisting principally of ingested hair found in the stomach or intestine of animals, especially ruminants.

**Bial's Reagent.** A mixture of orcinol in concentrated hydrochloric acid with 10% iron(III) chloride solution. It is used to detect the presence of pentose sugars in a test solution. A green colour after boiling indicates a positive reaction.

**Bibio Marci** (St. Mark's fly; suborder Nematocera, family Bibionidae). Fly that is usually found around St Mark's Day (April 25), and which is easily recognized as a large, heavy-looking, hairy, black fly that flies sluggishly. Care should be taken with identification, however, because of the large number of similar specias that fly at the same time of year. Males swarm over short grass. The head of the male seems to be entirely taken up with compound eyes, below which the antennae are inserted above the mouthparts. Females have smaller eyes that are widely separated. The larvae are structurally very primitive and may often be found gregariously at the roots of grasses, cereals, and in leaf mould.

**Bibionidae** (fever flies, March flies, St. Mark's fly; class Insecta, order Diptera, suborder Nematocera). Family of somewhat variable flies which has been subdivided by some authors into as many as five subgroups. The adults are, typically, robust flies with shorter legs and wings than those of other families of Nematocera. Their antennae have 8–16 beadlike segments and are usually shorter than the thorax. Wings are large, with prominent anterior veins. Males have holoptic eyes, and ocelli are present. The larve live in soil, roots, or decaying vegetation. The larvae of some species are among the most primitive of all dipteran larvae, having 12 segments, a large head, well-developed mouthparts, and no pseudopods. More than 700 species have been described.

**Bicapsular.** A capsule which consists of two chambers.

**Bicarpellary, Bicarpelate.** A gynoecium having 2 carpels.

**Bicentric Distribution.** The few endemics in the Scandinavian flora are mainly restricted to either one or both of two widely separated montane areas. If they occur in both areas their distribution is described as bicentric. About 25 species and subspecies of plants are involved. The bicentric pattern possibly reflects the former existence of nunataks above the late Pleistocene ice sheet.

**Biceps.** A muscle with two heads, as the biceps brachii.

**Bichir.** A primitive freshwater fish of tropical Africa whose body is covered with an armour of scales. The bichir has an air bladder connected with the throat, and it is able to breathe air in addition to obtaining oxygen through its gills. The front fins can be used as props, almost like legs, and the bichir may well represent one of the stages through which land animals passed during their evolution from fishes.

**Biciliate.** Having two cilia, flagella, or elaters.

**Bicipital**

1. Having two heads or points of origin, as a bicipital rib.
2. Pertaining to the biceps muscle.

**Bicollateral Bundle.** A vascular bundle in which the phloem occurs both internal and external to the xylem, as in the stems of some dicotyledons, *e.g.* members of the Solanaceae. The presence of bicollateral bundles distinguishes solanaceous plants from members of the Scrophulariaceae. Compare collateral bundle, concentric bundle.

**Biconic** Looking like two cones which are placed base to base.

**Bicornuate.** Having two horns, as a bicornuate uterus.

**Biconjugate.** A compound leaf having two main ribs, each bearing a pair of leaflets.

**Bicuspid**

1. Having two points or cusps, as a bicuspid tooth.
2. Having two leaflets, as the bicuspid or mitral valve of the heart.

**Bicuspid Valve.** Said of the mitral valve or left auriculo-ventricular valve in the mammalian heart; so-called due to the two cusps or flaps by which it can close.

**Bidder's Canal.** In male amphibia *e.g.*, frog, some urinary tubles connect with testes and transport sperms into a duct which is called Bidder's canal. It runs along medial edge of and outside the kidney and communicates with ureter.

**Bidder's Organ.** A vestigial ovary, sometimes having a mass of immature ova, in front of the testis or ovary in certain toads of both sexes.

**Bidentate.** Having two teeth.

**Biennial.** A plant that takes two years to complete its life cycle. It grows vegetatively in the first year and the photosynthates are stored in perennating organs. The stored food is used to produce foliage leaves, flowers and seeds the following year. The plant then dies. Some important crops are biennials, *e.g.* carrot (Daucus carota) and parship (Pastinaca sativa). Certain garden flowers that are in fact perennials are more successfully grown as biennials, *e.g.*, wallflower (Cheiranthus cheiri) and Antirrhinum. Compare annual, ephemeral, perennial.

**Biferous.** Bearing two crops of fruit in one season.

**Bifid.** Forked; divided into two parts by a median cleft.

**Bifidobacterium** (family Actinomycetaceae, order Actinomycetales). Genus of Gram-positive bacteria in which the cells are pleomorphic and often Y-or V-shaped. They are anaerobic, fermenting glucose to produce acetic acid and lactic acid. They are found in the gut in a wide range of mammals, fowls, and bees; certain species are common in human infants' intestines. The are non-pathogenic.

**Biflagellatae.** A group of the Phycomycetes with spores possessing two flagella.

**Biflagellate.** Possessing two flagella.

**Biflavonyls.** Flavonoids.

**Bifoliate, Biforlioate.** Used for a compound leaf with two leaflets.

**Bifurcated.** Two-pronged; forked.

**Biflavonyls.** The dimers of flavone apigenin. Belonging to flavonoids, widely found in gymnosperms, scarse or absent in other plant groups.

**Bigeneric.** Describing a hybird derived from an intergeneric cross, *e.g.* Triticale derived from a cross between Triticum and Secale.

**Bigheaded Turtle.** A heavily armoured freshwater turtle of south-eastern Asia whose head is very large in relation to its body and cannot be withdrawn into the shell.

**Bighorn.** A wild sheep living in the Rocky Mountains. The males have enormous horns which curve around the back of the head and come forward again to the eyes. The horns are marked off into segments, each of which represents one year of the animal's life.

**Bignoniaceae.** Family of mainly woody climbers, in which the leaves are pinnate and opposite. The flowers are showy, borne in cymose clusters, zygomorphic, and pentamerous, with fused sepals and petals, and with the ovary superior. The fruit is usually a capsule with numerous small, winged seeds. There are 120 genera, with 650 species, most occurring in tropical central or S. America.

**Bilabiate.** Having two lips, said of the corolla of certain flowers.

**Bilamellate.** Consisting of two layers or lamella.

**Bilaminar.** Consisting of two lamina or this plates.

**Bilateral.** Having two sides; pertaining to both sides of the body.

**Bilateral Cleavage.** Cleavage producing a bilaterally symmetrical arrangment of blastomeres which does not have the peculiar arrangement and oblique divisions of spiral cleavage. It takes place in Echinodermata, Chordata, etc.

**Bilaterally Symmetrically.** Of organisms or their parts that are capable of being halved in one, and only one, plane in such a way that the two halves become approximately mirror-images of each other. Almost all freely moving animals are bilaterally symmetrical, *e.g.*, all vertebrates, arthropods, and worm-shaped animals. Similar condition in flowers, *e.g.*, snapdragon, is often known as zygomorphy.

**Bilateral Symmetry.** A type of arrangement of the parts and organs of an animal in which the body can be divided into two halves that are mirror images of each other along one plane only (usually passing through the midline at right angles to the dorsal and ventral surfaces).

Bilaterally symmetrical animals are characterized by a type of movement in which one end of the body always leads. In botany this type of symmetry is usually called zygomorphy when applicable to flowers (*e.g.*, foxglove and antirrhinum flowers are zygomorphic). Compare radial symmetry.

**Bilberry.** Short deciduous under-shrub of the heath family. It produces a characteristic purple bloom, and an edible black berry often used for making jam. Usually found on moors and heaths, it can also survive at high altitudes.

**Bile** (gall). A bitter-tasting greenish-yellow alkaline fluid produced by the liver, stored in the gall bladder, and secreted into the duodenum of vertebrates. It assists the digestion and absorption of fats by the action of bile salts, which chemically reduce fatty substances and decrease the surface tension of fat droplets so that they are broken down and emulsified. Bile may also stimulate gut muscle contraction (peristalsis). Bile also contains the pigments bilirubin and biliverdin, which are produced by the break down of the blood pigment haemoglobin.

**Bile Acids.** Glycocholic and taurocholic acids present in bile.

**Bile Duct.** In vertebrates, the common bile duct formed by a union of the hepatic duct from the liver and cystic duct from the gall bladder. Just before entering the duodenum, it receives the pancreatic duct.

**Bile Pigments.** Pigments which are excreted in the bile as the products of the degradation of haemoglobin. When haemoglobin is degraded in the body the protein portion, globin, yields, amino acids while the porphyrin or haem portion yields the bile pigment.

**Bile Salts.** Components of bile which aid digestion in the duodenal region of the gut. Sodium taurocholate and sodium glycocholate emulsify fats by decreasing their surface tension, making them to break up into numerous tiny droplets and facilitating the digestive action of lipase.

**Bilharzia.** Schistosoma (q.v.)

**Bilirubin.** A bile pigment resulting from the reduction of biliverdin; the prinicipal pigment in the bile of humans and carnivores.

**Biliverdin.** A bile pigment resulting from the breakdown of hemoglobin and myoglobin. In the liver it is reduced to bilirubin.

**Bill**

1. The toothless jaws of a bird; the beak.
2. A corresponding structure in other animals, as the turtle and duckbill platypus.

**Billardiera** (family Pittosporaceae, tribe Billardicreae). Genus of eight species of subshrubs with climbing stems, endemic to Australia. They have bell-shaped flowers and fleshy fruits.

**Bilocular.** Having two cells, cavities, or compartments.

**Biloprotein.** Any of blue or red pigments occurring in blue-blue-green and red algae. They are accessory photosynthetic pigments but unlike cholrophylls and carotenoids are water soluble. Structully they are similar to porphyrin part of chlorophyll molecule but without magnesium. They incorporate 3 classes of pigments, phycocyanins, phycoerythrins and allophycocyanins.

**Binary.** Composed of two elements or parts.

**Binary Fission.** A method of asexual reproduction taking place in unicellular organisms in which nucleus and then

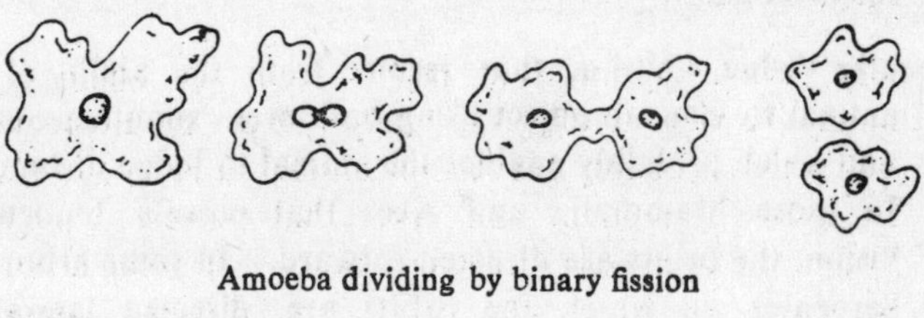

Amoeba dividing by binary fission

cytoplasm under go division mitotically to form two morphologically and genetically identical but smaller individuals.

**Bindweed.** A family of creeping or climbing plants with open trumpetshaped flowers and heart or arrowshaped leaves. There are several species of bindweed. The hedge bindweed

Hedge bindweed

is very common and covers hedges with a cloak of huge white flowers. The field bindweed has small pink and white blooms and is a weed of farms and gardens.

**Binocular.** Having two eyes or employing two eyes at the same time.

**Binocular.** An optical instrument with two eyepieces or two sets of lenses which permits the use of both eyes simultaneously in viewing an object; a stereoscopic microscope.

**Binocular Vision.** Vision that results from the ability of an animal to view an object using both eyes simultaneously, and which probably enables the animal to judge distances. In those Mammalia and Aves that possess binocular vision, the orbits are directed forward. In some arboreal Serpentes, in which the orbits are directed laterally, binocular vision may result from the possession of eyes whose pupils are long, horizontal slits located eccentrically and close to the anterior margins of the orbits.

**Binomial.** Consisting of two words or names.

**Binomial Nomenclature.** A system of naming species using a generic name and a specific epithet, established by the Swedish botanist Carl von Linne (also known by the Latinized form of his name, Carolus Linnaeus) in 1753. Previous to this the scientific names of species consisted of a short Latin description. This was too cumbersome as a name yet too short for a proper description. By separating the procedures of naming and describing, Linnaeous established the foundations of present-day nomenclature.

The generic name is a noun often based on a classical name as, for example, Endymion and Narcissus. The name can also be honorific, commemorating the plant's discoverer, such as Saintpaulia (African violets), named after Baron Walter von Saint Paul-Illaire. Alternatively, the generic noun may refer to the locality in which the plant was first found, Ligusticum (lovage) from Liguria (northwest Italy), for example. Specific names are adjectival and often describe a particular featuers of a plant, such as leaf shape or flower colour (*e.g.* longifolius, albus). Like generic names they may also be commemorative or geographical (*e.g.* wilsonii, lusitanica). Table 1 in the appendix for the meanings of some common specific epithets. Binomials are always Latinized and are usually pointed in italic script, the generic name beginning with a capital letter while the specific epithet is lower case throughout (*e.g.* Primula vulgaris). When naming a species the rules of the International Code of Botanical Nomenclature must be followed.

**Binturong.** The binturong or bear-cat is a tree-dwelling carnivore found in South-East Asia. It is about one metre long and has black fur. The binturong is clumsy on the ground, but it is an excellent climber. Its tail, which accounts for nearly half the animal's length, can be wrapped around branches as a brake or a fifth limb. The binturong feeds on birds and small mammals, together with a fair amount of fruit.

**Binucleate.** Having two nuclei.

**Bioassay** (biological assay). A controlled experiment for the quantitative estimation of a substance by measuring its effect in a living organism. For example, the amount of the plant hormone auxin can be estimated by observing its effect on the curvature of cat coleoptiles—the concentration of the hormone is proportional to the curvature of the coleoptile.

**Biocenose.** A community of organisms (plants and animals) which occupies a particular habitat.

**Biochemical Genetic.** The branch of genetics concerned with inheritance at the molecular level. It includes the study of the structure of DNA, its replication, the genetic code and transcription and translation in protein synthesis, and the regulation of gene expression.

**Biochemical Mutant.** An organism possessing a mutation that causes a particular enzyme either not to be synthesized or to be defective in some respect. The reaction that it catalyses therefore does not take place, and, if this reaction is an intermediate step in a metabolic pathway, the subsequent steps in the pathway are also prevented. Such mutants can be induced by various methods, such as irradiation with X-rays, and have proved particularly useful in elucidating the stages of a number of pathways.

**Biochemical Oxygen Demand** (BOD). The amount of oxygen taken up by microorganisms that decompose organic waste matter in water. It is therefore used as a measure of the amount of certain types of organic pollutant in water, BOD is calculated by keeping a sample of water containing a known amount of oxygen for five days at 20°C. The oxygen content is measured again after this time. A high BOD indicates the presence of a large number of microorganisms, which suggests a high level of pollution.

**Biochemical Taxonomy.** Chemotaxonomy.

**Biochemical Taxonomy.** Refers to the use of chemical characteristics which help to classify organisms. For example, the Asteroideae and Cichorioideae, are the two main divisions of the plant family. Compositae which are separated by the presence or absence of latex.

**Biochemistry.** The study of the chemistry of living organisms, especially the structure and function of their chemical components (principally proteins, carbohydrates, lipids, and nucleic acids). Biochemistry has advanced rapidly with the development, from the mid-20th century, of such techniques as chromatography, X-ray diffraction, radioisotopic labelling, and electron microscopy. Using these techniques to separate and analyse biologically important molecules, the steps of the metabolic pathways in which they are involved (*e.g.*, glycolysis and the Kerbs cycle) have been determined. This has provided some knowledge of how organisms obtain and store energy, how they manufacture and degrade their biomolecules, how they sense and respond to their environment, and how all this information is carried and expressed by their genetic material. Biochemistry forms an important part of many other disciplines, especially physiology, nutrition, and genetics, and its discoveries have made a profound impact in medicine, agriculture, industry, and many other areas of human activity.

**Biochore.** Little-used term from the early twentieth century ecological literature of central Europe, generally meaning a biotic district, *i.e.* a distinctive community and environment, and as such one of many precursors of the ecosystem concept. Also used by Raunkiaer to describe precise biological boundaries between major climatically determined plant regions and their main subdivisions, as identified by his life-form recording system (*i.e.*, percentages of phanerotypes, chamaephytes, etc.).

**Biochrome.** A natural pigment or coloring matter in a plant or animal.

**Biocide.** Natural or synthetic substance toxic to living organisms. Some ecologists advocate use of this term instead of 'pesticide', since most pesticides are also toxic to species other than the target pest species. Indirectly, pesticides may also affect non-target organisms detrimentally in many other ways, *e.g.* by loss of food species or loss of shelter, so that the effects of pesticides may be felt throughout a whole ecosystem. The term 'biocide' indicates this property more clearly than 'pesticide'.

**Biocies.** The climax animal or biotic community of a sere.

**Bioclimatology.** The study of climate, with particular reference to the environments of living organisms, especially to those of agricultural plants and animals, and humans; together with the disease vectors affecting humans and commercially important plants and animals.

**Biodegradable.** Pollution.

**Bioelectricity.** Electric currents generated within living tissues.

**Bioenergetics.** The study of energy transfer in living organisms. Almost all the energy used on Earth comes directly or indirectly from the sun. The way in which it is converted in cells depends on the principles and laws of thermodynamics. The first law concerns the relationship between work, heat, and internal energy; it is equivalent to the statement that energy can be converted from one form into another, but cannot be created or destroyed. Thus, when light energy falls on a plant some is reflected, some absorbed as heat, and some converted into chemical energy in glucose by photosynthesis, but the total amount of energy is constant. In fact energy transfers in living organisms tend to be inefficient. About 2% of the energy in incident radiation is converted into chemical energy. Heterotrophic organisms obtain energy from the nutrients they ingest; about 10-20% of the energy is passed on at each link in the food chain, which tends to have three or four links only.

The second law of thermodynamics concerns the way in which energy is transferred or converted. It states that any conversion of energy from one form into another involves some dissipation of energy as unavailable heat energy. The availability of energy in a system is determined by its entropy, which is a measure of randomness or disorder. In any process the total entropy increases (an alternative statement of the second law), and there is a constant degradation of energy in the universe into energy that is unavailable for work. The growth of organisms is characterized by decreases of entropy in the sense that disordered systems (*e.g.* $CO_2$ and $O_2$ gas) are converted into ordered chemical structures. However, the total entropy of the organism and its surroundings always increases in any change. All chemical reactions are given by a decrease of free energy.

**Bioengineering**

1. The use of artificial tissues, organs, and organ components to replace parts of the body that are damaged lost, or malfunctioning, *e.g.* artificial limbs, heart valves, and heart pacemakers.

2. The application of engineering knowledge to medicine and zoology.

**Biogenesis.** The theory postulating that living things originate only from other living things as opposed to non-living matter. The theory became accepted due to the work of

Redi and Pasteur, who proved that dirt, for example, does not itself produce bacteria or maggots, but that bacteria and maggots only come from spores or eggs already present in the dirt.

**Biogenetic Law.** An hypothesis which states that during its development, an individual repeats the evolution of its race in a shortened form.

**Biogeochemical Cycle.** Movement of chemical elements from organism in a more or less circular pathway. They are termed 'nutrient cycles' if the elements concerned are essential to life. The form and quantity of an element varies through the cycle, with amounts in the inorganic reservoir pools usually greater than those in the active pools. Exchange between the system components is achieved by physical processes (*e.g.* weathering) and/or biological processes (*e.*g. protein synthesis and decompo-tion). The latter form the vital negative-feedback mechanisms that regulate the cycles. Cycles may be described as varying from perfect to imperfect. A perfect cycle (*e.g.* the nitrogen cycle) has a readily accessible abiotic, usually gaseous, reservoir and many negative-feedback controls. By contrast, the phosphorus cycle, which has a sedimentary reservoir accessed only by slow-moving phvsical processes, has few biological feedback mechanisms. Human activities can disrupt these cycles, leading to pollution Theoretically, perfect cycles are more resilient than imperfect cycles.

**Biogeocoenosis.** Term equivalent to 'ecosystem', often used in Soviet and Central European literature. and attributed to Sukachaev (1947). A biogeocoenosis comprises a bio-coenosis (the biome, or living community), together with its habitat, which usually is termed an ecotope.

**Biogeographical Region.** Biological subdivision of the Earth's surface, delineated on the same general principles as a biogeographical province, but having superior taxonomic status. The provinces are grouped into regions, of which the following are generally recognized : Antarctic, Australian, Ethiopian, Nearctic, Neotropical, Oceanian: Oriental, and Palaearctic.

**Biogeography.** The science which deals with the geographical distribution of organisms.

**Biological Assay.** Bioassay.

**Biological Control.** Implies the introduction, or preservation and encouragement of a natural enemy of a pest, disease, or disease-carrying organisms, which may help in its control.

**Biological Clock.** The mechanism, presumed to exist within many animals and plants, that produces regular periodic changes in behaviour or physiology. Biological clocks underlie many of the circadian, tidal, and annual rhythms seen in organisms (*e.g.* hibernation in animals). They continue to run even when conditions are kept artificially constant, but eventually drift out of step with the natural environment without the specific signals that normally keep them synchronized.

**Biological Concentration** (biological magnification). Build-up through the food-chain of certain substances, natural or synthetic, in the bodies of living organisms. This is of particular importance to predators at the top of the chain, including humans, which may receive toxic doses. Substances concentrated in this way include heavy metals (*e.g.* lead) and organochlorine pesticides (*e.g.* DDT). The mechanism may cause especially serious problems where food-chains are long, as in aquatic ecosystems.

**Biological Conservation.** Active management to eusure the survival of the maximum diversity of species, and the maintenance of genetic variety within species. The term also implies the maintenance of biosphere functions, *e.g.* biogeochemical cycling, without which the basic resources for life would be lost. Biological conservation embraces the concept of long-term sustained resource use or sustained yield from the biosphere, which may conflict with species conservation in some circumstances. Conservation of species and biological processes is unlikely to succeed without simultaneous conservation of abiotic resources.

**Biological Control.** The control of pests by biological (rather than chemical) means. This may be achieved, for example, by breeding disease-resistant crops or by introducing a natural enemy of the pest, such as a predator or a parasite. This technique, which may offer substantial advantages over the use of pesticides or herbicides, has been employed successfully on a number of occasions. One notable example was the control of the prickly pear cactus (Opuntia) in Australia by introducing lhe cactus moth (Cactoblastis cactorum), whose caterpillars feed on the plant's growing shoots. Insect pests have been controlled by releasing large numbers of males of the pest species that have been sterilized by radiation : infertile matings subsquently cause a decline in the pest population.

**Biological Membrane.** The plasma membrane which is usually 7.5 nm (75 A) thick and made up of protein and lipids which are usually phospholipids *e.g.* phosphatidylcholine and phosphatidyl ethanolamine.

**Biological Oxidation.** Refers to such processes which deal with the production of energy in cell. Catalysed by enzyme and a particular protein enzyme being responsible in most cases.

**Biological Oxygen Demand** (BOD), biochemical oxygen demand). Indicator of the polluting capacity of an effluent where pollution is caused by the take-up of dissolved oxygen by micro-organisms that decompose the organic material present in the effluent. It is measured as the mass (mg) of oxygen used by one litre of sample effluent stored in darkness at 20°C for five days.

**Biological Spectrum.** A table which shows the percentage frequency of occurrence of the various plants and animals in a defined area.

**Biology.** The study of living organisms, which includes their structure (gross and microscopical), functioning, origin and evolution, classification, interrelationships, and distribution.

**Biology**

1. The science which deals with living things, comprising botany and zoology and all their subdivisions.
2. A treatise on living things.
3. All phenomena associated with a particular group of organisms, as the biology of protozoa.

**Bioluminescene.** The emission of light from living organisms. It results either from internal chemical reactions or from the reemission of absorbed energy as radiation. In plants, luminescence is probably the result of inefficiencies during oxidation-reduction reactions. Some of the energy released excites a molecule to a high-energy state and when the molecule returns to the ground state visible light is emitted. Luminescence is exhibited by certain fungi, including some of the genus Mycena, and also certain bacteria and planktonic algae.

**Biomass.** The total mass of organic material of a species per unit of area or volume, as 100 lbs. of perch per acre of pond surface. Term is used in expressing population density.

**Biome.** Biological subdivision of the Earth's surface that reflects the ecological and physiognomic character of the vegetation. Biomes are the largest geographical biotic communities that it is convenient to recognize. They broadly correspond with climatic regions, although other environmental controls are sometimes important. They are equivalent to the concept of major plant formations in plant ecology, but are defined in terms of all living organisms and of their interactions with the environment (and not only with the dominant vegetation type). Typically, distinctive biomes are recognized for all the major climatic regions of the world, emphasizing the adaptation of living organisms to their environment, *e.g.* tropical-rainforest biome, desert biome, tundra biome.

**Biometer.** A method used for assessing the amount of life by measuring the respiration, *e.g.* in a soil sample.

**Biometry.** Refers to the application of mathematics to the study of living things; particularly statistical study of resemblances and differences between groups of related organisms.

**Bionomics.** Means the study of the relation of an organism or population of organisms to its environment, animate and inanimate.

**Biophysics.** The application of the laws of physics to the study of the properties of living systems. Principal fields include physiological physics, molecular biology, radiation biology, theoretical physics, instrumentation, and measurement.

**Biopoiesis.** The development of living matter from complex organic molecules that are themselves nonliving but self-replicating. It is the process by which life is assumed to have begun.

**Biopsy.** The study of tissues taken from a living organism, especially the microscopic examination of excised tissue for diagnostic purpose.

**Biorhythm.** A roughly periodic change in the behaviour or physiology of an organism that is generated and maintained by a biological clock. A well-know example is the circadian rhythm occurring in many animals and plants. The term biorhythm has unfortunately also become associated with a pseudoscientific cult postulating that man's physical, emotional, and intellectual behaviour is influenced by three biological cycles with periodicities of exactly 23 days, 28 days, and 33 days respectively. There is no reliable evidence to support this theory.

**Bioseston.** The living components of seston.

**Bios Factor.** A substance which is essential for the growth of a plant, especially yeasts, obtained from the environment. It is a mixtute of aneurin, biotin, and, other substances. Biotin means Vitamin H, and is probably identical to the co-enzyme R.

**Bioseries.** In evolution, a historical sequence which is formed by the changes in any one inheritable character.

**Biosphere** The zone, including the earth's surface (and surface water), the adjacent atmosphere, and the underlying crust, where life can exist. The earth is usually considered as having three spherical zones: the solid lithosphere, the liquid hydrosphere, and the gaseous atmosphere. The biosphere encompasses parts of all three of these zones. Its limits are not well defined; most living organisms exist in a region extending about 100 m into the atmosphere and about 150 m below the surface of the oceans. The term can also include its of the earth and atmosphere that depend on the present or past existence of living organisms, *e.g.* coal deposits or atmospheric oxygen. The biosphere can be regarded as a single ecosystem and is often called the ecosphere.

**Biostatistics.** The branch of biometry that deals with vital data.

**Biosynthesis.** Synthesis of a substance which is taking place by some biochemical reaction or a series of biochemical reactions (biosynthetic pathway).

**Biosynthetic Pathway.** A series of enzymatic reactions in which more complex molecules are built from simpler ones. Biosynthetic pathways are energy requiring, this energy usually being supplied either as phosphate bond energy by ATP or as reducing power by NADPH. Three stages of biosynthesis can be recognized. The first stage is concerned with the manufacture of simple organic molecules from inorganic molecules like carbon dioxide and water. These few simple molecules are then converted in the second stage of building blocks for the many biological macromolecules. Finally macromolecules are synthesized from their constituent subunits. The major biosynthetic pathways in plants are shown in the diagram.

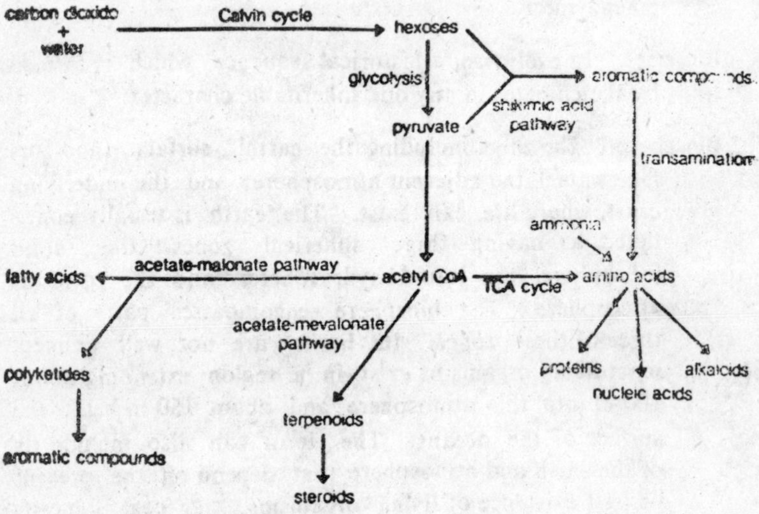


The main biosynthetic pathways in plants

**Biosystematics.** Involves the study of variations and relationships in populations rather than individuals. It is possible to assess genetic and evolutionary nature of groups by examining cytology, comparative morphology and ecology. It is often considered as the taxonomic application of genecology or occasionally as experimental taxonomy.

**Biota.** The flora and fauna either of a particular region or of a given geological period.

**Biotechnology.** The use of organisms (usually microorganisms), or the enzymes they produce, in industrial processes. Biotechnology has potential applications in food production, waster ecycling, alternative energy schemes, medicine, and a number of other spheres.

**Biotelemetry.** Remote-sensing method for monitoring animal movements using small transmitters attached externally to the body of the animal or implanted within the body cavity. It enables the precise locations of animals to be followed, and may also monitor changes in heart beat, *e.g.* in response to stress. It is especially useful for studying migratory animals in remote areas (*e.g.* elk, reindeer, and polar bear), and is an important aid to the study of bird migrations.

**Biotic.** Of or pertaining to life; biological.

**Biotic Adaptation.** Changes in form or physiology, which are believed to have arisen as a result of competition with other plants.

**Biotic Climax.** A climax community which is being maintained by living organisms *e.g.* grassland prevented from becoming forest by the grazing of animals.

**Biotic Environment.** The part of an organisms's environment that consists of other living organisms. These may affect it in many ways; for example, as competitors, predators, parasites, prey, or symbionts. In time, the distribution and abundance of the organism will be affected by its interrelatianships with the biotic environment.

**Biotic Factors.** The living components of the environment that by their activities affect the life of an organism. Compare abiotic factors.

**Biotic Index.** Scheme for grading river quality according to the diversity and abundance of the river fauna present, with particular reference to 'key species' with known pollution tolerances. The scale ranges from 10 (clean water with diverse fauna) to 0 (grossly polluted water with no fauna or with only a few anaerobic organisms).

**Biotic Region.** Biome.

**Biotin.** A vitamin in the vitamin B complex. It is the coenzyme for various enzymes that catalyse the incorporation of carbon dioxide into various compounds. Adequate amounts are normally produced by the intestinal bacteria in animals although deficiency can be induced by consuming large amounts of raw egg white. This contains a protein, avidin, that specifically binds biotin, preventing its absorption from the gut. Other sources of biotin include cereals, vegetables, milk, and liver.

**Biotopographic Unit.** Small habitat unit with distinctive topography formed by the activities of an organism, *e.g.* an ant hill, or a tussock. The term may also refer to small topographic units that, by their aspect, position, or other characteristics, generate distinctive micro-environments for living organisms. Examples include solar or shade slopes, windward slopes, and similar units in sand-dunes.

**Biotype**

1. A naturally occurring group of individuals all laving the same genetic composition, *i.e.* a clone or a pure line.

2. A physiological race or form within a species which is morphologically identical with it, but is different in genetic, physiological, biochemical, or pathogenic characteristics.

**Biovulate.** Having two ovules.

**Biparous**

1. *zool.* Producing two young at a single birth.
2. *bot.* Having two branches or parts.

**[1]Biped**

1. An animal with two feet, as man.
2. Any two limbs of a quadruped, as the two forelimb the anterior biped.

**[2]Biped.** Having two feet.

**Bipennate.** Resembling a feather, as certain muscles; bipenniform.

**Bipinnate.** Used for a pinnate leaf in which leaflets themselves have been further subdivided pinnately *e.g.* in Mimosa pudica.

**Bipinnaria.** The bilaterally symmetrical, ciliated larva of asteroid echinoderms.

**Bipinnate.** Describing a pinnate leaf in which the leaflets themselves are further subdivided in a pinnate fashion, as seen in the sensitive plant (Mimosa pudica).

**Bipolar**

1. Having two poles.
2. Having two processes, as certain neurons.

**Bipolar Cells.** A neuron having two axons which are emerging from opposite sides of the soma. One such class exists in retina of the eye where they transmit signals from visual receptor cell to ganglionic cells of optic nerve.

**Bipolar Distribution of Fish.** The distribution of certain families, genera, and species of fish (*e.g.* the families Petromyzonidae and Cottidae) is limited to the cooler waters of the northern and southern hemispheres, no immediate relatives being found in the more tropical regions of the world. The deep-sea anglerfish, Ceratias holboelli, is thought to occur only in the cold waters of the Arctic and Antarctic.

**Bipotentiality**. Having the potentiality of developing into two different structures, as an embryonic gonad developing into an ovary or testis.

**Biradial Symmetry**. A type of symmetry in which the body consists of radially arranged parts, half of which lie on each side of a median longitudinal plane, as a ctenophore.

**Biramous.** Having two branches, an inner endopodiate and an outer exopodite, with reference to appendages of various crustaceans.

**Biramous Appendage.** Forked, paired appendage. The parapodia of polychaetes are biramous, and so usually are the appendages in three arthropod groups, Trilobita, Crustacea, and Arachnida. The two branches may be similar, *e.g.* abdominal appendages of crayfish, or dissimilar.

**Biramous Limbs** (of Crustacea). The typical forked appendages of a crustacean, sometimes modified for various functions but essentially consisting of two branches arising from a basal portion.

**Birch**. A group of deciduous trees and shrubs, most of which have triangular leaves. The flowers are arranged in spikes called catkins. The male catkins are usually long and hanging; the female catkins are shorter, and some stand erect. The tiny seeds are scattered by the wind, and birches are among the first trees to spring up on bare ground The silver birch is one of the most common species It is a graceful tree that grow up to 30 metres high and produces winged fruit. Its bark, silvery white and peeling, gives the tree its name. Another species, the dwarf birch, grows further north than any other tree or shrub.

**Birch Bracket.** A bracket fungus found on birch trees throughout the year. The brackets are rather hoof-shaped and have a corky texture. The fungus attacks living trunks and often kills them.

**Bird.** A warm-blooded vertebrate of the class Aves that is unique in possessing feathers. Like the reptiles from which they are descended, birds lay shelled eggs. Another reptilian characteristic is the presence of scales on the legs and the feet. The forelimbs are modified as wings and the body of a bird is designed for flying: many of the bones of the skeleton are hollow and the large flight muscles may account for one-fifth of the entire body weight. Birds have no teeth but a tough horny beak. The food is not chewed but is stored in the crop after it is swallowed and is later ground up in the muscular gizzard which may contain stones.

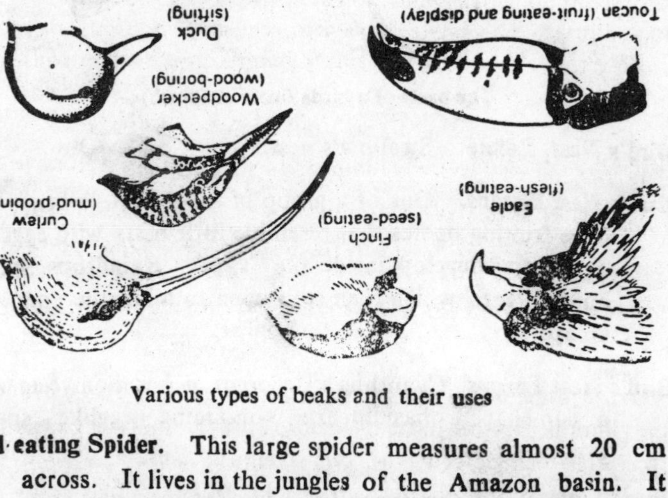


Various types of beaks and their uses

**Bird-eating Spider.** This large spider measures almost 20 cm across. It lives in the jungles of the Amazon basin. It does not spin a web, but catches birds and small mammals by dashing after them. The bird-eating spider has few enemies because it is covered with poisonous hairs.

**Bird Lice.** Parasitic insects of the order Mallophago.

**Bird of Paradise.** A group of birds found mainly in the forests of New Guinea and surrounding islands. The female birds are rather dull in colour, but the males of most species have beautiful plumes which they use in the most elaborate courtship displays.

**Bird-of-paradise Flower.** A South African plant with brilliant orange and purple flowers. It is related to the banana and has banana-shaped leaves.

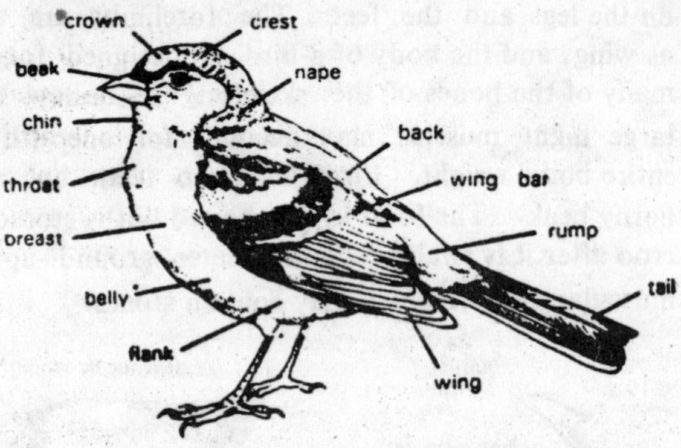


The parts of a birds (male chaffinch)

**Bird's Nest, Edible.** Swallow's nest.

**Bird's Nest Fungus.** One of a group of fungi that, when ripe, have fruiting bodies that resemble little nests with eggs in. The spores develop inside the 'eggs'. Raindrops splash out the 'eggs' which then split open to allow the spores to escape.

**Bird's Nest Fungus.** Cyanthus stirecoreus, a basidiomycete with a cup-shaped basidiocarp containing egglike spores producing bodies.

**Bird Pollination.** Ornithophily.

**Birdwing.** The birdwings are magnificent butterflies living in the forests of South-East Asia. Some have wing-spans exceeding 25 cm. The females are a little larger than the males, but they are less colourful. The males have velvety black wings, marked with beautiful shining greens are blues.

**Birth**

1. The production of offspring; delivery, parturition, labor.
2. That which is born or produced.

**Birth Control.** Control of limitation of the number of offspring; contraception.

**Birthmark.** A nevus; an area of pigmentation of vascularization of the skin present at birth or shortly afterward.

**Birth Rate.** The number of live births reported in a calender year per 1000 of actual or estimated population, known as crude birth rate. In the United States, in 1960 the rate was 22.6.

**Birthwort.** A species of low herbs or twining shrubs of the family Aristolochiaceae, especially those of the genus Aristolochia, whose aromatic roots were thought to aid in childbirth.

**Bisexual**

1. Of or pertaining to both sexes; having both male and female sex organs; hermaphroditic.
2. *bot.* Having both stamens and pistils.

**Bishop Bird.** A group of sparrow-like weaver birds found in many parts of Africa. The female has a dull brownish plumage throughout the year, but the male acquires brilliant plumage during the mating season. Some species are popular cage birds.

**Bison.** A massive, ox-like creature weighing well over one tonne. The largest ones stand almost 2 metres at the shoulder. The hair on the head, neck, shoulders, and forelegs is long and shaggy. There are two species; the European bison, or wisent, and the American bison. The latter, often wrongly called the buffalo, has longer hair than the wisent. Both species were almost exterminated during the last 100 years, but numbers have now increased again due to proper game management.

**Bisp Oragiate.** Used for strobilus having megasporophylls and microporophylls, with microsporangia, megasporangia.

**Biston Betularia** (peppered moth; order Lepidoptera). Moth which has been the subject of classical studies of industrial melanism, where there is selective predation by birds upon light moths that are consipicuous against a dark, sooty background, and conversely, upon dark moths against a light, soot-free background.

**Bistort.** A short unbranched flowering plant, frequently found near water in fields and woods. The amphibious bistort is often found growing in water. Both species have small pink flowers arranged in thick spikes.

Bistort

**Bitis Arietans** (puff adder; order Squamata, suborder Serpentes (Ophidia), family Viperidae) Highly venomous snake, dangerous to humans, which is common throughout Africa south of the Sahara. It grows up to 1.5 m long. When provoked it inflates the body and hisses, while preparing to strike. It feeds on small vertebrates.

**Bittercress.** Several species of white-flowered plant related to the cabbage. The hairy bittercress is a common garden weed with a rosette of hairy leaves at the base of its stem. The large bittercress has a bitter taste. It is found by streams and other damp places.

**Bitterling.** A freshwater fish belonging to the carp family, found all over central and eastern Europe. It is a small fish, never more than 9 cm long. It lives in weed-filled ponds and slow-running rivers. The female lays her eggs in freshwater mussels. The male then sheds his sperm over the shell to fertilize the eggs. When the larvae hatch they swim away, leaving the mussel unharmed.

**Bittern.** A heron-like bird of reeds and marshes. It has a brown, speckled plumage and when still, with its bill pointed skywards, it is hard to spot among the reeds. Bitterns feed on frogs, fishes and small water animals. The male bird has a deep booming call.

**Bittersweet.** A low-growing, downy plant, related to the deadly night-shade, and found in woods and scrub. Its bright purple flowers are arranged in loose clusters and the plant produces poisonous, red, oval-shaped berries.

**Bittersweet**

1. A poisonous, climbing, solanceous plant (Solanum dulcamara) with coral-red berries.
2. An American shrub (Celastrus scandens).

**Bitunicate.** Having a wall of two layers, with reference to an ascus.

**Biuret Reaction.** A reaction which occurs when proteins or other substances containing peptide bonds are treated with copper sulfate in an alkaline solution. A red, purple, or violet color results.

**Biuret Test.** A biochemical test to detect proteins in solution, named after the substance biuret ($H_2NCONHCONH_2$), which is formed when urea is heated. Sodium hydroxide is mixed with the test solution and drops of 1% copper(II) sulphate solution are then added slowly. A positive result is indicated by a violet ring, caused by the reaction of peptide bonds in the proteins or peptides.

Such a result will not occur in the presence of free amino acids

**Biuret Test.** A test for proteins in which sodium hydroxide is added to the test solution, followed by the careful addition of drops of 1% copper(II) sulphate solution. A violet colour indicates a positive result and is caused by the presence of peptide groups (NH·CO) in the proteins or peptides, which form a purple copper(II) peptide complex. Free amino acids will not give a positive result.

**Bivalent.** A pair of homologous chromosomes united by chiasmata. Bivalents are most clearly seen during late prophase of meiosis 1.

**Bivalent**

1. *biol.* Double or joined in pairs, said of chromosomes.
2. *chem.* Having a valence of two.

**[1]Bivalve**

1. *zool.* Having a shell consisting of two valves or valvelike parts.
2. *bot.* Having two valves, as diatoms.

**[2]Bivalve.** A mollusk of the class Pelecypoda.

**Bivalve.** Member of a group of aquatic, molluscs whose shells consist of two hinged valves. The group includes mussels, clams and oysters.

**Bivium.** The two rays of a starfish (sea star) between which lies the madreporite.

**Bivoltine.** Having two broods a year, said of insects.

**Blaberidae** (class Insecta, order Blattodea). Family of medium to large, broad-bodied cockroaches, most of which have short, stout legs, and relatively short antennae. Some species burrow in the ground, or live in rotting wood. Leucophaea maderae (Madeira cockroach) is able to stridulate, and produces an offensive odour when disturbed. Gromphadorhina spiracles can produce sound by forcing air through the species. This mainly tropical group includes the largest cockroaches known.

**Black-backed Gull.** Gulls similar in appearance to the herring gull but with darker grey, almost black backs. There are two species : the greater black-backed gull and the lesser (smaller) black-backed gull.

**Black Bass.** Bass.

**Black Bear.** There are five species of black bear, living in the Americas and southern Asia. They are much smaller than the grizzly and the other brown bears, weighing only about 200 kg. The American black bear is very common in North America, especially in the national parks. Like its relatives, it is a good tree climber. The black bears eat a wide variety of food, including fruits, berries, rodents and insects.

**Blackberry** (or bramble). A thorny, trailing plant with white or pink flowers. The fruits, called blackberries, are actually clusters of small Drupes. There are hundreds of kinds.

**Blackbird.** The name given to a variety of unrelated birds in different parts of the world whose plumage is mainly black. The European blackbird is a member of the thrush family. It is a familiar garden bird with a beautiful song and a clucking alarm note. The male is glossy black with a bright orange bill. The female is brownish with speckled underparts and can be mistaken for a thrush. The American blackbirds are insect-eating birds related to orioles.

**Blackbuck.** Also known as the Indian antelope, the blackbuck is found over much of India and Pakistan. It is about one metre long and the male has remarkably twisted horns. It is one of the fastest land animals and has been credited with speeds of 80 kp/h. It can also leap well. The blackbuck is one of the few antelopes in which males are dark brown above, while the does and young animals are yellowish brown.

**Blackcap.** A warbler whose dark crown—black for the male, dark brown for the female— distinguishes it from the similar garden warbler. The bird's song is sometimes mistaken for that of the nightingale. Blackcaps live in woods and heaths and most fly south for the winter.

**Black Death.** Plague.

**Black Earth.** Chernozem.

**Blackfish.** One of a number of species of small, toothed whales of the genus Globicephala.

**Black Fly.** A small, dark-colored dipterous insect of the genus Simulium, family Simuliidae, a pest to man and domestic animals; also called buffalo gnat.

**Blackhead.** Of turkeys : a disease caused by the protozoon Histomonas meleagridis. The disease affects the caecum and liver of the bird, and the mortality rate map be high. The disease is transmitted by a nematode worm parasitic in the intestines of turkeys.

**Black-headed Gull.** A seabird common around European coasts. In winter, it looks very like the common gull but in summer it is distinguished by its brownish-black head, It also has distinctive red legs and bill. Like many other gulls, the black-headed gull ranges inland, feeding in flocks; many now breed inland and never go to sea.

**Blackman Reaction.** A term including all the reactions in the photosynthetic process which do not require light (dark reactions). Named after the discoverer.

**Black Mold**. Any of the molds of the order **Mucorales, as** Rhizopus nigricans, the common bread mold.

**Black Molly**. This little fish, a favourite with acquarists, is a black variety of the sailfin or related fishes which live in the rivers of Central America. The black varieties crop up from time to time in nature and they are bred artificially by aquarists. The fishes can be recognized by the large sail-like dorsal fin of the male.

**Blackout**. Loss of vision and finally unconsciousness resulting from linear and centrifugal acceleration due to reduced blood supply to the head.

**Black Snake**. One of a number of dark-colored snakes especially Coluber constrictor, the blue racer, a nonpoisonous snake.

**Blackthorn**. A small deciduous tree or shrub belonging to the rose family and often found in hedges. It is also called sloe. It has black bark, long sharp thorns and small white spring flowers in dense spikes. Its small blackish-purple fruit is used for making jams or wine and sloe gin.

**Black Window**. This infamous spider has a number of sub-species distributed over the warmer parts of the world. The North American sub-species is noted for the female's powerful venom which produces severe pain and paralysis in a person. It can sometimes cause death, but fatal bites are rare. The female spider is about 1 cm long and shiny black in colour. There is a red 'hour-glass' mark on the underside of her spherical abdomen. The male is much smaller. The name of the spider comes from the belief that the female always eats her husband after mating, but this does not always happen.

The American black bear is highly popular in National Parks, where it begs food from the motorists.

**Black Widow Spider**. A poisonous spider (Lactrodecus mactans) identified by a reddish, hourglass-shaped spot on ventral surface of abdomen.

**Bladder**

1. (in anatomy) (*a*) A hollow muscular organ in most vertebrates, also known as the urinary bladder, in which urine is stored before being discharged. In mammals urine is conveyed from the kidneys to the bladder by the ureters and is discharged to the outside through the urethra. (*b*) Any of various other saclike organs in animals for the storage of liquid or gas. Gall bladder; swim bladder.
2. (in botany) (*a*) A modified submerged left of certain aquatic insectivorous plants, such as the bladderwort (Utricularia). It forms a hollow with a single opening that is sealed by a valve to trap small aquatic invertebrates after they have been sucked in. *b*. An air-filled cavity in the thallus of certain seaweeds, such as the bladderwrack (Fucus vesiculosus).

**Bladder Kelp.** Buil kelp.

**Bladdernose.** The hooded seal (Cystophora cristata).

**Bladdernut.** A bladderlike seedpod of Staphylea trifolia, a shrub or small tree; also the plant which produces it.

**Bladder Worm.** The bladder-like larva of a tapeworm which, because it is present in a different host from the adult worm, was orginally considered to be as a distinct species.

**Bladderworts.** A group of carnivorous water plants with no roots. The leaves and stems are covered with tiny bladders, each of which acts as a trap for minute insect larvae and other aquatic animals.

**Bladder Wrack.** Common name for the brown seaweed Fucus vesiculous. The thallus is variable; it is typically flatiened and strap-like, repeatedly forked, and has prominent midribs and (usually) paired air-bladders which give buoyancy to the plant. Bladder wrack grows, often abundantly, on rocks, breakwaters, etc., between the high-

**and low-water marks. ('Bladder work' is sometimes used a a synonym for 'egg wrack').**

**Bladdery.** **Inflated; having thin walls like a bladder.**

**Blade**

1. The leaf of a plant, especially that of an herb.
2. The thin expanded portion of a leaf, as distinguished from the petiole; lamina.
3. The flat, leaflike thallus of certain brown algae, as in kelps.

**Blandfordia** (family Liliaceae). Genus of five species of plants with stiff, fine leaves, and red to yellow flowers supported on a stiff stalk. The genus is endemic to Australia and often found in the wetter regions of the south, often under Eucalyptus.

**Blanket Bog.** It consists of acid peat which is formed from remains of bog plants. It varies in thickness and its high acidity (*p*H 3.0-4.5) is caused by continuous flow of water through peat which washes away bases and prevents minerals from underlying rocks reaching plants roots. Such bog can be formed over limestone.

**Blanketweed.** A group of filamentous green algae found in fresh or brackish water.

**Blast**

1. To ruin or destroy, as by a noxious wind.
2. To render incapable of producing fruit or seeds.
3. To become withered or blighted.

**Blastema**

1. An undifferentiated part from which an organ or structure develops.
2. The part of an organism which, in asexual reproduction, gives rise to a new organism. Compare anlage.

**Blastocoel.** The cavity of a blastula or blastocyst; the segmentation or cleavage cavity; the subgerminal cavity.

**Blastocyst.** Mammalian embryo at the stage at which, after cleavage, it is implanted in the wall of the uterus. It consists of a thin-walled, hollow sphere (trophoblast) enclosing a blastocoel : attached to the inner surface of the trophoblast at one end there is a sheet of cells designed to become the embryo proper.

**Blastoderm.** In eggs undergoing meroblastic cleavage, the disc of protoplasm in which cleavage takes place; in centrolecithal ova, the suface layer of cells enclosing the yolk.

**Blastodisc** (germinal disc). Disc-shaped layer of cytoplasm formed at the animal pole by the cleavage of a large, yolky egg, *e.g.* that of a bird or reptile. Mitosis within the blastodisc gives rise to the embryo and its membranes.

**Blastogenesis.** The development of a new individual by asexual reproduction; the development of a new individual or a part from a blastema. Compare embryogenesis.

**Blastoidea** (subphylum Pelmatozoa). Class of sessile, bud-like echinoderms, with biserial brachioles, well-developed, pentameral symmetry; theca composed of 17 major plates arranged in three circlets; and hydrospires (infolded, thin-walled, calcareous, linear structures) developed on each side of the ambulacra. Blostoidea range in age from Silurian to Lower Permian. They are uncommon as fossils, except in shallow-water calcareous rocks, often associated with 'reef' limestones.

**Blastokinesis.** Movement of an embryo within as egg, with reference to insects.

**Blastoma.** A tumor especially one that originates from embryonic cells.

**Blastomere.** One of the cells formed by the division of the fertilized egg during cleavage and prior to gastrulation. The blastomeres may differ in size, the larger ones being termed macromeres and the smaller ones micromeres.

**Blastomycetes** (subdivision Deuteromycotina). A class of fungi that characteristically form single yeast-like cells that reproduce by budding, *i.e.* a new cell is formed by extrusion from the periphery of the parent cell. In some cases a poorely-developed mycelium may be formed. There are two families.

**Blastopore.** Mouth-like opening of the archenteron or gastrocoel on the surface of an embryo in the gastrula stage. In many animals the blastopore becomes the anus, although in some it closes up at the end of gastrulation and may appear again at or near the same site. The blastopore is formed by an inward movement of the endoderm and mesoderm cells of the archenteron during gastrulation. Sometimes this movement is incomplete, so that an open pore does not develop; this explains the primitive streak of a bird or mammal embryo during gastrulation. In that case it is referred to as a 'virtual' blastopore.

**Blastophere.** An alternative name for the blastula.

**Blastostyle.** In colonial coelenterates, a modified reproductive polyp consisting of a central axis bearing numerous medusa buds.

**Blastozooid.** In tunicates, a zooid which arises by budding; a blastozoite. Compare oozooid.

**Blastula.** The first stage of development of an animal embryo, formed as a result of cleavage of a fertilized egg. This stage generally resembles a hollow ball with the dividing cells (blastomeres) of the embryo forming a layer (blastoderm) around a central cavity (blastocoel). Insect eggs have no blastula. In vertebrates the blastula forms a disc (blastodisc) on the surface of the yolk. In mammals the blastula stage is known as a blastocyst.

**Blattellidae** (class Insecta, order Blattodea). Large, cosmopolitan family of generally small cockroaches, which have long antennae and slender legs. Many species are fully winged in both sexes, and some species, most notably Blatella germanica (German cockroach), are domestic pests.

**Blattodea** (cockroaches, roaches; class Insecta). Order of medium to large, exopterygote insects in which the forewings are modified as rather strongly sclerotized tegmina. Wings are absent in some groups. The legs are gressorial (modified for running), and the body is dorsoventrally compressed. Auditory organs are absent. Females have a small, concealed ovipositor, and eggs are laid in an ohtheca. Most cockroaches are nocturnal, and during the day are usually found hiding in crevices. Burrowing and cave-dwelling species are known, and some species are even amphibious. Cockroaches may be adapted to desert conditions, or live in tropical rain forest. It is throught that most cockroaches are omnivorous. Of the approximately 3500 species known, some are of economic importance as domestic pests.

**Bleak**. A small silvery freshwater fish, generally about 13 cm long, which lives in shoals in slow-flowing streams and clear lakes. It belongs to the carp family and is found over most of central and northern Europe.

**Blechanaceae**. Family of terrestrial ferns with scaly rhizomes, to which the fronds are not jointed. The sori are short, or joined together in a continuous line, on a vein parallel to the midrib of the pinna. The indusium is outside the sorus, attached to the leaf surface or margin. Spore-bearing fronds are often distinct from the vegetable ones. There are 11 genera, of cosmopolitan distribution, containing more than 200 species, of which 180 are in the genus Blechmum.

**Bleed**

1. To lose blood, as from a wound.
2. To exude water or sap.

**Bleeding.** The exuding of sap from a wound. Bleeding Pressure=Root Pressure.

**Bleeding Time.** Used for describing the time when bleeding from some injured part ceases. Normally it is 2—6 minutes in most of the cases except under purpura when it is exceeded from 10—20 minutes.

**Blemmatogen.** A layer of hyphae having thickened walls, which covers the button of an agaric, and sometimes forms the veil.

**Blending Inheritance.** The intermingling of the characteristics of the parents so that the offspring are intermediate in form between their parents. It is usually seen when a characteristic is controlled by many genes, as for example, height or yield. If a characteristic is governed by single gene then blending inheritance is only seen when the alleles show incomplete dominance.

It was through that all characteristics become blended in the offspring. Until the rediscovery of Mendel's work this was the main criticism of Darwin's the ory of evolution by natural selection, for the variation upon which it depended would always be lost by such process. Mendel's demonstration of the particulate nature of inheritance removed this obstacle.

**Blenniidae** (blennies class Osteichthyes, subclass Actinopterygii, order Perciformes). Very large family of small, mostly marine fish found in shallow waters, even in tidal pools, in large numbers. They are identifiable by their long dorsal and anal fins, virtually naked skin, and two pronounced rays in each of the pelvic fins located below the gills; often they have tufts of skin (tentacles) above the head. Many species rely on skin coloration for protection. There are about 550 species, distributed worldwide in tropical and temperate waters.

**Blenny.** Member of a group of small fishes found around European coasts, usually on rocky shores. All blennies have a fin running nearly the whole length of their back. The group includes the Butterfish and the Eel-pout.

**Blepharoplast.** In flagellated protozoans, a deeply staining body from which the flagellum arises; basal granule.

**Blesbok.** Small sturdy antelopes standing about 1.25 metres at the shoulder. There is a white blaze on the face and a white patch at the base of the tail. The short horns diverge from each other near the base and then become more or less parallel. Blesbok were once in danger of extinction. Many now live a semi-domesticated life on South African farms.

**Blewit.** A stocky toadstool whose colour ranges from pale tan to grey. The stalk is violet, the gills are white to flesh-coloured and spores are pale pink. The fungus grows in grasslands where it often forms fairy rings. The wood blewit varies from chestnut brown to violet.

**Blight.** Any plant disease which results in withering and cessation of growth, especially one caused by a fungus, as the chestnut blight.

**Blind** Sightless; lacking a sense of vision.

**Blind Fish.** One of several species of fishes of the family Amblyopsidae inhabiting caves in the United States. Common genera are Amblyopsis and Typhlichthys.

**Blind Snake** This name applies to several hundred small, non-poisonous snakes living throughout the warmer parts of the world. They are worm-like creatures, usually only about 15 cm long, although some species reach one metre. They are not completely blind, but their eyes are very small and they can do no more than distinguish light from dark.

**Blind Spot.** The portion of the retina at which blood vessels and nerve fibres enter the optic nerve. There are no rods or cones in this area, so no visual image can be transmitted from it.

**Blindworm.** Blind snake; slowworm.

**Blister Beetle.** Blister beetles are most common in warm, dry climates. They get their name because their bodies contain a substance called cantharidin, which produces blisters on the skin of anyone touching them. The only British species has a shiny green body and is known as the Spanish fly.

**Blocking.** In synoptic meteorology, the establishment in the mid-latitudes of a high-pressure system that interrupts or diverts for a considerable period the typically eastward movement of depressions and other synoptic features in the zonal flow. Over W. Furope, for example, depressions are forced by blocking to move northward toward Scandinavia or southward over S. France and Spain.

**Blocking High** (blocking anticyclone). In synoptic meteorology, an anticyclone with deep circulation so placed as to interrupt or divert the eastward movement of the typical succession of low-pressure features (depressions) in the zonal flow of mid-latitudes. The usual zonal flow of middle latitudes is at such times diverted into more meridional flow around the high-pressure area, where settled weather can then result.

**Blood.** A fluid body tissue that acts as a transport medium within an animal. It is contained within a blood vascular system and in vertebrates is circulated by means of contractions of the heart. Oxygen and food are carried to tissues, and carbon dioxide and chemical (nitrogenous) waste are transported from tissues to excretory organs for disposal (excretion). In addition blood carries hormones and also acts as a defence system. Blood consists of a liquid (blood plasma) containing blood cells (erythrocyte; leucocyte) and platelets.

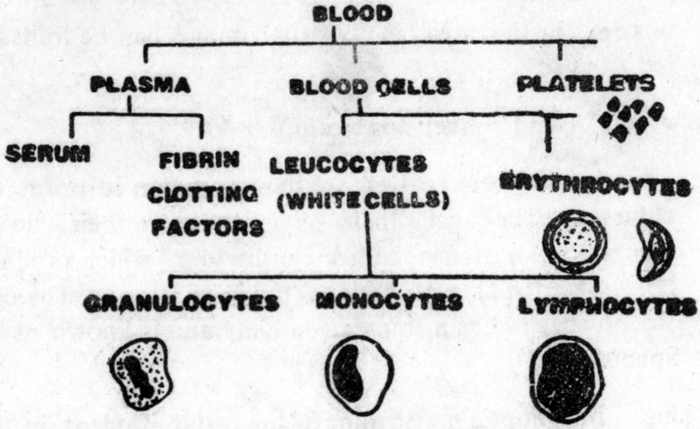


Composition of mammalian blood

**Blood-brain Barrier.** The mechanism that controls the passage of substances from the blood to the cerebrospinal fluid bathing the brain and spinal cord. It takes the form of a semipermeable lipid membrane permitting the passage of solutions but excluding particles and large molecules. This barrier provides the central nervous system with a constant environment, while not interfering with the transport of essential metabolites.

**Blood Cell** (blood corpuscle). Any of the cells that are normally found in the blood plasma. These include red cells (erythrocyte) and white cells.

**Blood Clotting.** Response to the injury of a blood vessel in which the escape of liquid blood is prevented by its conversion into a solid mass, or clot, composed of fibres of fibrin in which blood cells are enmeshed. In vertebrates, a soluble protein, fibrinogen, found in the blood plasma is acted upon by the enzyme thrombin. As a result, a negatively charged peptide is split off the fibrinogen molecule, leaving monomeric fibrin; this is capable of rapid polymerization to produce the tangle of insoluble threads that forms a clot. Active thrombin is formed from inactive prothrombin, also found in blood plasma, by a very complex process involving a lipoprotein factor liberated by rupturing blood platelets, a protein plasma thromboplastin component (PTC), antihaemophilic globulin (AHG), calcium ions, etc. Removal of free calcium from the blood, *e.g.*, by adding citrate or oxalate, inhibits the formation of thrombin.

Faciliated by different factors called clotting factors. The brief events of this process are summarised as follows :

Intrinsic — Extrinsic

Inactive F-XII — Tissue Thromboplastin (on injury)
↓ Collagen
Active F-XII
↓
Inactive F-XI→Active F-XI
↓
Inactive F-IX→Active F-IX Active F-VII←Inactive F-VI
F-VIII ↓ ↓
Inactive F-X ↓ Active F-X←—Inactive F-X Fibrinogen
Platelets F-V ↓ $Ca^{2+}$ ↓
Fibrin
Prothrombin————→Thrombin————→ ↓ F-XI
Clott

Blood clotting

**Blood Corpuscle**. The cells of the blood. There are two types found in vertebrate blood : red corpuscles and white corpuscles. Red corpuscles contain a pigment called Haemoglobin which carries oxygen through the body. White corpuscles are involved in the destruction of bacteria and any other parasites or foreign substances which invade the body. Certain of them are responsible for the production of Antibodies.

**Blood Gount**. The determination of the number of blood cells (erythrocytes or leukocytes) per cu. mm. of blood. In man, red cells average 5 million in males, 4½ million in females; white cells average 5,000 to 10,000 per cu. mm.

**Blood Fluke.** A trematode of the genus Schistosoma; a schistosome.

**Blood Groups.** In man, four primary types of blood based on the presence or absence of antigens (agglutinogens) in red blood cells and antibodies (agglutinins) in the serum. The principal groups and their frequencies are : 0 (47%), A (41%), B (9%), and AB (3%). Other blood groups include M, N, and Rh groups based on the presence of corresponding antigens in red blood cells.

**Blood Island.** An isolated mass of mesodermal cells from which the first blood cells and blood vessels in vertebrates arise.

**Blood Pigment.** A respiratory pigment present in the blood, as hemoglobin.

**Blood Plasma.** The straw-colured liquid left when all the cells have been removed from blood. It consists of 91% water and 7% proteins, which are albumins, globulins (mainly antibodies), and prothrombin and fibrinogen (concerned with clotting). Plasma also consists of the ions of dissolved salts, especially sodium, potassium, chloride, bicarbonate, sulphate, and phosphate. Plasma is slightly alkaline (pH 7.3) and the proteins and bicarbonate act as buffers to keep this constant. Its main function is to transport dissolved food (as glucose, amino acids, fat, and fatty acids), excretory products, (urea and uric acid), dissolved gases (about 40 $mm^3$ oxygen, 19 $mm^3$ carbon dioxide, and 1 $mm^3$ nitrogen in 100 $mm^3$ plasma), hormones, and vitamins.

**Blood Platelets.** Minute bodies in blood plasma consisting of non-nucleated fragments of the cytoplasm of megakaryocytes. They are the source of thromboplastin. Also called thrombocytes.

**Blood Pressure.** The pressure exerted by the flow of blood through the major arteries of the body. This pressure is greatest during the contraction of the ventricles of the heart (systolic pressure; systole), which forces blood into the arterial system. Pressure falls to its lowest level when the heart is filling with blood (diastolic pressure, diastole). Blood pressure is measured in millimetres of mercury using an instrument called a sphygmomanometer. Normal blood pressure for a young average adult human is in the region of 120/80 mm Hg (the higher number is the systolic blood pressure; the lower number the diastolic blood pressure), but individual variations are common. Abnormally high blood pressure (hypertension) may be associated with disease or it may occur without an apparent cause.

**Blood Proteins.** Proteins present in the blood plasma, principally serum albumin, serum globulin, and serum fibrinogen.

**Blood Rain.** Phenomenon of reddish coloured rainfall, caused by dust particles that have been lifted up from arid areas and carried long distances by the winds before they are washed out in precipitation. Saharan red dust sometimes occurs in rainfall over Europe, even as far north as Finland.

**Blood Serum.** Blood plasma from which the fibrin and clotting factors have been removed by centrifugation or vigorous stirring, so that it cannot clot. Serum containing a specific antibody or antitoxin may be used in the treatment or prevention of certain infections. Such serum is generally derived from a non-human mammal (*e.g.*, a horse).

**Blood Sinus,** An irregular space or channel through which blood flows, as those in the tissues of anthropods or in the meaninges of the brain of a vertebrate.

**Bloodsucker.** An animal that sucks blood, especially a leech. Term is also applied to certain red-throated Asiatic and Australian lizards and true vampires.

**Blood Sugar.** A carbohydrate, cbiefly glucose, present in blood plasma. Normal value in man—70-120 mg. per 100 ml.

**Blood Transfusion.** The introduction of blood (whole or fraction) or plasma into a blood vessel.

**Blood Typing.** The procedure used to determine the blood group to which a person belongs, consisting of adding anti-A and anti-B sera to suspensions of unknown cells.

**Blood Vascular System.** In mammals, it is a continuous system of vessels having blood, which transports food materials, excretory products, hormones, respiratory gases, etc., from one part of the body to another. Certain invertebrates (molluscs and arthropods) possess an open system in which blood flows in blood spaces (*e.g.* the haemoceol of Crustacea). Vertebrates and most invertebrates possess a closed system with the blood contained in blood vessels and generally circulated by muscular contractions of the vessels or a heart.

**Blood-vein Moth.** A European moth, with pink to purple wings, striped across with a single red 'vein'. It is seen around woodland edges and over damp ground. The caterpillar is grey with four dark spots along the back.

**Blood Vessel.** A tubular structure present in vertebrates and some invertebrates that is able to transport blood throughout the body. Blood vessels vary in diameter and hence are able to regulate the blood flow to different parts of the body; for example to the surface layers to regulate heat loss.

**Bloodworm.** The bright red larvae of certain non-biting midges which live in stagnant water.

**Bloody-nose Beetle.** Two species of beetle which like the blister beetle (which causes blisters on the skin), use a 'chemical' weapon for defence. They spit out a red blood-like liquid which, although not harmful, causes a would-be enemy to halt—giving the beetle more time to escape.

Bloody-nose beetle

**[1]Bloom.** To yield or produce blossoms or flowers.

**[2]Bloom**

1. The state of flowering, as roses are in bloom.
2. The delicate, waxy or powdery coating of the fruit or leaves of certain plants.
3. The sporadic seasonal occurrence of enormous numbers of algae in inland waters.

**[1]Blossom.** The flower of a seed plant, especially one which produces an edible fruit; a bloom.

**[2]Blossom.** To bloom or put forth blossoms.

**Blow.** Spout.

**Blow-fly.** The general name given to bluebottles and greenbottles. The flies are particularly unwelcome in kitchens since they lay their eggs on meat. The eggs hatch in about one day and the larvae or maggots feed on the decaying or 'fly-blown' meat.

**Blowhole.** The nostril or spiracle on dorsal surface of the head of whales and other cetaceans through which spouting takes place.

**Blow Snake.** The hognose snake (Heterodon), noted for feigning death. Also called puff adder or spreading viper.

**Blue.** Name of a widespread group of butterflies. The males are blue, the females often brown with only hints of blue.

The large blue is particularly interesting because its caterpillars are collected by ants and taken into the ants' nest. There they are fed on ant larvae, giving off, in exchange, a sweet fluid which is eaten by the ants. The caterpillars spend the winter in the ants' nest pupate, then fly away as winged adults in the spring.

**Blue Baby.** A baby with bluish skin (cyanosis) resulting from imperfect oxygenation of the blood. Such may be temporary as from obstruction of respiratory passageways or permanent due to a cardiac anomaly such as a patent foramen ovale or ductus arteriosus or both.

**Bluebell.** Short spring flower belonging to the lily family, which carpets woods sea cliffs and mountains in spring with its sky-blue bell-shaped flowers. The long narrow leaves grow directly from the bulb and the flowers are arranged in a long spike. The flowers can also be pink or white. In Scotland, the term bluebell is applied to the harebell and the bluebell is better known as wild hyacinth.

**Bluebottle.** Several species of large, metallic blue flies, also called belowflies. They have a buzzing flight and are disliked because they spread disease and spoil food.

Bluebottle

Bluebottles lay their eggs on rotting flesh, meat and fish The eggs hatch into white larvae or maggots about a day later.

**Bluebird.** A North American songbird (Sialia sialis) of the thrush family, Turdidae.

**Blue Crab.** The edible crab (Callinectes) of the Atlantic coast.

**Bluefish.** A voracious fish weighing up to 10 kg which lives in most of the warm seas of the world. It swims in large shoals, and attacks all kinds of fishes with astonishing ferocity. The bluefish occurs in exceptionally large numbers in the western Atlantic and is caught commercially for its tasty flesh.

**Blue Fox.** A color phase of the Arctic fox (Alopex lagopus).

**Blue-green Algae.** Small, often microscopic organisms in the kingdom Protista. They form a scum on rocks, in soil, and on still water.

**Blue Gill.** Lepomis macrochirus, a pan fish of the sunfish family, Centrarchidae, a highly esteemed sport and food fish.

**Blue Jay.** The common jay (Cyanocitta cristata) of the family Corvidae.

**Blue Racer.** Black snake.

**Blues.** A world-wide group of small butterflies, most of which are blue in colour, though the females are often partly or wholly brown. The catespillars of blues often secrete a sugary fluid called honeydew which is drunk by ants.

**Blueschist.** Metamorphic rock that has undergone regional metamorphism at low temperatures and high pressures. Blueschists contain abundant blue glaucophane, which is a blue amphibole derived from the metamorphism of geosynclinal deposits. Blueschists are usually associated with destructive plate-margin environments.

**Blue Shark.** A dangerous shark named for its colour. It grows up to 4 metres long and lives in the open oceans, occasionally visiting the North Sea. It is also called the blue whaler.

**Bluethroat.** A bird related to the robin. It nests close to the ground and frequents marshy woodland and heathland. The male has a blue throat. Scandinavian birds have a red spot in the blue patch; birds from further south have a white spot.

**Blue Tit.** The commonest tit and the one most adapted to life with people, frequently seen in gardens feeding at bird-tables. It has bright blue markings on its head, wings and tail, a green back and yellow underparts, and a black streak running through the eyes. It has an undulating flight and can climb up tree trunks in search of insects.

**Blue Whale.** This is the largest animal that has ever lived. It can reach 30 metres in length and nearly 150 tonnes in weight—as much as 30 elephants. Yet this huge creature feeds on tiny planktonic animals which it strains from the water through plates of a horny material called baleen, or whalebone, in its mouth. During the summer, blue whales live in the polar seas, but they move to warmer seas in the winter, and their calves are born in these warmer regions. The calves are over 7 metres long when they are born. The species is in great danger of dying out because whalers have killed so many of them.

**Blusher.** Common name for the fruit body of Amanita rubescens. It is mushroom-shaped, with reddish-brown or brown cap bearing scattered whitish patches (remnants of the universal veil). The flesh turns pink or reddish on breaking or bruising. The stem is white. It is common on ground in woodland during late summer and autumn.

**BMR.** Abbreviation of Basal Metabolic Rate. Metabolic rate.

**BNA.** Basle Nomina Anatomica, a system of antomical nomenclature.

**Boa.** Boas are large snakes found in the warmer parts of America, especially the Amazon basin. They kill their prey by coiling around it and suffocating it, but they are not poisonous. Large lizards, birds and some mammals are eaten. Best known of the boas is the boa constrictor, which sometimes reaches a length of about 4 metres. The Anaconda is the largest of the boas. There are also some much smaller boas, known as sand boas, in Africa and Asia.

**Boa Constrictor.** A large tropical American snake (Constrictor constrictor) which kills its prey by crushing it to death within its coils.

**Boar**

1. The uncastrated male of swine.
2. The male of a guinea pig.

**Boar, Wild.** A wild pig once common in Britain and northern Europe but now extinct in this area. It is still widely distributed in the forests of southern and central Europe.

**Boatbill.** A heron-like bird living in the swampy forests of South America. Its most remarkable feature is a wide, flat bill which is used to scoop small animals from the water.

**Boat Shell.** A marine gastropod of the genera Crepidula and Cymbium.

**Bobcat.** The wildcat of America, ranging from southern Canada to Mexico. It is actually a small lynx, about one metre long including its short tail. The bobcat hunts mainly a night and it is an excellent climber. It feeds mainly on rabbits (cottontails) and small rodents.

**Bobolink.** A songbird (Dolichonyx oryzivorus) of the family Icteridae. Also called reedbird or ricebird.

**Bobwhite.** A species of American quail, especially Colinus virginianus, an upland game bird. Called partridge in southern United States.

**BOD.** Biochemical oxygen demand.

**Body**

1. The total substance of an organism.
2. The trunk or main part of an organism as distinguished from its limbs or appendages.
3. The principal part of an organ or structure as distinguished from its ends or extremities, as of a bone.

**Body Cavity.** The internal cavity of the body of an animal, which is present in most invertebrates and all vertebrates and contains the major organs. The body cavity of vertebrates and many invertebrates is the coelom. In vertebrates the body cavity is divided by a transverse septum just posterior to the heart into the abdominal and thoracic cavities (abdomen; thorax). In mammals the septum is the diaphragm.

**Body Cell.** A fertile cell formed along with the infertile stalk cell after mitotic division of the generative cell in the gymnosperm pollen tube. It divides into two sperm cells.

**Body Cell.** A fertile cell which is formed along with infertile stalk cell after mitotic division of generative cell in the pollen tube of gymnosperms. It gets divided at a later stage to form 2 antherozoids (sperm cells).

**Body Louse.** A sucking, parasitic insect (Pediculus humanus corporis) of the order Anoplura, a transmitter of the causative organisms of epidemic typhus, trench fever, and relapsing fever.

**Body Stalk.** In mammalian development, a narrow stalk of mesoderm which connects the caudal end of the embryo to the chorion.

**Body Whorl.** The largest coil of a gastropod shell.

**Boehmeria** (family Urticaceae). Genus of trees and shrubs including B. nivea (China grass or rhea), which is cultivated in China for the long, touch, silky fibre of the inner bark, and in the tropics-as the variety tenacissima-for ramie fibre. There are 100 species, occurring in the tropics and northern subtropics.

**Bog.** Plant community of acidic, wet areas. Decomposition rates in it are slow, favouring peat development. Typical plants include bog-mosses (Sphagnum species), 'sedges' (*e* g. Eriophorum species), and 'heathers' (*e.g.* Calluna vulgaris and Erica tetralix). Insectivorous plants (*e.g.* sundews, Drosera species) are especially characteristic. They compensate for low nutrient levels by trapping and digesting insects. Three types of bog community are commonly distinguished : ombrogenous blanket, raised bogs, and valley bogs. There reflect the different physiographic and climatic conditions that may give rise to bog formation. Compare fen.

**Bogbean** (or buckbean). A marsh herb of Europe, northern Asia and North America. It has large, clover-like leaves and spikes of frilly pink and white flowers.

**Bog Moss.** Any moss which grows in bogs, especially those of the genus Sphagnum.

**Bohr Effect.** Decrease in the affinity of haemoglobin for oxygen, brought about either by a decrease in pH or by an increase in the partial pressure of carbon dioxide. It is an important mechanism in the release of oxygen by haemoglobin in the blood in respiratory tissues, where the partial pressures of carbon dioxide are high.

**Boidae** (constricting snakes; order Squamata, suborder Serpentes Ophidia). Family of large, tropical snakes that kill their prey by constriction. They have a flexible skull, paired lungs, and enlarged ventral scales; the pelvis and rudimentary hind limbs are present as anal spurs. The family includes the pythons (all Old World in distribution) and the boas (mainly New World in distribution). There are about 70 species.

**Bole.** The main trunk or stem of a tree; a caudex.

**Boletaceae** (order Agaricales). Family of fungi which form mushroom-shaped fruit bodies that typically bear a layer of tubes on the underside of the cap (in place of the gills of a mushroom). The hymenium lines the inner surface of the tubes. There are many genera, including both edible and poisonous species. They are found on the ground under trees, with which they commonly form mycorrhizal associations.

**Bolete.** The boletes are a group of fleshy fungi in which the underside of the cap is sponge-like with tiny pores. The pores are the openings of closely packed tubes in which spores are produced. The penny bun bolete or cep is an edible and excellent fungus which is used in the manufacture of many mushroom soups.

**Boll.** The pod or capsule of a plant, as a cotton boll.

**Boll Weevil.** Anthonomus grandis, a serious pest of cotton.

**Bollworm.** This name is applied to the caterpillars of several moths which attack the bolls or seed-pods of cotton Bollworms are widespread in the cotton-growing regions of the world and do a great deal of damage to cotton and also to many other crop plants.

**Bolting.** Used for the permature production of flowers and seeds in plants. It is common in biennial crops *e.g.*, sugar beet. If they run to seed in the first growing season then their yield is generally considerably reduced.

**Bolus.** A round mass, especially a moist mass of food formed in the mouth and prepared for swallowing.

**Bombacaceae.** Family of trees, closely related to Malvaceae, in which the trunk is often stout, and the leaves often palmately compound and usually scaly. The flowers are often large, and hermaphrodite; with five sepals and petals, usually partly united; numerous free stamens; and a superior ovary of 2-5 fused carpels. The fruit is a big, woody capsule, often spiny, or tessellated. There are 20 genera, with 180 species, distributed in the tropics.

**Bomb Calorimeter.** An apparatus that is used to measure the quantity of heat produced when a known amount of carbohydrate, fat, protein, or some mixture of these is burned. It consists of a strong cylindrical steel chamber, resistant to high pressures, surrounded by a jacket containing a known volume of water. The weighed foodstuff is placed in the chamber, oxygen is pumped in under pressure, and the food is ignited electrically. The rise in temperature of the surrounding water gives a measure of the amount of heat generated by the oxidized food.

**Bombina Bombina** (fire-bellied toad; order Anura (Salientia), family Discoglossidae). Species of primitive, essentially aquatic toads, which are grey-black, with a red, speckled belly. They grow to 4 cm long. The male has internal vocal sacs which inflate the throat. Nuptial pads develop on the lower arm and the first two fingers. The species occurs in C. and E. Europe.

**Bombycidae** (silk moths; order Lepidoptera). Family of moths with broad and generally brown wings. The antennae are bipectinate. The larvae spin very dense silk cocoons. There are few species, found mainly in tropical Africa and Asia.

Composition $Cu_5FeS_4$, which occurs in hydrothermal veins, in zones of secondary enrichment, and as a primary mineral in igneous rocks and pegmatites. It is distinguished by its iridescent colours, solubility in nitric acid, and its alteration to secondary copper minerals. It is reddish-brown to various shades of purplish blue, the colours iridescent on tranished surfaces, and it has a pale grey streak and a metallic lustre. It crystallizes in the cubic system. The crystals are rough cubes, rhombododecahedra, and also massive. It is an ore for copper.

**Bombycilla** (waxwings; family Bombycillidae). Genus of brown-grey birds with crests, and secondaries that have red, wax-like tips. The tail is tipped with yellow or red. They have short, stout bills, and short legs. They are arboreal, and gregarious in winter. They feed mainly on berries, and nest in pine trees. There are three species, found in Europe, N. America, and Japan.

**Bombycillidae** (hypocolius, silky flycatchers, waxwings; order Passeriformes). Family of variable, soft-plumaged, mostly crested birds, inhabiting forests, plains, and deserts, feeding on fruit and nesting in trees. There are five genera, with eight species, although the silky flycatchers are sometimes placed in a separate family Ptilogonatidae. They are found in N. and C. America, Europe, and Asia.

**Bombykol**. Refers to the sex attractant pheromone of female silk-worm moth Bombyx.

**Bombyliidae** (bee-flies; class Insecta, order Diptera, suborder Brachycera). Family of flies, most of which are medium to large, with densely pubescent bodies, and slender legs. The proboscis is elongate, points forward, and is adapted for feeding on nectar from flowers with long corollas. The third antennal segment is simple, with the style small or absent. Cell $M_3$ is absent from the wing venation. Their common name refers to their appearance and adult behaviour, and to their larvae, which are parasitic upon bees and wasps, although some species have larvae that parasitize other insects. Eggs are laid near the entrance to the nest of the specific bee host parasitized by that species of bee-fly. The tiny larvae enter the nest and usually wait until the bee larva has pupated before metamorphosing from a small, mobile animal to a smooth, fat larva which feeds on the bee pupa. The bee-fly pupa is dual-phased. The first pupa is 'normal'; the second stage has a sharp battering ram with which to break down the nest cell wall, which is made by the adult bee when closing the cell. The adult bee-fly emerges once the second-stage pupa has ruptured the seal. More than 2000 species of bee-flies have been described.

**Bombyx Mori** (common silk moth; order Lepidoptera, family Bombycidae). Moth used for the commercial production of silk; the species is no longer found wild. A silk cocoon is spun by the larva. After softening, the cocoon is unwound mechanically. A single cocoon may yield up to 3 km of silk. Commercial production may have started before 4700 BC in China. The larvae feed on mulberry leaves.

**Bone.** The hard connective tissue of which the skeleton of most vertebrates is formed. It comprises a matrix of collagen fibres (30%) impregnated with bone salts (70%), mostly calcium phosphate, in which are embedded bone cells (osteoblasts and osteocytes), which secrete the matrix. Bone generally replaces embryonic cartilage and is of two sorts—compact bone and spongy bone. The outer compact bone is formed as concentric layers (lamellae)

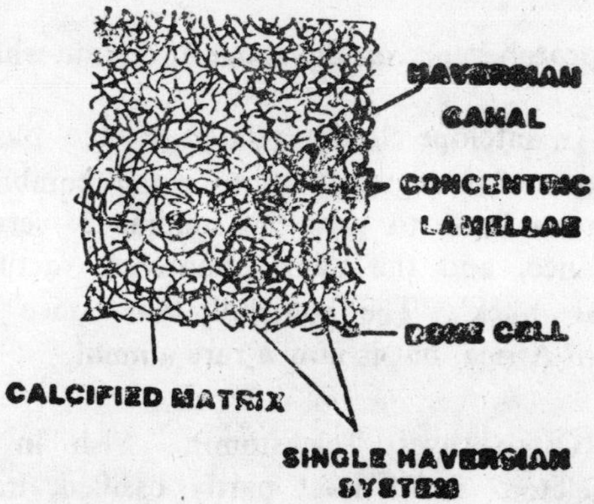


Structure of compact bone

that surround small holes (Haversian canals). The inner spongy bone is chemically similar but forms a network of bony bars. The spaces between the bars may contain bone marrow or (in birds) air for lightness.

**Bonebreaker.** A bird which breaks bones to feed on the marrow, as the giant fulmer, lammergeier, and osprey.

**Bone Cell.** A cell in bone tissue, as an osteoblast, osteocyte, osteoclast.

**Bone Marrow.** A soft tissue contained within the central cavity and internal spaces of a bone. At birth and in young animals the marrow of all bones is concerned with the formation of blood cells : it contains myeloid tissue and is known as red marrow. In mature animals the marrow of the long bones ceases producing blood cells and is replaced by fat, being known as yellow marrow.

**Bongo.** Boocercus euryceros. A large antelope of equatorial Africa.

**Bonito.** This name is given to several species of mackerel-like fish. The common bonito, found on both sides of the Atlantic in the tropical and subtropical zones, is a streamlined steel-blue fish about 60 cm long. Similar species occur in other parts of the oceans.

**Bonnet.** A protuberance on the snout of certain whales.

**Bontebok.** An antelope closely related to the blesbok. The white face, white legs and white rump combine with the dark brown back to give the animal a very attractive appearance, and the name bontebok actually means 'painted buck'. The bontebok was once common is southern Africa, but is now a rare animal.

**Bony Fish** (Osteichthyes, Teleostomi). Fish in which the endoskeleton is at least partly ossified, including the dermal bones of the upper and lower jaws. Characteristic features are the terminal mouth, homocercal tail, operculum covering the gills, scales on the skin, and the presence of a swimbladder (although sometimes this has been lost in the course of later evolution).

**Booby.** A group of birds belonging to the gannet family found in tropical regions. They have goose-sized bodies with thick necks and large heads. Boobies breed on coasts and islands and, like gannets, they feed by diving for fishes out at sea.

**Booklouse.** The name applied to a number of tiny plump-bodied wingless insects which feed on the paste and glue of book-bindings. They can become serious pests in libraries. Many related insects, some of them with-wings, feed on the dust and pollen grains on tree-trunks.

**Book Gill.** A gill composed of thin plates or lamella, as that of the king carb (Xiphosura or Limulus).

**Book Lice.** Wingless insects of the order Psocoptera, family Lipsocelidae.

**Book Lungs.** One of the two kinds of respiratory organ found in spiders. They are located in the abdomen, just below the pedicel, and are composed of many fine leaves. Blood is passed over a large surface area to absorb oxygen. The openings of the book lungs (branchial opercula) are situated on the ventral surface of the abdomen and may be closed to prevent water loss. The other type of organ is a tracheal spiracle located just anterior to the spinnerets. The fastest-moving spiders have no book lungs, but have instead two pairs of tracheal spiracles; these are also commonly found in small species, for which water loss is a special consideration. Book lungs are believed to be the ancestral type of respiratory organ in arachnids.

**Boomer.** A large male kangaroo hunted for sport.

**Boomsfang.** One of the rear-fanged snakes, in which some of the back teeth carry venom. Boomslangs are African snakes and they live in the trees, feeding on lizards, birds and small mammals. They average one metre in length and are ueually green or brown in colour. Their venom is extremely poisonous.

**Booplidae** (order Phthiraptera, suborder Amblycera). Family of chewing lice which are parasitic chiefly on Australian marsupials. Only two species are not found on marsupials; Heterodoxus spiniger has become established on dogs presumably having transferred to dogs since humans introduced them to Australia, and is now found all around the world between latitudes 40 °N and 40 °S; and Therodoxus oweni is found on the cassowary. Members of the family differ from other Amblycera in possessing a seta borne on a protuberance on each side of the mesonotum, and the fusion of the metanotum to abdominal tergum I. There are eight genera, with about 35 species.

**Bora**. Regional term for a cold and typically very dry wind from the north-east, blowing down from the mountains on the E. side of the Adriatic Sea. They are most common in winter on N. Adriatic coasts. The wind is probably a consequence of continental high pressure in central Europe with low pressure to the south in the Mediterranean. The wind is often accompanied by much precipitation when it is associated with depressions in the Adriatic. In other areas it is used as a generic term for cold squalls moving downhill from uplands.

**Borage.** A bristly garden plant with cucumber-scented juices and bright blue flowers arranged in leafy clusters. It was once commonly used in medicine and cooking.

**Boraginaceae**. Family of herbs, or rarely shrubs or trees, most of which are rough or hispid, usually with rounded stems, and with alternate, exstipulate, entire leaves. The flowers are usually regular, and borne in curved cymes. The calyx is five-toothed; and corolla five-lobed, and saucer-, funnel-, or bell-shaped; it is often pink in bud, changing later to blue. There are five stamens, alternating with the corolla-lobes. The ovary is four-celled, or less often two-celled, with the style inserted between the four lobes, or terminal. The fruit is normally composed of four nutlets.

There are about 85 genera, with 1600 species, which are cosmopolitan in distribution, but centred in S. Europe and E. Asia.

**Borassodendron** (family Palmae). Genus of stout, solitary palm trees with massive fan leaves, and a smooth, knife-edged stalk. They are dioecious, the little-branched, stout inflorescence forming among the leaves. The flowers occur in groups of 2·6, enclosed in bracts. The fruits are massive, globose, 12 cm in diameter, and in pendulous bunches, with a fibrous pericarp. There are three seeds, with thick, stony walls protruding as flanges into the endosperm. There are two species, native to rain forest in S. Thailand, Malaya, and Borneo.

**Borassus** (lontar, palmyra palm, tal; family Palmae). Genus of stout, solitary palm trees, with massive fan leaves which have short, spiny stalks split at the base, through which the sparsely-branched, stout inflorescence hangs. They are dioecious, the flowers sunken in groups. The fruits are big, globose, and 18 cm in diameter. The pericarp is fibrous or fleshy, and is edible when ripe. There are three seeds, with thick, stony walls. The leaves provide writing material; the flower is a source of toddy. The trees are much planted. There is one (or several polymorphic) species, native to Africa, Madagascar, Sri Lanka, India, and seasonal areas from SE Asia to Queensland.

**Borax Carmine.** A red dye, used in optical microscopy, that stains nuclei and cytoplasm pink. It is frequently used to stain large pieces of animal tissue.

**Bordeaux Mixture.** A mixture of copper sulphate and calcium hydroxide used as a fungicide. It was first used by P.M.A. Millardet in France in 1883-85 to control vine downy mildew (Plasmopara viticola). A common mixture is 40g copper sulphate and 40g calcium hydroxide in 51 water.

**Bordered Pit.** A pit possessing an extension of the secondary cell wall, *i.e.* a border, arching over part of the pit cavity.

In many gymnosperms, bordered pits also possess a thickening of the primary wall material, termed a torus, in the central part of the pit membrane, the remaining unthickened part being termed the margo. Bordered pits mainly occur in vessel elements, tracheids, and fibres in the xylem, but may also occur in some extraxylary sclerenchyma cells. Pit pairs may be half-bordered, in which case one member of a pit pair is bordered and the other is not. This is sometimes the case in pits linking parenchyma cells and tracheary cells. Compare simple pit.

**Border Parenchyma.** A sheath of one or more layers of parenchyma which are surrounding a vascular bundle.

**Bordered Pit.** A thin area in the wall between two vessels surrounded by overchanging rims of thickened wall.

**Bordetella.** Genus of bacteria not assigned to a taxonomic family. The cells are very small, ovoid, Gram-negative, and non-motile, or motile with many flagella. They are chemo-organotrophic, and can grow only in the presence of air. They are found as parasites and pathogens of the respiratory tract in mammals (B. pertussis is the causal agent of whooping cough).

**Bore.** Very rapid rise of the tide, in which the advancing flood waters form a wave with an abrupt front. Tidal bores occur in certain shallow estuaries aad river mouths where there is a large tidal range, *e.g.* the Amazon, the Bay of Fundy, the Tsing Kiang in China, and the Severn, Trent, and Ouse rivers in England.

**Boreal.** Northern.

**Boreal Climate.** The climate associated with the boreal ('taiga') forest zone of Eurasia, where it extends to 65-70 °N in the west and 50 °N in the east, and N. America, where it extends from the fringe of the tundra southwards to 55 °N in the east. Winters are long and cold, with temperatures below 6 °C for 6-9 months, and with short summers with temperatures averaging more than 10 °C. Precipitation, as snow in winter, typically amounts to 380-635 mm per annum.

**Boreal Forest.** Circumpolar, cold-temperate forest dominated by conifers, but with some broad-leaved hardwoods. To the north it is bounded by tundra and to the south by temperate mixed forest, steppe, or semi-desert. The American and Asian sectors of the forest are floristically more diverse than the European sector.

**Boreal Period.** Period in post-glacial (*i.e.* post-Devensian or Flandrian) times from about 8800-7500 BP, which preceded the climatic optimum of early Atlantic times. Pollen records typically show an increasing abundance of thermophilous tree species and also indicate the drier, more continental conditions that characterized the ensuing Atlantic period. The early Boreal corresponds to late Pollen Zone V; otherwise the Boreal is linked with Pollen Zone VI, which is sometimes subdivided to give Zones VIa, VIb, and VIc, according to the most abundant tree pollen represented. For Britain, the Boreal period is significant as the last period in post-glacial times in which Britain was joined to mainland Europe by a land bridge across the Dover Strait.

**Borhyaenoidea** (infraclass Metatheria, order Marsupialia). Extinct superfamily of S. American marsupial carnivores, the largest about the size of a wolf, which lived from the Palaeocene to Pliocene. Similarities between borhyaenoids and Thylacinus (the Tasmanian 'wolf') suggest that marsupials originated in S. America and moved across Antarctica to Australia. Borhyaenoids became extinct following the colonization of S. America by placental mammals.

**Boring Clam.** Any of a number of marine clams of the family Pnoladidae which bore into wood, coral, or soft rock, as Pholas.

**Boring Sponge.** A sponge which bores into the shells of oysters, clams, and other mollusks, as Cliona.

**Boron** Symbol : B. A metalloid element, atomic number 5, atomic weight 10.81, found in very low concentrations in plant tissues. Its role is uncertain though boron deficiency quickly results in changes in cell membrane function and in cell extension. Various plant diseases, *e.g.*, heart rot of beets and alfalfa yellows, have been attributed to boron deficiency. It has been suggested that a boron-sugar complex is involved in the movement of substrates through the phloem, though this idea is now largely rejected. Pollen germination and pollen tube growth are both greatly enhanced by addition of borate to the growth medium. Boron has been implicated in the uptake of calcium and appears necessary for the proper development of apical meristems.

**Boronia** (family Rutaceae, tribe Boroniaceae). Genus chiefly of shrubs less than a metre high, with strongly aromatic leaves, and four-petalled, star-like flowers which are usually pink. They are found on heathland and in dry sclerophyll forests in shady places. There are 70 species, endemic to and found throughout temperate Australia.

**[1]Boss.** A knoblike protuberance or umbo.

**[2]Boss.** In the United States, a cow or calf.

**Bossed.** Having a rounded surface with a projection in the center.

**Bostrichidae** (branch borer, limb borer, shot-hole borer; class Insecta, order Coleoptera). Family of black or brown beetles, 3-20 mm long, with the head tucked under a rounded, rugose thorax. The elytra are sharply declined at the rear, with several projecting, horizontal spines. The antennae have a loose club. Larvae are curved, white and fleshy, with a tiny head and enlarged thorax. They bore into felled or dying trees. There are many generations per year. Dinoderus minutus (bamboo borer) causes damage to bamboo, cane, and wickerwork products; originally from the Far East, it is now widespread. Rhyzopertha dominica (lesser grain borer) is a serious pest of stored grain. There are 434 species, largely tropical.

**Bostryx.** A coiled helicoid cyme in which the overall structure resembles a spring. Examples are the inflorescences of Hypericum species. Compare rhipidium.

**Bosvark.** The bushpig of South Africa.

**Bot.** The larva of a botfly.

**Botanical**

1. Any insecticide derived from plants, such as rotenone from roots of Derris and pyrethrum from Chrysanthemum flowers.
2. In horticulture, cultivated plants of an unimproved wild species rather than a cultivated variety.

**Botanic Garden.** An area in which a wide range of plants are grown for scientific, educational, and aesthetic purposes. Such collections aim either to include representative species of genera from all over the world or to specialize in one or more regions or types of vegetation. Large greenhouses are often maintained to provide appropriate growing conditions for exotic plants. As well as maintaining a large and varied collection of living plants, botanic gardens often also include herbaria, research laboratories, and increasingly, gene banks. In the past botanic gardens have been responsible for the introduction of many ornamental and crop plants into regions where they were previously unknown. The larger botanic gardens also finance plant-collecting expeditions to remote areas where the vegetation remains largely undescribed and uncollected.

**Botanize.** To study plants in the field or to collect plants for botanical purposes.

**Botany.** The scientific study of plants, including their anatomy, morphology, physiology, biochemistry, taxonomy, cytology, genetics, ecology, evolution, and geographical distribution.

**Botfly.** One of a number of flies belonging to the families Gasterophilidae (horse bots), Guterebridae (skin bots), and Oestridae (head bots), whose larvae called bots or warbles infest man and various animals causing myiasis.

**Bothidae** (left-eye flounders; class Osteichthyes, subclass Actinopterygii, order Pleuronectiformes). Large family of mainly marine, shallow-water flatfish, in which both eyey lie on the left side of the body. The dorsal fin originates in front of the eyes and spines are absent from all the fins. Many species are of small to moderate size. Others, *e.g.* Scophtalmus maximus (European turbot) and Paralichthys californicus (California halibut) are of considerable economic value. Flatfish are known for their remarkable colour adaptations to the prevailing background. There are about 425 species, with worlwide distribution.

**Bothridium.** One of four lappetlike outgrowths on the scolex of certain tapeworms.

**Bothriocephalidea** (phylum Platyhelminthes, class Cestoda). Order of parasitic, platyhelminth worms which possess a relatively simple scolex. All inhabit three hosts during their development.

**Bothrium.** A slitlike groove on the scolex of certain tapeworms, as the fish tapeworm.

**Botrychium** (family Ophioglossaceae). Genus of eusporangiate ferns with both the sterile and fertile blades of the leaf pinnately lobed or divided, the massive sporangia subsessile on the fertile pinnae, opening by a transverse slit without true annulus. There are about 30 species, cosmopolitan in distribution, but most are northern temperate.

**Botryoid.** Having many rounded prominences, thus resembling a cluster of grapes.

**Botryoidal Tissue.** A form of connective tissue present in the coelomic spaces of a leech.

**Bottle.** A unistratose involucre which encloses the sex organs of certain bryophytes.

**Bottlebrush Plant.** An Australian plant whose scarlet flower spikes resemble bottlebrushes. They are greenhouse plants in cooler climates.

**Bottle-neck Effect.** Type of genetic drift in which due to the rapid decrease in population size the genetic pool has been drastically diminished thus gene frequencies of remaining genes are greatly enhanced with respect to original pretrauma population values.

**Bottlenose Dolphin.** A favourite attraction of marine aquaria, the bottlenose grows to more than 3 metres in length and has a marked snout or 'beak'. These dolphins communicate with each other by an elaborate system of clicks and squeaks. They are particularly common off the east coast of the United States.

**Bottle-nosed.** Whale.

**Bottle-tree.** An Australian tree whose trunk is shaped like a bottle. There are two varieties, one with narrow leaves and the other with wide leaves.

**Bottom Yeast.** A yeast collecting at the bottom of the vessel during alcoholic fermentation.

**Botulism.** Severe, often fatal disease caused by the ingestion of foods contaminated with the botulinum toxin produced by the bacterium Clostridum botulinum. This toxin is one of the most potent known. Symptoms of botulism include nausea, constipation, dizziness, and dryness of the throat; later neurological disorders such as blurred vision and weakness develop, and finally death may occur due to paralysis of the respiratory system. Foods commonly responsible for cases of botulism are improperly cooked meats. ('Botulism' derives from the Latin botulus, 'sausage'.)

**Boudinage.** Minor structural feature in which competent strata resemble a series of sausages or 'boudins'. They are formed by the stretching or squeezing of the competent units which, unlike incompetent ones, cannot deform plastically. As deformation proceeds within the competent layer local thickening and thinning occurs, giving pinch and swell structures.

**Bougainvillaea.** Any of a group of South American shrubby climbing plants. Bougainvillaeas have small, insignificant flowers surrounded by brilliant red or purple Bracts.

**Boulder Clay.** Glacial deposit consisting of boulders of varying size in a clay-dominated matrix and laid down beneath a valley glacier or ice sheet. Typically it is unstratified and unsorted, and characterized by rocks types derived from the country crossed by the depositing glacier.

**Bouma Sequence.** Idealized sequence of sedimentary structures observed in turbidity-current deposits. It is named after the geologist, A. H. Bouma, who first emphasized its generality (Sedimentology, of some flysch deposits, Elsevier, Amesterdam, 1962). The lowest unit, A, a massive or graded sand, is overlain progressively by the B (lower division of parallel lamination), C (ripple or convolute laminations), D (upper division of plane parallel laminations), and E (pelagic shale) units. Examples showing the entire sequence are not common. The sequence can be interpreted in terms of deposition under waning current conditions.

**Boundary Layer.** A layer of liquid or gas next to a solid surface. It flows more slowly than that away from the surface. In plant there exists a boundary layer of air at a leaf surface, whose width is inversely proportional to wind speed. This layer also offers resistance to transpiration.

**Bourgueticrinida** (sea-lilies; class Crinoidea, subclass Articulata). Order of articulate sea-lilies (crinoids) in which the compact calyx, or cup, is made up of five basals and five radials only. The column consists of elliptical or rounded ossiccles which are united by synarthrial (bearing a fulcral ridge) articulations. Five or ten arms are present. The order first appeared in the Upper Cretaceous.

**Bouton**. The lappetlike terminal portion of the glossa in certain hymenopterans as the honeybee.

**Bouton Terminal**. The expanded end of the terminal branch of an axon which makes a synaptic connection with the cell body or dendrites of another neuron; an end bulb, end foot, or neuropodium.

**Bovichthyidae** (class Osteichthyes, subclass Actinopterygii, order Perciformes). Family of small, mainly marine fish, restricted to the cooler waters of the southern hemisphere, including oceanic islands, *e.g.* Tristan da Cunha. A freshwater representative, Pseudaphritis urvilli (congolli) or S. Australia, lives in rivers, where it reaches a length of some 35 cm. There are about six species.

**Bovid**. Any member of the Bovidae, a family of hollow-horned ruminants which includes cattle, sheep, goats, bison water buffalo, musk ox, and certain antelopes.

**Bovidae** (oxen, antelopes, gazelles, sheep, goats; order Artiodactyla, suborder Ruminantia, infraorder Pecora, superfamily Bovoidea). The largest by far of the artiodactyl families, including cattle bison, musk-ox, sheep, goats, antelopes, and allied groups. They are descended from the Oligocene traguloids, but do not appear as a distinct type until the Miocene. A major diversification followed in the Pliocene. Most are grazers but some are browsers. Horns, present in the male and often in the female, are covered with keratin and are not shed. The feet have two or four digits. Bovidae are of worldwide distribution, the family including Bison bison (N. American bison), Bison bonasus (European wisent, sometimes known, incorrectly, as the 'aurochs'), Bos taurus (all breeds of European cattle), Bos indicus (Zebu cattle), Bos grunniens (yak), Capra (goats, domesticated breeds being descended from C. aegagrus, the pasang), Ovis (sheep, descended from several wild members of the genus), Ovibos moschatus (musk-ox), Taurotragus oryx (eland), Aepyceros melampus (impala), and Saiga tataric (the saiga antelope of Siberia). In all there are 44 genera, with 111 species. The family is sometimes taken to include the family Antilocapridae.

**Bovine.** Cattlelike; of, pertaining to, or derived from cattle.

**Bovoidea** (order Artiodactyla, infraorder Pecora). Superfamily comprising two families, Antilocapridae and Bovidae, sometimes grouped together as a single family, Bovidae, sometimes grouped together as a single family, extinct allied forms have been distinct from the bovids since the Miocene and may have evolved from a cervid line. Bovoids are pecorans with lateral the digits reduced in some species to a nodule of bone. The upper canines are reduced or absent, the cheek teeth high-crowned. Horns are present, usually in both sexes though more developed in males, and covered with keratin (horn) rather than skin (as in cervids).

**Bowel.** The gut or intestine.

**Bower Bird.** There are several species of bower birds living in Australia and New Guinea. Some of them are beautifully coloured, but their most fascinating feature is the bower or courtship house which is built by the male. The bower usually consists of a platform of twigs and grasses partly or completely roofed over. The male normally decorates it with attractive pebbles, flowers, and other bright objects, and then he entices the female into it. Courtship and mating take place in the bower, but the female then makes a nest and lays her eggs elsewhere.

**Bowfin.** This freshwater fish of North America is a 'living fossil' with many primitive features. The head is covered with bony plates and the rest of the body bears thin scales. A soft dorsal fin runs most of the length of the body, which may be up to one metre long, and the body ends in a rounded tail. The bowfin lives in sluggish waters and can breathe air with its lung-like swim bladder. It can live out of water for up to 24 hours.

**Bowman's Capsule.** The cap-shaped end of a kidney nephron. It is named after its discoverer, the British physician Sir William Bowman (1816-92).

**Box.** An evergreen tree with small, leathery leaves. It grows very slowly, reaching a height of 10 metres. The single-sexed greenish flowers have no petals and grow in small clusters at the base of the leaves. The tree grows in many parts of Europe, especially on lime-rich soils.

**Brachial.** Of or pertaining to the brachium or arm.

**Brachial Plexus.** An interconnecting network of cervical and thoracic nerves which innervate the forelimb of vertebrates or the arm of man.

**Brachiate**

1. *bot.* Possessing widely spreading branches resembling arms, as the maple.
2. *zool.* Possessing arms.

**Brachiation.** In some arboreal Primates, a form of locomotion in which an animal swings hand over hand from branch to branch. In those species in which it is developed fully (species of Hylobatidae, and Pongo), apes are said to be able to move more quickly through the trees than a human can walk on the ground below.

**Brachiolaria.** The free-swimming, ciliated larva of asteroid echinoderms which develops from a bipinnaria.

**Brachionichthyidae** (warty angler; class Osteichthyes subclass Actinopterygii, order Lophiiformes). Small family of marine fish, differing from the related frogfish (Antennariidae) in having a thick membrane, separate from the rest of the dorsal fin, above the eyes. The pectoral and pelvic fins are arm-like in shape, making the fish more frog-like than the frogfish. There are a few species, found in the southern half of Australia.

**Brachiopod.** One of a group of bivalve marine animals. The name comes from a pair of food-gathering spiral arms (brachia). Brachiopods, also known as lamp-shells, resemble molluscs in appearance but there are sufficient differences for these animals to be placed in a phylum of their own, the Brachiopoda.

**Brachiopoda** (lamp shells). Phylum of solitary, marine, bivalved, coelomate invertebrates. The shell is chitinophosphatic or calcareous. Brachiopods are attached to the sea-bed by a muscular stalk (pedicle), or are secondarily cemented, or are free-living. Usually they consist of a larger, pedicle (ventral) valve and a brachial (dorsal) valve, lined by reduplications (mantle lobes) of the body wall which enclose the large mantle cavity. They are bilaterally symmetrical about the posterior anterior mid-line of the valves. The feeding organ (lophophore) surrounds the mouth and is covered by ciliated tentacles. The alimentary canal is divided into oesophagus, stomach, and intestine, with or without an anus. The nervous system is subepithelial, consisting of a ganglionate circum-oesophageal ring. The excretory organs are one or two pairs of metanephridia also acting as gonoducts. The circulatory system is open, with the contractile vesicle (heart) near the stomach. Brachiopods first appeared in the Lower Cambrian, and since then have undergone numerous radiations, the first involving the inarticulate brachiopods. The articulate groups became more important after the Cambrian. Many of the larger articulate groups, including the strophomenids, orthids, and spiriferids, are now extinct.

**Brachiopterygii** (class Osteichthyes). Group (subclass) of bony fish including the curious bichirs (Polypterus species) and reedfish (Calamoichthys species) of central Africa. This interesting group of fish possesses a number of primitive and specialized features, *e.g.* a series of spinous dorsal finlets, ganoid scales, lobate pectoral fins with special skeletal supports, a spiracle, a spiral intestinal valve, and a pair of ventral lung-like air bladders. The systematic position of the bichirs is not yet certain : the 11 living species, grouped together as the order Polypteriformes, have also been included in the subclass Actinopterygii.

**Brachium.** Used for describing the upper part of fore limb of a vertebrate. It is anteriorly articulated with shoulder and posteriorly with antibrachium. Skeleton support is provided by humerus bone.

**Brachycephalous.** Short-headed or broad-headed.

**Brachycera** (class Insecta, order Diptera). Suborder of the Diptera whose members are recognizable from their wing venation and porrect palps. With one exception (Stratiomyidae) all Brachycera larvae have the head retractile within the thorax. The antennae usually have fewer than six segments, with exceptions where segments have fused as a secondary feature. There are 16 families.

**Brachycerous.** Possessing short antennae.

**Brachychiton** (family Sterculiaceae). Genus of trees that are deciduous only at flowering, which is irregular. Their leaves are entire or lobed, and the bell-shaped flowers are cream, pink, or red. There are 18 species. 17 of them found in Australia and two in New Guinea. They occur widely in arid zones as well as in rain forest.

**Brachydactyly.** Having abnormally short fingers and toes.

**Brachydont.** Possessing or denoting teeth with short, low crowns, long roots, and reduced pulp cavity.

**Brachypteraciidae** (groundrollers; order Coraciiformes). Family of brightly-coloured, long-legged, short-winged birds, with the anterior toes joined at the base. They are ground-dwelling in humid forest, except for Uratelornis chimaera (long-tailed groundroller) which inhabits arid desert. They are insectivorous, also taking small amphibians and reptiles. There are three genera, containing five species, found only in Madagascar.

**Brachypterous.** Having short wings, especially wings that do not cover the abdomen.

**Brachypteryx** (shortwings; family Turdidae). Genus of small, robin-like birds with short wings and short tails. They are skulking, and found in dense forest undergrowth. They are insectivorous, and nest in moss or in holes in trees or in the ground. There are six species, found in India, SE Asia, Indonesia, and the Philippines.

**Brachysclereid** (stone cell). A relatively short, more or less isodiametric, sclerenchyma cell (sclereid). Brachysclereids are usually present singly or in small groups, although they occur in large numbers in some tissues, such as the fleshy part of the pear fruit.

**Brachythecium** (order Hypnobryales). Genus of pleurocarpous mosses in which branching may be irregular or pinnate. The leaves are imbricate to spreading, and each has a nerve extending at least half-way up the leaf. The capsule is inclined to horizontal, ovoid to cylindrical, and borne on a deep-red seta. Brachythecium is a cosmopolitan genus with about 300 species, found in a wide variety of habitats. B. rutabulum is common in all but the most acid habitats, particularly in damp, shady situations. It grows on rocks, soil, wood, and often in laws. It shoots grow to 12 cm. Branching is irregular, with the branches erect, ascending, or arcuate. The leaves are 2-3 mm long, broadly oval, and tapering to a sharp point. They are bright green to yellowish-green, and glossy.

**Brachyurous.** Having a short, reduced abdomen, as in crabs.

**Brachyury.** Having short tails, as in certain mutant strains of mice.

**Bracken.** A species of Fern, found world-wide. It is one of the first plants to grow on burned or newly-cleared ground, and spreads rapidly by means of underground stems.

**Bracken Fern.** The brake fern (Pteris aquilina).

**Bracket Fungi.** The pore fungi, basidiomycete fungi whose sporophores or basidiocarps grow horizontally on tree trunks forming shelflike structures (brackets or conks).

**Bracket Fungus.** A fungus that grows on trees, with a fruiting body shaped like a shelf or bracket. There are many species, nearly all belonging to the group known as polypores. The lower surface of the bracket bears thousands of tiny pores like those found in the boletes. Bracket fungi usually attack dead trunks and branches, but some attack living trees and may actually kill them.

**Brackish.** Applied to water that is saline, but less so than sea-water. According to the Venice system brackish waters are classified by the chlorine they contain and divided into zones. The zones, with their percentage chlorinity (mean values at limits) are : euhaline 1.65-2.2; polyhaline 1.0-1.65; mesohaline 0.3-1.0; alpha-mesohaline 0.55-1.0; beta-mesohaline 0.3-0.55; oligohaline 0.03-0.3; fresh water 0.03 or less.

**Bract**

1. *bot. a.* A small, specialized leaf in the axil from which a flower or floral axis develops; a modified leaf on the axis itself. *b.* A modified, scalelike leaf of a cone or strobilus.

2. *zool.* A modified medusoid (hydrophyllium, phyllozooid) serving a protective function, as in siphonophores.

**Bracteate.** Possessing bracts.

**Bracteolate.** Possessing small bracts or bractlets.

**Bracteole.** A leaflike organ subtending a flower in an inflorescence that is itself subtended by a bract.

**Bracteomania.** Used for the abnormal production of large numbers of bracts, generally at the expense of normal flowers.

**Bracteose.** Having many bracts.

**Bractlet.** A small bract situated in the axis of a larger bract; bracteole.

**Bract Scale.** The structure that subtends the ovuliferous scale in the female strobilus of gymnosperms.

**Bradycardia.** Abnormal slowness of heart beat.

**Bradykinin.** A hormone formed from precursor which is normally circulating in blood. It is an important vasodialator.

**Bradytelic.** Used in chronistics, to describe a species that has remained more or less unchanged for millions of years. Examples of bradytelic are certain gymnosperms like Podocarpous Ginkgo and Welwitschia. Evidence of such nature of these plants comes from studies of fossils and karyotypes of these plants.

**Bradypodidae** (tree sloths; order Edentata, infra-order Pilosa, superfamily Bradypodoidea). Family of edentates (toothless mammals) fully adapted for arboreal life and unable to walk on the ground : they use their limbs to hang upside-down from branches. The head is short and rounded. They are not actually toothless, but the five teeth have no enamel and by growing continuously provide a grinding surface. The forelimbs are longer than the hind limbs, the digits bearing hooked claws used in hanging. The tail is short. The fur is long, coarse and grooved; cyanobacteria grow in the grooves, giving the animals a greenish colour. There are six cervical vertebrae in Choloepus, nine in Bradypus. The stomach is large and chambered, the rectum very large, retaining faeces for several days. All movements are slow. The body temperature is low and variable, sloths neither shivering nor sweating but dying from hypothermia at temperatures below 40°C. They are distributed throughout the forests of tropical America. There are two genera, and six species.

**Bradypodoidea** (tree sloths; order Edentata, infraorder Pilosa). Superfamily comprising the family Bradypodidae (tree sloths). These animals are unknown as fossils, probably because their humid tropical habitat fails to preserve them after death. Structurally they appear to be related to the ground sloths of the superfamily Megalonychoidea.

**Bradytelic**. In chronistics, describing a species that has remained more or less unchanged for millions of years. Such species may appear primitive; however when they first appeared they may have represented the end of an increasing trend towards specialization in a particular group. Certain of the present-day gymnosperms, such as Welwitschia, Ginkgo, and Podocarpus are considered bradytelic The evidence for this comes partly from fossil studies, and also from investigations of the karyotype. Such species have strikingly asymmetrical karyotypes, a feature generally considered to be advanced.

**Bradytelic Evolution.** One of three types of evolutionary rates within groups. In this instance the rate is exceedingly slow, and is manifest by slowly evolving lineages which survive much longer than would normally be expected. Living fossils, *e.g.* the coelacanth, represent the low end of the bradytelic range; while the better-known groups that have remained relatively stable with time include opossums and crocodiles.

**Braided River.** River whose plan consists of a number of small channels separated by bars. The latter may be vegetated and stable (*e.g.* the eyots of the River Thames, England), or barren and unstable (as at glacial margins, where rapid changes occur).

**Brain**

1. The enlarged anterior part of the vertebrate central nervous system, which is encased within the carnium of the skull. Continuous with the spinal cord, the brain is surrounded by three membranes (meninges) and bathed in cerebrospinal fluid, which fills internal cavities (ventricles). It functions as the main coordinating centre for nervous activity, receiving information (in the form of nerve impulses) from

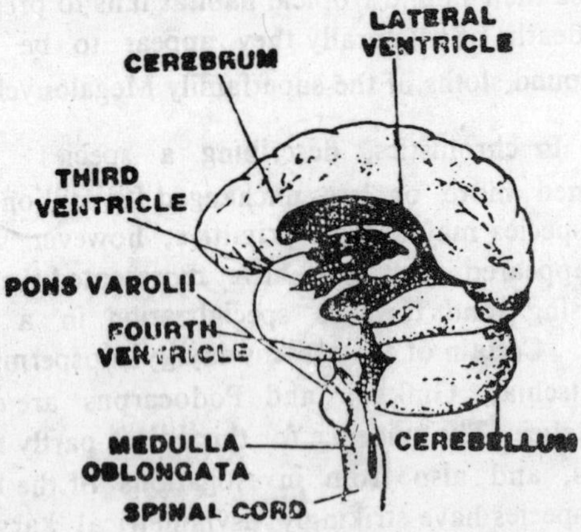


The human brain

sense organs, interpreting it, and transmitting 'instructions' to muscles and other effectors. It is also the seat of intelligence and memory.

The embryonic vertebrate brain is in three sections (forebrain; hindbrain; midbrain), which become further differentiated during development into specialized regions. The main parts of the adult human brain are a highly developed cerebrum in the form of two cerebral hemispheres, a cerebellum, medulla oblongata, and hypothalamus.

2. A concentration of nerve ganglia at the anterior end of an invertebrate animal.

**Brain Case.** The cranium or portion of the skull that encloses the brain.

**Brain Coral.** A coral (Meandrina or Meandra) which resembles the human brain in appearance.

**Brain Death.** The permanent absence of vital functions of the brain, which is marked by cessation of breathing and other reflexes controlled by the brainstem and by a zero reading on an electroencephalogram. Organs may be removed for transplantation when brain death is established, which may not necessarily be associated with permanent absence of heart beat.

**Brain Membranes.** The meninges. q.v.

**Brain Sand.** Corpora aranacea, sandlike particles present in the pineal body.

**Brainstem.** The part of the brain comprising the medulla oblongata, the midbrain, and the pons. It resembles and is continuous with the spinal cord. The midbrain controls and integrates, reflex activities (such as respiration) that originate in higher centres of the brain via a network of nerve pathways (the reticular formation).

**Bramble.** A thorny, rambling shrub belonging to the rose family. It has white or pink flowers and produces the blackberries that are so commonly collected for making jams and pies. Brambles are found in woods and hedgerows and on open waste ground.

**Brambling.** A bird belonging to the finch family, distinguished inflight by its white rump. The male has an almost black head and back in summer and an orange breast throughout the year. Females and winter males are duller, with brown heads. They breed in northernmost Europe but move south in winter in huge flocks in search of good crops of beech seeds. In their breeding area they feed largely on insects.

**Bramidae** (Atlantic pomfret, Ray's bream; class Osteichthyes, subclass Actinopterygii, order Perciformes). Family of deep-bodied, moderate to large oceanic fish. Oval in outline, the body shows long dorsal anal fins, a forked tail, and large, wing-like pectoral fins. Brama brama (Ray's bream or Atlantic pomfret), reaching a length of up to 70 cm, lives in depths of 100 m or more. There are about 18 species, found in all but polar seas.

**Branchia** pl. **Branchiae.** A gill; a ctenidium.

**Branchial.** Concerning the gills—*e.g.*, branchial arteries.

**Branchial Aperture.** The opening of gill a chamber to the exterior.

**Branchial Arch**

1. A gill-supporting structure between the gill clefts of fishes; a gill arch or visceral arch.
2. In a vertebrate embryo, the structure that develops in the wall of the pharynx between successive branchial grooves.

**Branchial Basket.** The cartilaginous framework supporting the gill pouches of cyclostomes.

**Branchial Chamber.** A cavity which contains gills, as that in crustaceans, amphibians, and fishes.

**Branchial Cleft**

1. A gill slit.
2. In a vertebrate embryo, the opening between two visceral arches.

**Branchial Cyst**. A cervical cyst, a closed epithelial sac located in the neck region, resulting from incomplete obliteration of a branchial groove or pouch.

**Branchial Fistula**. A cervical fistula, diverticulum in the neck region resulting from incomplete closure of a branchial groove or pouch.

**Branchial Groove.** One of a series of ectodermal invaginations in the neck region of vertebrate embryos corresponding in position to the pharyngeal pouches.

**Branchial Heart**. A supplementary, contractile structure located at the base of the gill in a squid.

**Branchial Musculature**. The muscles which move the visceral arches and jaws of lower vertebrates or homologues of these structures in higher vertebrates; muscles which are derived from splanchnic mesoderm of the hypomere instead of from myotomes.

**Branchial Ray**. A gill ray.

**Branchial Skeleton**. Visceral skeleton.

**Branchiate**. Possessing branchiae or gills.

**Branchiocardiac**. Pertaining to gills and to the heart.

**Branchiocardiac Sinus**. In crustaceans, one of the several channels through which blood passes from the gills to the pericardial sinus and thence to the heart.

**Branchiopod**. Any crustacean of the subclass Branchiopoda which includes various shrimps (brine, fairy, tadpole, clam) and water fleas, mostly freshwater forms with leaflike thoracic appendages which bear branchia (gills).

**Branchiopoda** (gill-footed shrimps; phylum Arthropoda, subphylum Crustacea). Diverse class of small, mainly freshwater, filter-feeding crustaceans, all characterized by flattened, leaf-like, trunk appendages in which the coxa bears a flattened epipodite which functions as a gill. The Branchiopoda includes the Anostraca (fairy shrimps), the Notostraca (tadpole shrimps), the Conchostraca (clam shrimps), and the Cladocera (water fleas). Many are pink or red owing to the presence of haemoglobin. They are often inhabitants of temporary bodies of water, and have drought-resistant eggs. There are 800 species.

**Branchiostegal Membrane.** A membrane supported by bony rods (branchiostegal rays) which, in most fishes, extends from the inner surface of the operculum to the body wall.

**Branchiostegite.** In crustaceans, the portion of the carapace that covers the gills.

**Branchiostomidae** (lancelets; order Amphioxiformes). Family of small, fish-like, marine, coastal animals. Lancelets are the only living representatives of the subphylum Cephalochordata. Although definitely not true fish, lancelets (*e.g.*, Branchiastoma lanceolata) are considered fairly close to the vertebrate ancestral lineage. The have an almost transparent body, no eyes or brains, a permanent notochord, and a dorsal hollow nerve cord; and they spend most of their lives buried in the beds beneath the world's oceans.

**Branchiura** (phylum Arthropoda, subphylum Crustacea). Small class of crustaceans, all of which are parasites, and which differ from the copepods in having a pair of sessile compound eyes, and a large, shield-like carapace covering the head and thorax. Branchiurans are common, blood-sucking ectoparasites on the skin or in the gill cavities of marine and freshwater fish and a few amphibians. Attachment to the host is via a large, claw-like modification of the first antennae, and by a pair of large suckers derived from the bases of the first maxillae, the rest of the maxillae being vestigial. A sucking mouth cone is formed from the labrum and labium. In Argulus there is a hollow spine in front of the mouth cone, which pierces the skin of the host and injects a supposedly poisonous secretion. There are no maxillipeds, and the second maxillae are uniramous well developed, with terminal claws. There are four large, biramous, thoracic appendages, armed with swimming setae. There are used when swimming between hosts. There are 75 species.

**Branchiuran.** Any crustacean of the subclass, Branchiura, which includes the fish lice.

**Braconid.** A hymenopterous insect of the family Braconidae, whose larvae parasitize other insects, as Microgaster tibialis, a parasite of the European corn borer.

**Brandling.** The stinking earthworm (Eisenia foetida).

**Brand Spore.** A thick-walled resting spore which is formed by the Ustilaginales. They are dark coloured and found in sooty masses.

**Brant.** A wild goose of the genus Branta.

**Branta** (geese; family Anatidae). Genus of medium to large geese. They are vegetarian, ground-nesting, and migratory. B. canadensis (Canada goose) has been introduced to Europe. B. sandvicensis (Hawaiian goose or ne-ne) is more terrestrial and non-migratory, having reduced webbing and short wings. There are five species, found in Europe, Asia, N. America, and Hawaii.

**Brassica** (family Cruciferae). Genus of annual to perennial herbs that have tap roots and erect, branched stems. The flowers are usually yellow, and are always four-petalled, the elongated fruit having a lower part (containing several seeds) that opens by two valves each with one strong vein, and an upper, indehiscent part (the beak) with 0—3 seeds. Several are important vegetables (cabbage, turnip, etc.)

or sources of useful oil (rape, black mustard, etc.). There are about 40 species, whose distribution is centred on the Mediterranean.

**Brassicaceae.** Cruciferae.

**Braulidae** (bee lice; class Insecta, order Diptera, suborder Cyclorrapha). Family of abnormal flies which lack wings and resemble members of the Hippoboscidae. The antennae are set in lateral grooves, and the eyes are reduced in size. The thorax appears to be joined to the abdomen. The tarsi are adapted to cling to the bodies of Hymenoptera, especially bees. Their eggs are laid near honey-or pollen-storage cells inside a been nest, and the larve of the bee lice feed on these substances and pupate within the nest of the host. The pupa is unique among the Cyclorrapha in being enclosed in the unmodified last (final instar) larval cuticle, and not a true puparium. Only five species have been described so far.

**Braun-blanquest Scale.** A method of describing an area of vegetation devised by J. Braun-Blanquent in 1927. It is used to survey large areas very rapidly. Two scales are used. One consists of a plus sign and a series of numbers from 1 to 5 denoting both the numbers of species and the proportion of the area covered by that species, ranging from + (sparse and covering a small area) to 5 (covering more than 75% of the area). The second scale indicates how the species are grouped and ranges from Soc. 1 (growing singly) to Soc. 5 (growing in pure populations.) The information is obtained by laying down adjacent quadrats of increasing size. One of a number of variations of Braun-Blanquet's method is the Domin scale, which is more accurate as there are more subdivisions of the original scale. The Braun-Blanquet scale also included a five-point scale to express the degree of presence of a plant. For example, 5=constantly present in 80—100% of the areas; 1=rate in 1—20% of the areas.

**Brazil Nut.** A large, three-angled nut (actually a seed) of a brazilian tree (Bertholletia excelsa), developing in a large globular fruit containing 18 to 24 closely packed nuts.

**Breadfruit Tree.** A tree of the Pacific Islands up to 15 metres tall. Its large fruits have a mealy pulp similar in appearance to bread.

**Breakage Plane.** In certain decapod crustaceans within exhibit autotomy, a region traversing one of the basal segments of an appendage at which self-amputation occurs.

**Breaker.** Wave that is collapsing or breaking as a result of the wave approaching the shore and reaching shallower water. The decreasing water depth causes the wavelength and speed to decrease and the wave height to increase. Consequently wave steepness increases and the wave becomes unstable : it breaks when the wave height is about 0.8 times the weter depth. Several types of breaker have been described, *e.g.* spilling breakers (in which the wave breaks forward, with broken water spilling down the front of the wave), and plunging breakers (in which the wave crest curls over a large air pocket and falls vertically into the trough).

**Breaking of Meres.** The sudden development of large masses of blue-green algae in small masses of fresh water.

**Bream.** A freshwater fish belonging to the carp family, with a deep, flattened body measuring about 35 cm long. It likes slow-moving or even stagnant waters. Some spend part of their time in brackish waters. Bream feed on worms and other animals of the muddy river bottom.

**Breast**

1. Refers to the fore part of the body between neck and abdomen; the anterior portion of the chest or thorax.

2. Refers to the human lactating apparatus. It arises as an invagination from surface epithelium which dips down into underlying connective tissue as a solid column; these gradually hollowed out to form ducts of mammary glands. It bears a nipple at which the various ducts open and surrounding it is areola. It is rudimentary at birth, little further development take place until puberty and fully developed after delivery. It further undergoes proliferative change with recurrence to each menstrual cycle.

**Breastbone.** The sternum.

**Breathing.** Means a physical process that is affected either by osmosis (aquatic animals) or diffusion (terrestrial animals) through which an exchange of oxygen and carbondioxide takes place between body and environment of an individual. Also termed as external respiration.

**Breathing Root.** A root which is produced by large plants growing in mud; it projects above the mud and water allowing the air to reach the root below.

**Breech.** The lower, posterior portion of the body; the buttocks or nates.

**[1]Breed.** To produce or bring forth young; to propagate.

**[2]Breed.** A race or variety of animals or plants, especially one developed through the influence of man.

**Bregmacerotidae** (codlets; class Osteichthyes, subclass Actinopterygii, order Gadiformes). Small family of marine, oceanic, warm-water fish related to the codfish. They are easily identifiable by their elongate body, deeply-notched dorsal and anal fins; the first dorsal ray reduced to one spine on the head, and long; and outer pectoral-fin rays trailing beside the body. The seven species are of worldwide distribution. Although not a true deep-sea fish, the Indo-Pacific Bregmaceros macclellandi, up to

12 cm in length, has been caught at depths exceeding 500 m.

**Brent** Goose. A winter visitor from Greenland and northern Russia which is usually found close to the sea, feeding on sea-grass and sand worms. Brent geese are smaller than other geese (roughly the same size as a mallard duck). The plumage is grey-brown, with a black head and neck, and white undersides.

**Brenthidae** (class Insecta, order Coleoptera). Family of narrow beetles, up to 40 mm long, often with an exceptionally lengthened head and rostrum; the elytra of some species comprise only one-quarter of the total body length. Many are sexually dimorphic. The females' long rostrum is used for boring into wood in which eggs are laid; the jaws are tiny. Males have a broad rudimentary rostrum but large jaws possibly for holding the female during mating. Larvae are fleshy, with short legs, and are found in decaying wood. There are 1230 species, largely of tropical woodland.

**Breviceps Adspersus** (rain frog, shorthead; order Anura (Salientia), family Microhylidae). Species of burrowing anuran, a small (about 4 cm long), round-bodied frog with a short head, and warty skin. They appear in large numbers after rain. The egg mass is laid in a damp burrow. Froglets develop without an aquatic phase. The species is found in southern Africa.

**Brier** or **Briar.** A plant bearing thorns or prickles, especially those of the genera Rosa, Rubus, and others; a bramble.

**Bright-field Illumination.** The normal method of illumination in light microscopy, in which the specimen appears dark against a bright background. Several methods of setting up the condenser lenses and light source are used, of which the two most common are critical illumination and Kohler illumination. Compare dark-ground illumination.

**Brill.** A flatfish closely related to the turbot. It is smaller and slimmer than its cousin, 50 cm long, and does not have any bony platelets. It feeds on bottom-living fishes and crustaceans, and normally lies on its right side.

**Brimstone Butterfly.** The male of this species is a bright yellow, while the female is greenish-white. Brimstone butterflies may be found flying in gardens, hedgerows and woodland; they feed on buckthorn. They hibernate in evergreen bushes during the winter, their leaf-like wings giving them good protection.

**Brimstone Moth.** A yellow moth with brown spots, usually

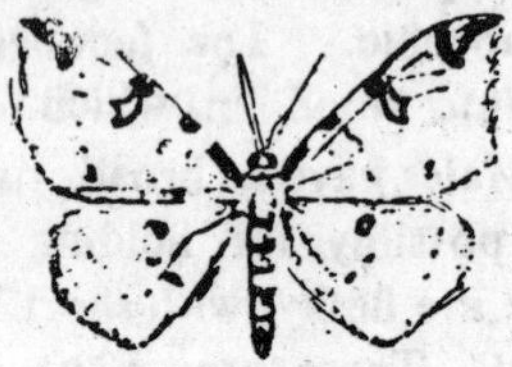

Brimstone moths

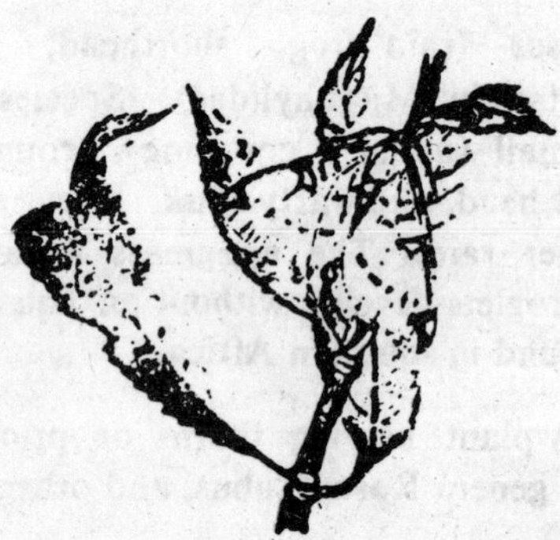

seen in early summer. The larva or caterpillar is a looper —that is, it moves by raising the middle section of its body into the air and pushing the front end forwards. It has legs only at the front and tail ends, and looks just like a brown twig.

**Brine.** Water saturated with salt; a strong, alkaline solution.

**Brine Shrimp.** A primitive relative of the crabs and lobsters which likes very salty water and is found in many parts of the world. Brine shrimps are about 1 cm long with two pairs of antennae, two compound eyes on stalks and a third small eye in the middle of the head. They swim upside down with their underside to the light.

**Bristle.** A stiff, coarse hair or hairlike structure.

**Bristlecone Pine.** The tree known to have the longest life-span. It is found in the dry mountains of California and Nevada. It has princles on its cones, gnarled, twisted branches, and is an evergreen. The oldest living specimen is known to be about 4600 years old. It is never more than 9 metres tall.

**Bristlemouth** One of the commonest fishes in the ocean, the bristlemouth lives in deep water where it preys upon small animals. It has small eyes and rows of light-organs (photophores) on its flanks.

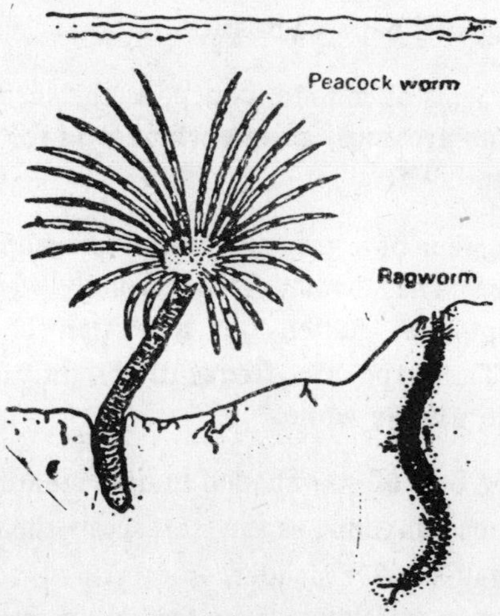


Bristleworms

**Bristletail.** A group of primitive wingless insects with either two- or three-pronged tails. They live beneath stones and leaves, and some live in houses. There are some 350 species, including the Silverfish which is a three-pronged bristletail.

Bristletails

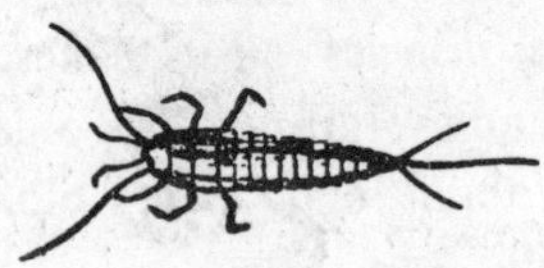

**Bristle Worm.** A group of marine annelid worms that have bundles of bristles on each segment of their bodies. They are commonly found on the seashore and include the lugworms, fanworms and ragworms.

**Bristly.** Bearing stiff hairs or bristles.

**Brit.** Dense swarms of minute, copepod crustaceans, especially Calanus finmarchicus, an important food for marine fishes and whales.

**Brittle Gill.** Member of a group of toadstools whose gills break very easily. The toadstools are usually strongly domed at first but they flatten out and often become funnel-shaped. The caps are frequently brightly coloured and the gills are usually white.

**Brittle Star.** A group of star-shaped marine creatures belonging to the same phylum as the starfishes—the echinoderms. Brittle stars have five slender, spiny arms that easily break off but regrow quickly. They feed by filtering tiny food particles from the water or by sifting through the debris on the sea bed. Those with many-branched, coiled arms are called basket stars. Brittle stars are also known as sand stars or serpent stars.

**Broad-leaved Evergreen Forest.** North of the tropics, broad-leaved forests are mainly deciduous, the evergreen variants being restricted to the coastal plain of the Gulf of Mexico, S. Japan and central China. South of the tropics, however, the broad-leaved forests are mainly evergreen, the only exception occurring in Chilean Patagonia. This forest type requires plentiful rainfall, well distributed throughout the year.

**Broccoli.** A vegetable of the cabbage family, closely related to the cauliflower. It has thick clusters of green or purple flower buds, the edible part.

**Brochidodromous.** Camptodromous.

**Broad-leaved Tree.** A tree with wide flat leaves. Most broad-leaved trees have strong hard timber and are frequently called hardwoods. They are all flowering plants and are Europe's most common trees, though they do not grow in the colder north or in high mountain regions. Most are deciduous but a few, such as the holly and the holm oak, are evergreen.

**Brochidodromous.** (camptodromous). Used for describing the venation in which there is a single primary vein and the secondary veins are rising from it curve upwards towards leaf margin and join together in a series of conspicuous loops at the margin *e.g.*, in Prunus avium.

**Brocket.** A small South American deer of the genus Mazama.

**Bromeliaceae** Distinctive family of monocotyledons with no close relatives, most of which are herbs and epiphytes, a few being terrestrial. Most have leaves crowded with an amplexicaul base forming a tank from which water is absorbed. The inflorescence is terminal, sometimes with showy bracts. The flowers are regular, and trimerous. The fruit is a berry, or capsule. There are 50 genera, with 2000 species, almost entirely confined to the New World, and mostly tropical.

**Bromeliad.** Any of a large group of American plants. They have rosettes of fleshy leaves which can absorb water and food. Many have no real roots and grow perched high up on forest trees. The Pineapple is a bromeliad.

**5-bromouracil** (5-BU). An analogue of the naturally occurring pyrimidine thymine (5-methyl uracil), in which bromine replaces the methyl group on carbon five of the pyrimidine ring. During chromosome replication the analogue may be incorporated into DNA in place of thymine, but it is less specific in its pairing properties. Over a series of replications a T : A nucleotide pair could thus eventually be replaced by a C : G pair resulting in a point mutation (diagram). The ability of 5-bromouracil to produce point mutations without significant chromosomal damage has made it a useful tool in genetic research. Other base analogues with similar effects include 2-aminopurine and 2,6-diaminopurine, which are analogues of adenine, and 5-bromodeoxycytidine, which is an analogue of cytosine.

**Bronchiole.** A fine respiratory tube in the lungs of reptiles, birds, and mammals. It is formed by the subdivision of a bronchus and in reptiles and mammals it terminates in a number of alveoli.

**Bronchus** (Bronchial Tube). Refers to one of the major air tubes in the lung. The trachea undergoes division into two main bronchi, one for each lung, which split into smaller bronchi and then into bronchioles. The walls of the bronchi become stiffened by rings of cartilage.

**Brontosaur.** A large, herbivorous dinosaur of the genus Brontosaurus.

**Brontotheriidae** (brontotheres, titanotheres; class Mammalia, order Perissodactyla). Suborder (ranked by some authorities as a family of the suborder Hippomorpha) of rhinoceros-like animals which flourished in the Eocene and Oligocene, and then became extinct. Probably they appeared first in N. America, but they spread to Asia and some lived in E. Europe. Brontotheres were large, some reaching 2.4 m at the shoulder (as large as modern elephants). The skull was long and low, the brain small. Bony horns were present in later forms, often large and presumed larger in males than females, carried as a pair, side by side on the front of the head. Some, *e.g.* Brontotherium, had Y- or V-shaped horns on their noses. The limbs were graviportal (short and massive). The teeth were primitive, the incisors and a premolar absent in some forms, the molars large, low-crowned, bunolophodont. The brontotheres seem to have evolved rapidly to large size, but their teeth must have restrieted their diet to soft plant material, perhaps making them vulnerable to minor environmental changes.

[1]**Brood**. The young of animals, especially birds, which are hatched and taken care of together, as a brood of chickens.

[2]**Brood**. To sit on and incubate eggs.

**Brood Capsule**. A hollow cyst which develops from the inner mall of a hydatid cyst or from the wall of a secondary cyst of Echinococcus granulosus, a tapeworm of carnivores. From its inner wall, scolices develop.

**Brood Chamber**. A brood pouch, a marsupium.

**Brood Parasitism**. Behavior exhibited by certain birds which deposit their eggs in the nests of other birds which incubate, hatch, and care for the young, as European species of cuckoos, cowbird.

**Brood Pouch**. A space or cavity other than the uterus in which young develop, as the modified outer gill of a freshwater clam; a brood chamber or marsupium.

**Brood Spot**. Refers to a prolactin induced bald area present on the ventral surface of some brooding birds which is richly supplied with blood for incubation of eggs.

**Brooklime**. A widespread, low-growing large speedwell plant which produces blue flowers arranged in stalked spikes. It grows in wet places, particularly in mud.

**Broom**. A shrub of Europe, Asia and Africa, with about 100 species. Brooms grow about 2 metres tall. They have small, often spiky leaves and produce seeds in pods. Most have yellow flowers.

**Broomrape**. A parasitic plant which grows on the roots of other flowering plants. It does not contain the green pigment chlorophyll and has scales instead of leaves. There are many species of this plant, each specific to one or two hosts. The common broomrape is the most familiar species, often found growing on peaflowers. Its flowers are purplish or creamy, arranged in a spike.

**Brosimum** (family Moraceae). Genus of trees whose flowers are aggregated in heads of one sunken female and many males. The fruit is an achene embedded in the fleshy receptacle. The achene of B. alicastrum is the breadnut. B. galactodendron is the cow-tree or milk-tree of Venezuela. It produces copious latex of appearance similar to cow's milk and is used as a substitute for this. There are 50 species, occurring in temperate and tropical S. America.

**Brotochore**. A plant spread or dispersed by man.

**Brown**. A fairly common family of butterflies, most of which are orange or brown in colour. Examples are the Speckled Wood, Ringlet, Gatekeeper and meadow brown butterflies. The caterpillars of brown butterflies generally feed on grasses.

**Brown Algae**. A large group of algae (singular alga) containing brown pigment. They all live in the sea and include the largest seaweeds—the kelps which grow to over 50 metres in length.

**Brown Bear**. The brown bear is found over a large area of the northern hemisphere and there are several subspecies.

These include the Kodiak, Syrian, and grizzly bears. They vary in size, but all are large omnivorous animals weighing up to 750 kg. They have poor sight and rely on their senses of smell and hearing which are acute.

**Brown Body**

1. In bryozoans, a dark brown mass formed by a degenerating polypide.
2. In holothurians, a mass of amebocytes present in the coelom.

**Brown Earth.** A type of zonal acid soil (pedalfer) characteristic of broad-leaved deciduous forest, such as that of Western Europe. The rainfall causes some leaching of lime from the A horizon, which is grey-brown in colour. The temperature is high enough for the rapid decomposition of organic matter resulting in the formation of mild humus (mull]. The B horizon is dark brown because of the accumulation of various iron and other compounds. Many of these deciduous-forest lands have been cleared for cultivation. The natural fertility resulting from decomposed leaf litter is thus no longer available and both liming and manuring are necessary. Compare podsol.

**Brown Fat.** A darker coloured region of adipose tissue found in newborn and hibernating animals (in which it may also be called the hibernating gland). Compared to normal white fat, deposits of brown fat are more richly supplied with blood vessels and have a higher proportion of unsaturated fatty acids. They can also be more rapidly converted to heat energy, especially during arousal from hibernation and during cold stress in young animals. Since the deposits are strategically placed near major blood vessels, the heat they generate warms the blood returning to the heart.

It has been said that some types of obesity in man may be linked to a lack of brown fat in affected individuals : in normal individuals, an intake of excess food is converted into brown fat and rapidly metabolized.

**Brown Hare.** Found over most of Europe with the exception of Ireland and northern Scandinavia, the brown hare is fond of open spaces. It has very long back legs and can run at speeds of more than 80 km/h. These hares spend most of the day resting in hollows called forms and go out to graze at night. Similar species are found in other parts of the world.

**Brownian Movement.** The continuous random movement of microscopic solid particles (of about 1 micrometre in diameter) when suspended in a fluid medium. First observed by the botanist Robert Brown (1773-1858) in 1827 when studying pollen particles, it was originally thought to be the manifestation of some vital force. It was latter recognized to be a consequence of bombardment of the particles by the continually moving molecules of the liquid. The smaller the particles the more extensive is the motion. It can be observed in the particles of a colloidal solution and in the protoplasm of dead cells.

**Brown Oak**

1. Wood from an oak tree that has been infected with Fistulina hepatica (beefsteak fungus). The wood has a rich, dark brown colour. Although mechanically weaker than wood from uninfected trees, it is nevertheless highly prized by cabinet-makers for decorative purposes.
2. Disease of oak trees caused by Fistulina hepatica.

**Brown Rot**

1. Very common disease of fruit caused by fungi of the genus Sclerotinia (usually S. fructigena). Fruits susceptible to it include apples, pears, cherries, plums, etc. Initially, soft brown patches appear on the fruit, often at a site of injury, and these gradually spread

until the whole fruit is affected. Fungal conidia are produced from small, pale-coloured, cottony patches which typically appear on the rotting fruit.

2. Type of timber decay in which the wood turns a reddish-brown colour and becomes cracked and eventually crumbly in texture. Fungi that cause brown rots are usually unable to break down the lignin component of wood.

**Browse Line.** In wooded regions, a line usually at a height of aboue 8 feet below which all available vegetation has been consumed, as that seen in overpopulated deer areas. Also called deer line.

**Brucella.** Genus of bacteria not assigned to a taxonomic family. The cells are ovoid or shortly rod-shaped, and are Gram-negative. They are chemo-organotrophic, and can grow only in the presence of air. There are several species, found as parasites and pathogens in a range of mammalian hosts. B. abortus can cause abortion in cattle and can also infect humans.

**Brucellosis.** A febrile disease resulting from infection by bacteria of the genus Brucella. Also called undulant fever, Malta fever, Mediterranean fever, contagious abortion.

**Bruits.** Refer to the abnormal sounds which are heard in various parts of vascular system; major cause is attributed to the disease of valves of heart.

**Brunoniaceae.** Monotypic family, comprising Brunonia australis, blue pincushion. It is a small herb with a rosette of leaves. The flowers are borne terminally on long stems in densely clustered, hemispherical, bracteate heads. They are regular and pentamerous. The five sepals are united in a lobed tube, and the five petals are narrow and not winged. The ovary is superior and enclosed in the hollow receptacle. The fruit is a small nut. The family is related to Goodeniaceae. It is endemic to Australia and Tasmania and present throughout temperate regions of the country in open communities.

**Brush-border.** A free epithelium or epithelial cell surface that is bearing numerous, small microvilli *e.g.*, epithelium of proximal urinary tubule.

**Brush-tail Opossum.** Also known as the vulpine, or fox-like opossum, the brush-tail opossum is found in Australia, Tasmania and New Zealand. It is about 60 cm long and its fur is thick and woolly, ranging in colour from silver grey to black. Its tail is prehensile at the tip.

**Brussels Sprouts.** Vegetables of the cabbage family. Each plant has a tall stalk on which the sprouts, like miniature cabbages, form. The tops are leafy. Sprouts are food-filled buds.

**Bruxism.** Teeth grinding which takes place during sleep in some individuals; also associated with dreaming.

**Bryales** (subclass Bryidae). Order of medium-sized to large acrocarpous mosses. The leaves are oval to lance-shaped; each usually has a nerve and a border of distinct cells. The capsule is spherical to cylindrical, inclined or drooping, with a double peristome. There are many genera, found in a wide range of habitats.

**Bryokinin.** A growth substance found in certain mosses, *e.g.* Funaria, that stimulates the formation of buds and subsequently leafy plants from the filamentous protonema.

**Bryony.** The common name of two unrelated perennial climbing herbs. White bryony, found in Europe, western Asia and North Africa, is related to the cucumber and has greenish-white flowers. It climbs with tendrils. Black bryony occurs in the same areas. It is related to yams and has small greenish blooms. It twines around the other plants.

**Bryophyta.** A division of nonvascular plants, mainly terrestrial in habitat containing about 25 000 species. It comprises the three classes Hepaticae (liverworts), Musci (mosses), and Anthocerotae (hornworts). Bryophytes are generally small low-growing plants, in most cases susceptible to desiccation and hence limited to damp or humid environments. Their life cycle shows a heteromorphic alternation of generations with the haploid gametophyte, which may be homo- or heterothallic, the dominant generation. The ephemeral sporophyte is partly or completely parasitic on the gametophyte and consists solely of a stalk bearing the spore capsule.

Certain similarities between mosses and algae, especially between algal filaments and the moss protonema, suggest that bryophytes evolved from algae, most probably green algae, since these also share similar photosynthetic pigments, food reserves, and cell-wall constituents. Bryophytes however exhibit considerably greater morphological differentiation than the algae and differ also in producing aerial spores and having enclosed sex organs. Nevertheless they still lack roots and water is needed for the dispersal of antherozoids and for fertilization.

Despite their primitive characteristics, bryophytes are the dominant vegetation in certain areas, notably the bogs of temperate latitudes.

**Bryophyte.** Any plant of the division Bryophyta which includes the mosses, liverworts, and hornworts.

**Bryopsida.** Taxon used by some authors as a synonym of Musci, and by others as a class which includes mosses more usually included in the subclass Bryidae, *i.e.*, mosses excluding Sphagnum and the Andreaeidae

**Bryopsidophyceae.** A class of the Chlorophyta consisting predominantly of macroscopic algae with coenocytic thalli. Certain of these algae contain distinctive carotenoid and xanthophyll pigments and reserve carbohydrates and include xylose, mannose, and callose among their cell-wall components. The class includes the orders Cladophorales, Acrosiphonales, Sphaeropleales, Siphonocladales, Dasycladales, and Caulerpales.

**Bryozoa** (moss-animals). Phylum of small, aquatic, colonial animals, related to the Brachiopoda, many of which possess a well-developed, calcite skeleton which comprises microscopic, box-like divisions, each housing an individual animal possessing ciliated tentacles and a coelom (internal body cavity). Food is collected by the tentacles which surround the mouth and are bone on a ridge called the 'lophophere'. Reproduction takes place by (a) asexual budding, and (b) the release of larvae which give rise to new colonies. Bryozoans have occurred from the Ordovician to the present day. Fossilized branched colonies are common in some rocks. They were important reef builders in the Phanerozoic, and underwent several great radiations.

**Bryozoan.** An invertebrate of the group Bryozoa (Polyzoa) which included organisms commonly called moss animals or zoophytes. The phylum has now been divided into two phyla, Entoprocta and Ectoprocta.

**Bryum** (order Bryales). Genus of mosses in which the plants are usually densely tufted. The leaves are ovate or broadly oblong-lanceolate; the cells composing the leaf are uniform and are mainly hexagonal or rhomboid. The capsule is pyriform to sub-cylindrical, horizontal or pendulous, but never erect; the peristome is double. Bryum is a large cosmopolitan genus, with about 1050 species, some of which are difficult to distinguish. They are mainly terricolous or saxicolous. B. argenteum is easily recognizabie on sight : it has a characteristic silvery-green colour, and grows abundantly in many places where little else can grow, *e.g.* on payements in towns, roadsides, etc.

**Bubble Shell.** A tropical marine gastropod with a thin, globose, or oval shell, of the family Bullidae, as Bulla, Hydatina.

**Bubo** pl. **Buboes.** Inflammation and swelling of one or more lymph nodes, especially those of the groin and axilla, as occurs in infectious diseases as syphilis and bubonic plauge.

**Bubonic Plague.** A form of plague characterized by buboes, primarily a disease of rodents but transmissible to man through the agency of fleas.

**Buccal**

1. Of a pertaining to the cheeks.
2. Of or pertaining to the sides of the mouth cavity.

**Buccal Cavity.** Refers to the mouth cavity, by which food is taken into the alimentary canal. In mammals it is surrounded by the lips and cheeks. Ducts from salivary glands open into the mouth so that food gets moistened and lubricated and, in some cases, digested. Other vertebrates are also having buccal cavities but without cheeks and cannot therefore chew their food, but must swallow it whole. Invertebrates are also having a variety of buccal cavities.

**Buccal Cirri.** The oral tentacles surrounding the vestibule of a lancelet.

**Buccal Field.** The area surrounding the mouth of a rotifer.

**Buccal Funnel.** The oral funnel, a suctorial structure by which the sea lamprey attaches itself to and secures food from its host.

**Buccal Incubation** (mouth brooding). In a number of species of fish, such as Sarotherodon mossambicus (cichlid), Scleropages leichardti (barramundi), of the family Osteoglossidae, and several sea-catfish (Ariidae), the male or the famale carries the fertilized eggs in the mouth until some time after hatching. During incubation the parent involved takes no food, and so may appear rather leant at the end of the incubation period.

**Buccal Mass.** A mass of tissue in the head of gastropods and other mollusks consisting principally of the radula and associated structures.

**Bucconidae** (puffbirds; order Piciformes). Family of small, black or brown and white birds with thick necks and large heads. The bill is stout with a hooked, often bifid, tip. There are rictal bristles, and the feet are zygodactylous. They are insectivorous and nest in holes in banks. There are 10 genera, with 32 species, found in tropical forests in C. and S. America.

**Bucerotidae** (hornbills; order Coraciiformes). Family of medium to large, typically black and white birds with huge, curved, red or yellow bills, a casque on the culmen, short legs, and a long tail. They are arboreal and terrestrial. They nest in holes in trees, the females being walled in with mud. They are omnivorous, feeding mainly on fruit. There are 12 genera, with 46—49 species, found in Africa, S. Asia, Malaysia, the Philippines, Indonesia, and the Solomons.

**Buck.** The male of various mammals (deer, antelopes, goats, hares, rabbits, rats).

**Buckeye.** A tree of the genus Aesculus, especially A. octandra, the yellow or sweet buckeye. Also called horse chestnut.

**Buckthorn.** A group of shrubs or small trees, with tiny green flowers arranged in clusters. The common buckthorn is a thorny shrub, often used for hedging. It produces clusters of black berries from which comes the dye 'sap-green'.

**Buckwheat.** A crop plant related to docks, grown for its seeds. It grows about 90 cm tall. Its seeds are like small beech nuts. The leaves are heart-shaped.

**Buckwheat.** Fagopyrum sagittatum, an herb of the buckwheat family, Polygonaceal, cultivated as a food plant.

**Bud**

1. (*in botany*). A condensed immature shoot with a short stem bearing small folded or rolled leaves. The outer leaves of a bud are often scalelike and protect the delicate inner leaves. A terminal (or apical) bud exists at the tip of a stem or branch while axillary (or lateral) buds develop in the axils of leaves. However, in certain circumstances buds can be produced anywhere on the surface of a plant. Some buds remain dormant, but may become active if the terminal bud is removed. It is common gardening practice to remove the terminal buds of some shoots to induce the development of lateral shoots from axillary buds.

2. (*in biology*) An outgrowth from a parent organism that breaks away and develops into a new individual in the process of budding.

**Budding**

1. A form of asexual reproduction in which a new individual develops as an outgrowth of a mature organism. Yeast cells exhiblt budding and sometimes the new cells so produced can themselves give rise to further bunds before the chain of individuals separates. Compare fission, fragmentation.

2. (*bud grafting*). A type of grafting in which a bud (the scion) of the desired variety, together with a small piece of bark, is removed and inserted into a slit made in the bark of the chosen rootstock (the stock), and secured with raffia or tape. The rootstock is

usually cut back and any buds removed. The technique is widely used to propagate rosebushes. Bush roses are produced by inserting buds as near to the ground as possible while standard roses are produced by inserting buds higher up on the stem of the rootstock.

**Buddleia.** A group of 100 species of deciduous and evergreen shrubs. They are native to the warmer parts of the world, especially eastern Asia. They are grown for their showy purple or organe flowers, which often form long spikes The flowers of the buddelia attract so many butterflies that it is sometimes known as the butterfly bush.

**Buddleja** (family Loganiaceae). Genus of plants, many of which are ornamentals. They are rich in alkaloids. The flowers are clustered, attractive to butterflies, tetramerous, and have a superior ovary. Perhaps they are related to Scrophulariaceae. There are 100 species, occurring in the tropics and subtropics, and especially in E Asia

**Budgerigar.** The commonest member of the parrot family in Australia, the budgerigar travels in huge flocks Being a seed-eating bird, it is a pest in grain-growing areas. The wild bird is bright green with black, yellow and blue markings but many different colour varieties have been produced by bird fanciers.

**Bud Grafting** Budding.

**Bud Scales.** Scalelike structures which form a protective covering for winter buds.

**Buffalo.** One of several species of heavily-built bovine animals, as the water buffalo (Bubalus bubalis), cape buffalo (Syncerus caffer), anoa (Anoa depressicornis), and North American buffalo or bison (Bison bison).

**Buffalo Fish.** One of several species of freshwater food fishes of the sucker family, Catostomidae, as the large-mouth buffalo fish (Ictiobus cyprinella).

**Buffalo Gnat.** A black fly.

**Buffer.** Solution of a weak acid and its conjugate weak base that resists changes in pH that would otherwise result from the addition of an acid or base. The buffering properties of weak electrolytes in living organisms are of great importance, since most cells can survive only within narrow pH limits.

**Buffered.** Treated in such a way as to resist changes in pH. said of solutions, bacteriological media, etc.

**Buffer Solution.** A solution consisting of a weak acid and a highly ionized salt of the same acid or base.

**Buffer Species.** An alternative food for a predator, which reduces pressure on the primary prey.

**Bufflehead.** Bucephala (Glaucionetta, Charitonetta) albeola, a small diving duck of the family Anatidae.

**Buff-tip.** When at rest, with its wings pulled in tight against its body, the buff-tip moth looks just like a deat twig. Its wings are greyish-brown, and it is often found in orchards. The forewings have a buff (sandcoloured) patch at the tip.

Buff-tip

**Bufo Bufo** (common toad, European toad; order Anura (Salientia), family Bufonidae). Species of toad in which the males are smaller than the females, and develop nuptial pads on three inner fingers in autumn for spring mating. Their colour is changeable, red-brown to grey. The species is native to Europe (including Great Britain), northern and temperate Asia, and N. Africa.

**Bufo Calamita** (natterjack toad; order Anura (Salientia), family Bufonidae). Species of toad which is tolerant of brackish water. They have a prominent yellow dorsal stripe. The hind limbs are short, and the toads run rapidly but do not jump. The male has a large vocal sac. They grow up to 8 cm long. The species usually inhabits sandy soils in Britain and W. Europe.

**Bufo Marinus** (marine toad; order Anura (Salientia), family Bufonidae). Species of toad comprising the largest bufonids, with females reaching 25 cm in length. The colour is mottled yellowbrown; there are red warts. Large parotid glands secrete a highly toxic posion. The species is a native of tropical America, but has been successfully introduced into Caribbean islands, Hawaii, Australia, and New Guinea.

**Bufonidae** (toads; class Amphibia, order Anura (Salientia), suborder Procoela). Squat-bodied amphibians which have short, powerful limbs for crawling. The skin is generally dry and warty. Teeth are absent. Vertebrae are procoelous, the pectoral girdle arciferal. A Bidder's organ (rudimentary ovary) is present in males. They are usually nocturnul or crepuscular land dwellers, only breeding in water. There are some 300 species, found in all continents except Australia and Antarctica.

**Bug.** A term popularly used for most insects but scientifically applied to any member of the insect order Hemiptera, sometimes known as the 'true bugs' to avoid any confusion. Bugs all possess piercing mouthparts suited for sucking the juices of plants and animals but they differ considerably in appearance. The group includes, among many others, Aphids, Assasin Bugs, Backswimmers, Bedbugs, Cicadas and Pond Skaters.

**Bug, True.** Many insects may be called 'bugs'. But true bugs are insects which look rather like beetles, though with different mouth parts. Bugs feed by piercing and sucking the juices from plants or animals, and their mouth parts form pointed 'beak'. (Beetles have jaws for chewing.) Bugs live on and under water as well as on land, and some, such as the aphid and leafhopper, can be pests. Other examples of bugs are the stinkbugs. water boatmen and cicadas.

**Bugle.** A low creeping plant with bright blue flowers arranged in a long leafy spike. It grows in woodlands and spreads by means of runners.

**Bugloss.** Several short hairy plants of the borage family. The viper's bugloss is a common species. Its pink buds and bright blue flowers add a splash of colour to gardens and wastelands. The name bugloss means 'ox-tongued' in Greek, an apt term for the rough, tongue-shaped leaves.

**Building Phase.** Stage in the cyclical pattern of changes typical of grassland and heathland communities. In grassland, the term refers to the accumulation of wind-borne particles to form a small hummock around any grass seedling that chances to invade a hollow, which in turn results from the erosion of a former hummock in the degenerate phase. In heathlands the term describes the bushy phase of growth in individual Calluna vulgaris (heather) plants, lasting from about 7—13 years of age. At this stage net primary production in the new shoots is at a maximum and the dense, bushy plant allows little light to reach the ground, hence it tends to suppress other species commonly associated with C. vulgaris in the pioneer, mature, and degenerate phases. Compare hollow phase; pioneer phase.

**Bulb.** A fleshy underground perennating organ formed by many members of the Liliaceae and Amaryllidaceae. It is a highly modified shoot, the bulk of which is made up of colourless swollen scale leaves or leaf bases. The central apical bud contains the immature foliage leaves, the future flower, and rudimentary adventitious roots at its base. It is surrounded by numerous layers of flesby scales, which may be complete modified leaves or the leaf bases of previous years' foliage leaves. The first sign of growth is the rapid elongation of the adventitious roots. When these have established themselves in the soil the apical bud sprouts and the foliage leaves and inflorescence emerge, growing at the expense of the food reserves in the scale leaves. In some bulbs, *e.g.* tulip, the inflorescence develops from the apex of the bud and further apical growth is consequently prevented. Photosynthates from the foliage leaves are

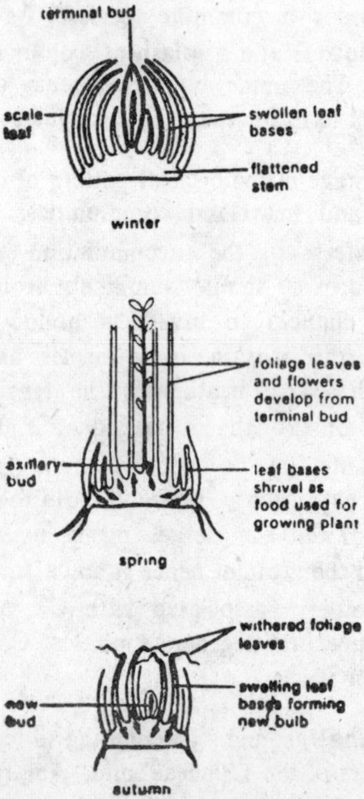


Development of a bulb

passed down to one or more lateral buds in the axils of the scale leaves. This is an example of sympodial growth. In other bulbs, *e.g.* daffodil, the inflorescence develops in the axil of one of the foliage leaves and the apex of the bud remains within the bulb. It persists from year to year, each year giving rise to foliage leaves and a lateral inflorescence. Propagation may be effected by the expansion of a lateral bud in the axil of the outermost scale leaf. Bulbs such as daffodil show monopodial rather than sympodial growth.

The food reserves of the bulb may be starch (as in tulip) or sugars (as in onion). The outermost leaves do not contain food but are thin, brown, and scaly and protect the bulb. Compare corm.

**Bulbil.** A small bulb that develops from an aerial bud. Bulbils are easily detached and function as a means of vegetative propagation. They may form from lateral buds, as in the lesser celandine (Ranunculus ficaria), or develop in place of flowers, as in many species of Allium Certain forms of apomixis give rise to bulbils, as seen in the lesser bulbous saxifrage (Saxifraga cernua). The term is also applied to various outgrowths formed by lower plants that become detached and develop into new plants. For example, the fern Asplenium bulbiferum produces bulbils on the upper surface of its fronds and Lycopodium selago has bulbils in the axils of the uppermost leaves.

**Bulbillus.** A contractile enlargement at the base of each of the lateral arteries leading to the gills in a lancelet.

**Bulblet.** A small bulb that develops in a leaf axil inflorescence or some other unusual location.

**Bulbose, Bulbous, Bulbar**

1. Having the structure of or resembling a bulb.
2. Producing or containing bulbs.
3. Growing from bulbs.

**Bulbourethral Glands.** Refer to the paired glands which are associated with urinogenital organs in mammals and are present surrounding urethra. They secrete a mucous-like substance that comes out before ejaculation. It lubricates vagina, neutralises aciditya of vagina, aids fertilisation by dissolving certain cells around the ovum. Also known as Cowper's glands.

**Bulbus Arteriosus.** The expanded proximal portion of the ventral aorta in lower vertebrates.

**Bulgaria** (order Helotiales). Genus of fungi that form gelatinous apothecia within which the unicellular brown and/or colourless ascospores are produced, B. inquinans ('Pope's buttons') is a common species, with black, globular to cup-shaped, rubbery fruit bodies, each 2-4 cm across, which grow in clusters on logs, especially those of oak.

**Bull.** The male of any bovine mammal; also the male of most large mammals, as the moose, elephant, seal, sea lion.

**Bulla**

1. A large bleb or blister.
2. In certain mammals, *a.* the expanded portion (auditory bulla) of the tympanic bone; *b.* an enlarged ethmoid cell which forms a rounded projection into the middle meatus.

**Bullate.** Having a blistered or puckered appearance, as the surface of certain leaves, as the Savoy cabbage.

**Bullfinch.** A beautiful bird, disliked by fruit-growers because it eats the buds of fruit trees. Both sexes have black caps and the male has a bright red breast. Bullfinches live in Europe all the year round and only the most northerly birds migrate south. They are usually seen in pairs and apparently mate for life. They nest in thick bushes or hedges.

**Bullfrog.** The bullfrog is a large North American frog up to 20 cm long, which is rarely found away from water. It feeds on a variety of insects caught at the surface of the pond but will also eat other animals, including small snakes and mammals.

**Bullhead.** Member of a group of mainly freshwater fishes belonging to the sculpin family. The most common species is the miller's thumb. It has a large bulbous head and gets its curious name from the tradition that a miller's thumb was wide through continually rubbing grains between thumb and fore-finger. It is a rather spiny fish, about 10 cm long, and lives in stony, swift-flowing streams.

**Bulliform Cells** (motor cells). Any of the large cells occurring at places in longitudinal rows in leaf epidermis of rolling xerophytes (that show rolling of lamina in dryness) which are mostly grasses. These cells are involved in rolling and unrolling of lamina due to rapid loss and reabsorption of water during dry and wet conditions respectively.

**Bull Kelp.** Nereocystis, the sea otter's cabbage or bladder kelp, a giant kelp sometimes reaching a length of 150 feet.

**Bull Snake.** One of several species of snakes of the genus Pituophis. They are large, harmless but pugnacious, killing their prey by constriction, as the pine snake and gopher snake.

**Bully Tree.** Balata.

**Bulrush.** A tall water or marsh plant with strap-shaped leaves. Also known as reed-mace. The flowers form dense spikes at the top of the stems and later give rise to the familiar velvety brown clubs. The name bulrush is also applied to a tall, dark stemined member of the sedge family which grows in still and slow-moving water.

**Bumble-bee.** A large bee whose lazy, noisy flight from flower to flower is a familiar summer sight in many parts of the world. The body of a bumble-bee is covered in stiff hairs, often black and yellow, which pick up pollen from the flowers. Bumble-bees build nests from grass and leaves in cavities such as old mouse burrows.

**Bundle**

1. *anat.* A group of elongated structures as muscle or nerve fibers; a fasciculus.
2. *bot.* An elongated group of conducting vessels in the stem of a vascular plant.

**Bundle Cap.** One or more layers of sclerenchyma or thickened parenchyma cells seen at the xylem and/or phloem poles of a vascular bundle.

**Bundle of His.** Refers to a specialised type of conducting tissue present within the heart of mammals, which is continuous anteriorly with AV-node and posteriorly gives off a left bundle branch. The left bundle branch and fassicles are running subendocardially down either side of septum and coming in contact with Purkinjie's system.

**Bundle of Kent.** Individuals having Wolff-Parkinson-white syndrome probably possess an additional aberrant muscular or nodal tissue connection between ataria and ventricle. It conducts more rapidly than slow conducting AV-node and is responsible for accelerated conduction.

**Bundle Scar.** A scar marking the end of a vascular bundle, one or more being present in a leaf scar.

**Bundle Sheath.** A region surrounding the small vascular bundles in the leaves of vascular plants. It usually consists of parenchyma cells but may sometimes consist largely of sclerenchyma. In angiosperms, the bundle sheath is a type of endodermis, which may be differentiated as a starch sheath. The cells of the bundle sheath have their long axes parallel to the direction of the vascular bundle. In dicotyledons, the parenchymatous bundle sheath is sometimes termed border parenchyma. Bundle sheath extensions, in which the cels of the bundle sheath extend to one or both epidermal layers, are present in many monocotyledons They are believed to be concerned with conduction or support.

**Bundle Tip.** The end of a vascular bundle in a leaf, usually a single vessel or tracheid.

**Bungarotoxin.** A group of neurotoxins which are isolated from venom of snake krait (Bungarus). It binds selectively and irreversibly to acetylcholine receptors.

**Bunner's Glands.** Refer to small coiled acinotublar glands in the duodenum that secrete a thick alkaline mucous which probably projects the duodenal wall from gastric acid. They open in the krypts of Loiberkuhn.

**Bunting.** A family of seed-eating birds that look similar to finches, with stout bills for cracking open seeds and nuts. Buntings tend to be less well known than finches because they are not so colourful and do not frequent parks and gardens.

**Buprestid.** A beetle of the family Buprestidae which includes the metallic wood-boring beetles, as Chrysobothris femorata, the flat-headed apple tree borer.

**Buprestidae** (jewel beetles; class Insecta, order Coleoptera). The most beautiful of beetle families, often used in jewellery. The more spectacular species are tropical; in Britain they emerge occasionally from imported timber. The elytra and thorax are elongate, with bright metallic colours; they are often of a considerable size. The eyes are large, the antennae short and filiform. The Buprestidae are daytime nectar feeders. The larvae are club-shaped, legless, and called 'flat-headed borers'; the head is tiny, the prothorax unusually broad, the body narrow and tapering. The larvae live in trees or roots, where they gnaw flattened tunnels. Some mine leaves or stems. There are 11 500 species.

**Bur** (burr). A type of pseudocarp in which the fruit is surrounded by a persistent barbed involucre as, for example, in burdocks (Arctium) and cocklebur (Xanthium). Often the term refers to any barbed fruits, *e.g.* those of cleavers (Galium aparine) and enchanter's night-shade (Circaes lutetiana) both of which have hooks borne directly on the pericarp. Burs cling to passing animals and are thus widely dispersed.

**Bunodont.** Having low, rounded cusps, as a molar tooth in man.

**Bunodont Teeth.** When cusps in molar tooth are distinct from one another, the tooth is turmed as bundont *e.g.*, man, monkey etc.

**Bunt** (stinking smut). Disease of wheat caused by the smut fungus Tilletia caries. The grain in an infected ear of wheat is replaced by masses of fungal spores which have a characteristic fishy smell; the spores are released when the wheat crop is harvested.

**Burbot.** The only member of the cod family that lives in fresh water. It is a slender fish, about 40 cm long. The barbel on its lower jaw serves as a feeler. Burbot live in lakes and slow-moving rivers, feeding on the bottom at dawn and dusk. They eat fishes and various invertebrates.

**Burdo.** A graft-hybrid formed by the fusion of vegetative nuclei from the stock and scion.

**Burdock.** A coarse hairy weed producing thistle-like flowers. The flower-heads (burs) are hooked and cling to the coats of animals when the seeds are ripe. Seeds are scattered from the burs as the animals walk about. The big lower leaves are heart-shaped, and are eaten as a vegetable in Japan.

**Burgundy Mixture.** A copper fungicide, similar to but stronger than Bordeaux mixture and used especially against.

**Burhinidae** (thick-knees, stone-curlews; order Charadriiformes). Family of sandy or grey-brown birds with large heads and eyes, shortish-stout bills, and long legs with thickened tibiotarsal joints. The feet are semipalmate with three toes. They are crepuscular and nocturnal, in open, stony and sandy country. They feed on invertebrates, mice and frogs, and are ground-nesting. There are two genera, with nine species, found in Africa, Europe, Asia, Australia, C. and S. America.

**Buried Soil**. Soil covered by an alluvial, colluvial, aeolian, glacial, or organic deposit, and being a product of a former period of pedogenesis. In US usage a buried soil is defined as lying beneath 30-50 cm if the covering layer is more than half the thickness of the buried soil, otherwise beneath more than 50 cm.

**Burl**. An abnormal outgrowth or excrescence on a tree trunk, usually due to stimulation of the cambium by insects or other agents.

**Burnet Moth**. A group of brightly-coloured, day-flying moths that are most abundant in the Mediterranean area. Most have metallic blue or greenish-black forewings with scarlet markings.

**Burro**. A small donkey, especially one used as a pack animal.

[1]**Burrow**. A hole or excavation used as a breeding place, shelter, runway, or habitat.

[2]**Burrow**. To make a passageway beneath a surface.

**Burrowing**. Fossorial.

**Burrowing Owl**. A small owl living over a wide area in the Americas. It hunts by both day and night, feeding mainly on rodents and insects. The bird gets its name from its habit of nesting in burrows on the ground, but it does not normally dig its own burrow. More often it takes over the deserted hole of a prairie dog or a fox.

**Burrowing Toad.** A small, oval-shaped Mexican toad which digs holes in which to escape the fierce heat of day. The burrowing toad inflates its body when alarmed to look half as large again as it really is.

**Bursa**

1. *anat.* A sac or saclike cavity, as *a.* one in connective tissue filled with synovia for minimizing friction; *b.* the cavity of the greater omentum.

2. *zool.* *a.* The flared, posterior end of male nematodes. *b.* An eversible, cuplike copulatory structure in male acanthocephalans. *c.* A sac in female turbellarians which stores sperm. *d.* An invagination on oral surface of ophiuroids.

**Bursa Entiana.** A small sac-like structure which is present between pyloric stomach and intestine in cartilagenous fishes like, Scoliodon. Its definite function is not known.

**Bursa Fabricii.** The bursa of Fabricius, a saclike lymphatic organ in young birds communicating dorsally with the cloaca.

**Burseraceae.** Important family of resiniferous, tropical timber trees, in which the leaves are pinnate, with stipules. The flowers are unisexual and small, their parts usually in threes or fives, with a disc. The fruit is a drupe or capsule. There are 16 genera, with 500 species.

**Bursicon.** Neurosecretory cells in brain and nerve cord of insects secrete a hormone that affects the cuticle development, including process of tanning which gets completed several hours after each moult; small molecular protein having molecular weight of about 40,000.

**Burying Beetle.** A group of carrion beetles (beetlss which feed on the bodies of dead animals). They are also known as sexton beetles, named after the people who tend graves in churchyards. The male and female beetles work together when they find a corpse such as that of a mouse, digging out the soil from underneath it so that eventually the body is bodies contain cyanide poison. Burnet moths have antennae with knobs at the ends, and so may be confused with butterflies. The larvae spin yellowish cocoons, often high up or grass stems. After the adult has emerged, the empty pupal skin can often be found hanaing from the cocoon. The most common species is the six-spot burnet which has six red spots on each of its shiny black fore-wings.

**Burnished Brass**. A brown moth with metallic yellow markings (sometimes almost green) on the wings. It is a relative of the silver-Y moth, and like it has clumps of hair along the back of its body.

**Bush**

1. A shrub, especially one with many branches and dense foliage.
2. Uncultivated land covered with scrubby vegetation, as in Australia.

**Bushbaby**. The four species of bushbaby, also called galagos, are relatives of the lemurs. All live in the African bush or scrub regions and they move around in the trees at night, feeding on insects, fruit, and birds' eggs. Bushbabies are furry creatures with large eyes and ears and long furry tails. The largest bushbaby is about '75 cm long including the tail.

**Bushbuck**. A browsing antelope found in the forest and bush throughout most of Africa. The bushbuck stands about 75 cm high at the shoulder. It has a brown coat with white markings and the male has a bushy mane along the back. The sharp horns may reach over 50 cm in length, but females only rarely bear them.

**Bush Cricket**. A group of insects related to grasshoppers. Bush crickets have longer antennae than the true grasshoppers and are sometimes (wrongly) called long-horned grasshoppers. Bush crickets 'sing' by rubbing their wings together and they feed mainly on other insects.

**Bush Dog.** A South American dog only distantly related to the domestic dog but behaving very like it when tamed. It stands about 40 cm high at the shoulder, but its legs are relatively short. It is brown in colour and, unlike most animals, it is paler on top than below. It ranges from Panama to Paraguay and hunts at night in small packs.

**Bushman.** One of a race of primitive peoples of Central and Southern Africa, related to the pygmies.

**Bushmaster.** Lachesis mutus, a large, venomous snake of Central and South America.

**Bushpig.** The bushpig, also known as the red river hog, is a stout-bodied pig found over most of Africa. The head is large in proportion to the body and it bears tufted ears. The adults are reddish-brown or black and weigh up to 140 kg. Their main food is roots and fruits.

**Butanedioic Acid.** Succinic acid.

**Bustard.** A group of large birds with stout legs and strong toes. Most species live in Africa, mainly on the ground in open country. The birds run well, but they can also fly in spite of their size. The great bustard is as large as a turkey, weighing up to 14 kg and having a wingspan of 2.5 metres.

**Butcher Bird.** The name given to various birds, including shrikes, which impale their prey on thorns.

**Buteo** (buzzards, hawks; family Accipitridae). Genus of mainly brown, broad-winged, broad-tailed, medium-sized birds, which are well adapted to soaring. The toes are short and thick, the tarsi sometimes feathered to the toes. They are found in open country and forests, and are mainly migratory. They feed on mammals and reptiles. They are mainly tree-nesting, but some nest on crags or on the ground. There are 25 species, found in the Americas. Europe, Asia, and Africa.

**Butterball.** A bufflehead, q.v.

**Butterbur.** A short plant related to the daisy, whose leaves may be up to 1 metre across when full-grown. The light clusters of pink flowers appear before the leaves. Male and female flowers grow on separate plants. Butterburs form patches in damp places such as riverbanks, water-meadows and roadsides.

**Buttercup.** Several species of flowering plant characterized by their waxy, yellow, five-petalled flowers. They have poisonous juices and are therefore avoided by grazing animals. The most common species is the meadow buttercup which grows mainly in meadows and other damp, grassy places. It grows up to 1.2 metres tall. The shorter bulbous buttercup can be identified by its downward-turned sepals. It likes drier ground than the meadow buttercup.

**Butterfish.** A small fish found in shallow coastal waters around northern Europe. It belongs to the blenny family and is also known as the gunnel. The fish grows up to 24 cm long and has 9-13 black spots along its dorsal fin. The female lays her eggs in a large ball, and wraps herself round it to protect them.

**Butterfly.** A large group of insects belonging to the order Lepidoptera which also includes the moths. Butterflies are generally day-flying creatures and moths night-flying, but there are many exceptions to this rule. A better way of telling the two apart is by the shape of the antennae. Butterflies have club-tipped antennae; the antennae of moths have many shapes but they are never club tipped. Butterflies and moths feed on flower nectar and other liquids. Their mouthparts are extended to form a long tube or proboscis through which they suck up the liquid. When not in use the proboscis is coiled beneath the animal's head. Butterflies and moths pass through four stages in their life cycle; egg, larva (caterpillar), pupa and finally the adult butterfly.

**Butterfly Flower.** A flower pollinated by butterfflies.

**Button**

1. *zool.* The cone shaped tip of the rattle of a rattlesnake.
2. *bot.* Any of a number of structures which resemble a button, as a bud, a rose hip, an immature fruiting body of a mushroom.

**Buttonquail.** Small ground-living birds of dry habitats, widely distributed from Spain through Africa and southern Asia to Australia. The female, unusually, is more brightly coloured than the male and attracts a partner in the breeding season with a strange booming call.

**Butterwort.** Insect-eating plants related to the bladderwort. The common butterwort has purple, two-lipped flowers and a rosette of sticky, insect-trapping leaves. It is found on moors and bogland.

**Butress Root.** A form of prop root that is asymmetrically thickened to give a planklike outgrowth on the upper side, providing extra support for the tree. Buttress roots are common in many tropical trees, *e.g.* certain figs (Ficus).

**Buxaceae**. Family of evergreen shrubs or trees whose leaves are without stipules. The flowers are small and regular, with two or three sepals and petals, 4-6 free anthers, and a superior ovary of three fused carpels. The fruit is a drupe or capsule. The seeds are black and shiny, sometimes with a caruncle. The family is related to the Euphorbiaceae. There are six genera, with about 100 species, occurring in temperate and tropical regions.

**Buxbaumiales** (subclass Bryidae). Order of small, sometimes minute, acrocarpous mosses. The leaves and shoots are often poorly developed, and the capsule is disproportionately large; in some species there are no leaves and the branched, filamentous protonema is persistent. They are found on acid soil on moorlands and in woods, and on soil-covered rocks in mountainous regions. (This characteristic group of mosses is sometimes elevated to subclass level : Buxbaumiideae).

**Buzzard.** A large bird of prey found over a large area of Europe, Asia and Africa. It inhabits open and lightly wooded country, especially hilly regions, and soars high in the air on its broad wings. It feeds on rabbits and other mammals. The name is also used in America for the New World vultures, especially the turkey vulture of the United States.

**Byrrhidae** (pill beetles; class Insecta, order Coleoptera). Family of dull, pubescent, highly convex beetles, 1.5-10 mm long. The antennae are clubbed. When disturbed, the legs are withdrawn completely into grooves on the underside of the abdomen. Byrrhus pilula, the most common British species, is found under stones, and in grass. Lorvae are fat and cylindrical, with a large, broad prothorax, and a pair of retractable false legs on the terminal segment. Larvae are found among roots and in mass. There are 270 species.

**Byssal Gland.** A glandular structure in bivalve mollusks which secretes threads of a viscid substance which harden on contact with sea water, forming byssal threads. Also called byssal pit.

**Byssochlamys** (family Eurotiaceae). Genus of fungi that are found chiefly in soil. B. fulva can cause spoilage of canned or bottled fruit. Its ascospores can survive heating to a temperature of 84-87 °C.

**Byssus.** A cluster of tough, hair-like threads by which certain aquatic molluscs anchor themselves to rock surfaces.

[illegible] (Gk. [illegible]) Order of small, sometimes [illegible]. [illegible] are [illegible] [illegible] there are [illegible] permanent. They are found on rocks and [illegible] and in woods, and on [illegible] rocks in mountainous regions. [illegible] [illegible]

[illegible] large area of [illegible] open and lightly [illegible] country [illegible] high [illegible] on rabbits and other [illegible] in America [illegible] the New World [illegible] of the United States.

[illegible] of the [illegible] [illegible] long. The [illegible] are [illegible] on the back side of the [illegible]. Larvae are [illegible] and a [illegible]. Larvae are found [illegible] and in [illegible]. There are 270 species.

Byssal Gland: A [illegible] gland in [illegible] which [illegible] of the [illegible] called byssus.

[illegible] (Gk. [illegible]) [illegible] of [illegible] that are [illegible] in [illegible] fruit. [illegible] temperature of [illegible].

Byssus: [illegible] threads by which [illegible] molluscs [illegible] to rock surfaces.

# C

**$C_3$ Plant.** Any plant that produces, as the first step in photosynthesis, phosphoglyceric acid, which contains three carbon atoms. Most plants of temperate regions are $C_3$ plants. They exhibit photorespiration and are relatively inefficient photosynthetically compared to $C_4$ plants. They generally have lower carbon dioxide fixation rates and higher compensation points than $C_4$ plants.

**$C_4$ Plant.** Any plant that produces, as the first step in photosynthesis, oxaloacetic acid, which contains four carbon atoms (Hatch-Slack pathway). Over 100 species of $C_4$ plants have been identified, most of which are tropical. Examples include maize, sugar cane, sorghum, Bermuda grass, and many desert plants. $C_4$ plants require 30 molecules of ATP and 24 molecules of water to synthesize a molecule of glucose ($C_3$ plants need only 18 molecules of ATP and 12 molecules of water). However $C_4$ plants produce more glucose for a given leaf area than $C_3$ plants and consequently grow more quickly. They can also continue to photosynthesize at high light intensities and low carbon dioxide concentrations (compensation point) and, most significantly, do not exhibit photorespiration. Compare crassulacean acid metabolism.

**Cabbage.** Several species of flowering plant with four-petalled flowers that resemble a cross. The wild cabbage is the ancestor of many cultivated vegetables. It has a spike of stalked, yellow flowers and greyish leaves. It is often found on sea cliffs and is also known as sea cabbage.

**Cabbage Moth.** A common moth whose larva feeds on cabbages and other low-growing plants, as well as the leaves of trees. The cabbage moth is a mottled dark brown, and flies throughout the summer. The caterpillar may be any shade from black to bright green.

**Cabbege White.** White.

**Cacao.** A South American tree (Theobroma cacao) extensively cultivated for its seeds, cocoa beans, the source of commercial cocoa and chocolate.

**Cacomistle.** An omnivorous relative of the raccoon, found in the southwestern US and Mexico. The cacomistle has been given a variety of names including ringtail, raccoon fox and catsquirrel. It is a small furry animal with a fox-like face and a long squirred like bushy tail ringed with black. Its fur is valuable and is sold as 'civet cat' and 'California mink'.

**Cactaceae.** A large family of dicotyledonous xerophytic plants, the cacti. It includes over 2000 species in about 87 genera; some authorities however recognize many more, over 300 genera being listed in some classifications. The cacti are limited in distribution to the drier regions of South and Central America and central and sonthern North America. Some have become naturalized elsewhere, *e.g.* prickly pears (Opuntia) in Australia and the Mediterranean, and Rhipsalis, which is probably naturalized rather than native, in southern Africa.

Cacti are succulents and, being, leafless (the leaves are reduced to spines), are a particularly distinctive group of plants. It is this that has led to their pomularity as unusual pot plants. Photosynthesis is carried out by the green expanded stems, which show various advanced characteristics in the arrangement of vascular tissues and many other features. The flowers however, which are borne singly directly on the stem, are comparatively primitive having large numbers of stamens, petals, sepals, and bracts arranged spirally. The fruit is a berry.

Very few cacti are of use to man, except as ornamentals, though prickly pears are grown for their fruits in California, Mexico, and some Mediterranean countries.

**Cactus**. A flowering plant adapted to desert conditions. Many cacti have vast spreading root systems covering large areas close to the surface of the ground, and able to absorb great volumes of water quickly when the rain comes. The stems are distended and fleshy, sometimes forming enormous water stores. Often they are pleated, which allows them to expand like a concertina, thus increasing their water-carrying capacity. Cacti are distinguished from all other succulents by the possession of areoles. These are tiny 'pincushions' from which spines and glochids (barbed hairs) project. The original home of the cactus family was in America but many species are now found in other parts of the world.

**Caddis Fly**. A group of insects which look similar to moths but whose wings are clothed with hairs instead of tiny scales. They are not true flies. Also called sedge flies, some 5000 species are known. Most are dull brown or black. These insects spend their larval stage in water, often building themselves cases of stones, shelll fragments and vegetable matter such as leaves. Inside the case, the larva is well hidden and protected from predators.

**Caducibranch.** An amphibian which loses its gills at metamorphosis.

**Caducous**. Describing parts that fall off easily or at an early stage, such as protective nonphotosynthetic stipules.

**Cae.** For words beginning with CAE not found here, words beginning with CE.

**Caecilian**. A limbless amphibian with a long cylindrical body. The animals vary in size from 20 cm to 1.3 metres and are usually a blackish colour. Their eyes are small and generally useless, but they have a sensory tentacle on each side of the head. Caecilians live underground in tropical regions of Central and South America, Southern Asia and parts of Africa.

**Caecum.** A pouch in the alimentary canal vertebrates between the small intestine and colon. The caecum (and its appendix) is large and highly developed in herbivorous animals *e.g.* rabbits and cows), in which it contains a large population of bacteria essential for the breakdown of cellulose. In humans the caecum is a vestigial organ and is poorly developed.

**Caeoma.** A spore-producing structure in rust fungi.

**Caenozoic** (Cainozoic, Cenozoic). The present geological era, which began some 65 million years ago, and divided into two periods, the Tertiary and the Quaternary. This era is characterized by the rise of modern organisms, especially mammals and flowering plants.

**Caespitous.** A plants which has a tufted form of growth as in many grasses like Deschampsia caespitosa.

**Cainozoic.** Caenozoic, Cenozoic.

**Caerulescent.** Bluish.

**Caespitose.** Having a tufted form of growth, as have many grasses, *e.g.*, Deschampsia caespitosa (tufted hair-grass).

**Caffeine.** An alkaloid, $C_8H_{10}N_4O_2$, present in tea and coffee, mate, kola, and other plants. It is a central nervous system, cardiac, and respiratory stimulant and a diuretic.

**Caiman.** A close relative of the alligator, differing mainly in having the skin of the underside covered in bony plates. There are five species, the smallest being the dwarf caiman up to one metre long, the largest the black caiman up to 4.5 metres long. They are found in the north of South America and Southern Mexico.

**Cainozoic.** Cenozoic.

**Calabash**

1. A gourd, especially one shaped like a flask.
2. The hard-shelled fruit of the calabash tree (Crescentia cujete).

**Calamint.** Several species of sweet-smelling flowering plant. The common calamint can be recognized by its clusters of purple flowers which bear small dark spots on the petals. It can be found in grassy areas and in woods, those found in woods having considerably large flowers.

**Calamitales.** Sphenopsida.

**Calamus**

1. The quill of a feather.
2. The sweet, aromatic rhizome of the sweet flag (Acorus calamus).

**Calamus Scriptorius.** Means a pointed depression in the floor of the fourth ventricle of the mammalian brain, which leads into the central canal of the spinal cord.

**Calathiform.** Cup-shaped.

**Calcaneus.** The heel bone, os calcis.

**Calcar.** A spur or spurlike process.

**Calcarate.** Bearing a spur or calcar.

**Calcarea.** A class of sponges whose skeletons have solely of calcareous and non-siliceous spicules.

**Calcaronea.** Refers to a group of calcareous sponges that comprise of most of those which are classed as Heterocoela, *i.e.*, those whose central cavity is lined by flattened cells and which are having collared cells in special flagellated canals.

**Calcareous.** Of the nature consisting of, or containing calcium carbonate.

**Calcareous Soil.** Rendzina, terra rossa.

**Calcicole.** Describing a plant that flourishes in lime-rich soil. The presence of such a plant is so characteristic of such conditions that it can be used as an indicator. An example of a calcicole plant is the common spotted orchid (Dactylorhiza fuchsii). Compare calcifuge.

**Calcicolous.** Preferring soils heavily impregnated with lime.

**Calciferol,** $C_{28}H_{43}OH$. Refers to a substance of the steroid group which is closely related to Vitamin D It can be produced by irradiation of ergosterol with ultra-violet light. Ergosterol is present in many animals and plants. It is concerned with the regulation of calcium and phospate absorption and the calcification of bones. Lack of Vitamin D produces rickets or softening of the bones.

**Calciferous.** Producing or containing calcite or carbonate of lime.

**Calciferous Glands.** Glands secreting calcium carbonate or other calcium compounds, *e.g.*, the oesophageal glands of an earthworm.

**Calcification.** The deposition of calcium or lime salts within an organ or tissue.

**Calcifuge.** Lime-hating. Plants of this type are rarely found where there is free calcium carbonate in the soil. They are typical of sandy soils. Examples include heather and rhododendron.

**Calcisol.** Rendzina.

**Calcite.** Calcium Carbonate.

**Calcitonin** (thyrocalcitonin). A hormone, produced by the mammalian thyroid gland, that lowers the concentration of calcium (and phosphate) in the blood. It operates in opposition to parathyroid hormone (parathyroid glands).

**Calcium** Symbol : Ca. A soft metal element, atomic number 20, atomic weight 40 08. It is essential to plant growth due to its role, in the form of calcium pectate, in the development of the middle lamella. Calcium ions increase the rigidity of the cell wall by cross-linking the carboxyls of adjacent chains of pectic acid. Calcium is also found as crystals of calcium ovalate in many plant cells. Calcium deficiency is first apparent in the younger parts of the plant because there is little or no translocation of calcium from mature tissues to the growing points.

Calcium is easily leached from soils resulting in an acid soil. This may be countered by adding calcium carbonate, calcium hydroxide (slaked lime), or calcium sulphate (gypsum) to the soil. These compounds also help improve soil structure.

**Calcium Carbonate.** $CaCO_3$, the most abundant and widdely distributed compound of calcium. It occurs in nature as calcite (limestone, marble, chalk) and appears as a white precipitate when $CO_2$ is passed through limewater. It is an important constituent of bone, animal shells, and skeletal structures of invertebrates.

**Calcium Cyclamate.** An organic calcium salt, $C_6H_{11}NHSO_3)$ Ca $2H_2O$, formerly used as a sweetening agent. Its use was banned in the UK in 1969 as it was suspected of causing cancer.

**Calcoblasts**. Refer to the specialised mesogloeal cells that are present in the body of sponges. They secrete calcareous spicules and are amoeboid in shape having calcareous inclusions in cytoplasm.

**Calculus**. A hard concretion composed principally of mineral matter which froms in hollow organs or ducts, as a gallstone.

**Calf**

1. The young of a cow or other bovine quadruped.
2. The young of most large mammals.

3. The fleshy portion of the leg below the knee.

**Call.** A simple, brief, vocal sound produced by birds usually for a distinct purpose, as an alarm call, begging call, or a call to bring the brood together.

**Callose.** A structural polysaccharide found in the sieve plates of the phloem of higher plants, consisting of glucose residues linked through β(1—3) glycosidic bonds. It is deposited steadily throughout the growing season eventually causing blockage of the pores of mature sieve tubes. The functions of blocked tubes are taken over by new phloem formed from the cambium. In some species the blockage is reversible, the callose being hydrolysed in the spring. Callose my be laid down very rapidly in response to injury of the pholem.

Callose was the first structural plant polysaccharide to be synthesized in vitro, using an enzyme isolated from bean (Phaseolus aureus) seedlings.

**Callosity** A callus.

**Callous.** Having a callus or callosities; hardened.

**Callus**

1. (*in botany*). A protective tissue, consisting of parenchyma cells, that develops over a cut or damaged plant surface. Callus tissue can also be induced to form in cell cultures by hormone treatment.

2. (*in pathology*). A thick hard area of skin that commonly forms on the palms of the hands and soles of the feet as a result of continuous pressure or friction.

3. (*in physiology*). Hard tissue formed round bone ends following a fracture, which is gradually converted to new bone.

**Caloric.** Of or pertaining to heat.

**Calorie.** The quantity of heat required to raise the temperature of 1 gram of water by 1°C (1 K). The calorie, a c.g.s. unit, is now largely replaced by the joule, an SI unit. 1 calorie=4.186 8 joules.

**Calorie** (kilogram calorie; kilocalorie). 1000 calories. This unit is still in limited use in estimating the energy value of foods, but is obsolescent.

**Calorific Value**. The heat per unit mass produced by complete combustion of a given substance. Calorific values are used to express the energy values of fuels; usually these are expressed in megajoules per kilogram ($MJ\ kg^{-1}$). They are also used to measure the energy content of foodstuffs; *i.e.* the energy produced when the food is oxidized in the body. The units here are kilojoules per gram ($kJ\ g^{-1}$), although Calories (kilocalories) are often still used in nontechnical contexts.

**Calorimetry.** The determination of heat exchange in an organism or in a system.

**Calvin Cycle** (Benson—Calvin—Bassham cycle). The sequence of reactions, making up the dark or light-independent reactions of photosynthesis, in which carbon dioxide is reduced to carbohydrate using ATP and NADPH derived from the light-dependent reactions (photophosphorylation). The Calvin cycle takes place in the chloroplast stroma and begins with the carboxylation and cleavage of ribulose bisphosphate (RUBP) to form two molecules of phosphoglyceric acid. The RUBP is then regenerated by a complex series of reactions involving 3-, 4-, 5-, 6-, and 7-carbon sugar phosphates. During this process glucose is formed by reversal of the glycolytic reactions (diagram). The overall series of reactions can be written as : 6 ribulose 1,5-bisphosphate$+6CO_2+18ATP+12$ $NADPH+12H^++12H_2O \rightarrow 6$ ribulose 1,5-bisphosphate$+$ glucose$+18P_i+18ADP+12NADP^+$. The glucose is subsequently converted to starch, cellulose, and other polysaccharides.

Calvin and his associates worked out this cycle of reactions by illuminating green algae in the presence of radioactive carbon dioxide for a couple of seconds and then immersing the cells in boiling water prevent further reaction.

**Calycanthemy.** Abnormal development of a calyx resulting in formation of petallike structures.

**Calyces.** Plural of Calyx.

**Calyciform.** Calyxlike.

**Calculate.** Resembling a calyx in shape.

**Calyculus.** A calyxlike structure composed of bracts or bractlets.

**Calypter.** In dipterous insects, a lobelike structure at the base of the wing; also called alula or squama.

**Calyptopis.** The protozoea larva of Euphausia and other shrimplike crustaceans.

**Calyptra**

1. A layer of cells that covers the developing sporophyte of bryophytes and pteridophytes. In mosses it forms a hood over the capsule and in liverworts it forms a sheadth at the base of the capsule stalk.

2. Root cap.

**Calyptrogen.** The layer of meristematic cells at the apex of a root tip that continually cuts off new cells to its outer edge. These replace the cells of the root cap (calyptra) that are worn away as the root pushes through the soil.

**Calyx** pl. **Calyces**

1. *bot.* Collectively, the sepals, the outermost floral whorl.

2. *zool.* *a.* The central cuplike portion of the crown of a crinoid. *b.* The body of certain pedunculate entoprocts. *c.* The thickened basal portion of certain corals.

3. *anat.* *a.* A division of the renal pelvis. *b.* The expanded cuplike termination of an axon.

**Calyx Tube**

1. A tube which is formed by the fusion of at least the lower part of the calyx.

2. The hollowed receptacle of a perigynous flower, on which the petals and stames grow.

**CAM.** Crassulacean acid metabolism.

**Camberwell Beauty.** A handsome butterfly with deep brown wings fringed with purple-blue and yellow. Often found in hilly areas, it is particularly fond of ripe fruit and sap oozing from trees. In winter it hibernates. It is named after the London suburb where it was first seen in Britain, but it is only a rare visitor to this country.

**Cambiform Cell.** An elongated, pointed parenchymatous cell which occurs in the phloem.

**Cambium** (lateral meristem). A plant tissue consisting of activity dividing cells (meristem) that is responsible for increasing the girth of the plant, *i.e.* it causes secondary growth. The two most important cambia are the vascular cambium and the cork cambium. The vascular cambium occurs in the stem and root; it divides to produce secondary xylem and secondary phloem (new food and water-conducting tissues). Compare apical meristem.

**Cambrian** The earliest geological period of the Palaeozoic era. It is estimated to have begun about 570 million years ago and lasted for some 100 million years. During this period marine animals with mineralized shells made their first appearance and Cambrian rocks are the first to contain an abundance of fossils. Cambrian fossils are all of marine animals; they include trilobites, which dominated the Cambrian seas, echinoderms, brachiopods, molluscs, and primitive graptolites (from the mid Cambrian). Trace fossils also provide evidence for a variety of worms.

**Cambrian Period.** The first or earliest division of the Paleozoic era; its rocks contain fossils of most invertebrate phyla, trilobites being abundant.

**Camel.** There are two species of camel : the Arabian or one-humped and the bactrian or two-humped. They are desert animals, although only the bactrian camel still survives in the wild. A dromedary is a special breed of the one-humped camel used for riding. Both species are remarkably well adapted for desert life. Their humps consist largely of far, which can be used to provide both energy and water when food is scarce.

**Canada goose**

**Camellia.** An evergreen tree of China and Japan, grown elsewhere for its showy Bowers. The 80 species have dark fleshy leaves. One species is the Tea plant.

**Camelopard.** The giraffe.

**Cam Plant.** Used for any plant which shows crassulacean acid metabolism for fixing atmospheric $CO_2$.

**Camouflage.** The means by which various animals avoid detection by would-be enemies by merging with their surroundings. Some animals do this by having a coloration that matches their background. Plaice, for instance, have a colour pattern similar to that of the sea bed on which they live, making them very difficult to detect. They can also change colour to match a chage in background colour. Other animals resemble leaves or twigs.

**Campion.** Flowering plants with sepals joined in a tube (inflated in the bladder campion). Red and white campion are common in hedgerows.

**Campanula.** A small bell.

**Campestrian.** Pertaining to the plains or open spaces.

**Camphor Tree.** A kind of laurel native to China, Taiwan and Japan. It is a tall tree with white flowers. When steamed its wood yields camphor, used in medicine and industry.

**CAM Plant.** Any of a group of succulent plants that employ crassulacean acid metabolism (CAM) for fixing atmospheric carbon dioxide.

**Camptodromous.** Describing a form of leaf venation in which there is a single primary vein and the secondary veins arising from it curve upwards towards the leaf margin. The secondary veins may join together in a series of conspicuous marginal loops (brochidodtomous venation, *e.g.* in wild cherry, Prunus avium) or may remain separate (eucamptodromous venation, *e.g.* in downy rose, Rosa tomentosa).

**Campylodromous.** Describing a form of leaf venation in which several primary veins originate at the base of the lamina and run in downward-curving arches towards the ape, as seen in black bryony (Tamus communis).

**Campylotropous.** Describing a form of ovule orientation in which the ovule develops horizontally and the funiculus appears to be attached half way between the chalaza and the micropyle (illustration at ovule). This arrangement is not very common but may be found in the Malvaceae and Caryophyllaceae. Compare anatropous, orthotropous.

**Canada Balsam.** A yellow-tinted resin used for mounting specimens in optical microscopy. It has similar optical properties to glass.

**Canada Goose.** A large goose introduced from North America as an ornamental bird. It now breeds in the wild in Britain and Scandinavia. The Canada goose is a pale brown in colour, with a black neck and head, save for white patches on the cheeks. Its call is a characteristic 'honk'.

**Canal.** An elongated intercellular space which is usually having secretions of various kinds, *e.g.*, oils, resins.

**Canal Cell.** The initial cell which later undergoes division to fill the central canal of the neck of the archegonia of Bryophyta and Pteridophyta. These cells get disintegrated when the archegonium gets ripened.

**Canaliculate.** Bearing longitudinal grooves or channels.

**Canaliculi.** Used for describing fine channels which are communicating with lumen of a canal or gland.

**Canaculus** pl. **Canaliculi.** A small canal, especially one of the minute canals extending from lacunae into the matrix of bone.

**Canal of Schlemm.** A passage which is connecting the aqueous humour with the scleral veins of the vertebrate eye and running through the junction between the cornea and the sclerotic.

**Canal System.** In sponges, the passageways through which water passes in its course from the surface pores to the osculum or excurrent opening. Types include asconoid, syconoid, and leuconoid.

**Canary.** A find coming originally from the Canary Islands. The wild bird is brownishyellow, but many yellow varieties have been produced in captivity. The canary is a very popular cage bird, with a sweet song. Like all finches it is a seed-eater.

**Cancellate.** Cancellous.

**Cancellous.** Having a porous or spongy structure; cancellate.

**Cancer.** Any disorder of cell growth that results in invasion and destruction of surrounding healthy tissue by the abnormal cells. Cancer cells arise from normal cells whose nature is permanently changed. They multiply more rapidly than healthy body cells and do not seem subject to normal control by nerves and hormones. They may spread via the bloodstream or lymphatic system to other parts of the body, where they produce further tissue damage (metastases) Malignant tumours are a form of cancer and leukaemia is cancer of white blood cells. Probable causative agents (carcinogens) include various chemicals, skin irritants (such as tobacco smoke), silica and asbeston particles, and oncogenic viruses. Hereditary factors and stress may also play a role.

**Cancroid**

1. Resembling a crab.
2. Cancerlike, with reference to growth characteristics.

**Candle Snuff.** A small, irregularly shaped fungus consisting of a leathery, strap-like stalk that is very tough and usually forked. Powdery white spores develop near the tips of young stalks, and there are black ones near the base. The fungi can be found at all times of the year on tree stumps and other dead wood.

**Candytuft.** Any of several flowering plants of the mustard family, mostly low-growing. There are perennial and annual varieties, producing tufts of white, pink or red flowers, often with very sweet scents.

**Candytuft, Wild.** A flowering plant of the cabbage family. It bears clusters of tiny white or purple flowers which are notable for their petals of unequal size. The plant is found in cereal fields and on open ground.

**Cane**

1. Any slender, jointed, hollow or pithy, more or less flexible stem, as that of various grasses and bamboo.
2. Rattan, especially the split stem used in wicker-work.
3. The stem of certain berries, as raspberry.

**Canescent.** Hoary; covered with a gray-white pubescence.

**Cane Sugar.** Sucrose.

**[1]Canine.** Any member of the dog family, a group of digitigrade carnivores which includes the dog, wolf, coyote, jackal, and fox.

**[2]Canine.** Of, pertaining to, or resembling a dog or doglike animal.

**Canine Tooth.** A sharp conical tooth in mammals that is large and highly developed in carnivores (*e.g.* dogs) for tearing meat. There are two canines in each jaw, each situated between the second incisor and the first premolar. In some animals (*e.g.* herbivores, such as giraffes and rabbits) canine teeth are absent.

**Canker.** A plant disease in which there is a well defined area of necrosis of the cortical tissue, which becomes surrounded by layers of callus tissue. Cankers occur mainly on woody stems but may also appear on herbaceous plants. For example, in apple canker, caused by Nectria galligena, the fungus penetrates the apple stem through a wound or leaf scar. As the fungus grows into the stem the tree produces callus tissue to seal off the infected zone. Further penetration by the fungus results in the production of more callus tissue, or wound wood, forming the characteristic canker.

**Cankerworm.** The larva of a moth of the family Geometridae.

**Canopy.** Top layer of vegetation in a wood or forest, formed by the upper foliage of the trees.

**Calabash.** A Gourd, growing on a tree or a vine of tropical America. People use the hard shells of the gourds as bottles, cups, and even cooking pots.

**Cantharophilous.** Pollinated by beetles.

**Canvasback.** A North American wild duck (Nyroca Aythya) valisineria).

**Cap**

1. *bot. a.* The pileus of a mushroom. *b.* The calpytra of a moss capsule.
2. *zool.* The acrosome of the head of a spermatozoan.

**Cap Cell.** The cell present at the apex of the fern antheridium. It is shed when the antherozoids get liberated.

**Cape Buffalo.** Reputed to be the most dangerous of the African big-game animals, this bulky ox-like creature stands some 1.5 metres high at the shoulder and adult males may weigh up to one tonne. It has large horns which sweep first downwards and then upwards. Cape buffaloes live throughout Africa south of the Sahara. They are not normally dangerous unless they are unexpectedly disturbed.

**Cap Cell.** A cell, seen in filaments of algae in the order Oedogoniales, that has one to several 'caps' of cell wall material at its anterior end. These result from a distinctive form of cell division that involves the formation of rings of new cell wall material prior to nuclear division.

**Cape Hunting Dog.** A ferocious carnivore, only distantly related to the domestic dog, that ranges over most of Africa. It stands about 60 cm at the shoulder and has a mottled black, yellow and white coat with large, round ears. The animals hunt in packs and run down the antelopes on which they feed.

**Capercaillie.** The largest member of the grouse family, the capercaillie is a bird of the northern coniferous forests. It is found over much of northern Europe and Asia. The male is a little under one metre in length and his plumage is predominantly black or dark grey. He has a fine tail, which he fans out and displays to the brown hen in the breeding season.

**Capers.** The flower-buds of a southern European shrub, the caper bush. They are pickled to make a sauce. The sprawling plant has white or pinkish flowers.

**Capillarity** (capillary action). The rise or fall of liquids within narrow tubes as a result of the surface tension of the liquid. Capillarity is also responsible for the formation of drops, bubbles, etc., and for the retention of water droplets on plants following dew formation, mist, rain, and guttation. The supply of water to all parts of a plant is due, in large part, to capillary action. Water will rise against gravity providing that the forces between the surfaces of the water and the solid it is in contact with are greater, than the cohesive forces within the body of water.

**Capillary.** The narrowest type of blood vessel in the vertebrate circulatory system. Capillaries conduct blood from arterioles to all living cells : their walls are only one cell layer thick, so that oxygen and nutrients can pass through them into the surrounding tissues. Capillaries also transport waste material (*e.g.* urea and carbon dioxide) to venules for ultimate excretion. Capillaries can be constricted or dilated, according to local tissue requirements.

**Capillary Water.** Water in the soil which is held by surface or capillary forces about soil particles or in the spaces between them. It is the principal source of moisture for plants.

**Capillitium.** A delicate, branched network within the sporangium of slime molds and certain fungi.

**Capillus.** A hair, especially one of the head.

**Capitate**

1. Having a head or headlike structure.
2. *bot.* Gathered into a dense cluster or head, with reference to flowers.

**Capitellum**

1. A capitulum.
2. *zool.* The expanded terminal portion of a halter.

**Capitular Facet.** A facet or demi-facet on the centurm of a throacic vertebra to which the capitulum of a rib has articulated.

**Capitulum.** A type of flowering shoot (racemose inflorescence) characteristic of plants of the family Compositae, *e.g.* daisy and dandelion. The tip of the shoot is flattened and bears many small stalkless flowers (florets) surrounded by an involucre (ring) of bracts. This arrangement gives the appearance of a single flower.

**Capitulum** (of Rib). One of two processes (the other being the tuberculum) by which the rib of a mammal or bird is articulating with the thoracic vertebrae. The capitulum is articulating with the centrum of the vertebra and the tuberculum with the transverse process.

**Capon.** A castrated cock, especially one fattened for use as food.

**Capreolate.** Having one or more tendrils.

**Caprification.** A method of pollination employed in the cultivation of figs in which fruits of the wild fig (caprifig) containing the fig wasp (Blastophaga) ar eplaced in trees of cultivated figs. The insects on emerging enter the flowers of edible figs, thus bringing about cross-pollination.

**Capri Fig.** A race of fig not producing edible fruit, but providing food for the wasps which pollinate the figs.

**Capsicum.** A perennial woody plant related to the tomato, native to Latin America. It has long pointed leaves. The fruits of some species, known as peppers, are used as food. The spices cayenne and paprika are made from two of the many other species.

**Capsid.** The protein coat of a virus, which surrounds and protects its nucleic acid. The nature of the capsid determines the virus' host range and the efficiency of its infectivity. Viruses can be identified by the serological reaction of the capsid proteins.

**Capsid Bug.** A large family of insects that are serious pests in many countries. Most have slender or oval brown or green bodies and feed mainly on plants. Some, such as the common green capsid, do great damage to fruit.

Capsid bugs

**Capsomere.** Any of the identical polypeptide subunits making up the capsid protein of a virus.

**Capsulate.** Enclosed within a capsule.

**Capsule**

1. (in botany) *a.* A dry fruit that releases its seeds when ripe; it is formed from several fused carpels and contains. many seeds. The seeds may be dispersed through pores (as in the poppy), through a lid (as in plantain) or by the splitting and separation of the individual carpels (as in the crocus). Various other forms of capsules include the silicula and siliqua. *b.* The part of the sporophyte of mosses and liverworts in which the haploid spores are produced. It is borne on a long stalk (seta) and sheds its spores when mature peristome).

2. (in microbiology) A thick gelatinous layer completely surrounding the cell wall of certain bacteria. It appears to have a protective function, making ingestion of the bacterial cell by phagocytes more difficult and preventing desiccation.

3. (in animal anatomy) *a.* The membranous or fibrous envelope that surrounds certain organs, *e.g.*, the kidneys, spleen, and lymph nodes. *b.* The ligamentous sheath of connective tissue that surrounds various skeletal joints.

**Capuchin.** A long-taffed South American monkey of the genus Cebus, family Cebidae.

**Capybara.** Also called the water cavy, the capybara is the world's largest rodent. It may reach well over one metre in length and looks like an enormous guinea pig. The capybara is found over much of South America but never far from water. It swims very well and feeds mainly on aquatic plants.

**Caracal.** Also called the desert lynx, the caracal is a medium sized cat. It has a short reddish-brown coat, long legs, and long black ears topped by very long tufts of hair. The caracal ranges over much of Africa and parts of Asia. It feeds on a variety of small mammals and will also catch birds in flight by leaping up at them

**Caracara.** A group of predatory birds related to falcons which are widely distributed throughout the Americas. Caracaras often chase and bully other birds until they release the food they are carrying. The caracaras then drop down and collect it.

**Carapace.** The hard protective shell which covers the head and thorax of many arthropods. It made of a protein substance called chitin and usually has calcium compounds deposited on it to make it even harder. Carapace is also the name given to the upper part (half) of tortoise and turtle shells.

**Caraway.** A herb of northern Europe and Asia, grown for its spicy seeds. It has a hollow stem and large, fern-like leaves. The small white flowers grow in large domed clusters (umbels).

**Carbamide.** Urea.

**Carbohydrate** (saccharide). A polyhydroxy aldehyde or ketone or a derivative of such a compound. Many carbohydrates have the structural formula $(CH_2O)_n$, which suggests that they were originally hydrates of carbon. The simplest carbohydrates are the monosaccharides or simple sugars. They are single polyhydroxy aldehyde (aldose) or ketone (ketose) units, most commonly containing five or six carbons. Oligosaccharides are more complex carbohydrates containing between two and ten monosaccharide units. Polysaccharides contain many monosaccharide units in long linear or branched clains. They function as energy storage molecules and as structural elements in the plant body.

**Carbon.** Symbol C. A nonmetallic element that occurs in all organic compounds and is therefore basic to the structure of all living organisms. It is an essential element for plants and animals, being ultimately derived from atmospheric carbon dioxide assimilated by plants during photosynthesis carbon cycle). The ubiquitous nature of carbon in living organisms is due to its unique ability to form stable covalent bonds with other carbon atoms and also with hydrogen, oxygen nitrogen, and sulphur atoms, resulting in the formation of a variety of compounds containing chains and rings of carbon atoms.

There are two stable isotopes of carbon (proton numbers 12 and 13) and four radio-active ones (10, 11, 14, 15). Carbon-14 is used in carbon dating.

**Carbon Cycle.** Carbon is an essential component of all living matter. Plants remove it from the air in the form of carbon dioxide and use It to make sugars, proteins and other materials. Animals obtain their carbon from the food they eat (derived ultimately from plants). But carbon is also returned to the atmosphere in many ways. Both plants and animals 'burn up' food materials to provide energy. This process (respiration) releases carbon dioxide back into the air. Bacterial decay of dead organisms also releases carbon dioxide. This interchange of carbon

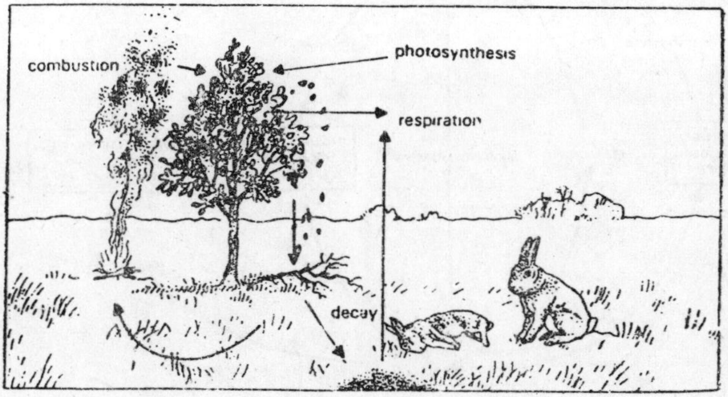

between the atmosphere and living organisms is called the carbon cycle.

The carbon cycle. Carbon dioxide is removed from the air by plants during photosynthesis and is used to make sugars and proteins. Both plants and animals release the gas during respiration, and it is also returned to the atmosphere when things decay or burn.

**Carbon Dating** (radiocarbon dating). A method of estimating the ages of archaeological specimens of biological origin. As a result of cosmic radiation a small number of atmospheric nitrogen nuclei are continuously being transformed by neutron bombardment into radioactive nuclei of carbon-14. Some of these radiocarbon atoms find their way into living trees and other plants in the form of carbon dioxide, as a result of photosynthesis. When the tree is cut down photosynthesis stops and the ratio of radiocarbon atoms to stable carbon atoms begins to fall as the radiocarbon decays. The ratio $^{14}C/^{12}C$ in the specimea can be measured and enables the time that has elapsed since the tree was cut down to be calculated. The method has been shown to give consistent results for

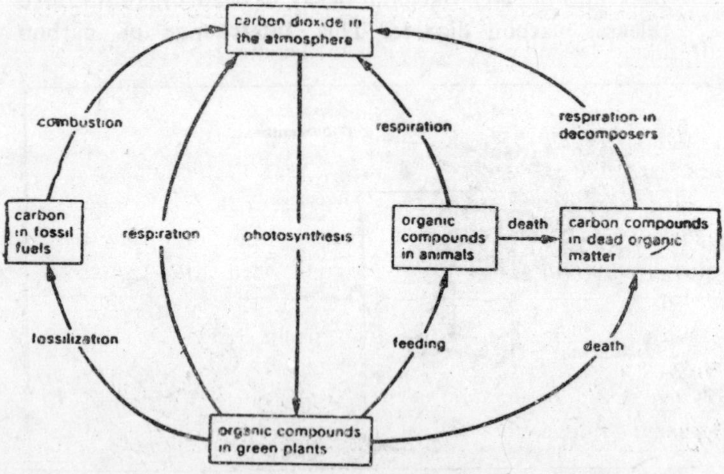


The carbon cycle in nature

specimens up to some 40000 years old, though its accuracy depends upon assumptions concerning the past intensity of the cosmic radiation. The technique was developed by Willard F. Libby (1908-80) and his coworkers' in 1946-47.

**Carbon Dioxide.** A heavy gas, formula $CO_2$, that makes up 0.033% by volume of the atmosphere. It is the basic carbon source of all life, being converted to carbohydrates by photosynthesis. The concentration of $CO_2$ remains relatively constant despite increased burning of fossil fuels and deforestation practices. This is due to the buffering capacity of the oceans, which contain large amounts of dissolved $CO_2$. The extreme solubility and rapid diffusion of $CO_2$ in water is a major factor in the maintenance of aquatic life.

The rate of photosynthesis can be increased by raising $CO_2$ levels. This has been put to practical use in the cultivation of some glasshouse crops. However yield increases are not as great as might be expected since increased $CO_2$ concentrations also increase stomatal closure.

**Carbonic Anhydrase.** An enzyme which catalyzes the reaction, $CO_2+H_2O \rightarrow H_2CO_3$.

**Carboniferous.** A geological period in the Palaeozoic era. It began about 345 million years ago, following the Devonian period, and extended until the beginning of the Permian period, about 280 million years ago. In Europe the period is divided into the Lower and Upper Carboniferous, which roughly correspond to the Mississippian and Pennsylvanian periods, respectively, of North America. During the Lower Carboniferous a marine transgression occurred and the characteristic rock of this division—the Carboniferous limestone—was laid down in the shallow seas. Fauna included foraminiferans, corals, bryozoans, brachiopods, blastoids, and other invertebrates. The Upper Carboniferous saw the deposition of the millstone grit, a mixture of shale and sandstone formed in deltaic conditions, followed by the coal measures, alternating beds of coal, sand stone, shale, and clay. The coal was formed from the vast swamp forests composed of seeds ferns, lycopsids, and other plants. During the period fishes continued to diversify and amphibians became more common.

**Carboniferous Period.** The Mississippian (Lower Carboniferous) and Pennsylvanian (Upper Carboniferous) periods of the Paleozoic era, during which time the great coal deposits were formed.

**Carbon Monoxide.** A colorless, odorless gas, CO, formed when organic substances are burned in an inadequate supply of oxygen. It is poisonous in that it forms a stable compound with hemoglobin.

**Carboxyamino Haemoglobin.** Haemoglobin on deoxygenation forms carbamine haemoglobine by reacting with carbon-dioxide and thus the transport of carbondioxide gets facilitated in the venous blood. About 20% carbondioxide is carried to lungs by this process. At respiratory surface the high partial pressure of oxygen breaks this association and carbondioxide is liberated.

**Carboxydismutase.** An enzyme catalysing the combination of ribulose-biphosphate and carbon dioxide to form two molecules of phosphoglyceric acid.

**Carboxy-haemoglobin.** This compound is formed by reacting carbon monoxide with haemoglobin. The affinity of haemoglobin for oxygen is much smaller than carbon monoxide and this substance tends to displace oxygen on haemoglobin reducing oxygen carrying capacity of blood thereby giving rise to the tissue anoxia.

**Carboxylase.** Any enzyme that catalyses the transfer or incorporation of carbon dioxide into a substrate molecule. Carboxylation reactions usually require energy in the form of ATP or a related compound; a coenzyme, usually biotin, is also a part of most carboxylases. An example is pyruvate carboxylase, which catalyses the formation of oxaloacetate from pyruvic acid. As with many carboxylases, this is an allosteric enzyme, its activity being increased by the binding of acetyl CoA.

**Carboxyl Group.** The univalent, acidic radical, —COOH, characteristic of organic acids, as formic, acetic, lactic.

**Carboxy-peptidase.** A type of proteolytic enzyme which occurs in pancreatic juice. It attacks peptide chain by stepwise removal of amino acid residues from carboxyl group at the end of the chain. Two such enzymes are known, carboxy-peptidase which is able to cleave carboxyterminal amino acids with aromatic or branched aliphatic side chains and carboxypeptidase which is able to cleave carboxy-terminal amino acids with basic chains.

**Carcerulus.** A dry fruit that is a type of schizocarp. It consists of a number of one-seeded fragments (mericarps) that adhere to a central axis. It is characteristic of mallow.

**Cercinogen.** Any agent that produces cancer, *e.g.*, tobacco smoke, certain industrial chemicals, and ionizing radiation (such as X-rays and ultraviolet rays).

**Carcinogenic.** Inducing cancer formation.

[1]**Carcinoid.** Of, pertaining to, or resembling crabs.

[2]**Carcinoid.** A trpe of benign tumor derived from argentaffin cells.

**Carcinoma.** A malignant, epithelial tumor; a cancer.

**Cardamom.** Any of several Indian plants, related to Ginger. It has lance-shaped leaves, small brownish flowers, and produces spicy seeds used as flavouring.

**Cardiac**

1. Relating to the heart.

2. Relating to the part of the stomach nearest to the oesophagus.

**Cardiac Arrest.** As a result of abnormality in heart beating ventricular extrasystoles take place, thereby leading to ventricular fibrillation due to ventricular tachycardia. The fibrillating ventricles fail to pump blood effectively and circulation of blood stops thereby resulting cardiac arrest. In absence of emergency treatment, death may take place in few minutes.

**Cardiac Cycle.** Refers to the contraction and relexation of heart which are responsible for receiving of blood and its supply out of heart. It involves atrial systole, isovolumetric ventricular contraction, ventricular ejection isovolumetric ventricular relaxation and ventricular filling. It gets completed in 0.8 second (artial systole 0 1 sec., ventricular systole 0.1-0.3 sec. and diastole 0 4-0.6 sec.)

**Cardiac Gland.** A large digestive gland which is present near the cardiac end of the stomach in certain mammals.

**Cardiac Glycoside.** Any of a group of steroid glycosides characterized by their stimulative effects on the heart. Cardiac glycosides resemble sayonins in being diterpenes and by foaming in solution. They differ however in having a lactone ring attached at carbon 17 of the steroid nucleus. An important commercial source is the foxglove (Digitalis purpurea), which yields digitonin.

**Cardiac Muscle.** A specialized form of muscle that peculiar to the vertebrate heart. The muscle fibres are branched and interlock, and the muscle itself shows spontaneous contraction and does not need nervous stimulation (pacemaker). The vagus nerve to the heart can, however, affect the rate of contraction.

**Cardiac Output.** Refers to the total volume of blood which is pumped out by heart per unit time. Cardiac output equals heart rate times stroke volume.

**Cardiac Stomach**

1. The large, anterior portion of the stomach of a decapod crustacean; the gastric mill.
2. The folded, adoral portion of the stomach of a sea star, the portion everted when feeding.

**Cardiac Valves.** The valves of a mammalian heart, comprising two atrioventricular valves (bicuspid and tricuspid) and two sets of semilunar valves (pulmonary and aortic).

**Cardinal.** A familiar songbird of North America, also known as the red bird. The male has a black 'bib', but otherwise he is bright scarlet. The female is more sombre, owing to a greater amount of brown in her feathers. Both sexes have a conspicuous crest and a stout, seed-cracking beak.

**Cardinal Beetle.** Several species of beetle which get their name from their red colour, resembling that of a Roman Catholic cardinal's dress. They live on trees and flowers, and have feathery antennae. The grubs feed on bark and wood.

**Cardinal Points of Temperature.** The minimum point is when growth starts the optimum when growth is best, and the maximum when growth stops.

**Cardinal Vein.** One of three pairs of veins (anterior, posterior, and common cardinal veins) present in fishes and the embryos of tetrapods. The common cardinal or duct of Cuvier empties into the sinus venosus.

**Cardio-accelerator Centre.** Refers to a region of the medulla oblongata from which impulses can accelerate the heart by involving the sympathetic nervous system.

**Cardioblasts.** Specialized cells that give rise to the wall of the heart in arthropods.

**Cardio-inhibitory Centre.** Refers to a region of the medulla oblongata from which impulses can slow down the rate of heart-beat by way of the vagus nerve.

**Cardiovascular.** Of or pertaining to the heart and blood vessels.

**Cardo.** A hinge or hingelike structure, as *a.* the basal segment of the maxilla of certain insects; *b.* the hinge in bivalve mollusks.

**Caribou.** One of several species of reindeer inhabiting North America and Greenland, best known of which is Rangifer caribou, the woodland caribou.

**Carina**

1. Any keellike structure.

2. *zool. a.* The prominent ridge on the breastbone of a bird. *b.* The median, dorsal plate of a barnacle.

3. *bot. a.* In irregular flowers, the structure which encloses the stamens and pistil, usually consisting of two fused petals lying opposite the banner. *b.* A longitudinal projection on the glumes of certain grasses.

**Carinal.** Pertaining to or possessing a keel or keellike ridge.

**Carinal Canal** (protoxylem lacuna). A longitudinal channel in the stem internode of Equisetum (horsetail) and some of its fossil relatives, positioned radially opposite a raised stem ridge (carina). Each carinal canal is arranged on the inner side of a vascular bundle. The carinal canals apparently result from breakdown of protoxylem and are believed to function in water conduction. Compare vallecular canal.

**Carmine.** A crimson dye substance obtained from cochineal.

**Carnassial Teeth.** Molar and premolar teeth modified for shearing flesh by having cusps with sharp cutting edges. They are typical of animals of the order Carnivora (*e.g.* tigers, wolves), in which they are the first molars in the lower jaw and the last premolars in the upper.

**Carnation.** A cultivated plant descended from various kinds of wild pinks—mainly Dianthus caryophyllus which is a native of southern Europe. Modern forms have many petals, unlike the native pinks with just five petals. The carnation has a strong, sweet scent.

**Carneous.** Resembling flesh in color.

**Carnivora.** An order of mainly flesh-eating mammals that includes the dogs, wolves, bears, badgers, weasels, and cats. Carnivores typically have very keen sight, smell, and hearing. The hinge joint between the lower jaw and skull is very tight, allowing no lateral movement of the lower jaw. This—together with the arrangement of jaw muscles—enables a very powerful bite. The teeth are specialized for stabbing and tearing flesh : canines are large and pointed and some of the cheek teeth are modified for shearing.

**Carnivore.** An animal that eats meat, especially a member of the order Carnivora (*e.g.* tigers, wolves). Carnivores are specialized by having strong powerful jaws and well-developed canine teeth. They may be predators or carrion eaters. Compare herbivore; omnivore.

**Carnivorous** Flesh-eating; preying or feeding upon animals. Compare herbivorous.

**Carnivorous Plant** (insectivorous plant). Any plant that supplements its supply of nitrates in conditions of nitrate deficiency by digesting small animals, especially insects. Such plants are adapted in various ways to attract and trap the insects and produce proteolytic enzymes to digest them. Venus' fly trap (Dionala), for example, has spiny-margined hinged leaves that snap shut on an alighting insect. Sundews (Drosera) trap and digest insects by means of glandular leaves that secrete a sticky substance, and pitcher plants (families Nepenthaceae and Sarraceniaceae) have leaves modified as pitchers into which insects fall, drowing in the water and digestive enzymes at the bottom.

**Carotene** (carotin). Any of a class of orange, red, or yellow pigments all of which are hydrocarbons containing eight isoprene subunits and hence have the formula $C_{40}H_{56}$. The most commonly occurring carotenes are α- and β-carotene (also vitamin A). Another carotene, lycopene, gives tomato fruits their red colour. Carotenes are accessory pigments in most photosynthetic cells, contributing to the process of gathering light energy. However they are relatively inefficient as light absorbers and are thought to have a second function of protecting the other photosynthetic pigments from photooxidation by ultraviolet light. Xanthophylls are oxygenated carotenes.

**Carotenoid.** Any of a group of yellow, orange, red, or brown plant pigments chemically related to terpenes. Carotenoids are responsible for the characteristic colour of many plant organs, such as ripe tomatoes, carrots, and autumn leaves. They also function in the light reactions of photosynthesis.

**Carotenol.** Xanthophyll.

**Carotid Artery.** The major artery that supplies blood to the head. A pair of common carotid arteries arise from the aorta (on the left) and the innominate artery (on the right) and run up the neck; each branches into an external and an internal carotid artery, which supply the head.

**Carotid Body.** One of a pair of tissue masses adjacent to the carotid sinus. Each contains receptors that are sensitive to oxygen and pH levels (acidity) in the blood. High levels of carbon dioxide in the blood lower the pH (*i.e.* increase the acidity). By responding to fluctuations in pH, the carotid body coordinates reflex changes in respiration rate.

**Carotid Sinus.** An enlarged region of the carotid artery at its major branching point in the neck. Its walls contain many receptors that are sensitive to changes in pressure and it regulates blood pressure by initiating reflex changes in heart rate and dilation of blood vessels.

**Carotin.** Carotene.

**Carp.** A family of fishes that includes many familiar fresh-water species, among them the roach, dace, chub, minnow, carp, and the goldfish so often kept as an aquarium fish. Some species are native to Europe, but others, including the goldfish and the carp itself, have been introduced. Members of this family have no teeth in their jaws, but have teeth in the back of the throat with which they grind up their food. The common carp is an Asian fish introduced into Europe by the Romans 2000 years ago. It is a good food fish, often kept in fish farms. In the wild, the carp likes stagnant water or slow-running rivers where it feeds on plants and various small animals. It has barbels on its mouth and, fully-grown, measures more than 20 cm long; a few which reach the age of 40 can be as much as 1 metre long. The crucian carps is a close relative that is smaller than the carp and has no barbels on its mouth. It can flourish in still, muddy waters with little oxygen.

**Carpal** (carpal bone). One of the bones that form the wrist (carpus) in terrestrial vertebrates.

**Carpal Bones.** Bones in the distal region of the forelimb of tetrapods; in man they constitute the wrist (carpus). In the typical pentadactyl limb there are 12 carpal bones, which are arranged in three rows. However, there are many modifications and reductions to this basic pattern; in man there are only eight which articulate with each other, and with the metacarpal bones distally. Three carpal bones are forming the wrist joint with the radius of the forearm.

**Carpel.** The structure that bears and encloses the ovules in flowering plants. It normally comprises the ovary, style, and stigma. The typical enclosed carpel of the angiosperms has probably evolved from an open carpel bearing megasporangia on the margins, and is thought by many to be homologous with the megasporophyll of pteridophytes and the ovuliferous scale of gymnosperms.

In more primitive angiosperms there are often large numbers of unfused carpels in the gynoecium. In advanced forms the number of carpels is reduced and they tend to be fused and inserted asymmetrically.

**Carpellate.** Pertaining to, bearing, or possessing carpels.

**Carpenter Bee.** A group of solitary bees, which make their nests in wood. The carpenter bee bores a tunnel up to 20 cm long, lining it with brood cells for its eggs. The cells are made of wood fragments cemented together. Each one is sealed once the egg and a food supply of nectar and pollen have been placed inside.

**Carpet Beetle.** Insects whose larvae feed on rugs, carpets and clothing, including furs. The beetles are about 3 mm long, and look rather like brown ladybirds. They feed on pollen. The larva is very hairy and is known as a woolly bear.

**Carpet Moth**. A group of moths which are mottled in colouring, ranging from black to brown, and often difficult to see on tree trunks or moss-covered rocks. There are several species, including the common, garden, green and twin-spot carpet moths all so named because their wings are patterned rather like traditional carpets.

**Carpet Pin.** A small fragile toadstool with a thin orange cap and yellowish-brown gills. It grows in damp grassy places in summer and autumn.

**Carpocephalon.** An erect, sporangium-bearing structure in certain liverworts.

**Carpogonium.** The female sex organ in the red algae, which has a swollen basal portion containing the egg and a number of hypogynous cells, and an elongated terminal projection or trichogyne, which attracts the male gamete. It develops by the expansion of a single cell.

**Carpometacarpus.** The fused carpal and metacarpal bones in the wing of a bird.

**Carpomyceteae, Carpomycetes.** The fungi having fruit bodies; the higher fungi, *i.e.*, the Ascomycetes and Basidiomycetes.

**Carpophore**

1. A structure which supports the sporocarp in certain fungi.

2. In the Umbelliferae, a slender stalk which supports a ripe carpel.

**Carposporangium.** A sporangium that develops directly from the zygote in situ in some of the red algae, and which is dependent on the parental tissue for nutrition.

**Carpospore.** A spore formed following division of the zygote in red algae. It may be haploid if formed following meiosis as, for example, in Porphyra. On germination it then gives rise to a haploid gametophyte or occasionally a short-lived juvenile form termed the Chantransia stage. The carpospores of the more advanced red algae, *e.g.* Polysiphonia, are diploid and give rise to a diploid plant similar in form to the haploid generation.

**Carpus** The wrist (or corresponding part of the forelimb) in terrestrial vertebrates, consisting of a number of small bones (carpals). The number of carpal bones varies with the species. The rabbit, for example, has two rows of carpals, the first (proximal) row containing three bones and the second (distal) row five. In humans there are also eight carpals. This large number of bones enables flexibility at the wrist joint, between the hand and forelimb.

**Carpotrophic.** The movement of the flower-stalk after fertilization to bring fruit into a favourable position for the ripening and/or dispersal of the seed.

**Carr.** Used for describing fern woodland with built-up of peat so that peat level gets raised sufficiently to allow establishment of certain woody plants which can tolerate wet conditions (*e.g.* Almus, Salix, Viburnum opulus etc.).

**Carragheen.** Also known as Irish moss, this is a small red tufted seaweed growing on the Atlantic coasts of Europe and North America. It produces a jelly-like substance used in food and medicines.

**Carrier**

1. *med. a.* A healthy individual who transmits pathogenic organisms but does not show symptoms of the disease. *b.* An organism which passively transmits pathogenic organisms, as the housefly. Compare vector.

2. *physiol.* A substance with which another substance combines in its transport through a cell membrane.

3. *genetics.* A heterozygous individual which transmits a recessive gene for an abnormal or pathologic condition.

**Carrion.** Dead flesh. The carrion-eaters are those creatures which live off already dead animals rather than hunting and catching live prey.

**Carrion Fungi.** Gasteromycete fungi of the order Phalles, whose odor attracts carrion-loving insects.

**Carrot.** A long reddish root vegetable, descended from ancestors growing wild in Europe and Asia. It is a biennial plant with lacy leaves and is related to parsley.

**Carrion Beetle.** A family of beetles that eat carrion, the best known being the Burying Beetles.

4-spot carrion beetle

**Cartilage** (gristle). A firm flexible connective tissue that forms the adult skeleton of cartilaginous fish (*e.g.* sharks). It comprises a matrix consisting chiefly of a mucopolysaccharide called chondroitin sulphate secreted by cells (chondroblasts) that become embedded in the matrix as chondrocytes. In other vertebrates cartilage forms the skeleton of the embryo, being largely replaced by bone in mature animals. It persists in areas of high wear (*e.g.* bone ends, joints, and intervertebral discs) and in the nose and pinna of the ear.

**Cartilage Bone** (replacing bone). Bone that is formed by replacing the cartilage of an embryo skeleton. The process, called ossification, is brought about by the cells (osteoblasts) that secrete bone. Compare membrane bone.

**Cartilaginous Fish**. Fishes with skeletons of cartilage (gristle) instead of bone, such as sharks, rays and skates. Cartilaginous fishes have no opercula (gill covers) and the gill slits are clearly visible. Their fins are clothed with thick skin, rather than being membranes as in body fishes.

**Caruncle**

1. *zool. a.* A small, fleshy outgrowth or excrescence, as the lacrimal caruncle of the eye. *b.* The wattles or comb of certain birds. *c.* An area of contact between

a placental cotyledon and uterine mucosa. *d.* A disclike structure on the tarsus of ticks and mites. *e.* A horny process on the beak of a newly hatched chick or turtle.

2. *bot.* A fleshy, water-absorbing structure attached to certain seeds, as the castor bean.

**ryophyllidae** (Centrospermae). A subclass of the dicotyledons containing mostly herbaceous plants usually with bisexual flowers. The seeds often contain perisperm and betalain alkaloids are usually present. Four or five orders are usually recognized: the Caryophyllales (or Chenopodiales); the Polygonales, containing the one family Polygonaceae (including buckwheat and sorrel); the Plumbaginales, including the one family Plumbaginaceae; the Batales, comprising the one species Batis maritima (saltwort), often placed on the Caryophyllales; and the Theligonales, the one genus of which, Theligonum, has been variously placed in the Caryophyllales or Haloragales (subclass Rosidae). The Caryophyilales is divided into some 10-16 families, the more important of which are the Cactaceae (cactus family), the Aizcaceae (including the mesembryanthemums), the Caryophyllaceae (carnation family), and the Chenopodiaceae (beet family).

**Caryopsis.** A dry, one-seeded indehiscent fruit characteristic of grasses, consisting of a single seed in which the seed coat and pericarp are fused, as in corn, wheat, oats, rice.

**C--ein.** One of a group of phosphate-containing proteins phosphoproteins) found in milk. Caseins are easily digested by the enzymes of young mammals and represent a major source of phosphorus.

**Caseinogen.** A soluble phosphoprotein in milk which, through the action of enzymes (renine, pepsin), is converted into insoluble casein, the basis of the curd of milk.

**Cashew.** A small evergreen tree, nativeto trooical America. It has long, smooth leaves and fragrant rosy flowers. It is

edible seeds inside its woody nuts. The trunk produces a gum used in varnish.

**Casparian Strip** (Casparian band). A band of suberized and/or lignified wall material in the radial (anticlinal) and transverse walls of cells of the endodermis. It ensures that water and solutes pass through the living protoplast of the endodermal cells, rather than through the cell walls, thus facilitating selective filtering of the sap solutes and control of the rate of flow.

**Cassava**. A South American shrub with a slender stem which can reach a height of 2.7 metres. Sweet cassava has roots eaten like potatoes; bitter cassava's roots [illegible] used to make tapioca.

**Cassia**. A tropical plant of the genus Cassia which yields senna, a drug with laxative properties.

**Cassowary**. A large flightless bird of the dense rain forests of New Guinea and northern Australia. It has coarse black plumage but the head and neck are naked and brightly coloured. Fruits and insects are the main foods.

**Cast**. A type of fossil in which the original organic substance has disappeared but counterparts of the organism are formed by the filling of the molds by uncrystallized substance, as casts of leaves, foodprints.

**Castaneous**. Dark brown or chestnut-colored.

**Caste**. A division found in social insects, such as the Hymenoptera (ants, bees, wasps) and the Isoptera (termites), in which the individuals are structurally and physiologically specialized to perform a particular function. For example, in honeybees there are queens (fertile females), workers (sterile females), and drones (males). There are several different castes of workers (all sterile females) among ants.

**Casting**. A mass of material discarded or thrown of by an animal, as the excrement of an earthworm or regurgitated food of a hawk.

**Castor Bean.** The seed of Ricinus communis, the source of castor oil, a cathartic.

**Castor Oil Plant.** A shrub native to India and Africa. It is grown in many tropical lands for its seeds, which yield castor oil. It grows up to 12 metres tall, with smooth leaves up to 90 cm across. Apart from the oil, the plant is extremely poisonous and the leaves have been used as an insecticide.

**Castration**

1. *zool. a.* Removal of the testes (orchiectomy) or ovaries *b.* Inactivation of the tests or ovaries by irradiation or through the action of hormones, parasites, or infections.

2. *bot.* Removal of the androecium of a flower.

**Cat.** The present-day domestic cat is thought to be descended mainly from the African bush cat. Domestication took place in Egypt where the cat was regarded as sacred. Today there are many breeds of domestic cat. Closest to the cats of Ancient Egypt is the Abyssinian. All domestic cats retain the hunting instincts of their ancestors and go feral, or wild, with surprising ease.

**Catabolism.** The metabolic breakdown of complex molecules to simpler ones. For example, respiration involves various catabolic reactions that degrade sugars to carbon dioxide and water and release energy, which is stored as ATP. Compare anabolism.

**Catacorolla.** A second corolla which is formed externally to the true one.

**Catadromous.** Migrating downstream and into the sea to spawn, as the freshwater eel. Compare anadromous.

**Catalase**

1. An oxidizing enzyme.

2. An enzyme present in tissues which decomposes hydrogen peroxide.

**Catalysis.** The process of changing the rate of a chemical reaction by use of a catalyst.

**Catalyst.** A substance that increases the rate of a chemical reaction without itself undergoing any permanent chemical change (also inhibition). The catalyst provides an alternative pathway by which the reaction can proceed, in which the activation energy is lower. It thus increases the rate at which the reaction comes to equilibrium, although it does not alter the position of the equilibrium. Enzymes are the catalysts in bio-chemical reactions; they are highly specific in the type of reaction they catalyse.

**Catamount.** A cougar or lynx.

**Cataphyll.** A small, scalelike leaf, as a bud scale.

**Catapult Mechanism.** A method of seed dispersal which depends on the jerking of a long stalk swaying in the wind.

**Catarrhine**. A primate of the suborder Catarrhini (now super-family Cercopithecoidea) which includes the Old World monkeys.

**Cat-bear**. The cat-bear, also called the red panda or lesser panda, is the nearest living relative of the gaint panda. It lives in the Himalayas. Its fur is a rich chestnut brown, with white marks on the face and dark rings on the long bushy tail. Although classified as a carnivore, the cat-bear feeds almost entirely on fruit and leaves. It spends most of its time in the trees, sleeping by day and coming out to feed by night.

**Catbird**. The name given to several unrelated birds. The Australian cat-birds are closely related to the Bower

Birds. The North American catbird is a member of the mockingbird family. It is a familiar garden bird throughout most of the United States, well known for the mewing notes of its song.

**Catecholamines.** A group of chemicals (amine derivatives of catechol) that are acting as neurohormones or neurotransmitters. Examples are noradrenaline, adrenaline, and dopamine.

**Catfish.** Any of a number of scaleless, mostly freshwater fishes, the upper jaw bearing whiskerlike barbels. North American forms belong to the family Ameiruridae and include the bullhead or horned pout, channel cat, and madtom.

**Catchfly.** Several species of flowering plant closely related to the campion. Their sepals are fused to form a tube and the flowers are usually either white or pink. The most common is the small-flowered catchfly, a sticky, hairy plant found in dry areas.

**Catecholamine.** Any of a class of amines (including dopamine, adrenaline, and noradrenaline) that function as neurotransmitters and/or hormones.

**Category.** Rank.

**Catenoid.** Linear or end, to end, with reference to the arrangement of individuals in a colony.

**Caterpillar.** The larval stage of various insects (especially butterflies and moths). The soft body carries three pairs of jointed legs on the thorax and a number of stumpy legs behind.

**Catfish.** A group of about 2000 species of fish, of which only one is native to northern Europe. Catfishes have no scales but all have long barbels on the mouth. The wels or European catfish is a large fresh-water fish with a long body and a broad, flat head. Most grow to about 1 metre long, but it has been known to reach 5 metres. It feeds mainly on other fishes, but also catches ducklings, frogs and water voles.

**Cathepsin.** An intracellular enzyme which catalyzes the hydrolysis of proteins; responsible for autolysis or liquification of tissus which occurs after death or in pathological conditions.

**Catkin.** A type of flowering shoot (racemose inflorescence) in which the axis, which is often long, bears many small stalkless unisexual flowers. Usually the male catkins hang down from the stem; the female catkins are shorter and often erect. Examples include brich and hazel. Most plants with catkins are adapted for wind pollination, the male flowers producing large quantities of pollen; willows are an exception, having nectar-secreting flowers and being pollinated by insects.

**Catmint.** A mint-scented, downy, grey plant with red-spotted white flowers growing in whorls. Found in hedge-banks and among rocks.

**Catodont**

1. Having teeth in the lower jaw only.
2. Pertaining to the sperm whale (Physeter catodon).

**Catothecium, Catathecium.** An inverted perithecium having the asc hanging from its base.

**CAT Scanner** (computerized axial tomography scanner) tomography.

**Cat's-ear.** A European perennial herb. It has dandelion-like flowers on 60 cm stalks bearing scattered scale-like bracts. The leaves are dull green. There are several species.

**Catshark.** A group of small sharks distinguished by their picturesque patterns of stripes and mottlings.

**Cattail.** A tall marsh plant of the genus Typha whose stem terminates in a dense, cylindrical spike.

**Cattle.** Domestic cattie probably originated from the aurochs, an extinct species of ox. Many strains have been bred for particular purposes, such as meat or milk production, and to suit particular environments.

**Cattle Tick.** Boophilus annulatus, a transmitter of Babesia, causative agent of Texas fever.

**Caudad.** Toward the tail or posterior end. Compare cephalad.

**Cauda Epididymis.** Refers to an enlargment at the distal end of the epididymis or tube which is leading from the testis to the vas deferens in mammals.

**Cauda Equina.** Used for describing the terminal spinal nerves of a mammal which together with the filum terminale form a bunch. The name has been derived from its resemblance to a horse's tail.

**Caudae Lobe.** Refers to a small lobe in the liver of mammals.

**Caudal.** Of, pertaining to, or resembling a tail; near or in the region of the tail; posterior.

**Caudal Fin.** The terminal or tail fin of an aquatic vertebrate; the primary organ of locomotion.

**Caudal Spine.** A spine which is forming the 'tail' or telson on some arthropoda, *e.g.*, scorpions.

**Caudal Styles.** Stylets or filaments, which are usually paired, on the hind-segments of many arthropods.

**Caudal Vertebrae.** The bones (vertebra) of the tail, which articulate with the sacral vertebrae. The number of caudal vertebrae varies with the species. Rabbits, for example, have 15 caudal vertebrae, while in man these vertebrae are fused to form a single bone, the coccyx.

**Caudate.** Bearing a tail or saillike appendage.

**Caudex**

1. The trunk of a palm or tree fern.
2. The persistent swollen stem base of certain herbaceous perennials.

**Caudicle**. The structure which connects a pollen mass or pollonium to the stigma, as in orchids.

**Caulerpales** (Siphonales). An order of the Bryopsidophyceae containing algae that lack any dividing walls. They also differ in containing α-carotene in addition to β-carotene. In some classifications these acellular algae are placed in the three orders : Derbesiales, Codiales (including Bryopsis and Codium), and Caulerpales (including Caulerpa and Halimeda).

**Caulicle**. A rudimentary stem, as the region between the radicle and cotyledons in a plant embryo; the hypocotyl.

**Caulid**. The 'stem' of a moss or liver-wort.

**Cauliflory**. The production of flowers on tissue that has been secondarily thickened, such as the branches or trunks, rather than at apical meristems. Flowers arising in this way normally develop from suppressed side shoots, but more infrequently they may be formed from the phellem. This trait is found most frequently in species that make up the lower canopy of tropical forests, *e.g.*, cocoa (Theobroma cacao). It is believed in some cases to be associated with pollination or fruit dispersal by bats.

**Cauliflower**. A kind of cabbage, similar to broccoli. It produces a dense head of white flower buds, packed with food, and it is these buds and their stalks that we eat. The flowers are yellow when they are allowed to open.

**Cauline**. Of the stem cauline leaves are carried on the upper part of a stem but do not bear flower shoots in their avils.

**Cauliflower Fungus.** A fungus that forms pale, cauliflower-like masses at the base of conifer trunks in autumn, up to 30 cm across.

**Cauline.** Pertaining to the stem, especically applied to leaves arising on the upper part of the stem, as compared to the radical leaves.

**Cauline, Bundle, Cauline Vascular Bundle.** A vascular bundle which is formed entirely from the tissue of the stem.

**Caulis.** The stalk or stem of a plant.

**[1]Caustic.** Corrosive, burning; capable of destroying by corroding or eating away.

**[2]Caustic.** A substance which destroys tissue by corrosive action.

**Caustic Potash.** Potassium hydroxide, KOH.

**Caustic Soda.** Sodium hydroxide, NaOH

**Cauterize.** To burn or sear.

**Cave Biology.** The study of cave-dwelling organisms (troglobionts).

**Cave Dweller.** A troglobiont; cavernicole.

**Cave Fishes.** A number of fishes spend their whole lives in underground caves and lakes. They have little or no pigment, and appear pinkish because the blood shows through the more or less scaleless skin. Most are blind and the largest is only 20 cm long. Cave fishes probably feed mainly on insects that fall into the water.

**Cavernicolous.** Inhabiting caves.

**Cavernous.** Full of cavities or hollow spaces.

**Caviar.** The prepared and salted roe of the sturgeon or other fishes.

**Cavitation.** The formation of vapour-filled cavities in a flowing liquid due to a decrease in pressure. It is the main cause of disruption of water columns in the xylem when a plant is suffering water stress.

**Cavy.** The name applied to a number of South American rodents of the genus Cavia, the best known being the domestic GUINEA-PIG which has been derived from the Peruvian cavy. The Patagonian cavy is a hare-like rodent found on the plains of Patagonia.

**Cayenne Pepper.** The dried and ground pod-like fruit of various species of capsicum pepper. The plant is a semi-woody many-branched perennial, native to tropical America.

**Cayman.** Caiman.

**Caytoniales.** An extinct order of gymnosperms known from fossils of the Jurassic period. Their habit is uncertain but it is known they had compound leaves consisting of three to six leaflets with reticulate venation. These arose from the tip of the rachis giving a fanlike or palmate leaf. The female reproductive axis bore short pinnae each of which ended in a round hollow structure or cupule containing the ovules. The pinnae of the male reproductive organs bore synangia longitudinally divided into four pollen sacs, which appear to have been very similar to the anthers of flowering plants.

**Cecidium.** An abnormal plant growth, as a gall.

**Cecropia Moth.** The giant silkworm moth (Samia cecropia), the largest native moth of the United States.

**Cecum.** A cavity open at one end; a blind pouch or cul-de-sac, as the first portion of the large intestine in mammals.

**Cedar.** Member of a group of tall coniferous trees belonging to the pine family. The needles are borne in dense whorls and the cones are like upright barrels which fall to pieces when the seeds are ripe. The cedar of Lebanon is a native of the eastern Mediterranean but is widely planted as an ornamental tree. It grows up to 40 metres tall and has a massive trunk with wide, sweeping branches, and a flat-topped crown. Some trees live up to 2000 years. There are three other kinds of true cedar, but the name also applies to certain members of the cypress family. Examples include the white cedar, a North American species grown in Europe for hedging or for ornament, and the western red cedar. The latter, also from North America, is quick-growing (up to 40 metres) and commonly planted for shelter and timber.

**Cedar-apple Rust**. A fungus disease of apples caused by Gymnosporangium juniperi, which also infects cedars causing swellings on branches called cedar apples.

**Celandine**. Two unrelated species of plant, both bearing yellow flowers. The greater celandine is related to the poppy and has an easily broken stem which has bright orange sap. The lesser celandine is related to the buttercup and

Greater celandine

has shiny heartshaped leaves. They are both common in hedgebanks.

**Celery**. A biennial vegetable related to parsley. It is grown for its crisp leaf stalks. It has large compound leaves, and if not harvested after its first season produces heads of small white flowers on a long stem.

**Celiac**. Coeliac.

**Cell**. The structural and functional unit of all living organisms. Cell size varies, but most cells are microscopic (average diameter 0.01-0.1 mm). Cells may exist as independent units of life, as in bacteria and protozoans, or they may form colonies or tissues, as in all higher plants and animals. Each cell consists of a mass of protein material (protoplasm) that is differentiated into a jelly-like substance (cytoplasm) and a nucleus, which contains DNA. The protoplasm is bounded by a cell membrane, which in plant and bacterial cells is surrounded by a cell wall. There are two main types of cell. Prokaryotic cells (bacteria and blue-green algae) are the more primitive. The nuclear material is not bounded by a membrane and chemicals involved in cell metabolism are associated with the cell membrane. Reproduction is asexual and involves simple cell cleavage. In eukaryotic cells the nucleus is bounded by a nuclear membrane and the cytoplasm is divided by membranes into a system of interconnected cavities and separate compartments organelles), *e.g.* mitochondria, endoplasmic reticulum, Golgi apparatus, lysosomes, and ribosomes. Reproduction can be either asexual (mitosis) or sexual (meiosis). Plants and animals consist of eukaryotic cells but plant cells possess chloro-

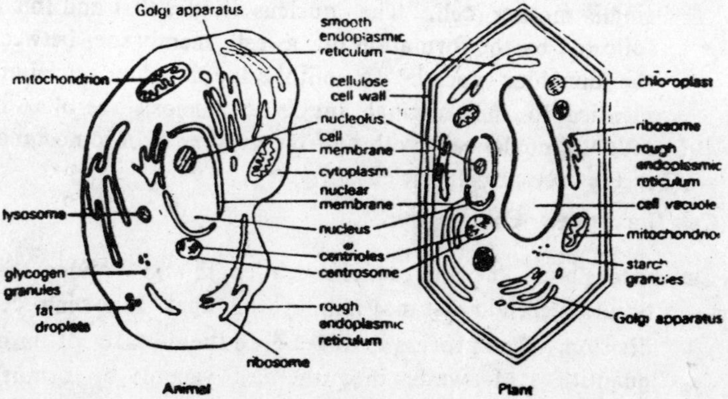


Generalized eukaryotic cells

plasts and other plastids and bear a rigid cellulose cell wall.

**Cell Biology.** Cytology.

**Cell Body** (perikaryon). The part of a neurone that contains the nucleus. The cell processes that are involved in the transmission and reception of nervous impulses (the axon and the dendrites respectively) develop as extensions from the cell body.

**Cell Cycle.** The sequence of events in a cell resulting in the formation of two complete daughter cells. In addition to the observable changes during mitosis, biochemical processes occur in the nucleus and cytoplasm. Cytokinesis is followed by a growth phase ($G_1$ phase) during which there is a high rate of RNA formation and protein synthesis. A lag phase of variable duration is followed by a period of DNA replication and histone synthesis (S phase) as the chromosomes divide into chromatids. Finally there is a short growth period ($G_2$ phase) before prophase of mitosis begins). The length of each period varies considerably. In actively dividing cells in culture the full cycle takes twenty four hours while in living tissue the time taken to double the number of cells can be as short as eight hours.

**Cell Division.** The formation of two daughter cells from a single mother cell. The nucleus divides first and this is followed by the formation of a cell membrane between the daughter nuclei. In mitosis the daughter nuclei are identical to the original nucleus; meiosis results in daughter nuclei each with half the number of chromosomes in the mother cell nucleus.

**Cell Doctorine.** Cell theory.

**Cell Extension.** The increase in cell length and volume that occurs a certain distance behind the apex following cell division. The process involves both the uptake of large quantities of water into the cell vacuole by osmosis (vacuolation) and the synthesis of new cytoplasmic and cell wall materials. Cell extension accounts for a far greater proportion of overall plant growth than cell division.

**Cell Fractionation.** The separation of cell components by differential centrifugation. The tissue is broken down in a homogenizer and the homogenate is spun in the cell of an ultracentrifuge. Protoplasmic particles settle out in order of size and weight, separation also depending on the speed and duration of centrifugation. The rate of sedimentation is expressed as the sedimentation coefficient, *s*. After sedimentation is complete the fractions can be identified by their biochemical activity and by electron microscopy.

**Cell Lineage.** The sequence of cells, produced by cell division and cytological changes, that results in the formation of differentiated cells with a specific function. For example, the germ cells in flowering plants are produced by the sequence of changes, commencing with undifferentiated cells in the anthers and nucellus respectively, that produce the microspores (pollen grains) and megaspores (embryo sacs) and eventually the male and female gametes.

**Cell Membrane** (plasmalemma; plasma membrane). The semipermeable membrane forming the outer limit of a cell. It consists mostly of protein and lipid. The membrane regulates the flow of materials in and out of the cell and plays a role in the production or assembly of the cell wall or capsule (when this is present).

**Cellobiose.** A reducing disaccharide composed of two glucose units linked by a $\beta(1\cdot4)$ glycosidic bond. It is formed by the incomplete hydrolysis of cellulose by the enzyme cellulase. Complete hydrolysis to glucose units is achieved by the enzyme cellobiase ($\beta$-glycosidase).

**Cell Plate.** An opaque colloidal layer established by membrane-bound cavities in the equatorial region of the spindle at the telophase stage of mitosis. It separates the cytoplasm into two daughter protoplasts, each with a nucleus. Pectic substances within the vesicles contribute to the formation of a middle lamella between the newly formed cells.

**Cell Sap.** The fluid contained within the vacuole of a plant cell, consisting of water and various substances in solution.

**Cell Theory.** The theosy attributed to M.J. Schleiden, botanist, and T. Schwann, zoologist, announced in 1838-39 that all plants and animals are made up of microscopic units called cells. From it developed the cell doctrine which holds that all organisms are composed of cells or the products of cells and that cells constitute the structural and functional units of an organism.

**Cell Tissue.** A group of cells formed from the division of one or a few cells, and functioning as a whole.

**Cellular**. Of or pertaining to cells; composed of or derived from cells.

**Cellular Slime Moulds.** Used for the members of class Acrasiomycetes of Myxomycota that feed on soil bacteria. Organisms are made up of an aggregation of myxamoebae forming preudoplasmodium. These yield naked masses of walled spores (pseudospores) by a process different from that of other fungi.

**Cellulase.** A hydrolytic enzyme found in bacteria and some seedlings that attacks alternate β(1-4) linkages in cellulose, degrading it to the pisaccharide cellobiose. Cellulase is one of the very few enzymes capable of attacking the β(1-4) glycosidic bond; cellulose is not degraded by other glycolytic enzymes such as amylase. Cellulase, produced by bacteria living in the gut of ruminant animals, enables such animals to derive nutrients from the fibrous component of their diet.

**Cellulosans** A group of carbohydrates similar to cellulose, bat with shorter chains, mainly of xylose residues may have uronic acid and mannose units.

**Cellulose.** A polysaccharide that consists of a long unbranched chain of glucose units. It is the main constituent of the cell walls of all higher plants. many algae, and some fungi and is responsible for providing the rigidity of the cell wall. The fibrous nature of extracted cellulose had led to its use in the textile industry for the production of cotton, artificial silk, etc.

**Cell Wall.** A rigid outer layer that surrounds the cell membrane of plant and bacterial (but not animal) cells. It protects and/or gives shape to a cell, and in herbaceous plants provides mechanical support for the plant body. Most plant cell walls are composed of the polysaccharide cellulose and may be strengthened by the addition of lignin. The cell walls of fungi consist mainly of chitin. Bacterial cell walls consist of complex polymers of polysaccharides and amino acids.

**Celsius Scale.** A temperature scale in which the fixed points are the temperatures at standard pressure of ice in equilibrium with water (0°C) and water in equilibrium with steam (100°C). The scale, between these two temperatures, is divided in 100 degrees. The degree Celsius (°C) is equal in magnitude to the kelvin. This scale was formerly known as the centigrade scale; the name was officially changed in 1948 to avoid confusion with a hundredth part of a grade. It is named after the Swedish astronomer Anders Celsius (1701-44), who devised the inverted form of this scale (ice point 100°, steam point 0°) in 1742.

**Cement** (cementum). A thin layer of bony material that fixes teeth to the jaw. It covers the dentine of the root of a tooth, below the level of the gum, and is attached to the periodontal membrane lining the tooth socket in the jawbone.

**Cenogenetic** or **Coenogenetic.** Pertaining to characters appearing during development which are not of phylogenetic significance. Compare palingenetic.

**Cenozoic (Cainozoic; Kainozoic).** The geological era that began about 65 million years ago and extends to the present. It followed the Mesozoic era and is subdivided into the Tertiary and Quaternary periods. The Cenozoic is often known as the Age of Mammals as these evolved to become an abundant, diverse, and dominant group. Birds and flowering plants also flourished. The era saw rise formation of the major mountain ranges of the Himalayas and the Alps.

**Cenozoic Era.** The most recent of geologic eras, characterized by the rise and spread of modern mammals and the red of land floras. It is called the "Age of Mammals" and covers about 60 million years.

**Censer Action.** The release of seeds from censerlike capsules from which seeds are shaken out through small openings, as in the poppy.

**Censer Mechanism.** A method of seed dispersal in which the seeds are shaken out of pores in the fruit when it sways in the wind.

**Centaury.** Several species of upright plant, of which only the common and the slender centaury are widespread. Both bear pink flowers, arranged in tight clusters, usually open only in bright sunlight.

**Center of Dispersal.** An area on the earth's surface where a species arose and from which it spread to occupy its present geographic range. Also called center of origin.

**Centi-.** Symbol c. A prefix used in the metric system to denote one hundredth. For example, 0.01 metre=1 centrimetre (cm).

**Centigrade Scale.** Celsius scale.

**Centipede.** A group of arthropods which have a pair of walking legs on almost every segment. Although the word centipede means '100 feet', the creatures have varying numbers of feet—from 15 to 177 pairs. Centipedes live in damp places, particularly under logs and stones. They are active hunters, killing insects and other small creatures with their poisonous claws.

**Central Body.** A colorless central region in certain blue-green algae.

**Central Capsule.** The inner, multinucleated portion of a radiolarian.

**Central Cell**

1. The cell present in the centre of developing archegonium of the Bryophyta and Pteriodophyta which divides to form the primary canal-cell and primary ventral cell.
2. The cell present at the base of the archegonium in the Gymnospermae, having the egg and ventral canal-cell.

**Central Cylinder.** Stele.

**Central Dogma.** The basic belief originally held by molecular geneticists, that flow of genetic information can only occur from DNA to RNA to proteins. It is now known, however, that information contained within RNA molecules of viruses can also flow back to DNA.

**Central Nervous System (CNS).** The brain and spinal cord or main nerve cord of the body. The central nervous system co-ordinates the activity of the whole body.

**Central Nervous System (CNS).** The part of the nervous system that coordinates all neutral functions. In invertebrates it may comprise simply a few nerve cords and associated ganglia. In vertebrates it consists of the brain and the spinal cord. The vertebrate CNS contains reflex arcs, which produce automatic and rapid responses to particular stimuli.

**Centre (in neurology).** A part of the nervous system, consisting of a group of nerve cells, that coordinates a particular process. An example is the respiratory centre in the vertebrate brainstem, which controls breathing movements. The stimulation of a centre will initiate the process, while destruction of the centre will prevent or impair it.

**Centre of Diversity.** Gene centre.

**Centre of Origin, Theory of.** According to this theory, the plant species originated in the area where they show the greatest genetical diversity.

**Centric Bundle.** Concentric bundle.

**Centrifugal.** Developing from the centre outwards so the oldest structures are in the middle and the youngest at the perimeter. An example is the differentiation of secondary xylem. Compare centripetal.

**Centrifugal Xylem.** A xylem in which differentiation takes place away from the centre of a stem or root.

**Centrifuge.** A device in which solid or liquid particles of different densities are separated by rotating them in a tube in a horizontal circle. The denser particles tend to move along the length of the tube to a greater radius of rotation, displacing the lighter particles to the other end.

**Centriole.** A cylindrical structure in a cell that has a role in cell division. Centrioles are not normally found in plant cells but are commonly present in pairs in animal cells. During cell division they move to opposite sides of the nucleus to form the ends of the spindle. The spindle fibres develop from them.

**Centripetal.** Developing from the outside inwards, so the oldest structures are at the edge and the youngest are in the middle. An example is the differentiation of xylem in club mosses (Lycopodium). Compare centrifugal.

**Centripetal Inflorescence.** Raceme.

**Centripetal Xylem.** A xylem in which differentiation takes place from the centre of the stem or root.

**Centrolecithal.** Having yolk centrally located and surrounded by a narrow layer of clear cytoplasm, as the eggs of insects.

**Centromere** (kinomere; spindle attachment). The part of a chromosome that contains no genes. It usually appears as a constriction when chromosomes contract during cell division (meiosis; mitosis). The position of the centromere is a distinguishing feature of individual chromosomes and it attaches them to the spindle fibres.

**Centroplasm** The inner, colorless region (central body) of a blue-green algal cell. Compare chromoplasm.

**Centroplast.** In certain heliozoans, a centrally located granule from which axopodia radiate.

**Centrosome.** The dense zone surrounding the centriole in a cell center; also called microcentrum.

**Centrospermae.** Caryophylidae.

**Centrosphere.** The clear region which surrounds a centriole.

**Centrum**

1. *anat*. The cylindrical mass forming the body of a vertebra.
2. *bot*. A large central air space in certain stems, as in Equisetum.

**Century Plant.** A Mexican plant (Agave americana) of the Amaryllis family, a longlived, monocarpic plant which flowers and produces seeds only once and then dies.

**Cephalad.** Toward the head or anterior end.

**Cephalic.** Referring to or situated near head.

**Cephalization.** In the evolution of animals, the development of a head, that is the concentration of nervous tissue (brain and sense organs) and the development of a mouth and food-getting apparatus at the anterior end.

**Cephalization.** The tendency among animal groups for the major sense organs, mouth, and brain to be grouped together at the front (anterior) end of the body. These are usually contained in a specialized cephalic region—the head.

**Cephalochordate.** Any chordate of the subphylum Cephalochordata which includes the lancelets.

**Cephalodium pl. Cephalodia.** A rounded body containing algae growing symbiotically in or on the thallus of a lichen.

**Cephalopod.** A member of the class of molluscs known as Cephalopoda, containing the squids, octopuses and cuttlefish, all of which are marine. There are many extinct members—ammonites, belemnites and others – typically with a chambered shell Modern forms, however, except for the pearly nautilus, have a very reduced shell. In size they vary from a few centimetres to 18 metres – the length of a giant squid including tentacles. Cephalopods have a large distinct head marked off from the rest of the body by a narrower 'neck' and a pair of prominent eyes. Eight or ten muscular arms surround the head. They are equipped with numerous suckers which brovide the animals with an extremely strong grip The mouth is armed with a horny beak made of chitin and the tongue is covered with rows of curved rasping teeth (radula). Compared with other molluscs, cephalopods lead a very active life and have a correspondingly better developed nervous system with a large brain. The animals feed on crabs, prawns, fish and other molluscs. Squids swim freely, others rend to rest on the seabed, though the cuttlefish can swim gently by flapping 'fins'.

**Cephalopoda.** The most advanced class of molluscs, containing the squids, cuttlefishes, octopuses, and the extinct ammonities. Cephalopods have a highly concentrated central nervous system within a protective cartilaginous case. The eye has a well-developed retina and is comparable to that of vertebrates. All cephalopods are predacious carnivores capable of swimming by jet propulsion; they have highly mobile tentacles for catching and holding prey.

**Cephalothorax.** The fused head and thorax of crustaceans and arachnids (spiders, scorpions), which is connected to the abdomen.

**Ceraceous.** Waxy.

**Ceral**

1. Of or pertaining to wax.
2. Of or pertaining to the cere of a bird's beak.

**Cerata.** Filamentous or club-shaped respiratory structures on the backs of nudibranch mollusks.

**Cercaria** pl. **Cercariae**. The free-swimming, larval form of a fluke which develops from a sporocyst or redia within the tissues of a mollusk (snail or bivalve).

**Cercariaeum.** A cercaria in which a tail is lacking; sometimes found within the molluscan host.

**Cerci.** Plural of Cercus.

**Cercocystis.** A cysticercoid with a tail.

**Cercopithicoid.** Old world monkeys having a tail which was not employed as limb.

**Cercopod.** A gegmented terminal process on the telson of branchiopods.

**Cercus** pl. **Cerci.** One of a pair of sensory appendages, usually segmented, found at the posterior end of insects ann other arthropods.

**Cere.** A cushionlike protuberance at the base of the beak in certain birds, as in the eagle, hawk, parrot.

**Cereal.** A member of the grass family (Gramineae) whose seeds are used for food. Examples include rye, oats, wheat, maize and barley.

**Cerebellum.** The part of the vertebrate brain concerned with the coordination and regulation of muscle activity and the maintenance of muscle tone and balance. In mammals it consists of two connected hemispheres, composed of a core of white matter and a much-folded outer layer of grey matter, and is situated above the medulla oblongata and partly beneath the cerebrum.

**Cerebral**

1. Of or pertaining to the bran.
2. Of or pertaining to the cerebral hemispheres.

**Cerebral Cortex** (pallium). The layer of grey matter that forms the outer layer of the hemispheres of the cerebrum in many vertebrates. It is most highly developed in mammals. The cortex is responsible for the control and integration of voluntary movement and the senses of vision, hearing, touch, etc.; it also contains centres concerned with memory, language, thougth, and intellect.

**Cerebral Hemisphere.** Either of the two halves of the vertebrate cerebrum.

**Cerebral Hemisphere.** A pair of structures that are originating from the forebrain. They have the centres which are concerned with the major senses, voluntary muscle activities, and higher brain functions, like language and memory.

**Cerebrospinal Fluid** (CSF). The fluid, similar in composition to lympth, that bathes the central nervous system of vertebrates. It is secreted by the choroid plexus into the ventricles of the brain, filling these and other cavities in the brain and spinal cord, and is reabsorbed by veins on the brain surface. Its function is to protect the central nervous system from mechanical injury.

**Cerebrum.** The largest part of the vertebrate brain. It consists of two cerebral hemispheres, which develop from the embryonic forebrain. The hemispheres have an outer convoluted layer of grey matter—the cerebral cortex—which contains an estimated ten billion nerve cells. Underneath this is white matter. The two halves of the cerebrum are linked by several neural structures. The function of the cerebrum is to integrate complex sensory and neural functions. The cerebrum is thought to play a critical role in the process of learning, which involves both short-term and long-term memory.

**Ceriferous.** Waxy; bearing or producing wax.

**Cernuous.** Pendulous, drooping, nodding.

**Ceroma.** A cere.

**Certation.** A gonisis; competition, as between pollen grains in rate of growth.

**Ceruloplasmin.** Refers to copper containing plasma protein. Its deficiency causes Wilson's disease, a familiar disorder of copper metabolism.

**Cerumen**

1. Earwax, a waxlike substance formed from the secretions of ceruminous and sebaceous glands of the external auditory meatus.
2. A substance produced by stingless bees of the genus Melipoma and used in nest construction.

**Cervical**

1. Of or pertaining to the neck.
2. Of or pertaining to the cervix of an organ.

**Cervical Vertebrae.** The vertebrae of the neck. The number of cervical vertebrae varies : for example, rabbits have 7 and humans have 12. Their main functions are to support the head and to provide articulating surfaces against which it can move relative to the backbone.

**Cervine.** Of or pertaining to deer or the deer family, Cervidae.

**Cervix pl. Cervices.** A neck or necklike part.

**Cervix.** Neck-like structure present between uterus and vagina in a typical mammal; opening of uterus in a mammal.

**Cespitose.** Growing in dense clumps or tuffs; matted.

**Cestoda.** A class of flatworms (Platyhelminthes) comprising the tapeworms-ribbon-like parasites within the gut of vertebrates. Tapeworms are surrounded by partially digested food in the host gut so they are able to absorb nutrients through their whole body surface. The body consists of a head (scolex), bearing suckers and hooks for attachment, and a series of segments (proglottides), containing male and female reproductive systems. The life cycle of a tapeworm requires tow hosts, the primary host usually being a predator of the secondary host. Taenia soleum has man for its primary host and the its secondary host. Mature segments, maining thousands of fertilized eggs, leave the primary host with its faeces and develop into embryos and then larvae that continue the life cycle in the gut of a secondary host.

**Cestodarian.** A tapeworm of the subclass Cestodaria characterized by lack of scolex and a body not divided into proglottids, as Amphilina, which lives in a sturgeon.

**Cestode.** A tapeworm, especially any member of the subclass Cestoda (Eucestoda) which includes the true tapeworms, parasitic worms with hody consisting of a scolex and a linear series of proglottids, as Taenia.

**Cetacea.** An order of marine mammals comprising the whales, which includes what is probably the largest known animal the blue whale (Balaenoptera musculus), over 30 m long any over 150 tonnes in weight. The forelimbs of whales are modified as short stabilizing flippers and the skin is very thin and almost hairless. A thick layer of blubber insulates the body against heat loss and is an important food store. Whales breathe trough a dorsal blowhole, which is closed when the animal is submerged. The toothed whales suborder Odontoceti), such as the dolphins and killer whale, are carnivorous; whalebone whales (suborder Mysticeti), such as the blue whale, feed on plankton filtered by whalebone plates.

**Cetacean.** A member of the aquatic mammalian order Cetacea which includes the whales.

**Chaeta.** A bristle, made of chitin, occurring in annelid worms. In the earthworm they occur in small groups projecting from the skin in each segment and function in locomotion. The chaetae of polychaete worms (*e.g.* ragworm) are borne in larger groups on paddle-like appendages (parapodia).

**Chaetoplankton.** Describing small aquatic organisms whose power to float is aided by small spiny outgrowths.

**Chafer.** A group of beetles which live on plants and may be seen in gardens. The best known chafer is the Cockchafer or maybug. Another common species is the rose chafer, a sturdy green insect sometimes found on rose flowers. The beetles' larvae feed on wood and roots.

**Chaff**

1. The husks or outer envelopes of the seeds of various cereal grains or grasses.
2. Small, degenerate bracts on the receptacle of flowers of various composites.

**Chaffinch.** The commonest of the finches, it lives in Europe all the year round, but moves south in winter from northern Scadinavia. The bird is easily identifiable by the two white wing bars on its dark wings. The female is a duller coloured bird than the male, which has a grey-blue crown and an orange-pink breast. The nest is built in an open site in a tree or hedge, but is well camouflaged.

**Chain Terminating Codon.** Refers to a sequence of three nucleotides which indicate the end of the information for assembly of amino acids in a polypeptide chain. It has three chain terminating codon each of which can bring translation to a halt. Also termed as non-sense codons.

**Chalaza**

1. A twisted strand of fibrous albumen in a bird's egg that is attached to the membrane at either end of the yolk and thus holds the yolk in position in the albumen.
2. The part of a plant ovule where the nucleous and integuments merge.

**Chalazogamy.** A method of fertilization in seed plants in which the pollen tube does not reach the nucellus through the micropyle (porogamy) but grows or digests its way through the placenta and chalaza instead. This may be observed in certain trees and shrubs, such as beech, elm, and hazel.

**Chalcid.** A small, hymenopterous insect of the superfamily Chalcidoidea, parasitic on other insects.

**Chalcidfly.** A chalcid.

**Chalcones.** Used for one of the two groups of anthochlor pigments, about 20 kinds of which are known.

**Chalimus.** A stage in the development of Lernaeocera, a copepod parasitic on the gills of fishes.

**Chalk.** A very fine-grained white rock composed of the fossilized skeletal remains of marine plankton known as coccoliths and consisting largely of calcium carbonate ($CaCO_3$). It is the characteristic rock of the Cretaceous period. It should not be confused with blackboard 'chalk' which is made from calcium sulphate.

**Chalcones.** One of the two groups of anthochlor flower pigments. Chalcones are less variable than other types of flavonoid pigments with only some 20 kinds being known. In the synthesis of the various flavonoids from acetates and cinnamic acid the chalcones are the first compounds to be formed along the biosynthetic pathway. This has led some to consider the possession of chalcones a primitive characteristic as compared to the possession of aurones, which are oxidized derivatives of chalcones. The yellow colours of gorse, dahlia, and carnation flowers are due to chalcones.

**Chalk Grassland.** Heath

**Chalone.** A substance present in mammalian tissue that can inhibit mitosis in the presence of, for example, adrenaline. It has been suggested that these substances play a role in the ageing process and in cancer.

**Chameleon.** A group of lizards which are famed for their ability to change colour. They do this by altering the distribution of pigment in their skins. Other unusual features include eyes which can be swivelled around independently, and a long tongue which is catapulted out to catch insects. Chameleons are rather flattened from side to side and they are often decorated with brilliant colours, 'warts' and horns. Most species live in Africa and range from 5-60 cm in length.

**Chamois.** A goat-like mountain animal found in various parts of Europe and Asia Minor. It is a study creature about 1.25 metres long and weighing up to 40 kg. Both sexes have sharply pointed horns. The long coat is tawny in summer and darker in winter. The animals live mainly in alpine forests and feed on a variety of plants.

**Chamomile.** A group of generally fragrant herbs that bear small daisy-like flowerheads.

**Cqannelled.** Bearing longitudinal grooves.

**Chanterelle.** A yellow funnel-shaped toadstool that smells of apricots and grows in deciduous woods. The outer or lower surface bears maze of irregular folds. The false chanterelle is less fleshy and more orange than the true chanterelle. It grows mainly in coniferous woods.

**Chaparral.** Vegetation consisting or thickets of dwarfed, drought resistant and often thorny thrubs and bushes characteristic of much of the western United States.

**Char or Charr.** A trout of the genus Salvelinus.

**Characin.** A large family of tropical freshwater fishes living in Africa and the Americas. Its members range from the brilliantly coloured Tetras of aquarium fame to the ferocious Piranha.

**Character.** A distinctive inherited feature of an organism. Organisms in a population may display different aspects of a particular character, *e.g.* the A, B, and O human blood groups (ABO system) are different aspects of the blood group character.

**Charlock.** An annual and a member of the cabbage family, charlock is a cornfield weed of Europe, North Africa and western Asia. It is also called wild mustard. It has bristly, 60 cm stems and leaves and small yellow flowers. Its seeds can remain dormant for 50 years.

**Charr Arctic.** A relative of the trout, commonly found in mountain lakes. Some Arctic charr migrate to the sea after spawning. They grow ap to 1 metre long.

**Chasmogamous.** Designating pollination which takes place in open flowers. Compare cleistogamous.

**Chasmogamy.** The production of flowers that open to expose the reproductive organs. This allows cross pollination but does not preclude self pollination. Compare cleistogamy.

**Chasmophyte.** A plant which is growing on rocks, rooted in the crevices.

**Cheek.** The region of the face below the eye and lateral to the mouth gena.

**Cheetah.** A long-legged cat with a spotted coat and a characteristic black stripe running from the eye to the corner of the mouth. Over short distances it is probably the fastest land animal in the world, with a speed approaching 100 km/h. It catches antelopes by a single leap or after a short sprint. The cheetah once ranged from India to South Africa, but its main stronghold is now in East Africa.

**Chela.** Claw or pincer of certain arthropods such as crabs and lobsters.

**Chelate.** Possessing or resembling chelae.

**Chelicera** pl. **Chelicerae.** One of the first pair of appendages used as feeding structures in chelicerates. In spiders, each bears a terminal fang on which a poison duct opens.

**Chelicerate.** Any arthropod of the subphylum Chelicerata which includes the classes Merostomata, Arachnida, and Pycngonoida.

**Cheliform.** Pincherlike.

**Cheliped.** A walking leg which bears at its tip a chela, especially the first walking leg of a lobster or crayfish.

[1]**Chelonian.** Of or pertaming to turtles or tortoises.

**₂Chelonian.** Any reptile of the order Chelonia (Testudinata), which includes the turtles, and tortaises, terrapins.

**Chelosis.** Inflamation and soreness of the corners of mouth. It is associated with deficiency of vitamin $B_2$.

**Chemical Dating.** An absolute dating technique that depends on measuring the chemical composition of a specimen. Chemical dating can be used when the specimen is known to undergo slow chemical change at a known rate. For instance, phosphate in buried bones is slowly replaced by fluoride ions from the ground water. Measurement of the proportion of fluorine present gives a rough estimate of the time that the bones have been in the ground. Another, more accurate, method depends on the fact that amino acids in living organisms are L-optical isomers. After death, these racemize and the age of bones can be estimated by measuring the relative amounts of D- and L-amino acids present.

**Chemical Fossil.** Any of various organic compounds founds in ancient geological strata that appear to be biological in origin and are assumed to indicate that life existed when the rocks were formed. The presence of chemical fossils in Precambrian strata indicates that life existed over 3000 million years ago.

**Chemoautotrophic.** Used for an organism which derives energy by the oxidation of simple inorganic molecules. An example is the oxidation of hydrogen sulphide to sulphur by Thiobacillus spp.

**Chemoautotroph.** An organism that synthesizes organic molecules using energy derived from the oxidation of inorganic compounds present in the environment. Examples are the bacteria Nitrosomonas, which obtains energy by oxidizing ammonia to nitrite, and Nitrobacter, which oxidizes nitrite to nitrate. Compare chemoheterotroph.

**Chemoheterotroph.** An organism that obtains the energy required for the synthesis of organic molecules from the oxidation of organic compounds. All heterotrophs, with the exception of the photoheterotrophs, are chemoheterotrophs.

**Chemoheterotrophic.** Refers to type of heterotrophic nutrition in which energy requirements for the synthesis of organic molecules from organic precursors are given by the chemical breakdown of organic molecules.

**Chemolithotroph.** An autotrophic organism which can obtain its energy from inorganic compounds, as the iron, sulfur, hydrogen, and nitrifying bacteria.

**Chemoorganotroph.** A heterotrophic organism, which uses prefabricated foods as a source of nutrition, as saprotrophic decay organisms, all metazoans.

**Chemoreceptor.** A receptor that detects the presence of particular chemicals and (in multicellular organisms) transmits this information to sensory nerves. Examples include the taste buds and the receptors in the the carotid body.

**Chemosterilant.** Any chemical used to sterilize pests and hence reduce the number of offspring in the subsequent generation. A common technique is to regularly release large numbers of laboratory-reared sterile males into the wild population, which compete with normal males. The method has been used successfully to control various fruit flies.

**Chemosynthesis.** The elaboration of organic materials by organisms (chemotrophs) using chemical energy derived from chemical reactions. Compare photosynthesis.

**Chemosynthetic.** Designating a type of autotrophic nutrition in which organisms obtain their energy from the oxidation of various inorganic compounds instead of from light.

**Chemosystematics.** Systematics.

**Chemotaxis.** A taxis in response to a chemical stimulus. For example, bacteria commonly show positive chemotaxis, swimming towards regions containing higher concentrations of food substances such as peptone and lactose. Negative chemotaxis may be shown in response to toxic substances.

**Chemotaxonomy** (biochemical taxonomy). The application of the principles and procedures of chemical analysis and the results obtained to the classification of plants. Although the science has disverse and ancient origins (*e.g.* the medicinal and ethnic interest in the chemical constituents of plants) it has only made significant growth in recent decades. Plant product analysis has been simplified by the development of chromatography and electrophoresis, which with other new techniques, make routine analysis of a representative selection of material a possibility that was not once available. Many different compounds are potentially of taxonomic value and three main groups are recognized; primary and secondary metabolites and semantides. Primary metabolites are those involved in the essential biochemical pathways of the plant. As such they are virtually ubiquitous through the plant kingdom and are rarely useful taxonomically. Secondary metabolites are those substances accumulated by plants that have traditionally been regarded as waste products, *e.g.* terpenoids, alkaloids, phenolics, etc. Often distinct discontinuities are found in the distribution of secondary metabolites, which have been used to delimit taxa.

**Chemotherapy.** The treatment of disease or the prevention of infection through the use of drugs which suppress growth or which kill pathogenic organisms in the body. Chemotherapeutic agents include synthetic substances (sulfonamides, arsenic compounds) and antibiotics (streptomycin, pencillin).

**Chemotroph.** An organism that derives the energy necessary for the synthesis of organic compounds from the oxidation of eitherorganic or inorganic compounds (as in chemoheterotrophs and chemoautotrophs respectively). Light energy plays no part in the process. Compare phototroph.

**Chemotropism.** The growth or movement of a plant or plant part in response to a chemical stimulus. An example is the growth of a pollen tube down the style during fertilization in response to the presence of sugars in the style.

**Cheraded.** A plant which inhabits wet sand bars.

**Chernozem** (black earth). A type of zonal alkaline soil (a pedocal) found in regions with light summer rainfall, as in the pampas of South America and the prairies of North America. The top of the A horizon is very thick, rich in humus, and black, and the brown lime-rich layer beneath, merges into, and is often indistinct from, the B horizon. The slight leaching due to the spring and summer rains is counteracted by surface evaporation in the hot summer resulting in the accumulation of lime in the A horizon. Such soils are very fertile over a long period of time.

**Cherry, Wild.** A deciduous tree belonging to the rose family and the ancestor of all cultivated sweet cherries. It grows up to 20 metres tall and is sometimes called the gean. Its small sweet fruit are eaten by birds which pass the stones and help to spread the trees. The closely related bird cherry is often found growing alongside streams, especially in more northerly regions. Both trees are covered with white flowers in spring.

**Cherry Laurel.** An evergreen shrub of the eastern Mediterranean with shiny leaves and white flowers. Leaves, fruit and bark are rich in prussic acid and are poisonous.

**Cherry Plum.** A deciduous tree belonging to the rose family, also known as the myrobalan. It originated in the Balkans and Asia, and is grown in many parts of Europe for its fruit. It is also used as a hedging plant and grows about 8 metres tall. Its white flowers look similar to blackthorn blossom, and the tree is one of the earliest to flower in spring.

Cherry plum

**Chersad.** A chersophyte.

**Chersophyte.** A plant which inhabits dry wastelands.

**Chervil.** A biennial herb of eastern Europe and western Asia, sometimes called sweet cicely. Its much divided leaves are used as flavouring.

**Chestnut.** The sweet or Spanish chestnut is a deciduous tree of the northern hemisphere with wide-spreading branches. It has broad, toothed oval leaves and reddish edible nuts enclosed in spiny green cases. The male flowers are Catkins. It reaches a height of 30 metres. The Horse-Chestnut belongs to a different family.

**Chestnut Blight.** Canker blight, a destructive disease of the chestnut tree, caused by an ascomycete fungus, (Endotheia parasitica).

**Chestnut-brown Soil.** A type of zonal alkaline soil (a pedocal) that forms in areas of dry grassland receiving about 340-360 mm of precipitation per annum. The A horizon is much thinner than in a chernozem soil because the supply of organic matter is limited.

**Chevrotain.** Also known as mouse deer, the chevrotains are the smallest of the ruminant animals. They are rarely more than 30 cm high at the shoulder. They are not true deer, and they lack antlers. There are four species, living in the forests of Africa and southern Asia. They eat mainly grass and leaves, but also take insects, fish, and small mammals.

**Chiasma** (*pl.* chiasmata). A point at which chromatids from different homologues in a bivalent are seen to be in close contact as separation of the paired chromosomes commences during the first meiotic prophase. Genetic evidence shows that at these points the chromatids break and rejoin so portions are exchanged, resulting in the recombination of maternal and paternal genes on the homologous chromosomes. Chiasma formation is also important for the distribution of chromosomes into the nuclei of gametes. If chiasmata fail to form, homologues do not pair effectively at first prophase and they are unable to move to the poles of the spindle.

**Chiasma Interference.** The effect a crossover occurring at one point has on the chances of a second crossover occuring in the same pair of chromatids. If the term is usen without qualification, it normally implies the chances of a second crossover are reduced (positive interference). Negative interference, where the chances of a second crossover are increased, is rater.

**Chigoe.** A chigger or sand flea. Sand flea.

**Chilopoda.** The class of arthropods containing the centipedes (*e.g.* Lithobius). They are characterized by a flat body that is divided into numerous segment, each bearing one pair of walking legs. They are terrestrial, and breathe air through tracheae. Excretion takes place by a Malpighian tubules.

**Chimaera.** An organism composed of tissues that are genetically different. Chimareas can develop if a mutation occurs in a cell of a developing embryo. All the cells arising from it have the mutation and therefore produce tissue that is genetically different from adjacent tissue, *e.g.* brown patches in otherwise blue eyes in humans. Graft hybrids are examples of plant chimaeras.

**Chickaree.** This is the red squirrel of North America. It is about two-thirds the size of the grey squirrel, and has a tawny brown coat. The eyes are ringed with white. The chickaree is found throughout coniferous and deciduous forests, and a related species is found along the west coast of the United States. The squirrels are active throughout the year and actually tunnel through the snow to find food.

**Chicken.** The domestic chicken is derived mainly from the jungle fowl of southern Asia. There are numerous varieties including egg-laying, meatproducing and dual-purpose breeds.

**Chickweed.** Several species of small, common weed that bear tiny white flowers. The common chickweed is a straggling plant with a single line of hairs running down its stem. It is found in abundance on cultivated land.

**Chicory.** A flowering plant related to the dandelion. It has a stiff, manybranched stem with bright blue flowers arranged in a spike. It is often found in areas of wasteland, and its leaves can be used for making salad.

Chicory

**Chiffchaff.** A small warbler that is easily distinguished from its close relatives the willow warbler and the wood warbler by its call, 'chiff-chaff, chiff-chaff', from which it gets its name. It has a greyish-green plumage and lives in woods and bushy places, building its nest in brambles or other undergrowth. The bird is a summer visitor from Africa and southern Europe.

**Chile Pine.** Also known as the monkey puzzle tree, the Chile pine is an evergreen native to the western slopes of the South American Andes where it grows up to 30 metres. It is widely planted elsewhere as an ornamental tree because of its strange branching form.

**Chimaera.** Like their relatives, the sharks and rays, the chimaeras are cartilaginous fishes. They are unusual among cartilaginous fishes in that the gill slits are covered by an operculum (gill cover). They are also known as rabbitfishes. The common rabbitfish lives close to the sea bed, feeding on crustaceans, molluscs and echinoderms, plus small fishes. The female is larger than the male, up to about 120 cm long.

**Chimpanzee.** One of the great apes and the nearest in intelligence to man, the chimpanzee lives in the rain forests of Africa and spends much of its time in the trees. Chimpanzees live in small bands, but there is little social structure and members come and go as they please. They eat mainly fruit and other vegetable food.

**Chinchilla.** Best known for its remarkably soft grey fur, the chinchilla is a South American rodent. It is about 25 cm long and looks rather like a squirrel, although its long back legs are more like those of a rabbit. Chinchillas live in burrows in parts of Chile. They feed on coarse grasses and herbs.

**Chinese Water Deer.** A native of China, now established in wild herds in England and France. It is a small deer, about 50 cm high at the shoulder, and has long upper canine teeth that project below the upper lip. Neither males nor females have antlers. The deer are not often seen because they feed mostly at night.

**Chinquapin.** The dwarf chestnut (Castanea pumila), which produces a small edible nut contained in a bur.

**Chionad.** A plant inhabiting snow-covered areas.

**Chipmunk.** A group of ground squirrels found in North America and Asia, where they live in open country and feed on berries, grasses, and a wide variety of small animals. They are great hoarders of food for the winter, although they do not actually hibernate. Chipmunks range from 10-25 cm in length, excluding the bushy tail.

**Chironomid.** Midge, a.

**Chiropter.** Any mammal of the order Chiroptera which includes the bats.

**Chiroptera.** An order of flying mammals comprising the bats. Their membranous wings are supported by very elongated forelimbs and digits and stretch along the sides of the body to the hindlimbs and tail. Whenever bats rest they allow their body temperature to fall, hibernating in winter when food is scarce. Most bats are nocturnal; their ears are enlarged and specialized for echolocation, which they use to hunt prey and avoid obstacles. Bats feed variously on insects, fruit, nectar, or blood.

**Chi-squared.** Describing the ratio of an observed sum of squares to the appropriate or corresponding variance as fixed by a hypothesis.

**Chi-squared Test** ($\chi^2$ test). A test usually used to find how well observed frequencies of results correspond with expected frequencies. It is used when the observations fall into discrete classes, such as red, pink, or white flowered plants. $\chi^2$ is found by calculating

$$(\text{observed}-\text{expected})^2/$$

expected for each class and adding these together. The sum is then checked in a table of $\chi^2$ values for different degrees of freedom at various probability levels.

**Chitin.** A polymer containing chains of acetylglucosamine units, having the empirical formula $C_{16}H_{26}O_{10}N_2$. Microfibrils of chitin make up the hyphal wall of most fungi.

**Chiton.** A group of primitive marine molluscs, also called coat-of-mail shells from the eight hinged plates that make up their outer coat. Chitons graze on algae on rocky shores, attaching themselves to the rocks like limpets. They can also crawi slowly using their long, single 'foot', and can roll up into a ball for protection.

**Chives.** A green vegetable of the onion family. It grows from a bulb and has long tubular leaves and globular heads of pale purple flowers. It is used as a flavouring.

**Chlamydobacteriales** (filamentous iron bacteria). An order of colourless rod-shaped gram-negative bacteria that aggregate into filaments, which sometimes become branched.

The filaments are surrounded by a sheath of organic material impregnated with ferric and manganese oxides. Such bacteria derive energy from oxidizing organic substrates. However they also oxidize ferrous compounds to ferric oxides and probably derive additional energy from these reactions.

**Chlamydospore.** A thick-walled resting spore formed by certain fungi. The term refers both to thickened segments of hyphae (gemmae), as found in the Saprolegniaceae and Mucoraceae, and to the dikaryotic brand spores of the Ustilaginales that develop in sori on infected plants.

**Chlamydozoa.** An obsolete phylum which is used to include the viruses.

**Chloranthy.** Describing an abnormal flower in which all the parts have developed as leafy structures.

**Chlorazol Black.** A temporary acid stain that colours walls grey or black and is especially suitable for demonstrating pitting. It is also used for chromosome counts, in which case the tissue is first fixed in acetic acid. After staining, a drop of acetocarmine is added and the chromosomes stain a deep reddish-black colour. The stain gives a clear-cut picture and is therefore useful for photomicrography.

**Chloranthus.** Possessing green and usually inconspicuous flowers.

**Chlorenchyma.** Photosynthetic tissue containing numerous chloroplasts and often having relatively large intercellular spaces. The mesophyll of leaves is composed of chlorenchyma.

**Chlorin.** A derivative obtained from chlorophyll when it loses the magnesium, phytol and methyl alcohol, and the 5-carbon ring is open.

**Chlorinated Hydrocarbon.** Any hydrocarbon with any or all of the hydrogen atoms replaced by chlorine atoms. Such compounds are often used as insecticides, examples being aldrin, dieldrin, and DDT.

**Chlorococcales.** An order of the Chlorophyceae containing nonflagellate unicellular (*e.g.* Chlorella), colonial (*e.g.* Scenedesmus), coenobial (*e.g.* Pediastrum), and coenocytic coenobial (*e.g.* Hydrodictyon) algae. Motility is restricted to the gametes and zoospores. Sexual reproduction is isogamous or anisogamous but never, so far as is known, oogamous. A sexual reproduction is by motile zoospores or nonmotile aplanospores (autospores).

**Chlorophyceae.** A class of the Chlorophyta. In some classification it contains all the orders of the Chlorophyta except the Charales (Charophyta). In other classifications the orders are divided between the Chlorophyceae, Oedogoniophyceae, Bryopsidophyceae, and Zygnemaphyceae. In the latter system the Chlorophyceae contains the orders Volvocales, Tetrasporales, Chlorococcales, Ulotrichales, Ulvales, Prasiolales, Microsporales, and Chaetophorales.

**Chlorophylls.** The main class of photosynthetic pigments. They absorb red and blue-violet light and thus reflect green light, so giving plants their characteristic green colour. Chlorophylls are involved in the light reactions of photosynthesis and are located in the chloroplast. The molecule consists of a planar porphyrin 'head' and a long phytol 'tail' (diagram). A molecule of magnesium is present in the centre of the porphyrin ring. In vivo the chlorophyll molecule is bound to membrane proteins via the phytol chain. Its function in photosynthesis is to absorb light energy and initiate electron transport. There are four groups of chlorophylls : *a*, *b*, *c*, and *d*. Chlorophyll *a* is found in all autotrophic plants, chlorophyll *b* in the Chlorophyta, Charophyta, and land plants, and chlorophylls *c* and *d* only in certain algae.

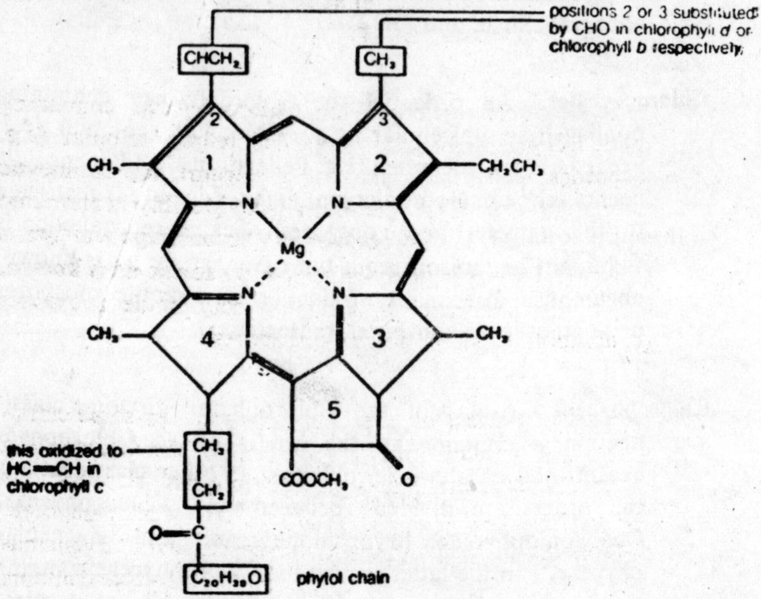


The structure of chlorophyll a

**Chlorophyta** (green algae). A large division of algae, the members of which possess chlorophylls *a* and *b*, store food reserves as starch, and have cellulose cell walls. In these respects they resemble higher plants more closely than do any of the other algal divisions. The Chlorophyta are widely distributed and diverse in form. Unicellular forms may occur singly (sometimes with flagella for motility) or in colonies, while multicellular forms may be filamentous (*e.g.* Spirogyra) or platelike (*e.g.* Ulva).

**Chloroplast.** Any of the chlorophyll-containing organelles (plastid) that are found in large numbers in those plant cells undergoing photosynthesis. Chloroplasts are typically lens-shaped and made up of stacks of membranes (granum) enclosed in a gellike matrix. The light reactions of photosynthesis occur on the membranes while the dark reactions take place in the matrix.

**Chlorosis.** The abnormal condition in plant stems and leaves in which synthesis of the green pigment chlorophyll is inhibited, resulting in a pale yellow coloration. This may be caused by lack of light, mineral deficiency, infection (particularly by viruses), or genetic factors.

**Chlor-zinc-iodide.** Schultze's solution.

**Choana** pl. **Choanae**. One of the two posterior or internal nares, the openings of the masal cavity into the mouth cavity or pharynx.

**Choanosome.** The inner portion of a leuconoid sponge consisting of groups of flagellated chambers.

**Cholesterol.** A sterol widely distributed in animal tissues being present in the brain and spinal cord, in animal fats and oils, egg yolk, and bile. It is a normal constituent of the blood and the main constituent of gallstones. It is the precursor of corticosteroids, androgens, and estrogens.

**Choline.** A nitrogenous substance, a member of the vitamin B complex, essential for the synthesis of amino acids.

**Choanae** (internal nares). Nares.

**Cholecalciferol.** Vitamin D.

**Cholecystokinin** (pancreozymin). A hormone, produced by the duodenal region of the small intestine, that induces the gall bladder to contract and eject bile into the intestine and stimulates the pancreas to secrete its digestive enzymes. Cholecystokinin output is stimulated by contact with the contents of the stomach.

**Cholesterol.** A sterol occurring widely in animal tissues and also in some higher plants and algae. It can exist as a free sterol or esterified with a long-chain fatty acid. Cholesterol is absorbed through the intestine or manufactured in the liver. It serves principally as a constituent of blood plasma lipoproteins and of the lipid-protein complexes that form cell membranes. It is also important as a precursor of various steroids, especially the bile acids, sex hormones, and adrenocorticoid hormones. The derivative 7-dehydrocholesterol is converted to vitamin $D_3$ by the action of sunlight on skin. Increased levels of dietary and blood cholesterol have been associated with atherosclerosis, a condition in which lipids accumulate on the inner walls of arteries and eventually obstruct blood flow.

**Choline.** An amino alcohol, $CH_2OHCH_2N(CH_3)_3OH$. It occurs widely in living organisms as a constituent of certain types of phospholipids—the lecithins and sphingomyelins. It is sometimes classified as a member of the vitamin B complex.

**Cholinergic Fibers.** Nerve fibers which release acetylcholine at their terminations.

**Chondrichthyes.** Elasmobranchii.

**Chondrification.** Conversion to cartilage.

**Chondriocont.** A rod-shaped or filamentous chondriosome.

**Chondriosome.** A mitochondrion or chondriocont.

**Chondroclast.** A cartilage-destroying cell.

**Chondrocranium.** In vertebrates, the cartilaginous portion of the embryonic skull forming a part of the base of the skull and the capsules enclosing the sense organs. In cyclostomes and elasmobranchs, it persists as the permanent skull; in higher vertebrates, it is partially or completely replaced by bone.

**Chordata.** A phylum of animals characterized by a hollow dorsal nerve cord and, at some stage in their development, a flexible skeletal rod (the notochord) and gill slits opening from the pharynx. There are four subphyla, the largest of which is the Vertebrata, in which the notochord is one present in the embryo or larva and become replaced by the backbone before birth of metamorphosis. The other three subphyla are often grouped together as the Protochordata. They are relatively primitive chordates including the lancelet (Amphioxus) and the sea squirts.

**Chordate**. Of, pertaining to, or possessing a notochord.

**Chordate.** Any member of the phylum Chordata which includes the tunicates, lancelets, and vertebrates, animals characterized by possession, at some stage during life, of a notochord.

**Chordate.** Any member of the large phylum of animals which includes all the backboned creatures and a few smaller groups such as the tunicates or sea squirts. In their early stages these animals all have a flexible skeletal rod called the notochord, and it is this that gives the group its name. But the notochord is rapidly replaced by the backbone in most species—even before birth. There is also a hollow nerve cord running along the back.

**Chordotonal Organ.** A sense organ in insects which is stimulated by body movements.

**Chorion**

1. A membrane enclosing the embryo yolk sac and allantois of reptiles, birds, and mammals.
2. The protective shell of an insect egg, produced by the ovary. It is pierced by a small pore (micropyle) that allows the entry of spermatozoa for fertilization.

**Choroid.** A pigmented layer, rich in blood vessels, that lies between the retina and the sclerotic of the vertebrate eye. At the front of the eye the choroid is modified to form the ciliary body and the iris.

**Choroid Plexus.** A membrane rich in blood vessels that lines the ventricles of the brain. It is an extension of the pia mater and secretes cerebrospinal fluid into the ventricles;

it also controls exchange of materials between the blood and cerebrospinal fluid.

**Chorology.** The science dealing with the distribution of organisms over the surface of the earth.

**Chough.** The two species of chough are members of the crow family. They are a little larger than jackdaws and have glossy black coats. The common chough, found mainly by the sea, ranges in a nrrrow belt from Ireland to China.

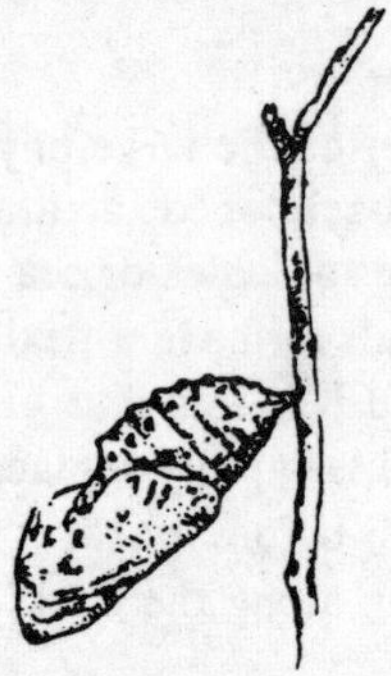

It has a long curved red beak. The alpine chough has a shorter yellowish beak and lives in the mountainous regions of Europe and Asia. Both species are scavenging birds.

**Christmas Rose.** A European evergreen herb of the buttercup family which produces its white flowers in winter. The similar lenten rose blooms in February-March. The plants are about 30 cm tall.

**Chromaffin Reaction.** Turning brown in the presence of chrome salts, a characteristic of cells containing epinephrine (adrenalin) or its precursor.

**Chromaffin System.** Collectively, structures in higher vertebrates which contain chromaffin cells. Includes the carotid bodies, paraganglia proper, aortic bodies, and the medulla of the adrenal gland.

**Chromatic**. Pertaining to, produced by, or consisting of a color or colors.

**Chromatid.** A threadlike strand formed from a chromosome during the early stages of cell division. Each chromosome divides along its length into two chromatids, which are at first held together at the centromere. They separate completely at a later stage. The DNA of the chromosome reproduces itself exactly so that each chromatid has the complete amount of DNA and becomes a daughter chrom some with exactly the same genes as the original chromosome from which it was formed.

**Chromatin.** The complex of proteins, DNA, and small amounts of RNA of which chromosomes are composed. Histones are the principal nuclear proteins, although nonhistone acidic proteins are also present.

**Chromatin Loop.** A region of relatively unwound DNA, about 200 nm long, extending outwards in a loop from the chromosome. It is thought that in this uncoiled condition transcription can occur. If so, chromatin loops correspond to genes actively involved in protein synthesis.

**Chromatogram**. A record obtained by chromatography. The term is applied to the developed records of paper chromatography and thin-layer chromatography and also to the graphical record produced in gas chromatography.

**Chromatography**. A technique used to separate and identify the components of mixtures of similar compounds, such as different amino acids or chlorophyll pigments, by selective adsorption. The mixture, dissolved in a liquid or gas mobile phase is passed through another solid or liquid medium the stationary phase This may be for example, a column of charged resin (ion-exchange chromatography) or a piece of filter paper (paper chromatography). Some of the compounds in the mixture will pass more slowly through the stationary phase than others, as they are more strongly adsorbed by the solid, or more soluble in the liquid. Consequently, the mixture will separate out. The column, strip of paper, or other material containing the separated components is termed a chromatogram. In some techniques, the compounds are collected as they emerge from the column, or their progress along the column is measured against a known standard. Colourless components of the mixture can be identified by electronic detection, ninhydrin developer, or radioactive labelling.

**Chromatophore**

1. A pigment-containing cell found in the skin of many lower vertebrates (*e.g.*, chameleon) and in the integument of crustaceans. Concentration or dispersion of the pigment granules in the cytoplasm of the cell causes the colour of the animal to alter to match its surroundings. A common type of chromatophore is the melanophore, which contains the pigment melanin.

2. Chromoplast.

**Chromidial Substance.** Basophilic material containing RNA present in the cytoplasm of neurons and gland cells. Also called chromophil substance.

**Chromocenter.** A karyosome; also called false, nucleinic, or chromatin nucleus.

**Chromogen** A colorless substance which, under suitable conditions, can become colored; a precursor of a pigment.

**Chromogenesis.** The production of pigment, as by a microorganism.

**Chromomere.** A particulate portion of a chromosome that becomes apparent as contraction and condensation of chromatin occurs in meiosis. Chromomeres vary in size and shape, homologous chromosomes having identical patterns along their lengths. An average chromomere has been found to contain sufficient DNA to code for approximately 30-35 polypeptides of average length. Genetic evidence, however, suggests that chromomeres contain only a single functional structural gene.

**Chromoneme**

1. The genetic material of a bacterium.
2. The thread-like structures which are running parallelly along the length of a chromosome and seen in certain stages of nuclear division. (pl. chromonemata).

**Chromopexy**. The ingestion and storage of vital dyes, as by macrophages.

**Chromophil** or **Chromaphil**. A cell whose cytoplasm stains readily, as certain cells in the anterior lobe of the hypophysis.

**Chromophobe**. A cell whose cytoplasm does not stain readily, as certain cells in the anterior lobe of the hypophysis. Compare chromophil.

**Chromoplasm**. The outer, pigmented portion of a blue-green algal cell. Compare centroplasm.

**Chromoplast** (chromatophore). Any of various organelles in plant cells that contain pigments. Red, orange, and yellow chromoplasts contain carotenoid pigments, while green chromoplasts (called chloroplasts) contain the pigment chlorophyll and provide the green coloration of most plants. Compare leucoplast.

**Chromosome** A threadlike structure several to many of which are found in the nucleus of plant and animal cells. Chromosomes are composed of chromatin and carry the genes, which determine the individual characteristics of an organism. When the nucleus is not dividing, individual chromosomes cannot be identified with a light microscope. During the first stage of nuclear division, however, the chromosomes contract and, when stained, can be clearly seen under a microscope. Each consists of two chromatids held together at the centromere meiosis; (also mitosis). The number of chromosomes in each cell is constant for and characteristic of the species concerned. In the normal body cells of diploid organisms the chromosomes occur in pairs (homologous chromosomes); in the gamete-forming germ cells, however, the diploid number is halved and each cell contains only one member of each chromosome pair. Thus in man each body cell contains 46 chromosomes (22 matched pairs and one pair of sex chromosomes) and each germ cell 23. Abnormalities in the number or structure of chromosomes may give rise to abnormalities in the individual; Down's syndrome is the result of one such abnormality.

**Chromosome Aberration.** Chromosome mutation.

**Chromosome Arm.** One of the two parts of a chromosome to which the spindle fibre has been attached along the side.

**Chromosome Complement.** The set of chromasomes characteristic of a cell of a species.

**Chromosome Cycle.** The complete changes in the chromosome taking place during the life-cycle.

**Chromosome Inversion.** Inversion.

**Chromosome Map** (linkage map). A plan showing the relative positions of genes along the length of the chromosomes of an organism. It is constructed by making crosses and observing whether certain characteristics tend to be inherited together. The closer together two allele pairs are situated on homologous chromosomes, the less often will they be separated and rearranged as the reproductive cells are formed (chiasma; crossing over). The proportion of offspring that show recombination of the alleles concerned thus reflects their spacing and is used as a unit of length in mapping chromosomes.

**Chromosome Mapping.** The assigning of genes to chromosomes and the calculation of their relative sequence and distance from each other on particular chromosomes. In initially assigning a gene to a particular chromosome, the inheritance of particular chromosome mutations may be studied, coupled with microscopic techniques. Linkage studies will indicate whether genes are on the same or different chromosomes and, if the former, their relative order and distance. Absolute distances cannot be determined by linkage studies. Chromosome mapping indicates that genes are arranged in linear order along chromosomes. In contrast to this, circular genetic maps are often obtained in prokaryotic (nonchromosomal) organisms and viruses.

**Chromosome Mutation** (chromosome aberration). An alteration in the number, order, or arrangement of genes caused by structural changes to a chromosome. Sometimes chromosome mutation may involve a large number of genes and the aberration may be visible by microscopy. There are four classes of chromosome mutations, deletions, duplications, inversions, and translocations.

**Chromosome Number.** The number of chromosomes possessed by a species, which may be given as either the haploid ($n$) or diploid ($2n$) number. Chromosome number is important taxonomically since it is usually constant within a species. There are however many exceptions especially in species exhibiting reproductive abnormalities, *e.g.*, apomixis. Among flowering plants the average haploid chromosome number is about 16 though this varies from $n=2$ in the composite Haplopappus gracilis to extremely high numbers in certain polyploid series. For example, in the allopolyploid Spartina townsendii (saltmarsh grass) $n=60$. It is thought that the original haploid chromosome number in angiosperms was in the region 7-9 and that numbers higher than $n=14$ are polyploid in origin.

**Chromosome Puff** (Balbiani ring). A swollen region of a polytene chromosome, corresponding to a site where messenger RNA synthesis (transcription) is actively occurring. It is probably the large size of polytene chromosomes that makes visualization of the process possible. Although polytene chromosomes are found only in dipterous insects, it is thought that the puffing phenomenon has wider genetic implications.

**Chronistics.** The study of the time taken for evolutionary events to occur. If phylogenetic trees are drawn with the vertical axis representing the time scale then a diagram is obtained showing the chronistic relationship between organisms. Organisms that, from fossil evidence, appear to have evolved rapidly are termed tachytelic while those that appear to have changed slowly are termed bradytelic. Horotelic is used of organisms showing moderate rates of evolution.

**Chroococcales.** An order of the Cyanophyta containing the unicellular and colonial blue-green algae. The colonial (or palmelloid) forms arise when daughter cells become bound together in a mucilaginous sheath after cell division. Heterocysts and hormogonia are lacking.

**Chrysalis or Chrysalid.** The pupa of a butterfly encased within a tough integument, often brightly colored.

**Chrysanthemum.** Any of about 100 species of perennial plants mostly native to China in which the stems are soft at first but become quite woody with age. Chrysanthemums have large composite flower-heads in which the florets are long and tubular and often ragged. Chrysanthemums are members of the daisy family.

**Chrysanthine.** Having yellow flowers.

**Chrysophyta** (golden-brown algae). A division made up predominantly of flagellate unicellular algae but also containing some colonial and filamentous forms. These algae usually have two golden-brown plastids in each cell and food is stored as leucosin or fat.

In some classifications the Chrysophyta also includes the yellow-green algae, the diatoms, and the Haptophyceae on the basis that these through groups share a number of features with the golden-browns. These include accumulating food reserves as the polysaccharide leucosin, having siliceous or calcareous cell walls more or less conspicuously divided into two parts, and having a flimmer flagellum.

**Chuckwalla.** The chuckwalla is a plump lizard, usually about 30 cm long. It is a mottled, brownish-black creature and it lives in the hot desert regions of North America. Unlike most lizards, it eats plant material. When disturbed, the chuckwalla scuttles into a rock crevice and wedges itself there by inflating its body with air. It is then very difficult to dislodge.

**Chub.** A freshwater fish belonging to the carp family, found mostly in rivers with clean, gravelly bottoms. It spends the spring and summer in shallow parts of rivers, but migrates to deeper waters, even to lakes, in the winter months.

**Chyle.** A milky fluid consisting of lymph that contains absorbed food materials (especially emulsified fats). Most chyle occurs in the lymphatic ducts (lacteals) in the villi of the small intestine during the absorption of fat.

**Chyme.** The semisolid and partly digested food that is discharged from the stomach into the duodenum.

**Chytridiales.** An order of the Chytridiomycetes containing unicellular or coenocytic fungi that are considered the most primitive members of the Eumycota. Chytrids number about 550 species in some 93 genera and are usually aquatic although some species, such as Synchytrium endobioticum (which causes potato wart disease), are found in damp soil. They produce motile cells, which may behave asexually as zoo-spores or sexually as gametes, fusing in pairs.

**Chytridiomycetes.** A class of the Mastigomycotina containing simple fungi that typically produce motile cells with a posterior whiplash flagellum. It contains 110 genera and some 685 species and comprises the four orders Chytridiales, Harpochytridiales, Blastocladiales, and Monoblepharidales.

**Cicada.** A heavy-bodied insect of the order Homoptera, the males producing a characteristic buzzing sound. Common species are the periodical cicada (17-year locust) and the dog-day cicada (harvest fly).

**Cicada Killer.** A large wasp (Sphecius speciosus) which provisions its nest with cicadas stung to insensibility.

**Cicatrix** pl. **Cicatrices**

1. A scar or scarlike mark.
2. *zool. a.* The fibrous connective tissue which replaces injured or destroyed tissue. *b.* A nonvascular area on the surface of an ovary which marks the point of rupture of a follicle, as in birds and reptiles.
3. *bot.* A mark or scar left after abscission of a leaf or bract.

**Cilia** sing **Cilium**

1. *anat.* The eyelashes.
2. *biol.* Minute, hairlike cytoplasmic processes of a cell which beat rhythmically. In lower forms, they serve as locomotor organelles; on ciliated surfaces they propel substances, as mucus.
3. *bot.* Minute hairs along a margin forming a fringe.

**Ciliary Body.** The circular band of tissue surrounding and supporting the lens of the vertebrate eye. It contains the ciliary muscles, which bring about changes in the shape of the lens (also accommodation). The ciliary body produces the aqueous humour.

**Ciliary Feeding.** A method of feeding used by Amphioxus and many aquatic invertebrates. The movement of cilia causes a current of water to be drawn towards and through the animal, and microorganisms in the water are filtered out by the cilia.

**Ciliate.** Describing a structure, such as a leaf margin, fringed with fine hairs.

**Ciliolate.** Minutely ciliated.

**Cilium.** Tiny hair-like structure, usually one of many, on the surface of certain protozoans such as paramecium. The wave-like motion of the cilia creates currents of fluid across the organism, helping it to move and feed. Cilia are also present internally in most other animals, lining passages to help the flow of liquids.

**Cinchona.** The dried bark of the stem or root of several species of Cinchona, a South American tree, the source of quinine and other alkaloids. Now extensively cultivated in the East Indies.

**Cincinnus.** A monochasium in which successive branches are borne on opposite sides of the stem. The inflorescence is often bent to one side. An example is that of Strelitzia reginae (the bird of paradise flower).

**Cingulate**

1. Resembling a girdle.
2. Possessing a girdle or girdlelike band.

**Cinnabar Moth.** A brightly patterned moth, with striking black and red markings which warm birds that it is unpleasant to eat. It flies, not very strongly, over grassy places and is often found near sea coasts. Its caterpillar also displays warming coloration—it is striped yellow and black. The caterpillars are commonly found on ragwort in July and August.

**Cinquefoil.** Several species of mostly creeping plant, of the rose family, with yellow or white flowers. The creeping cinquefoil is a common weed with yellow flowers and long stems that creep along bare ground. Another yellow-flowered member of the group, the spring cinquefoil, is mat-forming and is commonly found in dry grasslands. Tormentil is also a cinquefoil.

**Circadian Rhythm** (diurnal rhythm). Any 24-hour periodicity in the behaviour or physiology of animals or plants. Examples are the sleep/activity cycle in many animals and the growth movements of plants. Circadian rhythms are generally controlled by biological clocks.

**Circinate Vernation.** A form of vernation in which the leaf primordia are rolled in on themselves from the apex to the base, so that the apex is in the middle of the coil (illustration at vernation). It is seen in most ferns (except the Ophioglossales) and in certain of the cycads and extinct seed ferms.

**Circulatory System** The heart, blood vesseles, blood, lymphatic vessels, and lymph, which together serve to transport materials throughout the body.

**Circumnutation** (nutation). The circular or elliptical movement of the stem tips of many plants. Due to a shift in the region of most active cell division in the stem, the growing tip swings in a characteristic manner, either clockwise or anticlockwise depending on the species. If during these movements (which seem to be dictated both by internal stimuli and by gravity) contact is made with a solid object, the plant begins to twine around it. The importance of gravity to the response can be demonstrated by inverting a plant that has already entwined a support. The tip and the last two or three coils straighten out and become erect before once again coiling upwards around the support in the characteristic direction.

**Cirriped.** Any crustacean of the subclass Cirripedia which includes the barnacles.

**Cirrose.** Bearing tendrils or cirri; resembling a cirrus.

**Cirri.** Plural of Cirrus.

**Cirrus** pl. **Cirri**

1. *bot.* A tendril.
2. *zool.* A slender filamentous structure, as *a.* the fused cilia of certain protozoans, or hairs on the antennae or legs of certain insects; *b.* a blunt process or processes on the parapodia of polychaete worms, on the oral hood of lancelets, or about the mouth of fishes; *c.* rootlike processes of a feather start or whorled processes on the stalk of a crinoid; *d.* the protrusible copulatory organ of certain flat-worms and mollusks.

**Cis Arrangement** (coupling). The situation in which an individual is heterozygous for two linked genes (either two units of function or two mutations in the same functional unit), and one chromosome carries both the recessive (or mutant) allelles. The homologous chromosome thus carries both the dominant (or normal) alleles and will mask the effects of the recessives in the phenotype. Compare trans arrangement.

**Cisco.** A whitefish of the genus Coregonus, especially C. artedi, a food fish of northern United States and Canada; also called lake herring.

**Cisterna.** A reservoir or cavity, as the cisterna chyli.

**Cisternae.** Interconnecting intracellular compartments consisting of tubular or flattened channels and vesicles that extend throughout the cytoplasm. The endoplasmic reticulum and golgi apparatus are made up of membranes formed into cisternae.

**Cis-trans Test.** A method for deciding whether two mutations having similar effects occur in the same or different genes (defined as units of function). If the mutations occur in the same gene, only heterozygotes with the cis arrangement will show the normal phenotype because the gene in the homologous chromosome is dominant wild type and codes for normal protein. In the trans arrangement both copies of the gene contain a mutation and thus there is no wild-type copy of the gene and hence no normal protein. If the mutations occur in different genes, specifying different polypeptides, all heterozygotes will be normal in appearance because the homologous chromosomes carry wild-type copies of the genes.

**Cistron.** A gene defined as a unit of function, *i.e.* a length of DNA that codes for a single polypeptide. The end of one cistron and the beginning of the next can be determined by the cis-trans test.

**Citreous.** Lemon-yellow in color.

**Citric Acid.** A white crystalline hydroxy carboxylic acid, $HOOCCH_2C(OH)(COOH)CH_2COOH$. It is present in citrus fruits and is an intermediate in the Krebs cycle in plant and animal cells.

**Citric Acid Cycle.** Kerb's cycle; tricarboxylic acid cycle. A complex series of reactions in which pyruvic acid, a product of carbohydrate metabolism, is broken down, under aerobic conditions, to $CO_2$ and $H_2O$ with the release of energy which is utilized principally in the synthesis of adenosine triphosphate (ATP). In this cycle, an organism can also utilize fatty acids and amino acids, products of fat and protein metabolism; consequently it is considered to be the common pathway for the metabolism of the three primary classes of foods.

**Citron.** A thorny Indian tree of the orange family. It has lance-shaped leaves and purple and white flowers. The fruit is up to 23 cm long, with white flesh. Its thick rind is often candied.

**Citrus.** Any of a group of evergreen trees, producing juicy fruit. They include Citron, Grapefruit, Lemon, Lime, Mandarin and Orange.

**Citrus Fruit.** A fruit produced by one of several species of trees or shrubs of the genus Citrus, family Rutaceae. The principal fruits are the orange, lemon, lime, grapefruit, citron, and kumquat; minor fruits are bergamot, calamondin, and shaddock (pomelo).

**Civet.** A substance with a musky odor found in a pouch near the sex organs of civet cats. It is used in the manufacture of perfumes.

**Civet Cat.** One of a number of catlike carnivores of the genera Civettictis and Viverra of Africa and Southeast Asia.

**Clade.** A group of organisms that share a common ancestor.

**Cladistic.** Describing genetic relationships due to recentness of common ancestry. In describing cladistic relationships, as opposed to patristic relationships, more emphasis is placed on the actual pathways of genetic divergence.

**Chyme**. Food in the stomach is reduced to thick creamy paste called chyme It is formed due to addition of water, churning of food by stomach walls and by the action of gastric juices and spurted into duodenum in form of small jets.

**Cladistics.** A controversial method of classification in which animals and plants are placed into taxonomic groups

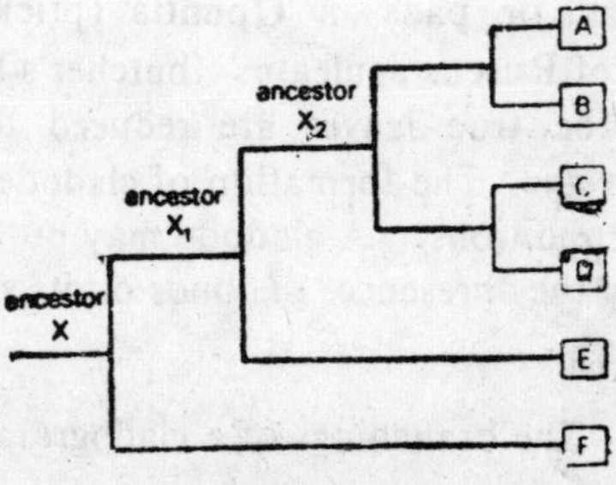


**A cladogram showing the relationships of six species (A-F)**

called clades when they share characteristics (known as homologies) that are thought to indicate common ancestry. It is based on the assumption that two new species are formed suddenly, by splitting from a common ancestor, and not by gradual evolutionary charge. A diagram indicating these relationships (called a cladogram) therefore consists of a system of dichotomous branches : each point of branching represents divergence from a common ancestor, as shown in the diagram. Thus the species A to F form a clade as they share the common ancestor X, and species A to D form a clade of a different taxonomic rank, sharing the ancestor $X_2$. Species C to F do not form a clade, since the latter must include all the descendants of a common ancestor.

Cladistics has been used as evidence by the opponents of neo-Darwinism in the debate on the nature of evolution. Cladists argue that the major branching patterns of cladograms correspond to large-scale evolutionary events that cannot be explained by orthodox new-Darwinism, which postulates a series of small changes occurring over a long period of time.

**Cladoceran.** Any member of the Cladocera, an order of branchiopod crustaceans which includes the water fleas, as Daphnia.

**Cladode** (phylloclade). A specialized stem structure resembling and performing the functions of a leaf Examples are the stem joints or pads in Opuntia (prickly pears) and the 'leaves' of Ruscus aculeatus (butcher's broom). In these genera the true leaves are reduced to spines or scales respectively. The formation of cladodes is an adaptation to arid conditions. A cladode may be distinguished from a leaf by the presence of buds on its surface. Compare phyllode.

**Cladogenesis.** The branchings of a cladogram.

**Cladogram.** A type of branching diagram (dendrogram) representing the relationships between organisms as determined by cladistic methods. A cladogram may be regarded as showing the phylogenetic relationships of organisms, in which case it is effectively an evolutionary tree, or it may be seen as simply representing a pattern based on shared characteristics. In the first case, the points of branching are thought of as actual or hypothetical ancestral species, while in the second case (the position held by 'transformed' cladists), the points simply represent shared characteristies.

**Cladophorales.** An order of the Bryopsidophyceae containing both freshwater and marine algae. The thallus of such algae is divided into a number of multinucleate cells.

**Coachwhip.** A long, slender snake (Masticophic flagellum) of the family Colubridae. It is common in southern United States and Mexico.

**Cladophyll.** A stem which resembles a leaf in form and color; a leaflike branch.

**Cladoxylales.** Filicinae.

**Clam.** The name given to many bivalve molluscs. The largest is the giant clam of coral reefs. It may measure one metre across and weigh 250 kg. In North America the name is most commonly used for edible shellfish such as the round or hard-shelled clam, the soft-shelled clam and the long clam or sandgaper.

**Clamber**

1. *zool.* To crawl or climb over a surface using hands and feet for holding.

2. *bot.* To grow over a surface using tendrils for attachment.

**Clam Shrimp** A crustacean of the suborder Conchostraca with a bivalve carapace with concentric markings, as Cyzicus.

**Clam Worm.** A marine polychaete (Neanthes (Nereis) virens).

**Clamp Connection**. A characteristic form of growth seen in dividing dikaryotic hyphae of basidiomycete fungi (illustration). Before cell division occurs the two nuclei divide simultaneously and at the same time a backward-pointing side branch develops. One of the daughter nuclei moves into this while another daughter nucleus of different genetic constitution moves down the main filament away from the hyphal tip Two cross walls are then formed, one across the main filament, so separating off the other two nuclei in the hyphal tip, and the other across the side branch. The wall between the branch and the subapical cell then dissolves so the nucleus in the side branch can pass through to join the remaining daughter nucleus This process has apparently developed to avoid the random movement of daughter nuclei, which could lead to the production of homokaryotic cells.

**Clary**. Several species of flowering plant, related to the dead-nettle, with fragrant leaves and blue flowers arranged in whorls around a tall spike. The wild clary has purplish stems and white spots on its flowers. It grows on dry grassy areas, particularly on chalk.

**Clasper.** A structure which enables the male to hold to the female during copulation, as in insects and elosmobranch fishes.

**Class.** A category used in the classification of organisms that consists of similar or closely related orders. Similar classes are grouped into a phylum in the case of animals and a division in the case of plants. Examples include, among animals, Mammalia (mammals), Aves (birds), and Agnatha (jawless fish).

**Classical Genetics** (Mendelian genetics). The branch of genetics concerned with the study of inheritance through observation of the progeny obtained in breeding experiments.

**Classification.** The division of all living things into various groups according to how closely the organisms within each group are related to each other. The first major division is into the two kingdoms : animals and plants. The animal kingdom is further divided into phyla (singular : phylum). There are about 25 invertebrate phyla (containing animals without backbones), but all the vertebrates (animals with backbones) belong to a single phylum, the Chordata. This phylum also includes the tunicates and lancelets (animals with a spinal chord but no backbone). The vertebrates form the sub-phylum Vertebrata. Phyla are divided into classes, *e.g.*, mammals all belong to the class Mammalia. Classes are divided into orders, *e.g.*, the flesh-eating mammals belong to the order Carnivora; orders are divided into families, *e.g.*, all cats belong to the family Felidae; and families are divided into genera (singular : genus). Animals within a genus are usually similar in appearance. The smallest division is the species; each different kind of animal is a separate species.

Plants are not divided into phyla as are animals but into divisions and sub-divisions. After this, the classification of the two kingdoms follows the same pattern of class, order, family, genus, species.

Many species of plant and animal do not have common names. For example, there are over a million species of insect and it would be difficult to give each one a popular name, particularly when some are so similar. Instead, each organism is given a Latin name that can be used throughout the world to identify it. This name consists of the name of the organism's genus followed by its specific name. For instance, the European wild cat is Felis (genus) silvestris (species). The closely related domestic cat, which belongs to the same genus, is Felis catus. The full classification of the wild cat is :

| | | |
|---|---|---|
| Kingdom | : | Animal |
| Phylum | : | Chordata |
| Class | : | Mammalia |
| Order | : | Carnivora |

| | | |
|---|---|---|
| **Family** | : | **Felidae** |
| **Genus** | ; | **Felis** |
| **Species** | : | **silvestris** |

**Clavate.** Club-shaped.

**Clavicipitales.** An order of the Pyrenomycetes whose members, which number about 175 species in 7 genera, produce small perithecia contained in the rounded heads of stromata. Each ascus contains eight threadlike asci. The order includes the ergot fungus, Claviceps purpurea.

**Clavicle.** A bone that forms part of the pectoral (shoulder) girdle, linking the scapula (shoulder blade) to the sternum (breastbone). In man it forms the collar bone and serves as a brace for the shoulders.

**Claviculate.** Possessing tendrils or hooks.

**Clawed Frog.** This animal belongs to the group of tongueless frogs which use their front teeth to catch small fish and other aquatic creatures. The front legs are short and weak but the back legs are strong and carry large webbed feet. The three inner toes of each back foot have sharp claws. The clawed frog rarely leaves the water.

**Clay.** Mineral particles with a diameter below 0.002 mm. They consist of aluminium and silica arranged to form a layered crystal structure.

**Cleaner.** An organism which removes ectoparasites, fungi, and diseased and injured tissue from the surface of another, as birds, fishes, and crustaceans which feed off the surface of other animals.

**Clearing.** A stage in the preparation of permanent slides for microscopical examination in which the stained dehydrated cells or tissue sections are immersed in a clearing agent to remove the alcohol that was used to dehydrate the preparation. The process is essential if the dehydrating agent and the mounting or embedding medium are not miscible. Examples of clearing agents include xylene (xylol), toluene, and 1,1,1,-trichloro-ethane and various essential oils, *e.g.*, clove oil and thyme oil. The term is sometimes used to mean the dissolving away of cell contents before staining so that the tissue distribution may be better observed. Sodium hypochlorite is commonly used for this.

**Cleavage** (in embryology). The series of cell divisions by which a single fertilized egg cell is transformed into a multicellular body, the blastula. Characteristically no growth occurs during cleavage, the shape of the embryo is unchanged except for the formation of a central cavity (the blastocoel), and the ratio of nuclear material (DNA) to cytoplasm increases.

**Cleavage Polyembryony**. The splitting of an embryo into several identical parts each of which is capable of developing into a mature embryo. It is seen in some gymnosperms and is particularly common in Pinus, where the zygote divides to form four nuclei each of which divides to give a chain of cells or suspensor. At the tip of each suspensor is a group of embryo initials. Usually, however, only one embryo develops to maturity.

**Cleavers**. Several species of plants closely related to the bedstraws, and otherwise known as goosegrass. The common cleavers bear tiny hooks that frequently cling to clothing or animal fur. Its flowers are a dull white and the plant is often found straggling over vegetation on waste ground and in hedgerows.

**¹Cleft**. A fissure; a narrow, cracklike slit or opening.

**²Cleft**

1. Divided or split, as a cleft palate.

2. *bot.* Divided into lobes or divisions by narrow sinuses which extend more than halfway to the midrib, with reference to leaves.

**Cleistocarp.** Cleistothecium.

**Cleistogamy.** The production of flower that do not open to expose the reproductive organs, so preventing cross pollination. Some species are obligately cleistogamous but others may be cleistogamous only under certain climatic conditions, as in Viola where flowers may not open at low temperatures. In some grasses only the lower florets are cleistogamous. The evolutionary origin of this mechanism is not known. Compare chasmogamy.

**Cleistothecium** (cleistocarp). The type of ascocarp characteristic of fungi in the Plectomycetes. It is a globose structure with no specialized opening to the exterior.

**Clag-fly.** Dull greyish insects related to the horse-fly. Clegs feed by sucking blood from animals. They fly silently and stab their victim before it is aware of their presence.

**Clematis.** A group of 250 woody climbing plants, many of which are grown for their beautiful flowers. The group also includes traveller's joy which smothers the hedgerows all over Europe. Some species are deciduous, others evergreen, and there are also some non-climbing species.

**Click Beetle.** A family of slender beetles named for their habit of righting themselves from an unsidedown position with a loud 'click'. The larvae of many click beetles are the garden pests known as wireworms.

**Climax.** The stable vegetation of an area under the prevailing environmental conditions.

**Climacteric.** The rise in respiration rate observed in certain fruit during ripening. It can be artificially induced by exposure to low concentrations of ethylene, a gas evolved by ripening fruit. Ripening can therefore be stimulated by placing unripe fruit alongside ripe fruit. Conditions that prevent the onest of the climacteric (low oxygen and high carbon dioxide concentrations) can be employed during storage to maintain the quality of stored fruit.

**Climatic Factors.** Those aspects of the weather, such as temperature, rainfall, light, humidity, and air movement, that influence the life of organisms.

**Climax.** The final stable community that results after a series of changes (succession) in the vegetation and animal life in a particular area. However, there are often factors that halt or slow down succession and prevent the establishment of a climax community. These factors include changes in climate, natural hazards, disease, animal interference, fire, and human activity. Often intensive grazing prevents the growth of shrubs and trees. The equilibrium achieved in this way is termed a biotic climax, disclimax, plagioclimax, or subclimax vegetation.

**Climax Vegetation.** A plant community, the composition of which is more or less stable, and whose character is mainly determined by the prevailing climatic conditions. In British lowland conditions, for example, open country is gradually invaded by trees of various kinds until oak becomes the dominant plant species, and in equatorial regions it is dense evergreen rain forest. In slightly drier areas it is grass-land, and in cold areas of northern Europe it is coniferous forest.

**Climax Community.** A relatively stable ecological community that is achieved at the end of a succession.

**Climber.** A plant which grows upward using other plants or objects for support.

**Cline.** A gradual change in a character over the range of a species. The term may also be applied to a change in the relative proportions of two or more distinct forms. For example, the leaves of lords and ladies (Arum maculatum) may or may not be spotted. The frequency of the spotted form increases towards the southern part of its range in Britain.

**Clingfish.** One of several fishes of the order Gobiesocida (Xenopterygii) which possess a ventral sucker by which they cling to stones, as Gobiesox.

**Clinostat.** A mechanical device that rotates whole plants (usually seedlngs), so removing the effect of any stimulus that normally acts in one particular direction. It is most often used to study the growth of plant organs when the influence of gravity has been removed.

**Clisere.** A succession of different climax communities in a particular area brought about by changes in the climate.

**Clitellum.** A swollen glandular region in the anterior portion of certain annelids.

**Clitoris.** An erectile rod of tissue in female mammals (and also some reptiles and birds) that is the equivalent of the male penis. It lies in front of the urethra and vagina.

**Cloaca.** The terminal portion of the digestive tract which serves as a common passageway for the products of the digestive, urinary, and reproductive systems. It is present in many invertebrates and most adult vertebrates except mammals.

**Clone.** A population of genetically identical cells or individuals. Such a population is obtained by mitotic division or by asexual reproduction. The term strain is sometime used synonymously.

**Clonus.** Alternate reflex contraction and relaxation of a voluntary muscle.

**Clot.** A semisolid mass of blood or lymph; a coagulum.

**Clotting.** Coagulation.

**Clotting Factors.** Substances that cause a blood clot to form at the site of an injury. Calcium ions and platelets trigger the release of the enzyme thromboplastin from injured tissues. This converts prothrombin in the blood to its enzymically active form thrombin. Thrombin catalyses the formation of insoluble fibrin from soluble fibrinogen; the fibrin forms a fibrous network in which blood cells become enmeshed, producing a clot.

**Clouded Leopard.** Found in the forests of South-East Asia and the islands of Indonesia, clouded leopards are agile tree-climbing cats. They have extremely long tails accounting for almost half of their 2-metre length. The coat is pale brown with greyish patches enclosing small dark spots.

**Clouded Yellow.** A butterfly which lives on grassy uplands and in open country. Its colour is deep yellow, with dark brown markings. It is a summer visitor to Britain from central and southern Europe.

**Clove.** An evergreen tropical tree which grows up to 9 metres in height and has purple flowers. The dried flower buds are used as a spice. Though native to Indonesia most of the spice production is done in Zanzibar and Malagasy.

**Cloven.** Split into two or more parts, as a cloven hoof.

**Clover.** A large group of small flowering herbs belonging to the pea family. Clovers produce dense rounded flowerheads and have trefoil leaves (leaves made up of three leaflats). They usually form patches in grassy areas. Two of the most common species are the red and white clover, often planted for cattle to eat. Clovers are popular with bees and make tasty honey.

**Clubbed.** Shaped like a club, as an insect antenna.

**Club Fungi.** The Basidiomycetes, which possess club-shaped basidia.

**Club Moss.** Any of a primitive group of plants related to ferns and horsetails. Club mosses have stems clothed with slender green leaves. They reproduce by spores which are generally borne in cones. Most are tropical but some are found on European heaths and moorlands.

**Club Root** (finger-and-toe disease). A disease of crucifers caused by the fungus in which the roots become swollen. Above ground the symptoms, which may not appear for a while, are wilting and later stunting and yellowing of infected plants. Infection occurs via the roots hairs and once the cambium is infected club roots develop rapidly. Spores can remain viable in the soil for several years making control difficult. Liming of the soil is a traditional control method.

**Clypeate.** Scutate; shaped like a shield.

**Clypeus.** A median sclerite on the head of an insect to which the labrum is attached.

**Cnidarian.** A coelenterate.

**Cnidoblast.** A cell in coelenterates which produces a nematocyst.

**Cnidophore.** A stalked structure bearing nematocysts present on the tentacles of certain medusae.

**Cnidosac Cells.** Cells in cerata of nudibranch mollusks in which ingested nematocysts from coelenterates are stored and later used for defense.

**CNS.** Central nervous system.

**CoA.** Coenzyme A.

**Coacervate**. Protobiont.

**Coachwhip**. A long, slender snake (Masticophis flagellum) of the family Colubridae, common in southern United States and Mexico.

**Coagulation**. The process in which colloidal particles come together to form larger masses. Coagulation can be brought about by adding ions to neutralize the charges stabilizing the colloid. Ions with a high charge are particularly effective (*e.g.*, alum, containing $Al^{3+}$, is used in styptics to coagulate blood), Heating is another way of coagulating certain colloids (*e.g.*, boiling an egg coagulates the albumin).

**Coagulum**. A semisolid mass; a clot or curd.

**Coal**. A brown or black carbonaceous deposit derived from the accumulation and alteration of ancient vegetation, which originated largely in swamps or other moist environments. Most deposits of coal were formed during the Carboniferous and Permian periods; more recent periods of coal formation occurred during the early Jurassic and Tertiary periods. As the vegetation decomposed it formed layers of peat, which were subsequently buried (for example, by marine sediments following a rise in sea level or subsidence of the land). Under the increased bear tiny hairs; it is filled with fluid (endolymph) and surrounded by fluid (perilymph). Sound-induced vibrations of the fenestra ovalis are transmitted through the perilymph and endolymph and stimulate the cells that line the cochlea. These in turn stimulate nerve cells that transmit information, via the auditory nerve, to the brain for interpretation of the sounds

**Coalfish**. Saithe.

**Coal Tit**. The smallest European tit, easily distinguished from the other black-headed tits (marsh and willow tits) by the white nape of its neck. It is a woodland bird and a frequent garden visitor in winter. It tends to feed on the ground, hunting for seeds and insects.

**Coarctate.** Crowded together; closely packed.

**Coati.** A carnivorous mammal related to the raccoons found in the forests of South and Central America. The body is about 60 cm long and the banded tail is the same length again. The general colour is reddish-brown. Coatis are industrious little creatures, foraging nearly all the time for small animals. They will also eat fruit and they often climb trees to reach it.

**Coat-of-mail Shell.** Chiton.

**Coating.** The application of a thin fil m of heavy metal, commodly gold, to the surface of a specimen during preparation for scanning electron microscopy. Coating is particularly useful in preparation of biological specimens because it results in the production of many more secondary electrons and the improved conductivity helps prevent a charge building up in the specimen and causing image deterioration. Coating units are of several types; some use fine filaments as the source of coating metal while others, known as sputter coaters, have a large solid block of metal that is ionized by a beam of ions.

**Cob.** A male swan.

**Cobalamine.** Generic name for vitamin $B_{12}$, a cobalt-containing vitamin.

**Cobra.** One of several venomous snakes, as Naja naja, the Indian cobra, and N. hannah, the King cobra of Southeast Asia. Also Hemachates haemachatus, the ringhals of South Africa.

**Cocci.** Plural of Coccus.

**Coccidiosis.** Any of a number of sporozoan infections caused by protozoans of the class Telosporidia, subclass Coccidia.

It includes a number of serious diseases of poultry and domestic animals.

**Coccus** pl. **Cocci**

1. A spherical bacterium.
2. A one-seeded locule of a lobed fruit.

**Coccyx.** A small bone terminating the vertebral column in man and apes, formed by a fusion of four rudimentary vertebrae.

**Cockchafer.** Two species of large beetle, also known as may-bugs, which fly noisily around gardens in summer. They frequently collide with lighted windows and outside lamps on summer evenings. Their large size (up to 3 cm long) and their orange-coloured feather antennae make them easily recognizable. The cockchafer larva is a white grub which can be a pest, damaging the roots of cereals and other crops.

**Coccolith.** Haptophyta.

**Coccolithophorids.** Haptophyta.

**Coccus.** Any spherical bacterium. Cocci may occur singly (monococcus), in pairs (diplococcus), in groups of four or more, in cubical packets (sarcina), in grapelike clusters (staphylococcus), or in chains (streptococcus). Diplococci, staphylococci, and streptococci include pathogenic species, causing pneumonia, suppurative infections, and scarlet fever, respectively. They are generally nonmotile and do not form spores.

**Coccyx.** The last bone in the vertebral column in apes and man (*i.e.*, tailless primates). It is formed by the fusion of 3-5 caudal vertebrae.

**Cochineal.** A crimson dye obtained from homopterous insects of the genera Epicoccus and Dactylopius, family Coccidae, which feed upon cacti of Mexico.

**Cochlea.** Part of the inner ear of mammals, birds, and some reptiles that transforms sound waves into nerve impulses. In mammals it is coiled, resembling a snail shell. The cochlea is lined with sensitive cells that canths are most abundant in deposits about 400 million years old and no fossils less than 70 million years old have been found.

**Cochleate.** Spiral or screw-shaped; coiled like a snail shell.

**Cock.** The male of barnyard fowls, also the male of other birds, especially gallinaceous birds; a rooster.

**Cockatoo.** The various species of cockatoo differ from the other parrots by having prominent crests on their heads. Most are white, but a few are black or grey. Cockatoos live in the Australasian region, often forming large bands. Some species are pests because they take a lot of grain and often attack fruit trees.

**Cockerel.** A young domestic cock, especially one less than a year old.

**Cockle.** Several species of bivalve mollusc with heart-shaped and often ribbed shells. Cockles have a long 'foot' with which to burrow into sand or mud on the sea bed. They can also make short leaps with their 'foot'.

**Cocklebur.** Any of a group of rough-leaved annual weeds, native to the Americas. The seeds are contained in spiny burs which cling to clothes and animals' coats.

**Cock-of-the-rock.** Two uncommon birds of South America recognizable by their fan-like crests. Females are dull brown, but the males are brilliantly coloured. One species is orange and one is bright red.

**Cockroach.** A group of beetle-like insects, related to the mantises. They are some of the most widespread and hard-to-destroy pests. Most species live in hot countries, but a few are found in NW Europe. Cockroaches like warmth, and often live in hotels, restaurant kitchens and in the central heating systems of buildings. The common cockroach is dark, with short wings; the German cockroach is paler. The smaller dusky cockroach lives outdoors, mostly in trees. All cockroaches have long antennae and long, spiky legs.

**Cocoa**. A powder prepared from the seeds of the cacao tree. The tree is native of tropical America but is grown in many tropical areas, especially in Africa. The cacao tree is up to 12 metres tall and has wide branches leathery leaves, and pink flowers growing directly on the trunk.

**Coconut**. The large, hard-shelled, oval fruit of the coconut palm (Cocos nucifera), its shell lined with an edible meas and containing a milklike fluid.

**Coconut Palm**. A tall palm tree, native to the Pacific islandt and South-East Asia but now growing throughout the tropical areas. It can reach 15 metres or more in height and has a crown of feathery leaves. The large seeds, inside a woody and fibrous fruit, hold a white 'meat' and a milky substance. Copra, the dried meat, yields a valuable oil.

**Cocoon**. A protective covering for eggs and/or larvae produced by many invertebrates. For example, the larvae of many insects spin a cocoon in which the pupae develop (that of the silkworm moth produces silk), and earthworms secrete a cocoon for the developing eggs.

**Cod**. One of the most important groups of fishes in Europe is the cod group. Nearly 20 species of the cod family are found in the waters of the North Sea, the Baltic Sea, and the Atlantic Ocean immediately west and north of the British Isles. Also belonging to the group are the lings, hake and rocklings. Most members of the group are large with a distinct lateral line and most have three fins along the back. Many have a barbel on the chin, which helps them to search for food. Most species are bottom-living and do noi form shoals. The cod itself is found in colonies across the Atlantic from Newfoundland to the Barents Sea. It grows up to 1.5 metres long.

**Codfish.** The cod (Gadus callarias and G. morrhua), an important North Atlantic food fish of the family Gadidae. Also G. macrocephalus of the North Pacific.

**Codiales.** Caulerpales.

**Codling Moth.** Carpocapsa pomonella, a small moth whose larva is a serious pest of apples and other fruits.

**Co-dominance.** The condition that arises when both alleles in a heterozygous organism are dominant and are fully expressed. For example, the human blood group AB is the result of two alleles, A and B, both being expressed. A is not dominant to B, nor *vice versa*. Compare incomplete dominance.

**Codon.** A sequence of three nucleotides (triplet) that codes for one amino acid in a polypeptide. A sequence of codons will thus determine the type and sequence of amino acids in a polypeptide. There are about 20 different kinds of amino acids in proteins. Most amino acids are coded for by more than one codon : the genetic code is thus said to be degenerate. The term codon is given both to the sequence of triplets on DNA and also to the sequence on messenger RNA. However these are not identical but complementary copies of each other.

**Coe-.** For words beginning with COE- not four.

**Coelacanth.** A primitive fish believed to have been extinct for more than 70 million years until a specimen was caught by a South African fishing boat in 1938. Several other specimens have been caught since. The coelacanth has fleshy lobes on its afins and heavy scales. It represents a very early stage in the evolution of the bony fishes.

**Coelenterata.** A phylum of aquatic invertebrates that includes Hydra, jellyfish, sea anemones, and corals. A coelenterate's body is diploblastic, with two cell layers of the body wall separated by mesoglea, and shows radial symmetry. The body cavity (coelenteron) is sac-shaped, with one opening acting as both mouth and anus. This opening is surrounded by tentacles bearing thread cells. Coelenterates exist both as free swimming medusae (*e.g.*, jellyfish) and as sedentary polyps. The latter may be colonial (*e.g* , corals) or solitary (*e.g* , sea anemones and Hydra). In many coelenterates the life cycle alternates between these two forms.

**Coelenterate.** Member of a group of aquatic invertebrates which includes jellyfishes, hydra, corals and sea anemones. Coelenterates have mostly rounded bodies and display Radial Symmetry. Their body wall consists of two layers of cells separated by a jelly-like material. They have a central cavity called a coelenteron where they digest their food, and an opening or mouth surrounded by tentacles. The tentacles bear stinging cells which the animals use to stun their prey.

Many coelenterates have to distinct forms during their life cycle—a tubular polyp (like a hydra) and a disc-shaped medusa (like a jellyfish). The two forms alternate with each other in a process known as alternation of genera tions. The polyps reproduce asexually by budding to produce medusae. These in turn produce sex-cells which fuse to form the polyps. In some coelenterates, such as jellyfishes, the medusa is the dominant form, with the polyp stage insignificant or absent. In other instances, such as with corals and sea anemones, the polyp stage is dominant. Some coelenterates, such as sea anemones, are solitary animals while others, such as corals, form colonies.

**Coelenteron.** The gastrovascular cavity of coelenterates.

**Coeliac.** Abdominal; of or pertaining to the belly.

**Coelom.** A fluid-filled cavity that forms the main body cavity of vertebrate and most invertebrate animals. It is formed by the splitting of the mesoderm. Ciliated ducts (coelomoducts) connect the coelom to the exterior allowing the exit of waste products and gametes; in higher animals these are specialized as oviducts, etc. The coelom is large and often subdivided in annelid worms (in which it functions as a hydrostatic skeleton) and vertebrates. In anthropods it is restricted to the cavities of the gonads and excretory organs, the body cavity being a blood-filled haemocoel.

**Coenozygote.** A multinucleate zygote, as in Mucor.

**Coelomoduct.** Coelom.

**Coelomycetes.** A class of the Deuteromycotina containing mycelial imperfect fungi in which the conidia are borne in pycnidia (as in the Sphaeropsidales) or acervuli (as in the Melanconiales). It contains over 7000 species in some 870 genera.

**Coelozoic.** Inhabiting a coelom or body, cavity, said of parasites.

**Coenenchyme.** In alcyonarian corals, the mass of tissue from which polyps project, consisting primarily of a gelatinous mesoglea containing skeletal elements.

**Coenobium.** A colony of cells that behaves as a single integrated unit, the number of component cells remaining constant. A coenobium often gives rise to internal daughter colonies. An example is the colonial alga Volvox.

**Coenocarpium.** A multiple fruit that incorporates the ovaries, floral parts, and receptacles of many flowers. It has a fleshy axis. The pineapple (Ananas comosus) is an example. Compare sorosis.

**Coenocyte.** A multinucleate plant body as that of certain slime molds, nonseptate algae and certain fungi in which cell walls are absent. Compare syncytium.

**Coenocytic** Describing a cell containing many nuclei or a thallus that lacks separating walls between nuclei. Such a structure is often threadlike. Examples are the hyphae of many fungi and the thalli of certain algae in the Xanthophyta and Siphonales.

**Coenosarc.** The hollow, soft tissues in the stem of a colonial hydrozoan or coral which unites the individuals of a colony.

**Coenosorus.** A continuous line of sporangia. It is seen in certain ferns, *e.g.* Pteridium, where discrete sori are not produced.

**Coenosteum.** The surface layer of the calcareous mass forming the skeleton of various corals.

**Coenozygote.** A multinucleate zygote, as in Mucor.

**Coenurus.** A type of tapeworm larva consisting of a bladder-like sac containing many scolices. Compare cysticercus, hydatid.

**Coenzyme.** An organic nonprotein molecule that associates with an enzyme molecule in catalysing biochemical reactions. Coenzymes usually participate in the substrate-enzyme interaction by donating or accepting certain chemical groups. Many vitamins are precursors of coenzymes.

**Coenzyme I.** NAD.

**Coenzyme II.** NADP.

**Coenzyme A (CoA).** A complex organic compound that acts in conjunction with enzymes involved in various biochemical reactions, notably the oxidation of pyruvate via the Kerbs cycle and fatty-acid oxidation and synthesis.

It comprises principally the B vitamin pantothenic acid, the nuclotide adenine, and a ribose-phosphate group.

**Coenzyme Q** (ubiquinone). A lipid-soluble electron-carrying coenzyme that participates in the transport of electrons from NAD to oxygen in the respiratory chain. It is a reversibly reducible quinone. Plastoquinone, a closely related compound, performs a similar function but in photosynthetic electron transport.

**Cofactor.** A nonprotein component essential for the normal catalytic activity of an enzyme. Cofactors may be organic molecules (coenzymes) or inorganic ions. They may activate the enzyme by altering its shape or they may actually participate in the chemical reaction.

**Coffee.** The green or roasted seeds of various species of a shrub or small tree of the genus Coffea or the plant which produces them.

**Coffee Tree.** A shrubby, evergreen tree which originated in Ethiopia. It has glossy leaves and white flowers. The red berries contain the seeds or 'beans' which are roasted to make the drink coffee.

**Coherent**

1. Sticking together by adhesion.
2. Touching and adhering but not fused.

**Cohesion Theory.** The currently accepted theory explaining the ascent of sap in the xylem. It postulates that the reduction in water potential in the leaf (due to an increase in the rate of evaporation) causes water to flow through the plant to replace the lost water. The column of water in the xylem can withstand considerable tension before breaking because of the very strong cohesive forces between the water molecules.

**Cohort.** A taxon between class and order.

**Coir.** The coarse, short fibers from the husk of a coconut.

**Colchicine.** An alkaloid derived from the autumn crocus, Colchicum autumnale. It inhibits spindle formation in cells, so preventing their division and inducing multiple sets of chromosomes (polyploidy). Colchicine is used in genetics, cytology, and plant breeding research and also in cancer therapy to inhibit cell division.

**Colchicum.** Also known as meadow saffron, this is a poisonous plant of European meadows. It has pale purple crocus-like flowers in the autumn, but the glossy green leaves appear in spring. It yields the drug colchicine.

**Cold-blooded.** An animal whose body temperature varies with the temperature of its environment is said to be cold-blooded. The animal tends to be slow and lacking in energy when its environment is cold and active when it is warmer. The temperature therefore has a major influence on the type of lifestyle the animal can lead. Fishes, amphibians and reptiles are cold-blooded, as are all invertebrates.

**Cold-bloodedness.** Poikilothermy.

**Cold Light.** Light emitted by bioluminescent organisms.

**Coleoptera.** An order of insects comprising the beetles and weevils and containing about 330 000 known species—the largest order in the animal kingdom. The forewings are hardened and thickened to form elytra, which meet at a precise mid-dorsal line and protect the underlying pair of hindwings and abdomen. The mouthparts are generally modified for biting and in some species assume antler-like proportions. Beetles occur in a wide variety of terrestrial and aquatic habitats; many feed on decaying organic matter, some eat living vegetation while others prey on other arthropods. A number of beetles and weevils are economically important pests of stored gain, timber, and crops. The young emerge as larvae and generally undergo metamorphosis via a pupal stage to form the adult beetle.

**Coleopteran.** Any insect of the order Coleoptera which contains the beetles and weevils; the largest insect order including over 250,000 known species.

**Coleoptile.** The sheathlike structure around the epicotyl in the seeds of grasses. It protects the erect plumule during its growth to the soil surface. In most grasses the coleoptile is very sensitive to light and has thus been used to investigate light-directed tropisms. Compare coleorhiza.

**Coleorhiza.** A protective sheath that covers the young root of the embryo in plants of the grass family.

**Coliphage.** Any DNA bacteriophage that infects the bacterium Escherichia coli. Examples are the intensively studied T series of phages (T1 through to T7), which have been developed on a particular strain of E. coli.

**Collagen.** An insoluble fibrous protein found extensively in the connective tissue of skin, tendons, and bone. The polypeptide chains of collagen (containing the amino acids glycine and proline predominantly) from triple-stranded helical coils that are bound together to form fibrils, which have great strength and limited elasticity. Collagen accounts for over 30% of the total body protein of mammals.

**Collagenous Fibers.** Wavy, white, nonelastic fibres found in connective tissue, especially tendons and ligaments.

**Collar Bone.** The clavicle.

**Collar Cell.** A choanocyte.

**Collared Dove.** An Asian bird almost unknown in Europe until 1930. Now it lives in most of Europe, where its call, 'coo-cooo-coo', is heard all the year round. It has a distinctive black strap across the back of the neck and nests in conifer trees, mainly near human habitation.

**Collateral.** Subsidiary, subordinate, indirect; acting secondarily.

**Collateral.** A branch of an axon other than one at the terminal arborization.

**Collateral Bundle.** A vascular bundle in which the phloem occurs on only one side of the xylem. In the stem the xylem is usually internal to the phloem. This type of bundle is common in both angiosperms and gymnosperms. Compare bicollateral bundle, concentric bundle.

**Collembolan.** A primitive insect of the order Collembola comprising the springtails, as Achoretes, the snow flea.

**Collenchyma.** A tissue composed of relatively elongated cells with thickened nonlignified primary cell walls. Collenchyma is sometimes considered to be parenchyma with exceptionally thick cellulose cell walls, specialized as a supporting and strengthening tissue in organs lacking (or almost lacking) secondary growth. Examples are young herbaceous stems and leaves. The thickened cell walls of collenchyma cell are sometimes used as a supply of cellulose for the other tissues in times of shortage. The wall thickenings may be mainly on the tangential walls (lamellar collenchyma), in the corners of the cells (angular collenchyma), or adjacent to the intercelluiar spaces (lacunar collenchyma). Compare sclerenchyma.

**Collencyte.** An amebocyte with slender, branching pseudopodia, as in snonges.

**Colletereal Glands.** Glands in a female insect which secrete an adhesive substance or provide material for the egg case.

**Collophore.** A tubelike structure on the ventral surface of the abdomen of springtails which functions as an adhesive structure.

**Collum**

1. A neck, collar, or collarlike structure.

2. The first, legless segment behind the head in millipedes and pauropods.

**Colobus Monkey.** A small group of monkeys which live in the dense forests of central Africa and rarely descend from the trees. They have long fur and reach up to 1.5 metres in length, including about one metre of tail. Colobus monkeys feed mainly on leaves.

**Colon.** The section of the vertebrate large intestine that lies between the caecum and the rectum. Its prime function is to absorb water and minerals from indigestible food residues passing from the small intestine, which results in the formation of faeces.

**Colonial.** Describing a type of growth form in which many cells of similar form and function are more or less loosely grouped together. Colonies of cells are characteristic of many algal genera, *e.g.* Volvox and Gonium. The colony is often surrounded by mucilaginous substances.

**Colony**

1. (in zoology). A group of animals of the same species living together and dependent upon each other. Some, such as the corals and sponges, are physically connected and function as a single unit. Others, such as insect colonies, are not physically joined but show a high level of social organization with members specialized for different functions.

2. (in microbiology). A group of microorganisms, usually bacteria or yeasts, that are considered to have developed from a single parent cell. Colonies that grow on agar plates differ in shape, colour, surface texture, and translucency and can therefore be used as a means of identification.

**Colorado Beetle.** An insect pest which can destroy potato crops. The beetle is about 10 mm long and striped black and yellow. It is native to North America but has spread to E rope where it does great damage. Drastic measures are taken to contain its numbers, particularly in Britain where it has not yet become properly established.

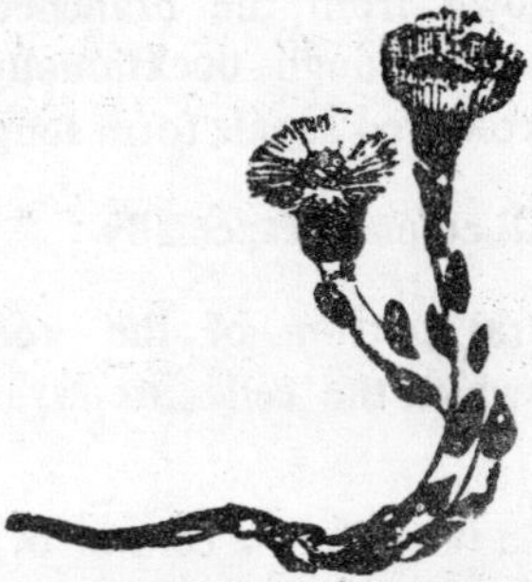

Coltsfoot

**Colostrum.** A liquid with a high content of nitrogen, antibodies, and vitamins that is secreted from the mammary glands before and just after giving birth. The change of secretion from colostrum to proper milk takes place gradually during the days after birth.

**Colour Blindness.** Any disorder of vision in which colours are confused. The most common type is red—green colour blindness. This is due to a recessive gene carried on the X chromosome (sex linkage), and therefore men are more likely to show the defect although women may be carriers. It results in absence or malfunctioning of nerve cells sensitive to coloured light (cones) in the retina of the eyes.

**Colpus.** An oblong to elliptic germinal aperture in a pollen grain, at least twice as long as it is broad. Pollen with such apertures is termed colpate. Compare pore.

**Coltsfoot.** A short creeping plant, with a scaly stem and bright yellow composite flowerheads. Its heart-shaped leaves grow from the roots only after the plant has flowered. Coltsfoot has been used since Roman times as a cough remedy. It is found on bare open ground.

**Colugo**. A flying lemur.

**Columbine.** A tall flowering plant related to the buttercup. It is a woodland plant with attractive hooded flowers which hang down from the branched stem. The petals are usually violet, though occasionally white or pink, and the similarly coloured sepals form long spurs.

**Columella**. A small column, especially :

1. The central portion of the root cap of certain roots in which the cells are arranged in longitudinal lines.
2. The sterile tissue in the centre of the sporangium in mosses, liverworts, and fungi.
3. A rodlike radial element in a pollen or spore wall.

**Column**

1. *zool.* Any column-shaped structure, as *a.* the body of an anthozoan; *b.* the central bony axis (spinal column) of a vertebrate; *c.* a longitudinal division of the spinal cord; *d.* an extension of the renal cortex into the medulla; *e.* a thickened stand of the ventricle of the heart or the mucosa of the vagina or anal canal.
2. *bot.* *a.* The united stamens and style forming a solid structure as in orchids; *b.* The twisted portion of an awn in grasses.

**[1]Coma**. *Pystol.* A state of unconsiousness from which a person cannot be aroused by ordinary stimuli.

**[2]Coma**

1. *bot.* A leafy crown or head, as in palms.
2. A tuft of hairs at the end of a seed, as in the milk weed.

3. A tuft of leaflike structures at the end of a fruit, as in the pineapple.

**Comb**. A serrated structure bearing teeth or teethlike parts, as *a.* the fleshy crest on the head of domestic fowl and other birds, especially the male; *b.* the pecten in the eye of a bird; *c.* the pecten on the third leg of a honeybee; *d.* a row of fused cilia on the comb plate of a ctenophore; *e.* the pecten of a scorpion.

**Comb Jelly**. Small marine animals related to jellyfishes, the comb jellies are so named because of the rows of tiny hairs that resemble minute combs on the sides of their bodies. They are also called sea gooseberries due to the size and shape of most of the species. Comb jellies are found in all the oceans and are usually colourless and quite transparent. They swim about by waving their hairs or cilia.

**Comb Plate**. A locomotor organ in a ctenophore. Also called plate row, comb row, comb column, rib or costa, paddle plate.

**Comet**. A single arm of an asteroid which is in the process of regenerating a new disc and arms, as in Linckia, a Pacific sea star.

**Comfrey**. Several species of hairy flowering plant related to the forget-me-not. The bell-shaped flowers of the common comfrey are either creamy white, pink or purple, and are arranged in clusters. The leaves are long and rough to touch. The common comfrey was formerly used to treat wounds. It is found in very wet areas.

**Comma**. A woodland and garden butterfly which has a comma-like mark on its brown underside; the upper side is russet and black. Both sets of wings have noticeably ragged edges. The caterpillar of the comma is disguised to look like a bird-dropping; it feeds on nettles, hops and tree leaves, including elm.

**Commelinidae.** A subclass of the monocotyledons containing mainly herbaceous plants, most of which have bisexual flowers with a more or less reduced perianth. It contains the following orders; Commelinales, which comprises four families including the Commelinaceae (spiderwort family); Eriocaulales; Restionales; Poales, which includes the one family Gramineae or Poaceae; Juncales, which consists of two families including the Juncaceae (rushes); Cyperales, made up of the one family Cyperaceae (reeds and sedges); Bromeliales, including the one family Bromeliaceae (bromeliads), which contains the pineapple (Ananas comosus); and the Zingiberates, which includes the families Musaceae (banana family), Strelitziaceae (containing bird of paradise flowers, Strelitzia), and Zingiberaceae (containing various aromatic plants, *e.g.*, ginger, Zingiber officinale). The Zingiberales is sometimes placed in the Liliidae. In some classifications the Typhales is included in the Commelinidae, while in others it is placed in the Arecidae.

**Commensalism.** An interaction between two animal or plant species that habitually live together in which one species (the commensal) benefits from the association while the other is not significantly affected. For example, the burrows of many marine worms contain commensals that take advantage of the shelter provided but do not affect the worm.

**Commissure**

1. *zool. a.* A band of never fibers which connects paired ganglia or the two halves of the brain or spinal cord. *b.* A seam or line of junction marking the union of two parts, as the labia.

2. *bot.* A line of junction between two united structures, as carpels.

**Communal.** Organized into societies, as man, social insects.

**Community.** An association of plants and animals in a given area or region in which the various species are more or less inter-dependent upon each other, as a desert community, pond community.

**Community** (of plants) is applied to any collection of plants which make up a distinct type of vegetation—from woodlands to the scant plant growth on the flanks of a sand-duce. A typical example is an oak-wood. In springtime, growing close to the ground are clumps of moss, white anemones, lesser celandines, winter aconites, and thick green spreads of dog's mercury; above is an undergrowth of woody shrubs such as hazel, hawthorn and sloe; higher still are branches of the oak trees themselves, supported on tough rigid trunks. All these plants are growing on a similar sort of soil; all are subjected to the same sort of climate. Together they make up a recognizable community of plants.

According to the scale of the plant community, a number of other terms can be used. A plant formation refers to a community in very broad terms. The great belts of vegetation found throughout the world—the rain forests, desert vegetation, deciduous forests, coniferous forests—are examples. Each plant formation breaks down into a number of subsidiary categories. An oak-wood, for example, is a smaller community falling within the deciduous forest plant formation. For such a community' dominated by a single species (*i.e.*, the oak tree) the term consociation is used. If there are two or more species of equal importance, then the community is called an association (*e.g.* mixed oak-ash woods). Finally, very small but distinct communities may occur inside associations or consociations. Within an oakwood for instance, there may be a local predominance of ash trees. This lowest category is referred to as a plant society.

Two different types of plant community. The amount of shrub and ground layers depends on the amount of shade cast by the dominant trees.

**Comose.** Having a tuft or tufts of hair.

**Companion Cell.** A type of cell found within the phloem of flowering plants. Each companion cell is usually closely associated with a sieve element. Its function is uncertain, though it appears to regulate the activity of the adjacent sieve element. In gymnosperms a similar function is attributed to albuminous cells, which are found closely associated with gymnosperm sieve elements.

**Comparative Biochemistry.** The recognition of discontinuities in biochemical variation and their subsequent use in the construction of classifications or correlation with existing classifications.

**Compass Plant.** A plant that has its leaves permanently orientated in a north-south direction. Such an arrangement enables the plant to take full advantage of morning and evening sun, while avoiding the stronger midday sunlight. An example is the compass plant of the prairies (Silphium laciniatum).

**Compensation Point.** The lowest steady carbon dioxide concentration achievable in a closed system containing a photosynthesizing plant. When this minimum level is reached, the photosynthetic uptake of carbon dioxide is exactly balanced by its respiratory release, indicating that the rate of synthesis of organic material is equal to the rate of breakdown by respiration. Low compensation points are indicative of photosynthetic efficiency as the plant is then using the maximum amount of available carbon dioxide ($C_3$ plant, $C_4$ plant). Following a period of darkness a plant will take a certain amount of time, termed the compensation period, to reach its compensation point. Shade plants often have shorter compensation periods than sun plants as they can make better use of dim light.

**Competence.** A characteristic exhibited by embryonic cells whereby they can go on to develop into any one of several different types of cell. Competence is therefore a feature that they possess before their ultimate cellular type is determined.

**Competent.** Describing embryonic tissue that is capable of developing into a specialized tissue when suitably stimulated.

**Competition.** The situation that arises when two or more organisms of the same or different species need the same limited resources. Organisms compete with one another for light, water, nutrients, etc. Competition may be resolved in various ways, namely : certain organisms or species being eliminated completely; migration of the less successful competitors; use of the resources at different times; physiological changes occurring; or the organisms involved living together, but not as successfully as they would at lower densities (*i.e.*, the reproductive rate falls off). When members of different species compete for most or all of the same resources, one species flourishes and the other declines. This is known as the competitive exclusion principle and means that two different species rarely occupy the same ecological niche.

**Competitive Inhibition.** A form of enzyme inhibition in which the inhibitor competes with the substrate for the enzyme active site. The inhibitor can bind to the active site but does not react to form products. An example is the inhibition of the enzyme succinate dehydrogenase by certain compounds resembling succinate, *e.g.*, malonate and oxalate. Studies of competitive inhibitors have provided valuable information about the way in which substrates are bound to the active site.

**Complement.** A group of proteins present in blood plasma and tissue fluid that aids the body's defences following an immune response. Following an antibody-antigen reaction, complement is activated chemically and becomes bound to the antibody-antigen complex (complement fixation); it becomes involved in destroying foreign cells and attracting scavenging white blood cells (phagocytes) to the area of conflict in the body.

**Complemental Males.** The small males of certain animals that live in or on the females and are usually more or less degenerate apart from the reproductive organs. They occur in certain crustaceans (*e.g.*, some branacles), in which the normal individuals are hermaphrodite but the complemental males have suppressed ovaries, lose their alimentary canal, and lead a semiparasitic existence in the mantle cavity of the larger partner. This may ensure that cross fertilization occurs.

**Complementary Genes.** Nonallelic genes that cooperate in the expression of a single characteristic. The genes may be linked or unlinked. In some cases a standard Mendelian ratio is maintained, but there may be unexpected phenotypes. Thus in the inheritance of flower colour in sweet peas, purple-flowered offspring may be obtained when two white-flowered plants are crossed. This is because flower colour is affected by two genes and if either is a double recessive then no colour develops. In other cases, no unusual phenotypes appear but there may be some apparent modification of the Mendelian ratio in the $F_2$, such as 9 : 3 : 4(=9 : 3 : [3+1]), or 9 : 7(=9 :[3+3+1]).

**Complement Fixation** An antigen-antibody-complement reaction in which the complement is destroyed or rendered unavailable, thus preventing certain reactions, such as hemolysis or bacteriolysis.

**Complementation.** The phenomenon whereby two recessive mutant strains can supply each other's deficiencies so that growth of both can occur. Thus adenine-requiring ($ad^-$) strains or histidine-requiring ($his^-$) strains of the fungus Neurospora will grow in the presence of the other in minimal media (lacking both adenine and histidine) but not separately.

**Complex Gene.** Super gene.

**Complicate.** Folded longitudinally.

**Compositae** (Asteraceae). One of the largest dicotyledonous families containing about 25 000 species in about 1100 genera and commonly referred to as the daisy or sunflower family. Its members are recognized by their characteristic headlike inflorescence, the capitulum, which superficially appears to be a single flower. The fruit (cypsela) often possesses a ring of hairs, the pappus, to aid dispersal, All composites have resin canals except most of those in the tribe Lactuceae, which have latex ducts. Commercially important composites include the sunflower (Helianthus annuus), grown for the oil in its seeds, and lettuce (Lactuca sativa), and numerous ornamental species, *e g.*, Dahlia, Chrysanthemum, and Aster.

**Composite Flower.** Flower made up of many tiny flowers called Florets, each with its own reproductive parts—carpels and anthers. Dandelions and daisies both have composite flowers.

**Composite Fruit.** A type of fruit that develops from an inflorescence rather than from a single flower.

**Compost.** Rotted plant material, made from garden rubbish and kitchen vegetable waste and used as an organic fertilizer. The decomposition of compost can be hastened by adding a compost activator, such as nitrochalk.

**Compound**

1. *biol.* Composed of several elements or parts united into a single structure, as a compound gland or leaf.
2. *chem.* A substance composed of two or more elements combined in definite proportions by weight.

**Compound Eye.** Eye of certain invertebrates, particularly insects, made up of thousands of tiny lenses called facets, each of which forms an image. The animal sees an object as a series of tiny images.

**Compound Leaf.** A leaf made up of several leaflets arising from a single point, such as the leaves of the horse chestnut.

**Compound Microscope.** Microscope.

**Compressed.** Flattened laterally or from side to side.

**Compression.** A fossil consisting of the carbonized remains of an organism brought about by compressive forces; an impression.

**Compression Wood.** Reaction wood.

**Conaria.** The early larva of certain siphonophores, as Velella.

**Concentration.** The quantity of dissolved substance per unit quantity of solvent in a solution. Concentration is measured in various ways. The amount of substance dissolved per unit volume (symbol *c*) has units of mol $dm^{-3}$ or mol $l^{-1}$. It is now called 'concentration' (formerly molarity). The mass concentration (symbol $\rho$) is the mass of solute per unit volume of solvent. It has units of kg $dm^{-3}$, g $cm^{-3}$, etc. The molal concentration (or molality; symbol *m*) is the amount of substance per unit mass of solvent, commonly given in units of mol $kg^{-1}$.

**Concentric Bundle** (centric bundle). A vascular bundle in which one vascular tissue surrounds the other so they appear to be arranged concentrically when viewed in transverse section. Compare bicollateral bundle, collateral bundle, meristele.

**Conceptacle.** A flask-shaped cavity with a small opening (the ostiole) that is found in the swollen tip of certain brown algae, such as Fucus. It contains the sex organs.

**Conception.** Fertilization of an ovum; the act of becomin pregnant; impregnation.

**Conch.** A large, marine gastropod of the family Strombidae, especially those of the genera Strombus and Cassis or their shells, used in the production of jewelry.

**Concha.** A structure shaped like a shell, as *a.* the deeper portion of the external ear; *b.* one of three scroll-like structures on the lateral wall of the nasal fossa; a turbinate bone.

**Conchiolin.** A nitrogenous substance present in the shells of mollusks.

**Conchology.** The science which deals with shells or the animals which produce them; the study of mollusks.

**Concrescence**

1. The growing together of parts originally separate, as the roots of teeth.
2. The movement of masses of cells toward each other and their eventual fusion, as in gastrulation.

**Concretion** A solidified mass; a calculus.

**Conditional Response** (conditioned reflex). A learned response that develops to an initially ineffective stimulus in classical conditioning.

**Conditioned Media.** Nurse tissue.

**Conditioning.** A process by which animals learn about a relation between two events. In classical (or Pavlovian) conditioning, repeated presentations of a neutral stimulus (*e.g.*, the sound of a bell or buzzer) are followed each time by a biologically important stimulus (such as food or electric shock), which elicits a response (*e.g.*, salivation). Eventually the neutral stimulus presented by itself produces a response (the conditional response, or conditioned reflex) similar to that originally evoked by the biologically important stimulus. For example, Pavlov's dogs learned to salivate in response to the sound of metronome that preceded the presentation of food. In instrumental (or operant) conditioning the animal is rewarded (or punished) each time it makes a particular response; this eventually causes the frequency of the response to increase (or decrease). For example, a rat will learn to press a lever in order to obtain food.

**Condor.** Condors are large American 'vultures'. They are not related to the true vultures of the Old World, although they look very much like them. They have naked heads and necks and wicked-looking hooked beaks. Like the true vultures, they are carrion feeders. There are two species, the Californian condor and the Andean condor. The former is very rare, but the Andean condor is found in the Andes for nearly the whole length of South America. Both birds have wingspans of about 3 metres and are among the largest of all flying birds.

**Cone** (of eye). Eye.

**Conducting Tissue**

1. Vascular system.
2. Transmitting tissue.

**Conduction.** The passage of electrons, atoms, or molecules through a suitable medium, as *a. bot.* the passage of water, minerals, or foods through conducting tissues, *b. zool.* the movement of heat, sound waves, or nerve impulses through cells or tissues.

**Conduplicate.** Folded, as certain grass leaves are. The term also refers to a form of vernation in which each leaf is folded in a U-shape around the next youngest leaf.

**Condyle.** A smooth round knob of bone that fits into a socket on an adjoining bone, forming a joint. Such a joint permits up-and-down or side-to-side movement but does not allow rotation. There are condyles where the lower jawbone (mandible) is attached to the skull, which permits chewing movements.

**Cone**

1. (in botany). A reproductive structure occurring in gymnosperms and some pteridophytes, known techni-

cally as a strobilus. It consists of sporophylls bearing the spore-producing sporangia. Gymnosperms produce different male and female cones. The large woody female cones of pines, firs, and other conifers are made up of structures called ovuliferous scales, which bear the ovules.

2. (in animal anatomy). A type of light-sensitive receptor cell, found in the retinas of all diurnal vertebrates. Cones are specialized to transmit information about colour and they function best in bright light. They are not evenly distributed on the retina, being concentrated in the fovea and absent on the margin of the retina. Compare rod.

**Cone Cell**

1. A photoreceptor cell in the retina of the eye.
2. In an ommatidium, one of four cells which produce the crystalline cone.

**Conelet**. A small cone, especially one of the first year's growth.

**Cone Shell**. A poisonous, carnivorous marine gastropod of the genus Conus.

**Conferted**. Densely or closely packed; crowded.

**Congenital**. Present at birth. Congenital disorders of the body may be due to genetic factors, *e.g.*, Down's syndrome, or caused by injury or environmental factors, *e.g.*, drugs (such as thalidomide) and chemicals (such as dioxin).

**Conger**. This is a stout-bodied marine eel, normally about 2.5 metres long. The body is brown or silvery and it is scaleless. The conger lives near the coast in many parts of the world. It is a fierce animal, eating more or less any animal that it can catch. It often hides among the rocks and darts out to catch its prey with powerful jaws and formidable teeth.

**Conger Eel**. A long slim fish, closely related to the common eel. Males grow up to 1 metre long, females up to 2 metres. The conger eel lives in rocky coastal waters around Europe and, unlike its cousin, does not spend part of its life in fresh water. It is a greedy predator, feeding on larger sea creatures such as herrings, lobsters and cuttle-fishes.

**Conglobate.** Spherical; grouped together into a ball or rounded structure.

**Conglomerate.** Grouped together into a dense cluster or mass, as a conglomerate fruit.

**Congo Red.** A scarlet benzidine dye of ten used to stain fungal hyphae.

**Conidiophore.** A specialized hypha which produces conidia.

**Conidiospore.** A conidium, q.v.

**Conidium** (conidiospore). An asexual spore produced by many fungi, especially ascomycetes, on specialized erect hyphae termed conidiophores. The conidia are usually formed in chains, which radiate from the globose or branched tip of the conidiophore.

**Conifer.** Member of a group of trees which bear their seeds in cones. Conifers are gymnosperms, and they include such trees as pines, firs, and cedars. Their leaves are generally long and very narrow and for this reason are known as needles. The trees are found throughout NW Europe, particularly in the colder northern parts and mountainous regions where they are able to withstand colder climates and higher altitudes than the broad-leaved trees.

**Coniferales** (Pinales). The largest and most widely distributed order of gymnosperms, containing about 49 genera with about 570 species most of which are evergreen trees. These are divided among the six families Pinaceae, Taxodiaceae, Cupressaceae, Podocarpaceae, Cephalotaxaceae, and

Araucariaceae. The Cupressaceae and Taxodiaceae are sometimes included as subfamilies in the Pinaceae.

Conifers are particularly abundant in the high latitudes of the northern hemisphere, where they form the climax vegetation. Typically conifers show a pyramidal growth pattern and bear simple leaves, often needles or scales. Most conifers are monoecious but bear the male and female reproductive organs in separate compact cones on different parts of the tree. Conifers are more advanced than the cycads and ginkgo in that they produce pollen grains; thus antherozoids are replaced by the two sperm nuclei, which are delivered to the egg by the pollen tube. It is thought this feature may have contributed to the success of the conifers as compared with other gymnosperms.

Conifers are commercially important as a source of timber for the paper-making, building, and furniture industries. They are generally faster growing and develop a less dense wood than angiosperm trees and are thus commonly called softwoods. In cross section distinct pores are normally absent in the wood (consequently termed nonporous wood) in contrast to the ring-porous or diffuse-porous wood of angiosperms.

**Coniferous**

1. Producing or bearing cones.
2. Composed of cone-bearing trees, as a coniferous forest.

**Conjugales** (Conjugatophyceae). In older classifications, an order (or class) of the Chlorophyta the members of which undergo the characteristic reproductive process of conjugation. More recently the order has been renamed Zygnemaphyceae.

**Conjugate**

1. To undergo conjugation.
2. *bot.* To join in pairs.

**Conjugated Protein.** A protein that contains other components besides polypeptide chains. Conjugated protein are classified according to the nature of the nonpeptide portion of the molecule. Glycoproteins are found in plant and bacterial cell walls, while cell and organelle membranes contain lipoproteins. Many enzymes contain metal ions and some dehydrogenases are flavoproteins Ribosomes and viruses are nucleoproteins.

**Conjugation**

1. The act of uniting or joining together, especially the temporary union of two individuals in which there is a transfer of nuclear material from one cell to the other, as occurs in various algae, fungi, and protozoans.

2. In certain algae, the union of isogametes.

**Conjunctive.** The delicate membrane that covers the cornea and lines the inside of the eyelid of a vertebrate eye. It is kept clean by secretions of the lachrimal (tear) gland and the reflex blink mechanism.

**Conker.** Fruit of the Horse Chestnut.

**Connate.** Describing similar organs that are joined together, such as petals fused to form a tube. The term is often used of paired leaves at a node, the bases of which have become fused to completely encircle the stem. Compare adnate.

**Connate-perfoliate.** United at the base and surrounding a stem, said of certain leaves.

**Connective.** The parenchymatous tissue that joins the pollen sacs in the anther. It is a continuation of the filament and contains the vascular strand supplying each lobe.

**Connective Tissue.** An animal tissue consisting of a small number of cells (*e.g.*, fibroblasts and mast cells) and fibres and a large amount of intercellular material (matrix). It is widely distributed and has many functions, including support, packing, defence, and repair. The individual constituents vary, depending on the function of the tissue. Different types of connective tissue include mesenchyme in the embryo, adipose tissue, loose areolar tissue for packing and support, blood, lymph, cartilage, and bone.

**Conoid**. Conoidal; cone-shaped.

**Conservation.** The sensible use of the earth's natural resources in order to avoid excessive degradation and impoverishment of the environment. It should include the search for alternative food and fuel supplies when these are endangered (as by deforestation and overfishing); an awareness of the dangers of pollution; and the maintenance and preservation of natural habitats and the creation of new ones (*e.g.*, nature reserves and national parks).

**Consociation**. A comparatively small climax community named after one dominant species, *e.g.*, oakwood, beechwood, etc. Consociations can be grouped together to form an association. For example, in England the deciduous-forest association consists of consociations, *i.e.*, smaller woods, of oak, ash, and beech.

**Consortium**. The symbiotic relationship between an alga and a fungus to form a lichen.

**Constitutive.** Constantly present, with reference to enzymes in bacteria. Compare inductive.

**Constitutive Enzyme.** An enzyme that is always present in nearly constant amounts in a given cell. A constitutive enzyme is part of the permanent and basic machinery of a cell. The enzymes of glycolysis are examples of constitutive enzymes in nearly all organisms. Compare induced enzyme.

**Consumer.** An organism that feeds upon those below it in a food chain (*i.e.*, at the preceding trophic level).

Herbivores, which feed upon green plants, are primary consumers; a carnivore that feeds only upon herbivores is a secondary consumer. Compare producer.

**Contact**. Describing an insecticide or herbicide that kills an insect or plant on contact rather than relying on ingestion or absorption. Examples of contact insecticides are DDT and pyrethrin. Contact herbicides include paraquat and diquat. Compare stomach insecticide, systemic.

**Contagious.** Readily transmissible from one individual to another, said of diseases.

**Continental Drift.** The theory that the existing continents moved to their present position following the break up to an ancient landmass. The idea was first proposed by A. Wegener in 1912 but was discarded by the geophysicists of the time. However evidence from biogeographic and oceanographic studies and the emergence of plate tectonics theory has established its validity. It is thought that the original landmass, Pangaea, broke up in the Mesozoic into Gondwana (or Gondwanaland) and Laurasia. The subsequent break-up of Gondwana resulted in the formation of the landmasses of the southern hemisphere, *i.e.*, Africa, India, South America, Australia, Antarctica, and New Zealand, while the break-up of Laurasia gave rise to North America and Eurasia. The theory helps to explain the present disjunct distributions of certain plant and animal groups.

**Continuous Variation** (quantitative variation). The range of differences that can be observed in many characteristics in a population. Characteristics resulting from multifactorial inheritance show continuous variation, *e.g.*, the wide-range of foot sizes in an adult human population. Compare discontinuous variation.

**Contorted.** Twisted; bent, convolute (in estivation).

**Contour Feathers.** Feathers that are arranged in regular rows on a bird's body, giving the body its streamlined shape

Each has a central horny shaft (the rachis) with a flattened vane on each side. Each vane is composed of two rows of filament-like barbs, which are connected to each other by means of hooked barbules to form a smooth surface. There is often a small second vane, the aftershaft, near the base of the feather.

**Contraception.** Prevention of conception; birth control; planned parenthood.

**Contract.** To shorten; to narrow or reduce in size; to draw parts together; to shrivel or shrink.

**Contractile Fibrils.** Myofibrils; myonemes.

**Contractile Root.** A specialized thickened root that serves to pull down a corm, bulb, rhizome, etc. to an appropriate level in the soil. Once the tips of the contractile roots are firmly anchored in the soil the upper region contracts, due to changes in the shape of the cortical cells. Prominent contractile roots are seen, for example, in Crocus ann Allium species.

**Contractile Vacuole.** A cavity in the cytoplasm of many freshwater unicellular algae that enlarges as it fills with water and contracts as water is expelled from it. The external medium is hypotonic with respect to the algal cell contents. To help prevent osmotic lysis, energy from ATP is used to pump water into the contractile vacuoles, the pulsations being visible with a light microscope. Water is released through the cell membrane or, in the case of Euglena, into the gullet. Such vacuoles are particularly important in those algae that do not have a rigid cell wall to help limit water intake.

**Contralateral.** Pertaining to or located on the opposite side. Compare ipsilateral.

**Conure.** A long-tailed New World parrot, especially one of the genus Aratinga.

**Convergence**

1. In phylogeny, the appearance of similar structures in unrelated organisms.
2. *physiol* *a.* The condition in which several axons synapse with one or a few motor neurons. *b.* The inclination of the visual axes toword a common point.
3. *embryol*. The movement of cells from lateral areas toward the midline resulting in formation of the primitive streak, as in the chick.

**Convergent.** Coming together, as veins in a leaf which pass from base to apex in a curving fashion.

**Convergent Evolution.** The development of superficially similar structures in unrelated organisms, usually because the organisms live in the same kind of environment. Examples are the wings of insects and birds and the streamlined bodies of whales and fish. Compare adaptive radiation.

**Convex.** Having a curved, rounded exterior surface, as that of a sphere. Compare concave.

**Convoluted.** Coiled or rolled up; having convolutions.

**Convolution**

1. A turn, twist, bend, or fold.
2. A permanent fold on the surface of the brain; a gyrus or folium.

**Cony.** A coney, rabbit, or pika.

**Coordinated Growth.** Symplast.

**Coot.** A water bird related to the rails. A plump, short-legged, black bird, the coot has flaps of skin on its toes which help it to swim by paddling. It has a white bill and a white patch on its forehead, and feeds on water animals and plants.

**Cooter.** A turtle (Pseudomys floridana).

**Cootie.** Common name for human body louse.

**Copal.** A hard resin of plant origin used in varnishes.

**Copepod.** Member of a large group of tiny crustaceans, many of which make up an important part of marine plankton, providing food for fish. Others live in fresh water or damp, mossy places on land. Some species are parasites. Swimming copepods have six pairs of legs arranged down their bodies like oars on a boat. They have large heads and forked tail-ends.

**Copepoda.** A subclass of crustaceans occurring in marine and freshwater habitats. Copepods are usually 0.5—2 mm long and lack both a carapace and compound eyes. Copepods are important members of plankton : some are free-living, feeding on microscopic organisms; others are parasitic. A familiar freshwater genus is Cyclops, so hamed because the members have a single median eye.

**Copper.** Butterflies with coppercoloured wings marked with darker spots. The large copper is an insect of marshland, while other coppers prefer hilly country. The caterpillars of copper butterflies feed on the leaves of dock and related plants.

**Copper.** Symbol : Cu. A metal element, atomic number 29, atomic weight 63.55, essential in trace amounts for growth. It is found in the enzyme cytochrome *c* oxidase, which is thought to catalyse the transfer of electrons from cytochrome $a_3$ to oxygen in respiration. In this reaction the two copper atoms of the molecule undergo transition from the cupric, Cu (II), to the cuprous, Cu(I) state. Copper also plys a role in photosynthetic electron transport, being found in the protein plastocyanin.

Copper deficiency leads to chlorosis, which suggests the elements may also play a role in the synthesis of chlorophyll.

**Copper Fungicide.** An inorganic fungicide containing copper. Some of the earliest known fungicides were copper compounds including the Bordeaux and Burgundy mixtures. Other copper-containing fungicides are often based on copper oxychloride or copper oxide and may be formulated with other types of fungicide.

**Copperhead.** A small group of venomous North American snakes. Most individuals are less than one metre long and bear live young. Copperheads hibernate during the winter in dens.

**Coppicing.** A from of woodland management in which trees are cut back to ground level regularly (every 10—15 years) to encourage growth of numerous adventitious shoots from the base. The resulting thicket is termed a copse or coppice. The young shoots are harvested for firewood, charcoal burning, fencing, etc. Many British woodlands have been managed in this way. Often selected trees may be left to mature, giving a coppice with standards.

**Copra.** The dried meat of the coconut.

**Coprophilous.** Describing organisms that live on or in dung as, for example, fungi of the Pilobolaceae.

**Coracidium.** The ciliated embryo of the fish tapeworm and related species.

**Coracoid Bone.** A bone of the pectaral girdle of amphibians, reptiles, and birds; absent in most mammals.

**Coral.** A large group of sea creatures that live either singly or in colonies. Corals are coelenterates, closely related to the sea anemones, and their bodies are polyps, encased in chalky cups or skeletons. The base of the polyp is attached to a solid surface and around the mouth is a ring of tentacles used for catching food. Only a few species of coral are found around the coasts of NW Europe, and the reef-forming varieties are found only in tropical waters.

[1]**Coralline.** *zool.* Of or resembling coral.

[2]**Coralline**

1. An animal which resembles a coral, as certain hydrozoans and bryozoans.
2. *bot.* A red alga with thallus heavily impregnated with lime, encrusting forms forming an important component of coral reefs.

**Corallum.** The entrie skeletal mass of a colony of corals.

**Coral Reef.** A calcareous mass formed by the deposition of coral skeletons over a long period of time. Types inciude : fringing reef, one that is close to land; barrier reef, one separated from the shore by a navigable channel; circular reef or atoll, one which encloses a lagoon.

**Coral Snacke.** One of several species of venomous snakes of the family Elapidae marked by distinctive black, red, and yellow bands, as the harlequin or Eastern coral snake (Micrurus fulvius) or the Western coral snake (Micruroides euryxanthus).

**Coral Spot.** A fungus whose threads grow through twigs and produce two different kinds of spore-bearing cushions on the surface. The commonest of these are the little pink or orange spots which give the fungus its name. The other kind of cushion is dark red.

**Corbie.** Crow.

**Cornea**

1. The anterior, transparent portion of the sclera of the eye of a vertebrate.

2. The outermost, transparent layer of a compound eye of an arthropod. It is divided into facets, each facet covering the end of an ommatidium and functions as a lens.

**Corbina.** Menticirrhus undulatus, of the croaker family, a game and food fish of the Pacific coast.

**Cord.** An elongated, cordlike structure, as the spinal cord, umbilical cord.

**Cordaitales.** An extinct order of gymnosperms, thought to have originated some time before the Carboniferous period and to have persisted into the Triassic. They were arborescent and in some of their vegetative structures resembled certain modern conifers, notably the monkey-puzzle (Araucaria araucana).

**Cordate.** Heart shaped, such as the leaves of the sweet violet (Viola odorata) or the lemmas of quaking grasses (Briza).

**Coriaceous.** Having a leathery texture.

**Cordiform.** Cordate.

**Core.** The central portion of a fleshy fruit, especically pome fruits, consisting of ripened carpels containing seeds, as in an apple.

**Coremium.** A cluster of hyphae forming a column which bears asexual spores (conidia).

**Coriaceous.** Tough, leatherlike.

**Coriander.** An annual herb of the Mediterranean area, the coriander is a member of the carrot family. It grows about 90 cm tall, and has much divided leaves and heads of small white flowers. The dried seeds are used as a spice

**Cori Cycle.** The process in which muscle glycogen is broken down to lactic acid which is carried to the liver and reconverted to glycogen, which in turn is broken down to glucose and returned to muscle where it is utilized.

**Corium**

1. The dermis or derma, the layer of skin immediately beneath the epidermis; the true skin.
2. The thickened, basal portion of a hemelytron.

**Cork** (phellen). A protective waterproof plant tissue produced by the cork cambium. It develops in plants undergoing secondary growth and replaces the epidermis. Its cells, whose walls are impregnated with suberin, are arranged in radial rows and fit closely together except where the cork is interrupted by lenticels. Some cork cells become air-filled while others contain deposits of lignin, tannins, and fatty acids, which give the cork a particular colour. The cork oak (Quercus suber) produces cork that can be used commercially.

**Cork Cambium** (phellogen). A type of cambium arising within the outer layers of the stems of woody plants, usually as a complete ring surrounding the inner tissues. The cells of the cork cambium divide to produce an outer corky tissue (cork or phellem) and an inner secondary cortex (phelloderm). Corks, cork cambium, and phelloderm together make up the periderm, an impermeable outer layer that protects the inner stem tissues if the outer tissues split as the stem girth increases with age. It thus takes over the functions of the epidermis.

**Cork Oak.** An evergreen species of oak growing in Portugal and around the Mediterranean. It has very thick bark, the outer layers of which are periodically removed to make the cork of everyday use.

**Corm.** Underground food store of certain plants, *e.g.* crocus, consisting of a short swollen stem. The corm bears buds and is capable of vegetative reproduction. After a plant has flowered a new corm swells up on top of the old one and new buds form. Corms differ from Bulbs in that a stem rather than leaves carries the food store.

**Cormatose.** Producing corms.

**Cormorant.** A sea bird also seen far up rivers. It is black, with short legs and a rather snake-like head. The bill is hooked for catching fish. Cormorants catch their prey by diving, and on land can be seen with wings outstretched when resting.

**Corn**

1. *a.* In the United States, Indian corn or maize (Zea mays), a tall cereal plant which produces seeds on large ears. *b.* The grain, seeds, or kernels of Zea mays used principally as food for livestock.
2. In various countries, the seeds of any of the cereal grasses which are used for food. In England the term is applied to wheat, in Scotland, oats.

**Corn Borer.** A moth (Pyrausta nubialis), the European corn borer of the family Pyralidae, whose larvae live in cornstalks, introduced into the United States about 1917.

**Corn Bunting.** The largest of the buntings, sometimes called the common bunting. It does not breed in Scandinavia and is rare in the western parts of the British Isles. It has no distinguishing features, being brown with darker streaks, but it can be told apart from similar-looking sparrows by its large size. Corn buntings live in open places such as fields, and in winter the birds gather in large flocks.

**Corncrake.** Rail.

**Cornea.** A transparent layer of tissue, continuous with the sclerotic, that forms the front part of the vertebrate eye, over the iris and lens. They cornea refracts light entering the eye onto the lens, thus assisting in the focusing of images onto the retina.

**Cornflower.** A pretty, blue-flowering plant related to the daisy and dandelion. It was once very common in cornfields but due to modern farming methods, it is now only found in waste ground.

**Cornification.** Keratinization.

**Corncob.** The central axis of an ear of Indian corn or maize upon which the grains or kernels develop.

**Cornea**

1. The anterior, transparent portion of the sclera of the eye of a vertebrate.
2. The outermost, transparent layer of a compound eye of an arthropod. It is divided into facets, each facet covering the end of an ommatidium and functioning as a lens.

**Corn Earworm.** A moth (Heliothis armigera) of the family Noctuidae, whose larvae feed on developing corn grains. It is also called tomato fruitworm or cotton bollworm as the larvae also feed on these plants.

**Cornicle.** One of a pair of tubes at the posterior end of an aphid through which a waxy fluid is discharged.

**Corniculate**

1. Bearing horns or hornlike structures.
2. Shaped like a horn.

**Cornu** pl. **Cornua.** A horn or horn-shaped structure.

**Corolla.** The petals of a flower, collectively, forming the inner whorl of the perianth. It encircles the stamens and carpels. The form of the corolla is very variable. The petals may either be free (polypetalous) or united to form a tube (gamopetalous).

**Corollate.** Possessing a corolla.

**Corona**

1. A crownlike outgrowth from a corolla tube. It is especially prominent in daffodils (Narcissus).
2. A crownlike structure at the tip of the oogonium in certain algae of the Charophyta.

**Coronal.** Designating a plane or section through the coronal suture, which separates the frontal and parietal bones.

**Corona Radiata.** A layer of follicle cells which surrounds a mature mammalian ovum.

**Coronary**

1. Resembling a crown.
2. Encircling, as the coronary arteries which supply the heart.

**Coronary Vessels.** Two pairs of blood vessels (the coronary arteries and coronary veins) that supply the muscles of the heart itself. The coronary arteries arise from the aorta and divide into branches that encircle the heart. A blood clot in a coronary artery (coronary thrombosis) is one of the causes of a 'heart attack'.

**Coronate.** Possessing a grown, corona, or similar structure.

**Coronoid.** Pointed, beaklike.

**Corpora.** Plural of Corpus.

**Corpora Allata.** A pair of neuroendocrine structures attached to the corpora cardiaca in certain insects; the source of the juvenile hormone (JH).

**Corpora Cardiaca.** A pair of neuroendocrine structures attached to the brain of certain insects.

**Corpora Cavernosa.** A pair of cylindrical bodies of erectile tissue present in the penis and clitoris.

**Corpus**

1. Tunica—corpus theory.
2. The main body of a bladdered pollen grain, as in many conifers, *e.g.* Pinus.

**Corpus Callosum.** A broad band of commissural fibres connecting the two cerebral hemispheres.

**Corpuscle**

1. A small body, as a renal or thymic corpuscle.
2. A cell, especially one floating in a fluid, as blood, coelomic fluid, or saliva.
3. An encapsulated sensory nerve ending, as Meissner's corpuscle.

**Corpus Luteum.** The yellowish body that forms in the cavity of a Graafian follicle in the ovary of a mammal after the release of the egg cell. It secretes the hormone progesterone. Some species of sharks, reptiles, and birds have similar structures in their ovaries but the function of these is less well understood.

**Correlative Inhibition.** The suppression of the growth of certain plant parts by a compound, such as a food substance or growth substance, produced in another area of the plant. An example is the production of a substance by the root system that suppresses the development of roots on the stem. If the influence of the root is removed a detached petiole or stem may subsequently produce a profusion of adventitious roots.

**Cortex**

1. (in botany). The tissue between the epidermis and the vascular system in plant stems and roots. It is composed of parenchyma cells and shows little or no structural differentiation. Cortex is produced by activity of the apical meristem.

2. (in zoology). The outermost layer of tissue of various organs, including the adrenal glands (adrenal cortex), kidneys (renal cortex), and cerebral hemispheres.

**Corticate.** Possessing a cortex.

**Corticosteroid.** Any of several hormones produced by the cortex of the adrenal glands. Glucocorticoids regulate the use of carbohydrates, proteins, and fats in the body and include cortisol and cortisone. Mineralocorticoids regulate salt and water balance.

**Corticotrophin.** A hormone which stimulates the adrenal cortex, as ACTH.

**Cortisol** (hydrocortisone). A hormone (corticosteroid), produced by the adrenal glands, that promotes the synthesis and storage of glucose and is therefore important in the normal response to stress, suppresses or prevents inflammation, and regulates deposition of fat in the body. It is used as treatment for various allergies and for rheumatic fever, certain skin conditions, and adrenal failure (Addison's disease).

**Cortisone.** A hormone (corticosteroid), produced by the adrenal glands, that is closely related to, and has an action similar to that of, cortisol. Cortisone is also the name for a synthetic version of cortisol.

**Corymb.** A simple racemose inflorescence in which the flowers are formed on lateral stalks of different lengths, the longest at the base, resulting in a flattopped cluster of flowers (illustration at racemose inflorescence). This form of floral arrangement, found frequently in the Cruciferae, may aid insect pollination by giving easy access to individual flowers and in providing a flat landing platform, as in candytufts (Iberis).

**Corymbose.** Corymbiform; corymbous.

**Cosmine.** A hard, dentinelike substance present in certain types of fish scales.

**Cosmoid Scale.** A type of scale found in primitive fishes, as in crossopterygians and dipnoans.

**Cosmopolitan.** Describing species that have a worldwide distribution and are not restricted to specific areas. Compare endemic.

**Cosmozoic.** Pertaining to life of other planets.

**Costa**

1. A rib.
2. *zool.* A riblike structure, as *a.* a ridge on the shell of certain mollusks; *b.* a vein in the wing of certain insects usually forming the anterior margin; *c.* a rodlike structure in the base of the undulating membrane of trichomonads; *d.* a comb row in ctenophores; *e.* an extension of the sclerosepta of corals connecting the theca to the epitheca.
3. *bot. a.* The midvein of a simple leaf *b.* The rachis of a pinnately compound leaf.

**Costal.** Of or pertaining to a rib or costa.

**Costate.** Bearing a longitudinal rib or ribs, said of leaves.

**Cotinga.** A group of often brilliantly coloured birds living mainly in the rain forests of South and Central America. One of the most spectacular is the Cock-of-the-Rock.

**Cotton** A soft, white, fibrous material obtained from fibers enclosing seeds of various plants of the family Malvaceae, especially that from the cotton plant (Gossypium hirsutum or G. barbadense).

**Cotton Grass.** Several species of sedge, commonly found on wet moorland. The flowers are bristly and, after flowering, produce a white cottony material that helps to disperse the seeds.

**Cottonmouth** The water moccasin.

**Cottontail.** Any of several species of North American rabbits of the genus Sylvilagus, especially S. floridanus, the Eastern cottontail.

**Cotyledon.** Leaf inside a seed which, in many cases, grows to form part of the young plant. In some seeds, *e.g.* beans, the cotyledons act as a food store. Flowering plants are grouped according to whether their seeds contain one cotyledon (the monocotyledons) or two (dicotyledons). In gymnosperms the number varies.

**Cotylosaur.** A primitive reptile of the order Cotylosauria, a group considered to have given rise to modern reptiles, as Seymouria.

**Couch Grass.** Also known as twitch or spear grass, couch grass is a persistent weed in cultivated ground. It is a species of Grass which spreads rapidly by underground runners.

**Coumarin.** A toxic white crystalline substance with the formula $C_9H_6O_2$, found in certain plants, particularly in the testa or fruit where it inhibits germination. Only when it has been removed or destroyed, for example by exposure to light, will the seed germinate. It has a characteristic smell of new-mown hay and has been manufactured artificially for use in the perfume industry.

**Counterstaining.** Staining.

**Coupling.** Cis arrangement.

**Courser.** A long-legged, plover-like shore-bird, living in the Old World from Africa to Australia.

**Covered Smuts.** Smuts.

**Covert.** One of the small feathers which covers the bases of the wing and tail feathers in birds; a tectrix.

**Covey.** A brood, hatch, or small flock of birds, especially of quail and partridges.

**Cow.** The mature female of any bovine animal or of any animal, the male of which is designated bull.

**Cowberry.** A flowering shrub of the heath family. It is a low creeping evergreen with clusters of pink or white flowers and touch leaves. It produces edible red berries and is found in woods and on heaths.

**Cowbird.** Molothrus ater of the family Icteridae, a small blackbird which lays its eggs in the nests of other birds.

**Cow Parsley.** A tall, slightly hairy flowering plant of the carrot family. Its small white flowers are arranged in umbrella-like clusters. The hollow ridged stems are often reddish in colour. It is a common plant, often found in hedgerows.

**Cowrie.** A carnivorous mollusc related to the sea snails but with the shell whorls enveloped during growth until only the final whorl is visible. Most cowries live in the Indian and Pacific oceans.

**Cowslip.** A hairy plant related to the primrose that grows in grassy areas. Its short stem supports clusters of deep

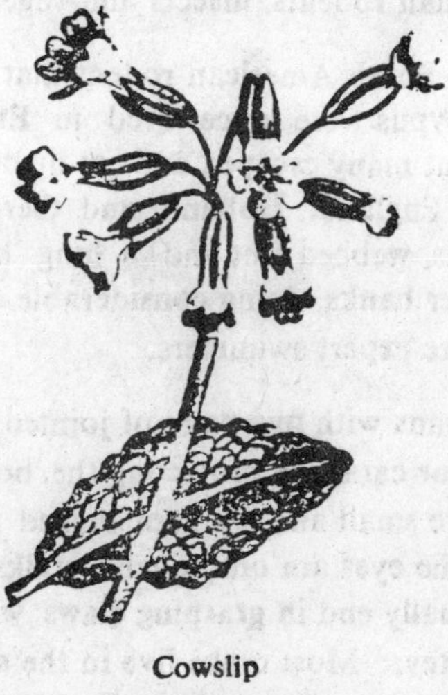

Cowslip

yellow flowers that bear an orange spot at the base of each petal.

**Cow-wheat.** Several species of small, thin, flowering plant. The common cow-wheat bears pale yellow two-lipped flowers which are arranged in pairs. It is semi-parasitic and is often found in woods attached to the roots of other flowering plants, from which it draws water and minerals.

**Coxa.** The first segment, attached to the thorax, of an insect's leg.

**Coxite.** The basal segment of certain abdominal appendages in insects.

**Coxopodite.** In crustacean appendages, the proximal or basal segment of the protopodite. Compare basipodite.

**Coyote.** A relative of the wolf, the coyote is slightly smaller, measuring about one metre from nose to tail. The fur is tawny coloured and it has a bushy black-tipped tail. Coyotes used to live all over the western part of North America but their range has decreased considerably over the last century. They eat a variety of food including rabbits, small rodents, insects and vegetable matter.

**Coypu.** A large South American rodent that grows up to 60 cm long. Coypus were once bred in Europe for their fur (nutria) but many escaped and set up colonies, particularly in eastern England, Holland and Germany. They have large heads, webbed feet and a long hairless tail. They live in river banks, doing considerable damage by burrowing, and are expert swimmers.

**Crab.** Crustaceans with five pairs of jointed legs and a broad, flat cover or carapace protecting the body. The abdomen and tail are small and are kept tucked up underneath the trunk. The eyes are on movable stalks and the first pair of legs usually end in grasping claws which the crab uses to catch prey. Most crabs live in the sea but a few are found in fresh water and some on land. One type of crab that does not have a protective cover is the Hermit crab. Instead it lives inside the empty shell of other sea animals, especially whelks.

**Crab Apple.** A deciduous tree belonging to the rose family and the ancestor of our eating apples. It grows to a height of 10 metres. Its fruit is too bitter to eat but makes good jelly.

**Crabeater Seal.** One of the most common antarctic seals reaching some 3 metres in length. Despite its name, the crabeater seal feeds mainly on krill—the minute crustaceans which abound in the surface waters.

**Crab-eating Fox.** A South American member of the dog family which is fox-like both in appearance and behaviour. As the name implies it does eat freshwater crabs, but small mammals, frogs and insects are more typical food items.

**Crab-eating Monkey.** A common macaque monkey of South-East Asia measuring 50 cm in the body with a slightly longer tail. In swampy coastal areas this monkey supplements its diet of fruit and other plant food with crabs and bivalve molluscs. It also lives in mountain areas, in the jungle and along rivers.

**Crab Louse.** Phthirus pubis, a sucking louse which frequents the pubic and perianal regions of man.

**Crab Plover.** A black and white wading bird found along the shores of the Indian Ocean. It feeds mainly on crabs and shellfish which are smashed open against a rock.

**Crab Spider.** So called because of the curvature of their legs and the way they scuttle sideways, crab spiders are found almost everywhere. They do not make webs but lie in wait for their prey and then pounce on it. They are sometimes found in flowers, the colours of which they often match perfectly.

**Crake.** A group of water birds related to the rails and coots. They have mainly streaky brown plumage, and short tails. They seldom fly, preferring to skulk among the reeds of marshes and ponds. The spotted crake is one of the most widespread species though it is not commonly found in Britain. The corncrake is rather rare and, unlike the others, prefers to live on dry ground.

**Crampon.** A hooklike, aerial, adventitious root which serves as a supporting structure, as in the ivy.

**Cranberry.** A low-growing creeping evergreen shrub of Europe and North America. It has small leaves, pink flowers and small red acid fruits. It grows on damp moorlands.

**Crane.** A long-legged bird, rather like a stork but with a shorter bill. Cranes are found in most parts of the world, but most species are rare. They breed in marshy regionr, and migrate in flocks, often flying for long distances.

**Crane-fly.** A family of several hundred species of large mosquito-like insect, also known as daddy-long-legs. They have thin bodies with spindly legs and fly rather clumsily. Crane-flies live in gardens and near water. The larvae of many species are known as leatherjackets. They live in the soil and can cause serious damage to crops.

**Cranesbill.** A group of flowering plants related to the garden geranium, with mainly pink, five-petalled flowers. The name comes from their characteristic fruit which is shaped like a crane's beak.

**Cranial.** Of or pertaining to the cranium or the skull.

**Cranial Nerves.** Ten to twelve pairs of nerves in vertebrates that emerge directly from the brain. They supply the sense organs and muscles of the head, neck, and viscera. Examples of cranial nerves include the optic nerve (II) and the vagus nerve (X). With the spinal nerves, the cranial nerves form an important part of the peripheral nervous system.

**Craniata.** Vertebrata.

**[1]Craniate**

1. Possessing a cranium.
2. Of, pertaining to, or belonging to the subphylum Vertebrata (Craniata).

**[2]Craniate.** An animal with a skull and vertebral column.

**Cranium.** The portion of the vertebrate skull which encloses the brain.

**Cranium** (brain case). The part of the vertebrate skull that encloses and protects the brain. It is formed by the fusion of several flattened bones, which have immovable joints (sutures) between them.

**Craspedote.** Possessing a velum, as in medusae.

**Craspedromous.** Describing a form of leaf venation in which there is a single primary vein running down the centre of the leaf with secondary veins branching off this in an essentially parallel fashion. In traditional terminology such venation is described as penni-parallel. An example is the leaf of the sweet chestnut (Castanea sativa).

**Crassula** (bar of Sanio). One of a pair of barlike thickenings made up of primary wall and intercellular material found adjacent to the bordered pits of most gymnosperm tracheids.

**Crassulacean Acid Metabolism** (CAM). A form of photosynthesis first described in the family Crassulaceae and since found in many other succulent plants. CAM plants keep their stomata closed during the day to reduce water loss by transpiration. Carbon dioxide can therefore only enter at night when, instead of combining with ribulose bisphosphate (as in conventional $C_3$ plants) it combines with the three-carbon compound phosphoenol pyruvate (PEP) to give the four-carbon oxaloacetic acid. This is then converted to malic acid, which can be stored in the cell vacuoles until daylight, when it is transferred to the cytoplasm. Here it is broken down to release carbon dioxide, which is then fixed in the normal manner. This adaptation allows such plants to flourish in arid habitats but their growth rate is slow. CAM can be induced in certain $C_3$ plants by water stortage.

**Crateriform.** Shaped like a saucer or hollow, shallow bowl.

**Craw**

1. The crop of an insect or bird.
2. The stomach of an animal.

**Crawdad**

1. In the United States, a crayfish.
2. In England, the spiny lobster.

**Crawler**

1. An animal which crawls, as the night crawler; an annelid.
2. The first instar of a scale insect.

**Crayfish.** The crayfish is a freshwater crustacean, rather like a small lobster. There are several species distributed widely over the world, although absent from Africa. The largest species lives in Tasmania and may weigh up to 4 kg. Crayfishes eat a variety of small water creatures, and some actually leave the water at night to feed on nearby vegetation.

**Creatine.** A compound, synthesized from the amino acids arginine, glycine, and methionine, that occurs in muscle. In the form of creatine phosphate (or phosphocreatine), it is an important reserve of energy for muscle contraction, which is released when creatine phosphate loses its phosphate and is converted to creatinine, which is excreted in the urine.

**Crealionism** (special creation). A view that opposes evolutionary theory and anvisages the vast variety of living organisms, both existing and fossilized, as having been specially designed by a Creator. The attempted construction of phylogenetic pathways based on the idea that living forms have evolved from ancestral forms is interpreted by creationists as evidence of a 'Great Design'. Creationism is difficult to disprove by experiment. Some creationists believe in the theory of catastrophism in which it is thought that there have been a number of creations at different times, each having been destroyed by some kind of natural catastrophe, such as a flood.

**Creationist.** A proponent of the theory of special creation.

**Creeper**

1. *bot.* *a.* A plant which spreads along the surface of the ground. *b.* A plant which climbs by means of aerial roots, as the Virginia creeper.
2. *zool.* *a.* A small bird of the family Certhiidae, as the brown creeper (Certhia familiaris). *b.* Any small creeping animal.

**Creeper Fowl.** A heterozygous fowl with short, crooked legs. Homozygous recessives die due to a lethal factor.

**Creeping Jenny.** A low creeping plant related to the primrose. It has yellow, bell-shaped flowers and grows in damp woods.

**Cremocarp.** A dry fruit that is a type of schizocarp formed from two one-seeded carpels. The carpels remain separate and form indehiscent mericarps that are attached to a central supporting strand (carpophore) for some time before dispersal. It is characteristic of the Umbelliferae (carrot family).

**Crenad.** A plant which grows near a spring.

**Crenate.** Describing a leaf margin that has rounded projections. A leaf margin with very small such projections is termed crenulate.

**Crenicolus.** Inhabiting brooks fed by springs.

**Crenulate.** Minutely or finely crenate.

**Creodont.** A primitive, fossil mammal.

**Creophagous.** Carnivorous said of insect-eating plants.

**Crepitation.** Production of a grating or crackling sound.

**Crepuscular**

1. Pertaining to dusk or twilight.
2. Active at twilight or in dim light, as bats.

**Cress.** A popular salad vegetable, originally native to Iran. It is usually eaten as a seedling. The leaves have a pungent flavour.

**Crest**

1. A tuft of hair or a process on the head of a bird or mammal, as the comb of a cock.
2. A prominent ridge, as *a.* that along the neck of newts; *b.* that on certain bones or seeds.

**Crested.** Bearing a crest or crestlike structure.

**Crested Newt.** Also called the warty newt because of its coarse black skin. It is up to 14 cm long including the tail, and the male has a ragged crest running down its back in the breeding season. It spends much of its time in water and emits a strong smell when disturbed.

**Cretaceous.** The final geological period of the Mesozoic era. It extended from about 136 million years ago, following the Jurassic, to about 65 million years ago, when it was succeeded by the Palaeocene epoch. The name of the period is derived from creta (Latin : chalk) and the Cretaceous was characterized by the deposition of large amounts of chalk in western Europe. The Cretaceous was the time of greatest flooding in the Mesozoic. Angiosperm plants made their first appearance on land and in the early Cretaceous Mesozoic reptiles reached their peak. At the end of the period there was a widespread extinction of the dinosaurs, flying reptiles, and ammonites, the cause of which is not definitely known, although it may be partly related to changing environmental conditions at the time.

**Cretaceous Period.** The third and final period of the Mesozoic era characterized by great swamps, formation of the Rocky Mountains, the rise of flowering plants, modern insects, archaic mammals, and birds, and the extinction of dinosaurs, pterodactyls, and toothed birds.

**Cricket.** A group of insects similar to grasshoppers but with much longer antennae. Male crickets sing to the females by rubbing together their wing-cases. There are two main groups of cricket : the true crickets, which live mainly on the ground and include the field cricket and house cricket; and the bush crickets which live in bushes and other undergrowth. Bush crickets include the great green bush cricket, wart-biter and speckled bush cricket.

**Crinoid.** Any echinoderm of the class Crinoidea which includes the sea lilies and feather stars, abundant during the Paleozoic era. Most were sessile forms, attached by a jointed stalk. Living species include Antedon, a feather star of the Atlantic coast.

**Crisp.** Curled; in curls or ringlets; brittle.

**Crissum.** Undertail coverts constituting the circumanal plumage of birds.

**Crista.** A shelflike structure in a mitochondrion formed by infolding of the inner membrane. The cristae greatly increase the surface area of the inner mitochondrial membrane so providing a large area for the reactions of the electron transfer system to occur.

**Crista Ampullaris.** A sensory structure on the inner surface of the ampulla of a semicircular duct containing hair cells which are stimulated by movement of the endolymph.

**Cristate.** Bearing a crest or crista.

**Critical Day Length.** The period of daylight, specific in length for any given species, that appears to initiate flowering in long-day plants or inhibit flowering in short-day plants. In actual fact long-day plants will not flower if the dark period exceeds a certain maximum and conversely short-day plants will not flower unless the dark period exceeds a certain minimum. These periods are termed critical dark periods and must be continuous to have effect (night-break effect).

**Critical Group.** A large group of related organisms that, although variations exist between them, cannot be divided into smaller groups of equivalent taxonomic rank to the parent group.

**Critical-point Drying.** A technique for removing the water from biological specimens without causing shrinkage or collapse. The specimen is dehydrated by suspending it in acetone or alcohol and driving off the solvent under controlled conditions of temperature and pressure. Compare freeze drying.

**Croaker.** The name given to a widely distributed family of fishes remarkable for the noise they make. This ranges from humming and purring to hissing and croaking. The sounds are produced by vibrations of the muscles surrounding the swim-bladder. The Atlantic croaker and the meagre or weakfish of warm waters are two common members of this family.

**Crocodile** A large, long-tailed, aquatic reptile of the order Loricata (Crocodilia), as Crocodylus americana, the American crocodile.

**Crocus.** Small flowering plants of the iris family, growing from a corm. The wild spring and autumn crocus have solitary flowers like those of the garden crocuses: six-petalled, purple or white (or both), with orange styles. The flowers of the spring crocus appear between March and April, while those of the autumn crocus come out in September to October, after the long, slim leaves have died.

**Cromagnon Man.** The earliest form of modern man (Homo sapiens), which is believed to have appeared in Europe about 35 000 years ago and possibly earlier in Africa and Asia. Fossils indicate that these hominids were taller and more delicate than Neanderthal man, which they replaced. They used intricately worked tools of stone and bone and left the famous cave drawings at Lascaux in the Dordogne. The name is derived from the site at Cromagnon, France, where the first fossils were found in 1868.

**Crop.** An enlarged portion of the anterior section of the alimentary canal in some animals, in which food may be stored and/or undergo preliminary digestion. The term is most commonly applied to the thin-walled sac in birds between the oesophagus and the proventriculus. In female pigeons the crop contains glands that secrete crop milk, used to feed nestlings.

**Crop-milk.** Pigeon Milk.

**Crosier.** A curled structure, as a young frond of a fern.

**Cross**

1. A mating between two selected individuals. Controlled crosses are made for many reasons, *e.g.* to investigate

the inheritance of a particular characteristic or tc improve a livestock or crop variety.

2. An organism resulting from such a mating.

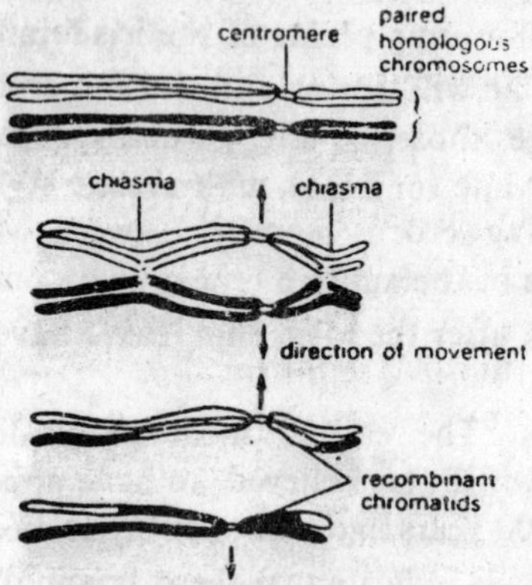


Crossing over at two chiasmata in a pair of homologous chromosomes

**Crossbill.** A bird belonging to the finch family. The male is predominantly red, the female yellowish-brown. The crossbill gets its name from its unusual beak, the lower part of which crosses to the left of the upper part. With this beak the bird can extract seeds from the fir cones on which it feeds. The bird is found in scattered areas of the British Isles. The similar parrot crossbill lives in Scandinavia.

**Crossbreed.** To mate two unrelated individuals, especially those of different breeds.

**Cross-fertilization.** The union of gametes of two different individuals.

**Cross Field.** In the wood of conifers, the area where the walls of ray cells about onto those of axial tracheids, as seen in radial longitudinal section. This region is usually pitted and the form of these cross-field pits is often characteristic of a genus or group of genera.

**Crossing Over.** The exchange of corresponding segments between chromatids of homologous chromosomes. The process is inferred genetically from the recombination of linked genes and cytologically from the formation of chiasmata. Normally crossing over is reciprocal (equal) but unusual segregation products is ordered tetrads indicate that it can very occasionally be nonreciprocal (unequal). Work with imperfect (asexual) fungi indicates that crossing over can also occur during mitosis. Chromosome reassortment and crossing over together constitute the main source of genetic variation in sexually reproducing organisms. Crossing over is suppressed by chromosome inversions.

**Crossopterygian.** A primitive lobe-finned fish of the superorder Crossopterygii, a group considered ancestral to amphibians and higher verrebrates.

**Crossover.** An individual resulting from a new combination of linked genes brought about by crossing-over.

**Crossover Suppressor.** Inversion.

**Cross Pollination.** The transfer of pollen from the anthers of one individual to the stigma of another individual of the same species. This is achieved by intermediary agents such as insects (entomophily), wind (anemophily), or water (hydrophily). Birds (ornithophily) and bats often act as pollinators in the tropics. Cross pollination does not necessarily preclude self pollination, although some mechanisms, such as the closing of the stigma lobes after pollination with compatible pollen (as in Mimulus), may reduce the possibility of it occurring.

**Cross Protection.** The inoculation of a young plant with a mild strain of a virus to protect it from other virulent strains. This procedure has been used in the control of tobacco mosaic virus and citrus tristeza virus.

**Crotalid.** A pit viper.

**Croton Bug.** The German cockroach (Blattella germanica).

**Crow.** A family of mainly black birds which includes the rook, jackdaw, jay and magpie. Crows are the largest of the perching birds. They are active and aggressive, with harsh, noisy voices. They eat almost anything, including grain and vast quantities of caterpillars and other insects. Rooks and jackdaws tend to flock together and build their nests in colonies, usually in tree-tops. The carrion crow is completely black with a black beak. It is known as the corbie in Scotland. Carrion crows are found almost anywhere. They gather in large flocks in the autumn but, for the rest of the time, they are solitary birds. They have a bad name because they rob nests and eat carrion. The grey-backed hooded crow is a northern form of the carrion crow, but behaves in just the same way.

**Crown**

1. A corona; the top portion of a structure.
2. *bot*. *a.* The junction between stem and root in a seed plant. *b.* A portion of a rhizome with a large bud, used in propagation. *c.* A circle of processes on the inner surface of a corolla. *d.* The branches of a tree with their leaves.
3. *zool.* *a.* The body of a crinoid with its projecting arms. *b.* The crest of a bird.
4. *anat.* *a.* The exposed portion of a tooth covered by enamel. *b.* The top portion of the head.

**Crown Gall.** A gall disease caused by the soil-borne bacterium Agrobacterium tumefaciens. Galls are produced above and below ground on a wide range of host plants—particularly fruit trees. It is not generally a serious disease and even large galls on fruit trees seem to have little economic effect.

The galls are of interest to physiologists because they display habituation and are self-sufficient for auxin when grown in culture.

**Crown of-thorns**

1. *zool.* A sixteen-armed, spiny starfish, Acanthaster planci, destructive to living coral, especially in the islands of Oceania.
2. *bot.* A climbing spurge, Euphoria splendens.

**Crowfoot.** A European and North American aquatic plant of the Butter-cup family. Most of the plant is under water. Its white, buttercup-sized blooms grow above the surface. There are many species.

**Crozier.** The hooked dikaryotic tip of an ascogenous hypha. Its two nuclei divide simultaneously and the resulting four daughter nuclei are partitioned by two septa into three cells. The middle cell contains two genetically different nuclei and the apical and basal cells either side contain one nucleus each. The apical cell bends round to fuse with the basal cell, thus reestablishing the dikaryotic condition in both cells resulting from the cell division. The middle cell, now at the tip of the ascogenous hypha, develops into an ascus. The cell below may extend and go on to form another crozier. Similarities between this process and the clamp connections of certain basidiomycetes have led to the suggestion that basidiomycetes evolved from ascomycetes.

**Cruciate.** Resembling or shaped like a cross; bearing the mark of a cross.

**Cruciferae** (Brassicaceae). A large dicotyledonous family, commonly called the mustard family, members of which occur predominantly in north temperate latitudes. It contains about 3000 species in about 375 genera. Most cruciferous plants are herbs with alternate leaves and four-petalled flowers borne in a raceme or corymb. The petals are inserted in the shape of a cross (cruciform), hence the name of the family. The fruit is also characteristic (siliqua, silicula, lomentum).

Many crucifers are important crop plants. Cultivars of Brassica oleracea include the cabbage, cauliflower, and Brussels sprout, while other species include the turnips, swedes, and oilseed rape. Ornamental crucifers include the wallflower (Cheiranthus cheiri), honesty (Lunaria annua), and stocks (Matthiola).

**Cruciferous.** Of or pertaining to the mustard family, Cruciferae.

**Cruciform.** Cruciate.

**Crumble Cap.** A fragile toadstool, often found in thousands on rotten logs and tree stumps. The pale yellow cap is bell-shaped and grooved; the gills are grey or black.

**Crura.** Plural of Crus.

**Crustacea.** A class of arthropods containing over 35 000 species distributed worldwide, mainly in freshwater and marine habitats, where they constitute a major component of plankton. Crustaceans include shrimps, crabs, and lobsters (Decapoda), barnacles, water fleas (Daphnia), copepods (Copepoda), and the terrestrial woodlice The segmented body usually has a distinct head (bearing compound eyes, two pairs of antennae, and various mouthparts), thorax, and abdomen, and is protected by a shelllike carapace. Each body segment may bear a pair of branched (biramous) appendages used for locomotion, as gills, and for filtering food particles from the water. Appendages in the head region are modified to form jaws and in the abdominal region are often reduced or absent. Typically, the eggs hatch to produce a free-swimming nauplius larva. This develops either by a series of moults or undergoes metamorphosis to the adult form.

**Crustacean** Member of a group of largely aquatic arthropods which includes crabs, shrimps, barnacles, water-fleas and woodlice. The body is segmented and often divided into three—head, thorax and abdomen. There are several pairs of limbs (the number varying from species to species), commonly branched into two at the end. The head bears two pairs of antennae, the front pair being called antennules. Their function is mainly sensory. Most crustaceans also have compound eyes. The hard exoskeleton is made of chitin, frequently strengthened with deposits of chalk. In several species, *e.g.*, crabs, it forms a large plate or carapace over the front end of the body.

**Crustaceous.** Hard; brittle, with a crustlike surface or shell.

**Crustose** (crustaceous). Describing lichens that have a crustlike thallus closely appressed to and virtually inseparable from the substratum. An example is Lecanora.

**Cryophyte**. A plant which grows on ice or snow.

**Cryoplankton**. The plankton of glacial or polar waters.

**Crypt.** A slender sac or cavity; an intestinal gland (crypt or Lieberkuhn).

**Cryptanthous.** Cleistogamous; having hidden flowers or stamens.

**Cryptic**

1. Hidden or concealed.
2. Adapted for concealing, as cryptic coloration.

**Cryptic Coloration.** The type of colouring or making of an animal that helps to camouflage it in its natural environment. It may enable the animal to blend with its background or, like the stripes of zebras and tigers, help to break up the outline of its body.

**Cryptococcales.** Blastomycetes.

**Cryptogam**. In early classifications, a plant whose method of reproduction is not immediately apparent, *i.e.* a plant in which the reproductive structures are not borne in conspicuous flowers or cones. Cryptogams thus included the algae, fungi, bryophytes, and most pteridophytes. Compare phanerogam.

**Cryptophyta.** The division of unicellular flagellate algae that are dorsoventrally flattened and have an oblique furrow. Cryptophytes contain green, blue, and red pigments and store food as starch in a pyrenoid outside the plastid. Reproduction is by longitudinal fission and sexual reproduction does not occur.

**Cryptophyte.** A plant with its perennating buds hidden either below ground (geophyte, helophyte) or in water (hydrophyte). Cryptophytes are more common in arctic and temperate regions than in tropical regions.

**Cryptozoic.** Living in concealed places, as under stones, in crevices.

**Cryptozoite.** The preerythrocyte stage of the malarial organism found in liver cells.

**Crystal.** A nonliving cytoplasmic inclusion, often of calcium oxalate or less frequently of calcium carbonate. Crystals occur in a variety of forms (druse, raphide).

**CSF.** Cerebrospinal fluid.

**Ctenidium**

1. A gill, especially in a mollusk.
2. A row of stiff bristles forming a comblike structure, as that on the head of a flea.

**Ctenoid.** Resembling a comb; pectinate.

**Ctenoid Scale.** A type of dermal scale with an edge bearing comblike projections, as that in most teleost fishes.

**Cub.** Young of certain mammals, *e.g.* fox, bear and badger.

**Cuckoo.** A long-tailed, grey bird, about the same size as a kestrel, that is often heard and seldom seen. The familiar 'cuckoo' call of the male heralds the spring. Both sexes have a grey head and chest, and grey bars on their pale underparts. They winter in southern Africa and spend

April to August in Europe. The female lays her eggs in the nests of other birds, one egg in each nest, removing one of the existing eggs as she does so. When hatched the young cuckoo quickly gets rid of any other chicks or eggs. The foster parents, often much smaller than the cuckoo, have to work very hard for three weeks to satisfy the alien chick's enormous appetite. The young birds follow their parents south in September.

**Cuckoo Flower.** Also called lady's smock, the cuckoo flower is a declicate plant belonging to the cabbage family. Its lilac or white flowers appear in the spring; at the same time as the arrival of the cuckoo. The leave sarising from the roots are much finer than those growing from the stem. The plant grows in damp areas, particularly meadows.

**Cuckoo-pint.** Lords and Ladies.

**Cuckoo-spit.** Foam produced by froghopper nymphs to protect themselves from drying up while they feed on plant juices.

**Cuckoo-shrike.** Bearing little resemblance to cuckoos or shrikes and related to neither, this group of insecteating birds is distributed through tropical Africa, southern Asia and Australia. One of the best known is the black-faced cuckoo-shrike of Australia, locally called the blue-jay or shufflewing.

**Cuckoo Wasp.** A group of parasitic wasps that lay their eggs in the nests of other wasps and bees. The Ruby-tailed Wasp is a common species.

**Cucullate**

1. Hooded.
2. Shaped like a hood.

**Cuckoo Wrasse.** Wrasse.

**Cucumber**. A trailing or climbing hairy-stemmed plant, originally from southern Asia. It is cultivated for its long, pulpy green fruits. It has triangular leaves and yellow or white flowers, each one either male or female. Young fruits are often called gherkins, although the true gherkin is the fruit of a related plant from the West Indies.

**Cucurbit.** Any member of the melon or gourd family, Cucurbitaceae, as the gourd, pumpkin, squash, cucumber, muskmelon, and watermelon.

**Cud.** In ruminants, a mass of food which is regurgitated from the rumen, chewed, and swallowed a second time.

**Culm.** The jointed stem of a grass, usually hollow except at the nodes.

**Culmicolous.** Growing on grass stems, said of fungi.

**Cultellus.** A sharp, lancetlike mouth part of certain flies.

**Culm**. The jointed stem of members of the Gramineae and Cyperaceae. In grasses it is usually hollow or more rarely filled with pith. In sedges it is usually solid and triangular in cross section.

**Cultivar.** A variety of a plant that has been developed by cultivation as a result of agricultural or horticultural practices. The term is derived from cultivated variety.

**Cultured**. Grown or produced artificially, as cultured pearls.

**Culture Medium** (nutrient medium). A mixture of nutrients used to support the growth of microorganisms or of the cells, tissues, or organs of animals or plants. Such media may be solid, if mixed with a gelling agent (*e.g.* agar), or liquid. Whenever possible media used in experimental work should be chemically defined, *i.e.* the identity and concentration of their constituents should be known. Sometimes however a culture can only be grown when complex undefined additional substances, *e.g.*

coconut milk, are added. A culture medium must contain all the macro and micronutrients essential to growth. A carbohydrate source is necessary and is usually supplied as sucrose. Carbohydrates are necessary even for plant tissue cultures since photosynthesis either does not occur or is insufficient in culture. Plant tissue cultures also require growth substances, normally an auxin or cytokinin or very often both in a particular ratio. Other factors, *e.g.* gibberellins or vitamins, are often necessary. Ideal media for plant tissue culture are usually also suitable for the growth of microorganisms. Culture must therefore be carried out under sterile conditions to avoid contamination.

**Cuneate.** Describing leaves that are wedge shaped with the point of the wedge forming the base of the lamina.

**Cuneiform Bones.** Three tarsal bones lying proximal to the first three metatarsal bones.

**Cunner.** A small, marine percomorph fish (Tautogolabrus adspersus).

**Cup.** A shallow, open organ or structure, as the involucre of an acorn.

**Cup Fungus.** A fungus whose fruiting body is a shallow cup-shaped disc, often brightly coloured, with the spore-producing cells scattered over the upper surface Most species are small and all are rather brittle. The majority live on the ground, although some grow on dead wood.

**Cup Fungi.** Ascomycetes of the order Pezizales which possess cup-shaped fruiting bodies or apothecia, as Peziza.

**Cupula**

1. A gelatinous mass surmounting *a.* the neuromasts of a lateral line system; *b.* a crista ampullaris of the inner ear.

2. The rounded tip of the osseous cochlea
3. The dome of the diaphragm.

**Cupule**

1. A hard or membranous cupshaped structure formed from bracts and enclosing various fruits, such as the hazelnut and acorn.
2. A structure in club mosses (Lycopodium species) that protects the gemma (resting bud) during its development. It is composed of six leaflike structures.
3. They bright red tissue around the seed of yew (Taxus), forming the yew 'berry'.

**Curlew.** The common curlew is a large wading bird, with streaky brown plumage and the down-curved 12-cm beak. It breeds across Europe and Asia, frequenting moorlands and marshes. The curved beak is used for digging small animals from the soil or mud. Several other species breed in the northern hemisphere, and some cover huge distances in their annual migrations to the southern hemisphere.

**Currant.** Small deciduous shrubs commonly cultivated for their edible berries. The red and black current have greenish, five-petalled flowers arranged in drooping spikes, and palmate, lobed leaves. They grow in damp woods and by fresh water.

**Cursorial.** Adapted for running.

**Cuscus.** An Australasian tree-dwelling marsupial about one metre long including its long prehensile tail. The various species are all nocturnal and they feed on fruit, leaves and insects.

**Cusp**

1. A sharp raised protuberance on the surface of a molar tooth. The cusps of opposing molars (*i.e.*

on opposite jaws) are complementary to each other, which increases the efficiency of grinding food during chewing.

2. A flap forming part of a valve.

**Cuspidate**. Suddenly narrowing to a point. The terms is especially used of leaves.

**Cutaneous**. Of or pertaining to the skin.

**Cuticle**. Protective outer covering of most plants and invertebrates. In plants it is made of the substance cutin and its main function is to prevent excessive water loss. In the invertebrates it is either made largely of protein or, as in the case of arthropods, a substance called chitin. The cuticle forms the tough exoskeleton of insects and in crustaceans it is frequently strengthened by deposits of chalk.

**Cuticularization**. The secretion by the outer (epidermal) layer of cells of plants and many invertebrates of substance that then harden to form a cuticle.

**Cutin**. A mixture of complex macromolecules forming the waxy cuticle that covers the aerial parts of most higher plants. Cutin contains long-chain fatty acids and polyhydroxy derivatives of these fatty acids (*e.g.* 10, 16-dihydroxypalmitic acid). These molecules are cross-linked through ester bonds in a more or less random fashion to form a large interlinking matrix, relatively impervious to water and gases.

**Cutinization**. The impregnation of the walls of epidermal cells with cutin.

**Cutis**. The skin.

**Cutlass Fish**. A long, slender marine fish of the family Trichiuridae; hairtail.

**Cutting**. A detached portion of a living plant, such as a bud or leaf, that can produce a new daughter plant if grown in soil or in a suitable culture medium. Taking cuttings is a common horticultural practice for plant propagation. Often the cut end of a stem cutting is dipped into a rooting powder, which contains a natural or synthetic auxin that stimulates the rapid development of adventitious roots and the establishment of a new daughter plant.

**Cuttlefish.** A marine mollusc resembling a squid. Cuttlefishes vary in length from about 4 cm to 1.5 metres. The head bears eight arms and two long tentacles, all with horny suckers. Inside the body there is a chalky 'shell', often washed up on the beach at the 'cuttle-bone'. Cuttlefishes feen on small fishes, which are caught by the tentacles. The animals are famed for their ability to change colour.

**Cupule.** A cup-shaped structure, as *a.* the involucre of an acorn consisting of bracts fused at their bases; *b.* the structure in liverworts which produces gemmae; *c.* the apothecium of a cup fungus.

**Cupuliform.** Cup-shaped.

**Curare.** An extract of tropical plants of the genera Chondrodendron and Strychnos of the Amazon valley used by South American Indians for poisoning arrows. It contains alkaloids which block impulses at the myoneural junction. It is used medicinally as a muscle relaxant.

**Curculio.** Any snout beetle of the family Curculionidae, as the plum curculio (Conotrachelus nenuphar).

**Cuttle Fish.** A group of cephalopod molluscs related to the squids, with a chalky inner shell or 'cuttle-bone'. Cuttlefish have streamlined bodies, up to 1.5 metres long. At the head end are eight arms and two long tentacles, all bearing suckers and used to seize prey. Cuttlefish can change colour to camouflage themselves when danger threatens.

**Cyanobacteria.** Cyanophyta.

**Cyanocobalamin** (vitamin $B_{12}$) A complex molecule consisting of a corrin ring (similar to a porphyrin ring) and a sibonucleotide. The corrin ring contains a cobalt atom, which is bonded to a cyanide group and to the ribonucleotide. Cyanocobalamin is not synthesized by plants or animals and commercial production is from bacterial cultures, *e.g.* of Streptomyces olivaceus. It is not needed by plants but animals need it for the normal development of erythrocytes.

**Cyanogenesis.** The production of cyanide glycosides by certain plants, including cherry laurel (Prunus laurocerasus), birdsfoot trefoil (Lotus corniculatus), and white clover (Trifolium repens). The glycosides, found largely in water solution in the vacuole, yield a sugar and hydrogen cyanide on hydrolysis. Their function is uncertain but they may serve to detoxify harmful by-products of necessary metabolic reactions. They may also act as an emergency sugar store and, because of their poisonous nature, can play a role in deterring invasion or damage by disease and pest organisms.

**Cyanophycin.** A food reserve characteristic of algae belonging to the Cyanophyta.

**Cyanophyta** (blue-gree algae). A division containing very simple algae that resemble photosynthetic bacteria in their internal organization (prokaryote). Cyanophytes are unicellular but sometimes become joined in colonies or filaments by a sheath of mucilage. They occur in all aquatic habitats. A few species fix atmospheric nitrogen and thus contribute to soil fertility (nitrogen fixation). Others exhibit symbiosis (Lichenes).

**Cyanophyte.** Any member of the Cyanophyta, a division of the plant kingdom which includes the blue-green algae, simple organisms lacking a distinct nucleus and plastids, as Gleocapsa, Nostoc.

**Cyanosis.** Blueness of the skin due to an excess quantity of reduced hemoglobin in the blood.

**Cyathium.** A specialized cup-shaped type of inflorescence found in members of the Euphorbiaceae. It resembles a single flower and consists of a female flower in the centre surrounded by many simple male flowers enclosed within an involucre. The involucre also bears a number of petaloid glands along its rim.

**Cyathium.** A type of inflorescence in which modified unisexual flowers are borne on a cup-shaped involucre, as in Euphorbia (spurge).

**Cybernetics.** The application of statistical mechanics to communication systems, especially in relation to human control systems.

**Cycad.** A primitive, gymnospermous plant of the subclass Cycadophytae, with large divided leaves borne on the tip of a short, unbranched stem, abundant during the Mesozoic era. Living forms comprise about 100 species.

**Cycadales.** An order of tropical and subtropical gymnosperms containing one family, the Cycadaceae, divided into some 9 genera and about 100 species. Cycads have a thick, generally unbranched, stem bearing a terminal rosette of large palmlike leaves. Scale leaves are also present on the upper part of the stem and apex. Cycads are very slow-growing and vary considerably in height between species : some have a large proportion of the stem underground and reach a height of only a few metres, while others attain heights up to 15 m. Most of the mechanical support of the stem is provided by the sclerenchymatous leaf based. The starchy nature of the stem (and of the seeds) has led to the use of certain cycads, the sago palms, as a food source.

Cycads are dioecious and bear exceptionally large female cones and ovules. The egg cell of the archegonium is larger than that found in any other group of plants. Cycads first appeared in the late Palaeozoic and are thought to be most closely related to the Pteridospermales.

**Cycadeoidales.** Bennettitales.

**Cycadicae.** Pinophyta.

**Cycadofilicales.** Pteridospermales.

**Cyclamen.** A flowering woodland plant related to the primrose. Its heart-shaped leaves, borne on long stems, have a purple tinge on the underside, and the pink or white flowers have backward-turned petals.

**[1]Cycle.** A complete course of operations or a series of events which occurs repeatedly in the same sequence, as a line cycle.

**[2]Cycle**

1. *zool.* An alternating circle of tentacles on the oral disc of a sea anemone.
2. *bot. a.* One turn of a helix or spire, with reference to leaf arrangement. *b.* A whorl of floral parts.

**Cyclic**

1. Pertaining to or occurring in cycles.
2. *bot.* Whorled, said of floral parts.

**Cyclic AMP.** A derivative of ATP that is widespread in animal cells as an intermediate messenger in many biochemical reactions induced by hormones. Upon reaching their target cells, the hormones activate the enzyme that catalyses cyclic AMP production. Cyclic AMP ultimately activates the enzymes of the reaction induced by the hormone concerned. Cyclic AMP is also involved in controlling gene expression and cell division, in immune responses, and in nervous transmission.

**Cycloid Scale.** A type of fish scale which is thin, lacks enamel, is roughly circular in outline, and bears concentric lines of growth.

**Cyclomorphosis.** Seasonal changes in form which occur in various plankton organisms.

**Cyclops.** A freshwater crustacean. The female is easily recognized by the pair of trailing egg-sacs on either side of the clearly segmented body.

**Cyclosis** (cytoplasmic streaming). The movement of cytoplasm within cells. The viscosity of cytoplasm can vary as a result of chahges in the nature of protein molecules, particularly actin. In the fluid form it flows freely and can be observed carrying organelles and other inclusions in the cell. Cyclosis is very variable in plant cells. For example, in leaves of Elodea (waterweeds) it is more active in cells in the midrib region than in cells near the margin. The rate of flow increases with rise in temperature but is normally less than 0.1 mm per second. It is probable that contractile forces generated by F-actin microfilaments in the cytoplasm contribute to the movement. The streaming of cytoplasm probably assists the distribution of metabolites between cells via plasmodesmata, augmenting diffusion, which is a slower process. It is also believed to contribute to the passage of material through sieve tubes and is more pronounced in young phloem sieve tubes than in the older elements. Cyclosis is not seen in prokaryotic cells.

**Cyclostomata** Agnatha.

**Cyclostome.** The most primitive kind of fishes. Cyclostomes have no jaws, only a circular sucking mouth with which they attach themselves to their prey. The skeletons are made of cartilage (gristle) instead of bone. They include Lampreys and Hagfishes.

**Cydippid Larva.** The free-swimming larva of certain ctenophores.

**Cyesis.** Pregnancy.

**Cygnet.** A young swan.

**Cymba.** A woody, boatlike spathe which encloses the inflorescence in certain palms.

**Cyme.** A determinate type of infloresence in which flowers form a flat-topped or convex cluster in which the terminal flower of each axis blooms first.

**Cymose**

1. Of or pertaining to a cyme.
2. Bearing cymes.

**Cymose Inflorescence** (cyme; definite inflorescence). A type of flowering shoot (inflorescence) in which the first-formed flower develops from the growing region at the top of the flower stalk. Thus no new flower buds can be produced at the tip and other flowers are produced from lateral buds beneath. In a monochasial cyme (or monochasium, the development of the flower at the tip is followed by a new flower axis growing from a single lateral bud. Subsequent new flowers may develop from the same side of the lateral shoots, as in the buttercup, or alternately on opposite sides, as in forget-me-not. In a dichasial cyme (or dichasium), the development of the flower at the apex is followed by two new flower axes developing from buds opposite one another, as in plants of the family Caryophyllaceae (such as stitchwort). Compare racemose inflorescence.

**Cynarrhodium.** A type of fruit characteristic of roses, as a rose hip.

**Cynipid.** A gall-producing insect of the family Cynipidae, order Hymenoptera.

**Cyperaceae.** A large family of monocotyledonous plants, the reeds and sedges, numbering some 4000 species in about

90 genera. It is cosmopolitan in distribution but members are concentrated in the wetter regions of temperate and cold latitudes. Reeds and sedges superficially resemble grasses but may be distinguished by their solid three-angled stems, by the absence of ligules, and by the leaf sheaths, which are usually closed as compared to the open sheathing bases of grasses. The plants arise from swollon underground stems, which in some species, *e.g.* Chinese water chestnut (Eleocharis tuberosus), are edible. The flowers are small, having a reduced perianth, and arranged in spikes, each flower being subtended by a single glume. The fruit is an achene.

A few species are of limited commercial importance being used for making mats, baskets, hats, and paper. Others are used as ornamentals in water gardes.

**Cyphonautes.** A ciliated larva which develops from a non-brooded egg in ectoprocts.

**Cypress.** A group of coniferous trees found in the cooler northern and southern parts of the world, and on mountains in warmer regions. Cypresses belong to the same family as the junipers. Most species have over-

Lawson cypress Leyland cypress

lapping scale-like leaves, though young leaves may be needle-shaped. The cones are small and woody. One of the most popular species is the Lawson cypress from the mountains of Oregon and California. It has a conical shape reaching about 35 metres, and is commonly grown in Europe for ornament or shelter.

**Cypris Larva.** The free-swimming larva of certain crustaceans, as barnacles.

**Cypsela.** A dry single-seeded fruit that does not split open during seed dispersal and is formed from a double ovary in which only one ovule develops into a seed. It is similar to an achene and characteristic of members of the family Compositae, such as the dandelion.

**Cyrtopia Stage.** The postlarval stage of euphausiaceans, shrimplike crustaceans.

**Cyst**

1. A small, closed sac or vesicle; a bladder.
2. *zool.* A thick-walled structure containing an organism in an inactive stage, as that of various protozoans and flukes.
3. *bot.* A resistant, sporelike body formed by various algae, bacteria, fungi, and myxomycetes.
4. *med.* An abnormal, saclike structure or closed cavity containing fluid or other material, as a hydatid cyst.

**Cystacanth.** The infective form of an acanthocephalan.

**Cysteine.** A polar sulphur-containing amino acid with the formula $HSCH_2CH(NH_2)COOH$ (illustration at amino acid). It is synthesized from the amino acids methionine and serine. Breakdown is to pyruvate and may occur by several routes.

**Cystic Duct.** The duct leading from the gall bladder to the common bile duct.

**Cysticercoid.** A larval form of a tapeworm resembling a cysticercus but with a solid body and usually a taillike appendage, as in Hymenolepis.

**Cysticercus.** A bladder worm, the larva of a tapeworm consisting of a fluid-filled sac into which a scolex is invaginated; found in the intermediate host.

**Cystid.** In bryozoans, the exoskeleton and body wall.

**Cystine.** A molecule resulting from the oxidation reaction between the sulphydryl (—SH) groups of two cysteine molecules (amino acid). This often occurs between adjacent cysteine residues in polypeptides. The resultant disulphide bonds (—S—S—) are important in stabilizing the structure of protein molecules.

**Cystocarp.** A swollen urn-shaped fruiting body found in some red algae, *e.g.* Polysiphonia. It forms following fertilization of a carpogonium and contains the developing carpospores. The surrounding pseudoparenchymatous tissues develop from cells of the filament below the carpogonium.

**[1]Cystoid.** Bladderlike; resembling a cyst.

**[2]Cystoid** A fossil echinoderm of the class Cystoidea.

**Cystolith.** A large intracellular structure formed by the deposition of lime on an in growth of the cell wall. An enlarged epidermal cell containing such a structure is termed a lithocyst. Species in which cystoliths are formed include Ficus elastica (rubbr plant) and Urtica dioica (stinging nettle).

**Cytase.** An enzyme in seeds which acts on hemicelluloses.

**Cytidine.** A nucleoside comprising one cytosine molecule linked to a D-ribose sugar molecule. The derived nucleotides, cytidine mono-, di-, and triphosphate (CMP, CDP, and CTP respectively) participate in various biochemical reactions, notably in phospholipid synthesis.

**Cytochemistry.** The science which deals with the constituents of cells.

**Cytochrome.** Any iron-porphyrin containing electron-carrying protein forming part of the electron transport chains of respiration and photosynthesis. The porphyrin prosthetic group of cytochromes contains a chelated Fe ion, which changes oxidation state from ferric, Fe (III), to ferrous, Fe(II), when the cytochrome is reduced. Most cytochromes are tightly membrane bound.

**Cytochrome Oxidase.** One of several enzymes which catalyze the final steps in Krebs cycle in which water is an end product.

**Cytogamy.** In protozoa, a process resembling conjugation but differing in that the synkaryon is formed from fusion of the male and female nuclei of the same cell.

**Cytogenetics.** The application of techniques used in cytology to the problems of inheritance, particularly the study of chromosome structure and its relation to the phenotype.

**Cytokinesis.** The process of cytoplasmic division as distinct from nuclear division or karyokinesis. As telophase proceeds, a cell plate is organized in the cytoplasm in the equatorial region of the spindle. The cell is thus divided into two daughter cells.

**Cytokinin** (kinin). Any of a group of plant growth substances chemically related to the purine adenine. Cytokinins stimulate cell division in the presence of auxin and have also been found to delay senescence, overcome apical dominance, and promote cell expansion. Zeatin is a naturally occurring cytokinin.

**Cytology.** The study of the structure and function of cells. The development of the light and electron microscopes has enabled the detailed structure of the nucleus (including the chromosomes) and other organelles to be elucidated. Microscopic examination of cells, either live or as stained sections on a slide, is also used in the detection and diagnosis of various diseases, especially cancer.

**Cytolymph.** The fluid matrix of cytoplasm.

**Cytolysin.** A substance which brings about the dissolution of cells, as an antibody (bacteriolysin or hemolysin) or a non-specific substance, as snake venom or a hypotonic saline solution.

**Cytolysis.** The breakdown of cells, usually as a result of destruction or dissolution of their outer membranes. Certain drugs (cytotoxic drugs) have this effect and are used in the treatment of some forms of cancer.

**Cytomegalovirus.** A virus belonging to the herpes group (herpesvirus). In man it normally causes symptoms that are milder than the common cold, but it can produce more serious symptoms is those whose immune response is disturbed (*e.g.* cancer patients). Infection in pregnant women may cause congenital handicap in their children.

**Cytomixis.** The apparent migration of cytoplasm and nuclear material from one pollen mother cell to another through pores (cytomictic channels) in the cell walls. It occurs prior to and during the prophase stage of meiosis. The reason for this is unknown though it may be a response to the nutritional problems of developing reproductive cells.

**Cytomorphosis** *bacteriol.* A succession of morphological types from large, young cells through smaller, uniformly staining, mature forms, to senescent, degenerating forms, as may appear in a bacterial culture.

**Cyton.** The cell body of a neuron; perikaryon.

**Cytopathic.** Causing injury to cells.

**Cytopharynx.** A cavity in certain protozoans which leads from the cytostome (mouth) into the endoplasm; the gullet.

**Cytoplasm** (hyaloplasm). The part of the protoplasm outside the nucleus in which the cisternal elements and membrane-bound organelles lie. The soluble phase of cytoplasm contains the principal components of the cell's biochemical pathways, *i.e.*, ions, dissolved gases, and most of the enzymes and substrate molecules for metabolic processes. The cytoplasmic matrix also contains storage products, *e.g.*, lipid droplets, aleurone grains, and starch grains. Complex networks and linear arrangements of fine microfilaments and microtubules are commonly present. The microfilaments, 0.5—7.0 nm in length, are composed of helical chains of F-actin, and when supplied with ATP they contract. Those at the periphery of the cell are involved in movements of the components of the plasma membrane, *e.g.*, in endocytosis. Cytoplasm shows transitions between viscous (plasmagel) and fluid (plasmasol) phases. This is displayed in cyclosis and in amoeboid movement shown by some algal unicells. The F-actin molecules of the microfilaments, particularly at the periphery of cells, are unstable, readily breaking up into soluble components so that the cytoplasm becomes fluid.

**Cytoplasmic Inheritance**. The inheritance of genes contained in the cytoplasm of a cell, rather than the nucleus. Only a very small number of genes are inherited in this way. The phenomenon occurs because certain organelles, the mitochondria and (in plants) the chloroplasts contain their own genes and can reproduce independently. The female reproductive cell (the egg) has a large amount of cytoplasm containing many such organelles, which are consequently incorporated into the cytoplasm of all the cells of the embryo. The male reproductive cells (sperm or pollen), however, consist almost solely of a nucleus. Cytoplasmic organells are thus not inherited from the male parent. In plants, male sterility can be inherited via the cytoplasm. The inheritance of any such factors does not follow Mendelian laws.

**Cytoplasmic Streaming**. Cyclosis.

**Cytoproct.** The anal opening of a protozoan; cytopyge.

**Cytopyge.** Cytoproct.

**Cytosine.** A nitrogenous base, more correctly described as 4-amino-2-oxypyrimidine, derived from amino acids and sugars and found in all living organisms. Cytosine is found in one of the nucleotides present in DNA and RNA and pairs specifically with the purine base guanine. Substantial amounts of cytosine in DNA and RNA are found in the modified forms of 5-methylcytosine and 5-hydroxymethyl-cytosine. The affinity of these substances for guanine is similar to that of cytosine but the significance of their occurrence is uncertain. Recent evidence suggests that the regions of DNA with a large number of methylated cystosines are inactive. Thus gene activation may be brought about, at least in part, by selective demethylation.

**Cytosome.** The cytoplasm of a cell.

**Cytostome.** In protozoans, the mouth or opening leading to the cytopharynx.

**Cytotaxnomy.** The use of chromosome studies (*i.e.*, number, structure, and behaviour) in taxonomic work. Chromosome number is probably the most frequently quoted feature of the karyotype used by taxonomists. Chromosome counts are usually made on sporophytic tissue at mitosis and are therefore the diploid number (2n). When dealing with a polyploid series, the base number (*i.e.*, the number of chromosomes present in the original haploid genome) may be given.

**Cytozoan.** An animal which lives as an intracellular parasite, as Plasmodium.

**Cytozoic.** Living within cells, said of animal parasites.

**Cytorrhysis.** Wrinkling of a when schizophyte placed in a hypertonic solution.

# D

**2, 4-D.** 2,4-dichlorophenoxyacetic acid : a synthetic auxin frequently used as a weedkiller of broad-leaved weeds.

**$D_2$** (Vitamin-$D_2$). It is formed by ultraviolet irradiation of ergosterol (a substance occurring in lower plants like yeast and fungi); also known as calciferol. It is able to regulate calcium and phosphorus metabolism in the body.

**$D_3$** (Vitamin-$D_3$). A naturally occurring substance present in yolk, butter, and fish liver oils. In the body skin it is produced from 7-dehydrocholesterol at present the surface by activation through ultraviolet light. It is also known as cholcalciferol.

**D-600.** An organic compound (drug) that is able to block calcium influx through cell membranes. Chemically the substance is alphaisopropyl-alpha [(N-methyl-N-homo-veratryl)-alpha-amino-propyl] -3, 4, 5-trimethexyp/ohenyl acetonitrile.

**Dab.** A flatfish similar to the plaice, but slightly smaller (up to 38 cm long) and found in shallower water. It lives on the sandy sea bed and is particularly common in the North Sea.

**Dabbler.** A surface-feeding or dabbling duck.

**Dace.** A freshwater fish belonging to the carp family. It is like a slimmer version of its relative the roach, although it does not have red fins. It can move very quickly and lives in shoals in cool streams and lakes, eating mostly insects.

**Dactyl.** A digit (finger or toe).

**Dactylogram.** A fingerprint.

**Dactylozooid.** Sensory polyp which is found in hydrozoan coelenterates such as Obelia.

**Daddy-loug-legs.** This name is given to several long-legged Crane-Flies common in gardens and grasslands. The larvae are known as leather-jackets, and they feed on plant roots. Some of the long-legged Harvestmen (relatives of the spiders) are also called daddy-long-legs.

**Dahlia.** A plant of the genus Dahlia, propagated by root tubers.

**Daisy.** The name given to many flowers of the family Compositae with petal like rays. The common daisy frequently seen in lawns is a biennial with leaves growing close to the ground and white, pink or red flower-heads borne on short stalks. The name was originally 'day's eye', because the daisy closes its petals at night or on dull days

**Dalmanite.** A fossil trilobite of the genus Dalmanites.

**Dam.** A female parent, especially of a quadruped.

**Damping-off.** A disease of seedlings encouraged by cold wet soil and crowded conditions. In pre-emergence damping-off the germinating seed rots before the plumule breaks through the soil surface. In post-emergence damping-off the seedlings rot at soil level and then collapse and die. Damping-off is caused by numerous soil-inhabiling fungi including Fusarium, Phytophthora, Pythium, and Rhizoctonia (Corticium). Correct planting conditions, seed dressings, and the use of sterile soil in seed trays are the usual preventative methods.

**Damselfish.** A group of small brightly-coloured fishes found mainly in tropical waters, particularly along coral reefs. One of the best known is the clown fish which shelters among the stinging tentacles of a giant sea anemone. Each fish becomes gradually acquainted with, and accepted by, a particular anemone; if the fish enters the tentacles of a different anemone it is liable to be stung to death.

**Damselfly.** Any of a number of slender-bodied, rapid-flying insects of the order Odonata, suborder Zygoptera. They differ from dragonflies in that wings are held vertically over the body when at rest.

**Dance of the Bees.** A celebrated example of communication in animals, first investigated by Karl von Frisch (1886-1982). Honeybee workers on returning to the have after a successful foraging expedition perform a 'dance' on the comb that contains coded information about the distance and direction of the food source. Other workers, sensing vibrations from the dance, follow the instructions to find the food source.

**Dandelion.** A widespread flowering plant related to the daisy. Its leafless stems support solitary, bright yellow flower-heads made up of 'ray' Florets. The longiagged leaves form a rosette at the base of the stem. The fruits are topped by feathery white 'parachutes' which form the familiar dandelion clock. Dandelion stems contain a milky white juice that was once used in medicine. The leaves may be used in salads and the flowers are used for wine. The name dandelion is a corruption of 'dent delion', meaning lion's tooth, and referring to the lagged leaves.

**Daphnia.** A genus of crustaceans belonging to the suborder Cladocera (water fleas). Daphnia species have a transparent carapace and a protruding head with a pair of highly branched antennae for swimming and a single-median compound eye. The five pairs of thoracic appendages form an efficient filter-feeding mechanism. Reproduction can take place without mating, *i.e.* by parthenogenesis.

**Dark-ground Illumination.** A microscopical technique used to examine living cells or microorganisms. These are not suitable for examining under a normal light microscope (bright-field illumination) as they are usually transparent. Thus little detail can be seen against a light background. In dark-ground illumination direct light is prevented from forming an image by illuminating the specimen from the side so only diffracted light from the specimen passes through into the objective. The image of the specimen then appears luminoustagainst a completely dark background. This technique exploits the differences in refractive index between organelles and the surrounded protoplasm that causes the organelle boundaries to reflect more light.

**Dark Reactions.** The sequence of light-independent reactions that utilize the energy (in the form of ATP) and reducing power (in the form of NADPH), produced during the light reactions of photosynthesis, to reduce carbon dioxide. In eukaryotes, this process usually occurs in the chloroplast stroma and it can take one of two forms, depending on whether the subject is a $C_3$ or a $C_4$ plant. The details of the fixation of carbon dioxide differ in the two types of plants but the end result in both cases is the production of carbohydrates via the Calvin cycle.

**Dark Seed.** A seed which will germinate, only when kept in the dark, when other conditions would normally favour germination.

**Darter**

1. One of a large number of small, fresh water fishes of the family Percidae characterized by swift, sudden movements, as Etheostoma and Percina.

2. Water Turkey.

**Darwinism.** The theory of evolution proposed by Charles Darwin (1849-82) in On the Origin of Species (1859), which postulated that present-day species have evolved from simpler ancestral types by the process of natural selection acting on the variability found within populations. On the Origin of Species caused a furore when it was first published because it suggested that species are not immutable nor were they specially created—a view directly opposed to the doctrine of special creation. However the wealth of evidence presented by Darwin gradually convinced most people and the only major unresolved problem was to explain how the variations in populations arose and were maintained from one generation to the next. This became clear with the rediscovery of Mendel's work on classical genetics in the 1900s and led to the present theory of neo-Darwinism.

**Darwin's Finches.** A group of birds living in the Galapagos Islands that helped Charles Darwin to arrive at his theory of evolution by natural selection. Several species live in the various islands, all derived from a few finches that were blown to the Galapagos from South America. Before they arrived there were few birds on the islands, so the newcomers were able to evolve into many different forms, each having a different way of life.

**Dasyphyllous.** Having thick, hairy leaves.

**Date.** The fruit of the date palm (Phoenix dactylifera).

**Date Palm.** A kind of palm with a tall stem and a feathery crown. It bears large bunches of rich red fruits which are often dried and eaten. The tree originated in North Africa, and grows to more than 30 metres in height.

**Dating.** The determination of the age of rocks, minerals, and organic materials. Organic materials may be dated by radiocarbon dating and dendrochronology. However these methods can only date specimens from the later part of the Quaternary period. Varve dating is also limited to this period. Age determinations of older rocks rely on radiometric dating.

**Dating Techniques.** Methods of estimating the age of rocks, palaeontological specimens, archaeological sites, etc. Relative dating techniques date specimens in relation to one another; for example, stratigraphy is used to establish the succession of fossils. Absolute (or chronometric) techniques give an absolute estimate of the age and fall into two main groups. The first depends on the existence of something that develops at a seasonally varying rate, as in dendrochronology and varve dating. The other uses some measurable change that occurs at a known rate, as in chemical dating, radioactive (or radiometric) dating (carbon dating; fission-track dating; potassium-argon dating; rubidium-strontium dating; uranium-lead dating), and thermoluminescence.

**Dauer Humus.** Humus which is resistant to the attack of micro-organisms.

**Dauermodification.** A lasting inheritable change which is possibly cytoplasmic, and is produced by some treatment.

**[1]Daughter.** A female child.

**[2]Daughter.** Designating first generation offspring without regard to sex, as a daughter chromosome.

**Dawn Stone Age.** The Eolithic Age, the first of the cultural ages of man based on the existence of crude stone instruments called eoliths. It lasted from the Miocene through most of the Pliocene epoch.

**Day Length.** Critical day length.

**Day-neutral Plant.** A plant that is capable of flowering regardless of the amount of light it receives each day. The onset of flowering is therefore controlled by other factors. Compare long day plant, short-day plant.

**Day Position.** The situation adopted by leaves of plants during the day, if they alter this position when the light intensity decreases.

**Day Sleep.** Used for the folding of leaflets of a compound leaf in bright light. This brings the slomatal surfaces together, thereby reducing the water-loss.

**D-cells.** In human beings 1-8% cells of islets of Langerhans are D-cells which have somstostatin [(substance acting on anterior pituitary and also inhibiting secretion of insulin, glycogen and gastrointestinal hormones) also contain gastrin.

**DDT.** Dichlorodiphenyltrichloroethane; a colourless organic crystalline compound, $(ClC_6H_4)_2CH(CCl_3)$. DDT is the best known of a number of chlorine-containing pesticides used extensively in agriculture in the 1940s and 1950s. The compound is stable, accumulates in the soil, and concentrates in fatty tissue, reaching dangerous levels in carnivores high in the food chain. Restrictions are now placed on the use of DDT and similar pesticides.

**Dead.** Lifeless; not alive.

**Dead-leaf Butterfly.** An Indo-Malayan butterfly of the genus Kallima which, when resting, resembles a dead leaf.

**Dead-man's-fingers.** A soft coral (Alcyonium digitatum) found on beaches after storms.

**Dead-nettle.** Several species of usually fragrant, flowering plants, whose leaves resemble those of the stinging nettle, though they do not sting. The stem is square and the flowers are two-lipped, arranged in whorls at the base of the leaves. The two most c mmon species are the white dead-nettle, found by the wayside, and the red dead-nettle, an abundant weed of cultivated areas.

[1]**Dealate.** Having lost or been deprived of wings.

[2]**Dealate.** An insect which has lost its wings, as a termite.

**Deamination.** The removal of an amino group from a compound. Breakdown of amino acids is by oxidative deamination. Glutamate, which is formed from many amino acids by tronsamination, is deaminated by the enzyme glutamate dehydrogenase, yielding $\alpha$-ketoglutarate ammonium, ions, and reduced NAD or NADP.

**Death**. Cessation of life or vital activities beyond the possibility of resuscitation; termination of the existence of an organism.

**Death Cap**. A deadly poisonous toadstool that is fairly common in deciduous woodlands. It has a greenish cap, white gills, a white ring on the stalk, and a ragged bag surrounding the base. The harmless false death cap has a much yellower cap, often with patches of white skin on it. There is no bag at the base, but the stalk is swollen like a bulb.

**Deathwatch Beetle**. A wood-boring beetle, renowned for the damage it causes to timber. It gets its name from the sound the adult beetle makes by tapping its head against the walls of its tunnel; this sound was once believed to foretell a death. The larva of the deathwatch beetle feeds on old timber, especially oak. Old buildings, such as churches, are most at risk from deathwatch beetles.

**Deca-**. Symbol da. A prefix used in the metric system to denote ten times. For example, 10 coulombs=1 decacoulomb (daC).

**Decacanth**. The ciliated larva of Amphilina foliacea, a cestodarian tapeworm. Also called lycophore.

**Decacanth Embryo**. Ten hooked embryo present in the tapeworm Taenia saginata and infectious to secondary host.

**Decalcification**. Removal of lime or calcareous matter.

**Decapod**

1. Member of a group of crustaceans characterized by having five pairs of walking legs. The group contains the crabs, prawns and lobsters.
2. Member of a group of cephalopod molluscs that have ten arms or tentacles. The group contains the squids and cuttlefishes.

**Decapoda**. An order of crustaceans distributed worldwide, mainly in marine habitats. Decapods comprise swimming forms (shrimps and prawns) and crawling forms (crabs, lobsters, and crayfish). All are characterized by five pairs of walking legs, the first pair of which are highly modified in crawling forms to form powerful grasping pincers. The carapace is fused with the thorax and head forming a cephalothorax. The antennae are especially long in shrimps and prawns, which also possess several pairs of well-developed swimming appendages (pleopods) posterior to the walking legs Following fertilization by the male, females usually carry the eggs until they hatch. The larvae undergo several transformations before attaining adult form.

**Decarboxylase.** Any enzyme that catalyses the removal of carbon dioxide from a substrate. An example is the enzyme pyruvate decarboxylase, which catalyses the formation of acetaldehyde from pyruvate, a reaction in the alcoholic fermentation of glucose. Decarboxylases have a tightly bound coenzyme, often biotin or thiamin pyrophosphate, which acts as an intermediate carboxyl carrier.

**Decarboxylation.** The loss or removal of carbon dioxide from an organic acid, especially an amino acid.

**Decay**

1. Decomposition, putrefaction, fermentation, rotting; the transformation from a more or less solid or perfect state to a less perfect state.
2. *bacteriol.* The decomposition of organic matter, especially carbohydrates through the action of aerobic organisms such as bacteria, yeasts, and molds.

**Decerebration.** Removal of the brain, especially the cerebrum.

**Deceiver, The.** A toadstool that is common to all kinds of woods and heaths. It gets its name because it occurs in so many forms. The cap is a rich red brown when moist and the stalk is often twisted. The gills are flesh-coloured and widely spaced.

**Decerebration.** Refers to the experimental elimination of cerebral activity by section of brain stem by interrupting blood supply to the brain stem by interrupting blood supply to the brain region.

**Deci-.** Symbol d. A prefix used in the metric spstem to denote one tenth. For example, 0.1 coulomb=1 decicoulomb (dC).

**Decidua.** The mucosa or endometrium of a pregnant uterus.

**Deciduate Placenta.** On higher animals, the part of the inside skin of the uterus touching the placenta which is changed while the development of off spring is taking place and pushed out after it at birth.

**Deciduous.** Describing woody perennial plants that shed their leaves before the winter or dry season. Leaf fall is an adaptation that reduces water loss by transpiration when little or no water is available to the plant roots (physiological drought). Various environmental factors, such as daylength, temperature, and light intensity, influence the onset of leaf abscission. Compare evergreen.

**Deciduous Forests.** Forests having deciduous trees (leaves fall off annually). Found in moderate climate.

**Deciduous Teeth** (milk teeth). The first of two sets of teeth or a mammal. These teeth are smaller than those that replace them (the permanent teeth) and fewer in number, since there are no deciduous molars.

**Decomposer.** An organism that feeds on dead organic material, breaking it down into simpler substances and bringing about decay. In this way, organic material is recycled as the products of decomposition can be used by plants (producers). Examples of decomposers are some bacteria and fungi. Compare consumer.

**Decumbent.** Describing a stem that lies along the ground. Decumbent stems often have an upturned tip.

**Decompound.** Compound more than once, said of leaves.

**Deconjugation.** Used for the separation of chromosomes before the end of prophase of meiosis.

**Decortication**

1. *bot.* Removal of the bark or outer covering of a plant or plant product.
2. *zool.* Removal of the cortex of an organ.

**Decumbent.** Lying on the ground but with end ascending.

**Decurrent.** Describing leaf bases that extend down the stem beyond their point of insertion, forming a wing on the stem. The leaves of the common mullein (Verbascum thapsus) are examples. The term is also used of the gills of basidiomycete fungi that run down the stem, as seen, for example, in the genus Clitocybe.

**Decussate**

1. *anat.* Crossed or intersected so as to form an X-shaped structure, as the optic chiasma.
2. *bot.* Arranged in pairs alternately crossing at right angles, as decussate leaves or branches.

**Dedifferentiation.** The loss of the specialized features and reversal to a meristematic state of a differentiated cell. Dedifferentiation often occurs immediately prior to further reorganizational changes as in the production of a secondary meristem. The process may also be brought about by wounding or stimulation by growth substances. It is thought to involve the removal of inhibitors that normally prevent the expression of the complete genetic complement.

**Dediploidization.** Used for the production of haploid cells (or hyphae) from a dikaryotic diploid cell (or mycelium).

**Deer.** In a broad sense, any of a number of ruminants of the family Cervidae whose males possess solid antlers which are shed and grown anew each year, as the white-tailed deer (Odocoileus virginianus).

**Deer Mouse.** A rodent (Peromyscus leucopus) and related species, of the family Muridae. Also called white-footed mouse.

**Defaunate.** To make free of animal inhabitants.

**Defecation.** Evacuation of the bowel; passage of feces or a stool.

**Deficiency.** Deletion.

**Deficiency Disease.** A disease caused by the lack of an essential nutrient element. Mineral deficiencies can often be recognized by characteristic symptoms. For example, nitrogen deficiency results in stunting of the plant and chlorosis of older leaves. Iron deficiency results in interveinal chlorosis, particularly of younger leaves, giving a striped appearance in cereal and grass leaves. Boron deficiency causes the disease of heart rot in sugar beet and mangolds (Beta vulgaris).

**Definite Growth.** A form of growth where a maximum size is reached beyond which there is no further increase, *i.e.* growth is limited. It is seen in annual and biennial plants and in many plant organs, *e.g.* internodes, which do not continue to lengthen throughout the life of the plant. The term is also used of cymose inflorescences, in which growth is terminated by the production of a terminal flower bud. Compare indefinite growth.

**Definite Inflorescence.** Cymose inflorescence.

**Definitive Nucleus.** The diploid nucleus found in the centre of the embryo sac after the fusion of the two haploid polar nuclei. A male gamete released from the pollen tube may fuse with this to form the triploid primary endosperm nucleus from which the endosperm develops.

**Deflexed.** Bent abruptly downward; reflexed.

**Deflorate.** To deprive of flowers.

**Defoliation.** The loss of leaves, as that occurring in the natural shedding or that resulting from the depredations of insects.

**Degenerate Code.** Refers to the genetic code in which two or more codons may be representing the same amino acids.

**Degeneration**

1. Changes in cells, tissues, or organs due to disease, etc., that result in an impairment or loss of function and possibly death and breakdown of the affected part.
2. The reduction in size or complete loss of organs during evolution. The human appendix has undergone this process and performs no function in man. Degeneration of external organs may cause animals to appear to be more primitive than they really are; for example, early zoologists believed whales were fish rather than mammals because of the degeneration of their limbs.

**Deglutition** (swallowing). A reflex action initiated by the presence of food in the pharynx.

**Dehiscence.** The spontaneous and often violent opening of a fruit, seed pod, or anther to release and disperse the seeds or pollen Examples are the splitting of laburnum pods and primrose capsules.

**Dehiscent.** Fruits that split open and release their seeds are said to be dehiscent. The poppy capsule is a good example and so is the pod of the pea.

**Dehydrase.** An enzyme catalysing the removal of water, *i.e.* condensation, *e.g.*,

$$2C_6H_{12}O_6 \rightarrow C_{12}H_{22}O_{11} + H_2O.$$

**Dehydrogenase.** Any enzyme that catalyses the removal of hydrogen atoms in biological reactions. Dehydrogenases occur in many biochemical pathways but are particularly important in driving the electron-transport-chain reactions of cell respiration. They work in conjunction with the hydrogen-accepting coenzymes NAD and FAD.

**Dehydroretinol (vitamin-$A_2$).** Form of vitamin-A which is present in the liver and retina of fresh water fishes, some invertebrates and amphibians.

**Delayed Inheritance.** When each successive generation is having the genotype of the female parent for a particular character.

**Delayed Lethal Gene.** A lethal gene which affects the carrier after attainment of reproductive age. Thus, it is the only type of lethal gene that may be transmitted.

**Deletion** *genetics.* The loss of a portion of a chromosome with its contained genes. Also called deficiency.

**Deletion Mutation**. Genetic mutation in which one or more codons are knocked; a shorter protein.

**Delignification.** Describing the destruction of lignin in wood by a fungus.

**Deliquescence**. A gradual dissolving of tissue by autolysis. It is seen, for example, in Coprinus (ink-caps), in which the gills change into an inky black fluid after the basidio-spores have been discharged.

[1]**Deliquescent.** *chem.* Capable of absorbing atmospheric moisture and going into solution in the water absorbed.

[2]**Deliquescent.** *bot.*

1. Becoming semiliquid, applied to the perianth of certain flowers, as the water hyacinth, or to certain fungi upon maturing.

2. Designating a type of branching in which the main stem divides and then divides repeatedly forming many small branches.

**Deltoid**. In man, a large muscle which covers the shoulder joint, an abductor of the humerus.

**Deme**. A group of organisms in the same taxon. The term is used with various prefixes that denote how the group differs from other groups. For example, an ecodeme occurs in a particular ecological habitat, cytodemes differ from each other cytologically, and genodemes differ genetically.

**Dementia**. Disease of mind in which there is a more or less complete loss of reasoning power, common sense and generally of interest and the power of feeling.

**Demology**. The study of population genetics.

**Denaturation**. Change in the structure of a globular protein or a DNA molecule following exposure to temperatures above 60-70°C, to pH outside the normal physiological range, or to certain chemicals. Denaturation of proteins involves the uncoiling of the polypeptide chain so that its tertiary structure is lost, resulting in loss of biological activity. The process is sometimes reversible, the protein regaining its characteristic coiled structure (native form) and its activity. This is termed renaturation. Denaturation of DNA involves the uncoiling of the double helix, forming single-stranded DNA. The double helix molecule will quickly reform if denaturation has not proceeded too far (*i.e.* if a small part of the molecule has retained the double helical form). Renaturation (or annealing) is slow if the strands have completely separated.

**Denature**. To produce a structural change in a protein or nucleic acid that results in the reduction or loss of its biological properties. Denaturation is caused by heat, chemicals, and extremes of pH. The differences between raw and boiled eggs are largely a result of denaturation.

**Dendrite.** A slender branching process of the cell body of a neurone. It forms connections (synapse) with the axons of other neurones and transmits nerve impulses from these to the cell body.

**Dendritic.** Branching like a tree : Arborescent.

**Dendrochronology.** The use of the annual rings of trees to date historical events. The dating of archaeological sites depends largely on cross dating. This involves taking small cores from old living trees and comparing them with the rings of timbers at the site. The year the timbers were felled is determined by finding the point at which ring patterns of the living tree correspond to those of the archaeological specimens. Bristlecone pines (Pinus longaeva) are often used as they can live for over 4000 years. If sufficiently aged living trees cannot be found in a particular region then chronologies may be built up successively further back in time by matching the ring patterns of a number of wood samples whose ages overlap.

Annual rings also provide a record of past environmental conditions. Thus ring width is normally positively correlated with water abundance. The presence and level of certain pollutants, *e.g.* lead, may also be recorded in the rings. It is necessary in such work to ensure that only those tree species that produce one growth ring a year are used. Certain trees, *e.g.* many juniper species, produce multiple rings each year, while in others it may not be possible to distinguish one season's growth from the next.

**Dendrogram.** A branching usually 'rooted' diagram that reflects the relationships of a group of taxa. The taxonomic hierarchy can be represented in a dendrogram, with kingdom at the base and subform as the terminal branches. Specific types of dendrogram can be recognized. Phenograms represent the degree of phenetic similarity and are based solely on phenetic, data. Phenon lines drawn at right angles to the phenogram (diagram), show values of similarity as percentages (the greater the value the higher the level of similarity). Clusters of similar groups are termed phenons and phenons may be assigned rank according to the level on the phenogram at which they branch off. Thus in the diagram the four clusters above the 80% phenon line could be assigned the rank of genus while the two clusters at the 55% similarity level might be assigned the rank of subfamily. Phylogenetic trees are also dendrograms, but unlike phenograms, the vertical axes represent time (though not necessarily to scale) or relative advancement.

**Dendrograph.** An instrument used to measure the periodic shrinking and swelling of tree trunks.

**Dendroid.** Treelike; resembling a tree in shape.

**Denervation.** Used for describing the destruction of nerve to any part of body which results in atrophy of the organ. In skeletal muscles it brings about muscular atrophy and abnormal excitability of muscle and increases its sensitivity to acetylcholine. Fine irregular contractions of individual fibres (fibrillations) become evident.

**Denitrification.** A chemical process in which nitrates in the soil are reduced to molecular nitrogen, which is released into the atmosphere. This process is effected by the bacterium Pseudomonas denitrificans, which uses nitrates as a source of energy for other chemical reactions in a manner similar to respiration in other organisms. Compare nitrification.

**Denitrifying Bacteria.** A group of soil bacteria which break down nitrites and nitrates anaerobically to evolve nitrogen.

**Denizen** A species of plant which could maintain itself in the wild, but was probably introduced by man.

**Dens.** A tooth or toothlike process; the odontoid process of the axis.

**Density-gradient Centrifugation.** A technique for separating and isolating pure samples of cell organelles, *i.e.* cell fractionation. The cells are first broken up in a homogenizer to release the contents and the homogenate is filtered to remove cell wall fragments. It is then poured on top of prepared salt or sucrose solutions of different concentrations that have been layered according to their density in a glass tube. Provided an appropriate centrifugal force is applied, the cell inclusions will band together at the regions in the density gradient that correspond to their own density and can then be separated off by various methods. Another method of isolating cell organelles, differential centrifugation, involves the filtered homogenate being centrifuged and decanted several times in sequence, increasing the time and speed of centrifugation at each successive stage. Nuclei, membranes, chloroplasts, mitrochondia, vesicles, endoplasmic reticulum, and ribosomes, are collected in that order.

**Dental.** Of or pertaining to teeth or dentistry.

**Dental Formula.** A representation of the dentition of an animal. A dental formula consists of eight numbers, four above and four below a horizontal line. The numbers represent (from left to right) the numbers of incisors, canines, premolars, and molars in either half of the upper and lower jaws. The total number of teeth in both jaws is therefore obtained by adding up all the numbers in the dental formula and multiplying by 2. Representative dental formulas are shown in the illustration.

$$\frac{2\quad 1\quad 2\quad 3}{1\quad 1\quad 2\quad 3} \text{ man (32 teeth)}$$

$$\frac{2\quad 0\quad 3\quad 3}{1\quad 0\quad 2\quad 3} \text{ rabbit (28 teeth)}$$

$$\frac{3\ \ 1\ \ 4\ \ 2}{3\ \ 1\ \ 4\ \ 3} \text{ bear (42 teeth)}$$

Representative dental formulas.

**Dentary.** One of several bones of the lower jaw in vertebrates. In man, it alone forms the mandible.

**Dentate.** Describing a leaf margin that is toothed, with outward-pointing notches. Leaf margins finely toothed in this way are termed denticulate.

**Denticle.** Any small tooth or toothlike projection.

**Denticulate.** Describing leaf-margins that are finely toothed with outward projecting notches.

**Dentine.** The bony material that forms the bulk of a tooth. Dentine is similar in composition to bone but is perforated with many tiny canals for nerve fibres, blood capillaries, and processes of the dentine forming cells (odontoblasts). Ivory, the material that forms elephant tusks, is made of dentine.

**Dentition**

1. Teething or the eruption of teeth.
2. The teeth of an individual or species taken collectively or as expressed by a dental formula.

**Deodar.** A kind of Cedar which grows in the western Himalayas. It has a distinctly pyramidal shape. The deodar can be distinguished from the other cedars by the distinctly drooping leading shoots and the shoots at the tips of its branches.

**Deoxycorticosterone** (deoxycortone). A steroid hormone, produced by the adernal cortex. It is having mineralocorticoid activity.

**Deoxyhaemoglobin.** Haemoglobin in which oxygen is not combined to $Fe^{3+}$ of haeme-moeity.

**Deoxyribonuclease.** An enzyme which catalyzes the hydrolysis of deoxyribonucleic acid (DNA).

**Deoxyribonucleic Acid.** DNA, a substance present in nuclei of cells consisting of phosphoric acid, a sugar, and nitrogenous bases. The sugar is deoxyribose, a pentose sugar; the bases are purine bases, adenine and guanine, and pyrimidine bases, thymine and cytosine. It is a nucleic acid localized principally in the chromosomes. It regulates protein synthesis and is the key molecule of the genes which give each cell its hereditary qualities and characteristics.

**Deoxyribose.** A pentose sugar and a component of the nucleotides present in DNA, *i.e.* adenosine, cytosine, guanidine, and thymidine phosphates (AMP, CMP, GMP, and TMP). Although not conforming to the general formula of monosaccharides ($C_x(H_2O)_y$), deoxyribose ($C_5H_{10}O_4$) is in other respects a typical five-carbon sugar.

**Deplasmolysis.** Refers to increase in intracellular pressure which is usually accompanied by cell membrane bursting. It takes place when cell is kept in hypotonic solution.

**Depolarization.** A reduction in the difference of electrical potential that exists across the cell membrane of a nerve or muscle cell. Depolarization of a nerve-cell membrane occurs during the passage of an action potential along the axon when the nerve is transmitting an impulse.

**Depressor**

1. A muscle which depresses or draws a part downward.
2. A nerve which, when stimulated, lowers blood pressure by reflexly inducing vasodilation or a slowing of heart beat.

**Derbesiales.** Caulerpales.

**Dermal**. Pertaining to the skin especially inner connective tissue layers of vertebrate skin.

**Dermal Bone**. Refers to a bone which develops from mesenchyme of dermis. Such bones are usually present in dermatocranium of tetrapods skull.

**Dermal Branchia**. A papula.

**Dermal Plate**. Underneath the dermis, many reptiles are having specialised scales which are forming the plates called dermal plates. Such plates are present over the head of lizards and in the armature of turtles (carapace and plastron).

**Dermal Scales**. Typical scales of fishes present in the epidermis but of mesodermal origin.

**Dermal Skeleton**. Skeletal structures which originate from the dermis, as the dermal scales of fishes, dermal plates of reptiles and, in birds and mammals, certain membrane bones of the skull.

**Dermaptera**. An order of insects comprising the earwigs. Earwigs typically have long thin cylindrical bodies with biting mouthparts and a stout pair of curved forceps at the tip of the abdomen, used for catching prey and in courtship. Some species have a single pair of wings, which at rest are folded back over the abdomen like a fan; others are wingless. Most earwigs are nocturnal and omnivorous.

**Dermatitis**. Inflamatory development/skin troubles, which are usually caused by deficiency of biotin, pantothenic acid (vitamin B complex).

**Dermatocranium**. In bony fishes and tetrapods, a part of brain box is not roofed over by cartilages in embryo, but is covered by dermal bones forming the dermatocranium. It includes, ethmoid region nasal capsules etc.

**Dermatogen.** Meristem tissue in plants which gives rise to the epidermis.

**Dermatome.** One of the skin divisions in the development of embryo.

**Dermatophyte.** A parasitic fungus causing a disease of skin, hair, or nails.

**Dermatosome.** One of the small pieces into which a cell wall can be resolved by prolonged treatment with dilute hydrochloric acid, followed by heating at 50-60°C.

**Dermestid.** Any beetle of the family Dermestidae, small dark beetles, some of which are serious household pests, as the black carpet beetle (Attagenus piceus).

**Dermis.** The under-coat of the skin in which are nerve-endings and blood vassels.

**Derris.** The plant or root (tuba root) of various species of Derris, a leguminous plant of Southeast Asia It is the source of rotenone, an insecticide.

**Desert.** A major regional community (biome) characterized by low rainfall and consequently supporting little or no vegetation. The term true desert is used of regions completely devoid of higher plant life. Cold deserts include the tundra and regions permanently covered with ice and snow. Hot deserts have a mean annual rainfall of under 250 mm while hot semideserts have a mean annual rainfall of under 400 mm. The rain falls in brief heavy showers and varies in amount from year to year. The plants are few in number and are usually short and sparsely distributed. The permanent perennial plants consist of succulent or xerophytic trees, shrubs, and herbs. There are also ephemeral plants whose seeds lie dormant until a brief rainstorm prompts them to germinate, flower, and set seed in a short space of time.

**Desman.** An aquatic, molelike mammal of the family. Talpidae, order Insectivora.

**Desmid.** A group of single-celled, free-floating algae, often found on the surface of ponds forming a green film.

**Desmolases.** Enzymes breaking, or forming a C-Clink, without hydrolysis *e.g.*, Carboxylase catalyses the change of pyruvic acid to acetaldehyde and carbon dioxide.

**Desmoneme.** A nematocyst with a threadlike tube coiled like a corkscrew and closed at one end. Also called volvent.

**Desmosome.** A condensation of protoplasm at points of contact between cells, as those of the epidermis of the skin.

**Desynapsis.** The abnormally early breaking of synapsis in meiosis.

**Deterimental Gene.** A gene imparting a disadvatageous effect to individual that is having it. The carrier gets hampered in some way by the gene so that chances of reproduction or survival are less than those individual which are free from the gene.

**Determined.** Describing embryonic tissue at a stage when it can develop only as a certain kind of tissue (rather than as any kind).

**Desor's Larva.** The ciliated larva of Lineus, a nemertine.

**Despeciate.** To remove all species of organisms from a specific habitat.

**Determinate Cleavage.** Spiral cleavage, as in protostomes, in which the early blastomeres have specific fates.

**Detorsion.** A reversal in rotation as occurs in some gastropods whose ancestors had undergone complete torsion.

**Deuteromycete.** Any fungus of the Deuteromycetes which comprises the Fungi Imperfecti, fungi whose sexual stages are lacking or unknown.

**Deuteromycotina** (Fungi Imperfecti). An artificial subdivision of the Eumycota containing all those fungi in which the sexual stage has either not been found or appears to have been replaced by other mechanisms, *e.g.* by parasexual recombination. It contains over 15,000 species in some 1875 genera. Most of the imperfect fungi show affinities with the ascomycetes. Fungi in which the sexual (perfect) stage is found may be given a different generic name from closely related speeies only showing the imperfect stage, *e.g.* the name Aspergillus is given to certain moulds that show no sexual stages but similar species that form ascocarps are called Eurotium. Some imperfect fungi are classified with their perfect forms. The group is subdivided into the classes Blastomycetes. Hyphomycetes, and Coelomycetes.

**Deutesostome.** Any member of the Deuterostomia, animals in which the blastopore becomes the anal opening, the mouth being formed later as an independent opening, as as in the echinoderms and chordates.

**Deuterostomia.** Animals in which blastopore is forming anus while the second embryonic opening is forming mouth opposite the anus.

**Deuterotoky**. Parthenogenesis in which individuals of both sexes are produced from female gametes.

**Deutobroque**. A stage which is proceeding leptotene in cogenisis. The chromosomes radiate from the nucleolus and wind about just under the nuclear membrane.

**Deutocerebrum.** The second or middle portion of the brain of an arthropod.

**Deutonymph.** The second stage in the development of certain trombiculid mites.

**Development.** Used for the succession of stages in the life of the plant, as distinct from simple growth.

**Developmental Spiral**. Genetic spiral.

**Devil Fish**. Related to skates and rays, these fishes live in the warmer seas of the world. The front fins are greatly enlarged as 'wings' and they also have forward-pointing extensions at the front of the head. These look like horns and give the fishes their common name. The largest of the species is the mantaray, which may be 8 metres across and weigh nearly 2 tonnes.

**Devonian**. The first period of the Upper Palaeozoic era from about 395 to 345 million years ago in which the first extensive invasion of the land by plants and animals took place. A possible bryophyte fossil, Sporognites, with a well developed capsule has been found in the Lower Devonian, but most fossil bryophytes appear later. Many well preserved fossils of the Psilophytales have been found in the Rhynie chert of the Devonian in Scotland. Lycopsids and sphenopsids are also found. The ferns (Filicinae) arose in Devonian times possibly from a form resembling Protopteridium, an intermediate between the psilophytes and the Filicinae. The gymnosperms probably arose in the late Devonian, being represented by the extinct Pteridospermales, which include the earliest seed plants Archaeopteris and Archaeosperma, and also the extinct Cordaitales.

**Dextrin**. A polysaccharide resulting from incomplete hydrolysis of starch.

**Dextrose**. $C_6H_{12}O_6$, d-glucose or grape sugar.

**Dextrosinistral**. From right to left.

**Dhole**. This is the wild dog of India. It is not a true dog, and can be distinguished by its rounded ears and short muzzle. The fur is greyish-brown and the bushy tail is tipped with black. Dholes range from India and Malaysia to China and parts of the Soviet Union. They hunt in packs of 100 or more individuals, running down deer and other animals.

**Diabetes Insipidus.** Refers to the physiological abnormality which is characterised by passing of large amounts of dilute urine (polyuria) and drinking of large amounts of water/fluids (polydipsia). Insufficient secretion of ADH (antidiuretic hormone) is the main cause for less absorption of water from glomerular filtrate which passes out in urine.

**Diabetes Mellitus.** A disorder of carbohydrate metabolism resulting from inadequate production of insulin by the pancreas. It is characterized by presence of sugar in the urine and excessive production of urine.

**Diadelphous.** Describing stamen filaments that are fused into two groups.

**Diageotropic.** Transversely geotropic, said of leaves or roots which grow horizontally.

**Diagnosis**

1. *biol.* A concise, technical description of a taxonomic group.
2. *med.* The recognition or determination of the existence of a disease or pathological condition.
3. The scientific examination and analysis of a situation or condition.

**Diakinesis.** The period at the end of the first prophase of meiosis when the separation of homologous chromosomes is almost complete and crossing over has occurred.

**Diallel Cross.** A breeding experiment in which each of a number of males is mated to each of a number of females.

**Dialysis.** A process in which large molecules, such as proteins and starch, and small molecules, such as amino acids, glucose, and salts, are separated by selective diffusion through a semipermeable membrane. For example, a mixture of starch and glucose molecules in solution can be separated by placing them in a semipermeable dialysis tube made, for example, of cellophane, which is immersed in a container of distilled water. The large starch molecules remain in the dialysis tube and the small glucose molecules pass out through the membrane and can be detected in the water in the container.

**Diaminopimelic Acid** An amino acid found in bacteria and blue-green algae. It is involved in the biosynthesis of lysine in such organisms. It is also often found in the peptide side chains of the acetylmuramic acid molecules that partly make up the mucopeptides of bacterial cell walls.

**Diapause.** A period of suspended development or growth occurring in some insects during which metabolism is greatly decreased. It is often triggered by seasonal changes and regulated by an inborn rhythm and enables the insect to survive unfavourable environmental conditions so that its offspring may be produced in more favourable ones.

**Diapedesis.** A term used for describing the process by which many of the neutrophils enter the tissues that are insinuating themselves through the walls of capillaries. Both the plasma proteins and leucocytes pass through endothelial system and in most cases injury brings about leakage of plasma proteins long before emigration of leucocytes occurs. The escape of plasma proteins is a purely passive affair and is partly true for leucocytes which, however, undergo active amoeboid movements in this process.

**Diaphototrophic.** Used for a plant member which grows into a fixed position across the direction of incident light.

**Diaphragm.** The muscular membrane that divides the thorax (chest) from the abdomen in mammals. It plays an essential role in breathing (respiratory movement), being depressed during inhalation and raised during exhalation.

**Diaphysis**

1. *anat.* The shaft of a long bone.

2. *bot.* The elongated axis of an inflorescence.

**Diapohysis.** Means transverse process which arises from neural arch but often from centrum; an articular surface which serves for attachment of tuberculum of biheaded ribs.

**Diapsid.** A type of vertebrate skull in which two temporal fossae are present, as in Sphenodon and crocodiles.

**Diarch.** Having two strands of xylem.

**Diarthrosis.** A type of articulation in which there is considerable freedom of movement. The joint possesses a joint cavity lined with synovial membrane. They are also known as movable joints. They may be of following types :

*Ball and socket.* It is also known as enarthroses. In this one bone has rounded end and the other a cavity to receive it. It shows greatest degree of movement, *e.g*, joints of humerus with glenoid cavity and that of femur with acetabulum.

*Hinge.* It is also known as ginglymusi; it is same as ball and socket but movement is somewhat restricted, *e.g.*, elbow joint.

*Pivotal.* It is also known as rotaria. In this one bone is shaped like fixed pivot while other rotates on it *e.g.*, on odantoid process of axis rotates the atlas together with head.

*Sliding.* It is also known as arthrodium. In this two articulating bones can slide over one another *e.g.*, joints in zygapophyses of vertebrae and in pronation (palm facing downwards) radius is on thumb-side and ulna on little finger side.

*Saddle.* It is similar to ball and socket but since both ball and socket do not develop, the movement of joint may take place in many planes *e.g.*, joints between matacarpals of our thumb and wrist bones.

**Desoxyribose Nucleic Acid.** Deoxyribose nucleic acid (DNA).

**Diastase.** An enzyme which hydrolyzes starch to maltose, as ptyalin.

**Diastema.** A natural gap or space between two types of teeth.

**Diaster.** In cell division, when the daughter chromosomes are situated in two groups near the poles of the spindle and ready to form the daughter nuclei.

**Diastole.** The phase of a heart beat that occurs between two contractions of the heart, during which the heart muscles relax and the ventricles fill with blood. Compare systole.

**Diatoms.** Golden-brown algae of the division Chrysophyta, class Bacillariophyceae. They possess a siliceous cell wall consisting of two valves which fit together, one overlapping the other.

**Diatropism.** A tropism in which the plant part is aligned at right angles to the direction of the stimulus acting on it.

**Dicaryotic.** Dikaryotic.

**Dicentric.** Possessing two centromeres, with reference to a chromatid or chromosome.

**Dicarpellary.** Composed of two carpels.

**Dichasium** (dichasial cyme). A cymose inflorescence in which apecies are developed into flowers and two lateral flowers are developed below each apex from axillary buds of common node. This gives symmetrical appearance to the inflorescence.

**2 4-dichlorophenoxyacetic Acid.** 2,4-D.

**Dichogamy.** The condition in which the male and female reproductive organs of a flower mature at different times, thereby ensuring that self-fertilization does not occur. Compare homogamy.

**Dichopodium.** A sympodial branch system which is made up of successive parts of a dichotomizing branch system, of which only one of part is assisting in forming the axis.

**Dichotomous.** Describing the system of branching where each division is into two equal parts. It occurs in many lower plants, for example the branching of the thallus in Fucus and the branching of the stem in Lycopodium and Selaginella.

**Dichotomous Key.** In taxonomy, a key in which each division is divided into two subdivisions.

**Diclinous.** Having separate staminate and pistillate flowers borne either on the same plant or on separate plants.

**Dicliny.** The separation of male and female reproductive parts into different flowers. Diclinous plants may either have female and male unisexual flowers on the same individual (monoecy) or on different individuals (dioecy). The term diclinous may also refer to the flowers themselves, in which case it is equivalent to the term unisexual. Compare hermaphrodite.

**Dicoelous.** Having two cavities.

**Dicotyledon.** A kind of flowering plant which possesses two seed-leaves, known as cotyledons. Most flowering plants are dicotyledons. Their mature leaves are generally fairly broad and have a distinct network of veins, and their flowers generally have four or five petals.

**Dicotyledonae.** One of the two classes or subclasses of plants within the Angiospermae, distinguished by having two seed leaves (cotyledons) within the seed. The dicotyledons usually have leaf veins in the form of a net, a ring of vascular bundles in the stem, and flower parts in fours or fives or multiples of these. Dicotyledons include many food plants (*e.g.*, potatoes, peas, beans), ornamentals (*e.g.* roses, ivies, honey-suckles), and hardwood trees (*e.g.* oaks, limes, bones). Compare Monocotyledonae.

**Dictyoptera.** An order of insects comprising the cockroaches (suborder Blattaria) and the mantids (suborder Mantodea) occurring mainly in tropical regions. Cockroaches are oval and flattened in shape; some have a single well-developed pair of wings, folded back over the abdomen at rest, while in others the wings may be reduced or absent. They are usually found in forest litter, feeding on dead organic matter, but some species, *e g*, the American cockroach (Periplaneta americana), are major household pests, scavenging on starchy foods, fruits, etc. In most species the females produce capsules (bothecae) containing 16-40 eggs. These are either deposited or carried by the female during incubation.

**Dictyosome**. The Golgi complex in invertebrates.

**Dictyospore**. A multicellular spore divided by transverse and longitudinal walls.

**Dictyostele**. A type of dissected siphonostele in which the vascular tissue (as viewed in transverse section) is divided into a number of amphicribal vascular bundles called meristeles. These are separated by parenchymatous areas, which are usually associated with large closely placed leaf gaps. Dictyosteles are typical of many ferns, *e.g*. Dryopteris, and are essentially similar to solenosteles, except that the amphiphloic cylinder of the solenostele is reduced to a meshwork by the occurrence of numerous overlapping leaf gaps.

**Dicyclic**

1. Arranged in two whorls.
2. Biennial.
3. Having two sexual cycles a year.

**Didymous**. Used for describing arrangement of anthers in two equal pairs in the androecium.

**Didynamous**. Having two long stamens and two short stamens, as do plants in the family Labiatae.

**Diencephalon**. Used for the region of vertebrate brain which is just posterior to cerebrum in adult. In embryo it refers to the second part of two divisions of prosencephalon (fore brain).

**Diestrus.** Sexual inactivity between two estrous periods.

**Differential Centrifugation**. Used for describing a method of isolating cell organelles. This method involves the breaking up of cells in homogenizer, followed by filtering the homogente to separate cell fragments and then certifuging it and decanting several times in sequence with increasing the time and speed of certifugation at each successive stage. Nuclei, membranes and ribosomes have been collected in that order.

**Differentiation**

1. The process by which amorphous cells, produced by meristematic cell division, undergo various physiological and morphological changes during maturation in order to become specialized for a particular function. Differentiation thus produces the specific cell types that make up the separate tissues composing a plant body. At a higher level, differentiation results in the formation of the various plant organs and the division into shoot and root and into vegetative and reproductive structures. Compare growth.
2. Staining.

**Diffuse Nucleus.** The chromatidia sometimes present in non-nucleated cells.

**Diffuse Porous.** When the vessels are scattered evenly throughout the xylem, or when there is little difference in the size of the vessels formed in different seasons.

**Diffuse-porous Wood.** Secondary xylem in which there is little or no seasonal variation in tracheary-element diameter as, for example, in the wood of yellow birch (Betula lutea). Growth rings are therefore difficult to discern. Compare ring-porous wood.

**Diffusion**. The movement of molecules or ions in a fluid from areas of high concentration to areas of low concentration. In a closed system this will continue until the solution or gas mixture is evenly mixed. Diffusion is responsible for such processes as transpiration and the uptake of carbon dioxide. The rate of diffusion depends on concentration differences and on the nature of the pathway the molecules have to take. Thus transpiration is greater when the air is dry and when the stomata are fully open.

**Diffusion Pressure Deficit** (DPD, suction pressure). In older terminology, the net force or pressure that causes water to enter a plant cell. Its magnitude is the difference between the osmotic pressure (Π) and the turgor pressure (TP), *i.e.*, $DPD = \Pi - TP$.

**Digenetic**

1. Pertaining to or exhibiting alternation of generations.
2. Pertaining to flukes of the subclass Digenea in which one or more asexual generations are interposed between sexual generations. Compare monogenetic.

**Digestion**. The breakdown of complicated food substances into simpler compounds which can be used by the animal to build up its own body and to provide energy. Digestion is performed by enzymes, mainly in the food canal, and the products are absorbed into the body.

**Digestive System**. The alimentary canal and its accessory organs (salivary glands, liver, pancreas).

**Digit**. A finger or toe. In the basic limb structure of terrestrial vertebrates there are five digits (pentadactyl limb). This number is retained in man and other primates, but in some other species the number of digits is reduced. Frogs, for example, have four fingers and five toes, and in ungulate (hooved mammals, the digits are reduced and their tips are enclosed in horn, forming hooves.

**Digitate.**

1. Having or resembling fingers or digits.
2. *bot.* Having parts resembling the fingers of a hand, as a palmately compound leaf.

**Digitiform.** Shaped like a finger.

**Digitigrade.** A type of foot posture in which the animal walks upon the ventral surfaces of the digits with posterior portion of the foot raised, as a dog or cat. Compare plantigrade, unguligrade.

**Dihybird.** An organism that is heterozygous for two particular genes, as in AaBb. Dihybrids are most conveniently produced from crossing parents that are homozygous for the genes in question, *e.g.* AABB×aabb or AAbb×aaBB. A test cross normally yields four kinds of offspring: A—B—(both dominant characters expressed); A—bb, and aaB—(only one dominant character expressed); and aabb (no dominant characters expressed). If the genes A/a and B/b are not linked, equal numbers of all kinds of offspring will be produced. If they are linked, two classes, the parentals, will be more common, and two classes, the recombinants (cross overs), will be rarer. Selfing a dihybrid normally yields a 9 : 3 : 3 : 1 ratio (dihybird ratio) in the case of independent assortment but a much more complex result in the case of linkage.

**Dihybrid Ratio.** A 9 : 3 : 3 : 1 ratio of phenotypes among the offspring of a single cross. Such a ratio can only be obtained providing that all the following conditions are met: two genes at different loci are involved, *e.g.* gene A/a and gene B/b; the immediate parents of these offspring are heterozygous for both genes, *i.e.* AaBb; these heterozygotes are selfed or crossed with one another, *i.e.* AaBb×AaBb; the genes are unlinked, *i.e.* independent assortment; there is no interaction between the genes, *e.g.* no epistasis; A is dominant to a, and B is dominant to b, *i.e.* no codominance, etc.; fertilization is random, and all the gametes, zygotes, and offspring have an equal chance of survival.

If there is reason to expect a 9 : 3 : 3 : 1 ration in a particular cross and this result is not obtained, one or more of the above conditions is not being fulfilled. For example, the ratio may be modified to 9 : 3 : 4 (=9 : 3 : [3+1]) in some cases of gene interaction (epistasis).

A dihybrid ratio is an example of a simple Mendelian ratio, being an expansion of the monohybrid 3 : 1 ratio, viz : $(3 : 1)^2$.

**Dikaryotic.** A plant thallus (the fungus mycelium of Basidiomycetes) in which each segment is having two genetically distinct nuclei. Such mycelium is formed from fusion of two monokaryotic mycelia of different strains.

**Dik-dik.** A small antelope distributed over most of Africa. The males have short horns, partly hidden in a tuft of hairs on the head. The tail is a mere stump, and the animal also has a longish snout.

**Dilatation.** The state of being expanded or dilated.

**Dilate.** To enlarge, expand, or widen.

**Dilation.** Dilatation.

**Dilleniidae.** A subclass of the dicotyledons containing both woody and herbaceous plants. The flowers may be unisexual or bisexual and the stamens develop in a centrifugal manner. Some 12—17 orders are recognized including : the Dilleniales; the Theales, including the Theaceae (*e.g.* camellia, tea) and Guttiferae; the Malvales, including the Tiliaceae (*e.g.* limes) and Malvaceae (*e.g.* mallows); the Violales, including the Violaceae (*e.g.* violets), Flacourtiaceal, and Begoniaceae (begonias); the Salicales, containing the Salicaceae (*e g.* willows); the Capparales, including the Capparaceae (*e.g.* capers), and Cruciferae (*e.g.* mustards); the Ericales, including the Ericaceae (heath family); the Diapensiales; the

Ebenales, including the Sapotaceae (*e.g.* sapodillas) and Ebenaceae (*e.g.* ebonies); and the Primulales, including the Primulaceae (primrose family). Other orders sometimes recognized include : the Paeoniales (often placed with the Dilleniales); the Passiflorales, Cucurbitales, and Tamarales (often placed with the Violales); the Euphorbiales (often placed in the subclass Rosidae); and the Thymeleales (often placed either with the family Flacourtiaceae or in the order Myrtales of the subclass Rosidae). The Urticales, including the Ulmaceae (*e.g.* elms), Moraceae (*e.g.* mulberries, figs), and Urticaceae (*e.g.* nettles), is sometimes included in the Dilleniidae, and sometimes in the Hamamelidae.

**Dilute.** To diminish in strength or flavor; to weaken or decrease the concentration.

**Dimerous** (2-merous). Describing flowers in which the parts of each whorl are inserted in twos, as in the enchanter's nightshades (Circaea).

**Dimorphic.** Of or pertaining to dimorphism.

**Dimorphism.** The existence of a species in two distinct forms. Sexual dimorphism, in which males and females differ, occurs to some extent in all bi-sexual animals of course, but it is particularly marked in many birds and insects. Some insects also show seasonal dimorphism, with spring broods quite different from summer ones.

**Dingo.** This is the wild dog of Australia—one of the few placental (nonpouched) mammals to arrive before the Europeans. It arrived with the Aborigines when they reached Australia from southern Asia. It is a reddish-brown animal, about 50 cm high at the shoulder. The ears are erect and pointed, and the tail is bushy. Dingoes live in small packs and hunt sheep, wallabies and kangaroos.

**Dinitro Compounds.** A group of chemicals including dinocap, which is effective in controlling powdery mildews, and dinitro-orthocresol (DNOC), used as a fungicide, herbicide, and insecticide.

**Dinoflagellate**. A protozoan of the order Dinoflagellata possessing two flagella, one longitudinal and one transverse, as Noctiluca, a luminescent, marine form.

**Dinophyta** (Pyrrophyta). A division consisting predominantly of flagellate unicellular marine algae, often dark brown in colour due to the presence of the xanthophyll pigment peridinin. It is divided into two classes, the Desmophyceae, and the Dinophyceae, or dinoflagellates. The Dinophyceae are abundant in the phytoplankton. They characteristically have one longitudinal and one transverse groove in the cell wall and two flagella, one situated in each groove. The Desmophyceae either lack a cell wall or hove a wall divided into two semicircular halves by a transverse groove. Certain tropical members of the Desmophyceae exhibit bioluminescence.

**Dinosaur**. An extinct terrestrial reptile belonging to a group that constituted the dominant land animals of the Jurassic and Cretaceous periods, 190—65 million years ago. There were two orders. The Ornithischia were typically quadrupedal herbivores, many with heavily armoured bodies, and included Stegosaurus, Triceratops, and Iguanodon. They were all characterized by birdlike pelvic girdles. The Saurischia included many bipedal carnivorous forms, such as Tyrannosaurus (the largest known carnivore), and some quadrupedal herbivorous forms, such as Apatosaurus (Brontosaurus) and Diplodocus. They all had lizard-like pelvic girdles. Many of the herbivorous dinosaurs were amphibious or semiaquatic.

**Dinucleotide**. A unit which is derived from deoxyribose and is linked through a phosphate radical. Some are important as prosthetic groups of enzymic globular proteins.

**Dioecious**

1. *zool.* Unisexual; having separate sexes.

2. *bot. a.* With sex organs on separate gametophytes. *b.* With staminate and pistillate flowers borne on separate plants.

**Diphosphopyridine Nucleotide** (DNP) (Coenzyme I). **Trivial name for NAD.** A coenzyme which gets oxidized and reduced during the early stages of respiration. The pyridine ring is the active group. It oxidizes glyceradehyde-3-phosphate to 3-phosphoroglyceric acid by removing hydrogen.

**Diphtheria.** An acute, infectious disease of the respiratory passageways caused by a bacterium (Corynebacterium diphtheriae).

**Diphycercal.** Designating a type of caudal fin in which the vertebral column extends to the tip of the tail dividing it into dorsal and ventral portions which are approximately equal, as in dipnoan fishes.

**Diphygenic.** Producing embryos of two types.

**Diphyodont.** Describing a type of dentition that is characterized by two successive sets of teeth : the deciduous (milk) teeth, which are followed by the permanent (adult) teeth. Mammals have a diphyodont dentition. Compare monophyodont; polyphyodont.

**Diplanetic.** Describing organisms that successively produce two different types of zoospore (planospore), as do certain species of Saprolegnia. Compare monoplanetic.

**Dipleurula.** The hypothetical, bilaterally symmetrical, ciliated, ancestral larva of echinoderms or an existing larva resembling this form.

**Diplobiontic.** Describing a life cycle in which two types of vegetative plant are formed, one haploid and the other diploid (*i e.* a life cycle in which there is an alternation of generations). The life cycles of ferns are diplobiontic. Compare haplobiontic.

**Diploblastic.** Describing an animal with a body wall composed only of two layers, ectoderm and endoderm, sometimes with a noncellular mesoglea between them. The Coelenterata are diploblastic; all other Metazoa are triploblastic.

**Diploid.** Having a double set of Chromosomes in the cell nucleus. Normal body cells are diploid. Sex cells are formed by a special process in which only one set of chromosomes goes to each cell. Cells with only one set of chromosomes are called haploid. When sev cells join together at fertilization the diploid number is regained in the resulting zygote or embryo.

**Diplontic.** Describing a life cycle in which the diploid phase predominates and where the haploid stage is limited to the gametes. Such life cycles are seen in the diatoms and members of the Fucales. Compare haplontic.

**Diplosegment.** A double segment resulting from the fusion of two segments.

**Diplosome.** The two centrioles of a cell center or centrosome.

**Diplospondyly.** The condition in which a vertebra possesses two centra, as in Amia. Compare monospondyly.

**Diplospory.** A form of apomixis in which the embroy forms directly from the megaspore mother cell. It is found, for example, in mountain everlastings (Antennaria).

**Diplostemonous.** Describing stamens that are inserted in two whorls with the outer opposite the sepals and the inner opposite the petals. Compare obdiplostemonous.

**Diplotene.** The period in the first prophase of meiosis when paired homologous chromosomes begin to move apart. They remain attached at a number of points.

**Dipnoi.** A subclass of bony fishes that contains the lungfishes, which have lungs and breathe air. They are found in Africa, Australia, and South America, where they live in freshwater lakes and marshes that tend to structures (*e.g.* the caecum and appendix in the alimentaiy canal) or abnormally, from a weakened area of the organ.

**Dipper.** A bird of streams and rivers, also called the water-ouzel. It has dark brown feathers, with a white breast, and hops in a characteristic bobbing fashion about the pebbles in a stream, catching insects and other small creatures under the water. The name comes from its constant dipping movement.

**Diptera.** An order of insects comprising the ture, or two-winged, flies. Files possess only one pair of wings—the forewings; the hindwings are modified to form small club-like halteres that function as balancing organs. Typically fluid feeders, flies have mouthparts adapted for piercing and sucking or for lapping; the diet includes nectar, sap, decaying organic matter, and blood. Some species prey on insects; others are parasitic. Dipteran larvae (maggots) are typically wormlike with an inconspicuous head. They undergo metamorphosis via a pupal stage to the adult form. Many flies or their larvae are serious pests, either by feeding on crops (*e.g.* fruit flies) or as vectors of disease organisms (*e.g.* the house fly (Musca domestica) and certain mosquitoes).

**Dipteran.** Any insect of the order Diptera which includes the true flies, gnats, midges, and mosquitoes, characterized by a single pair of wings, the second pair represented by a pair of halteres.

**Dipterous**

1. *zool.* Of or pertaining to the order Diptera.
2. *bot.* Possessing two wings or winglike processes.

**Disacchairde.** A double sugar, one of a group of carbo-hydrates which upon hydrolysis yields two monosac-charide molecules, at lactose, maltose, and sucrose. Basic formula is $C_{12}H_{22}O_{11}$.

**Disk** or **Disk.** *bot.* A flat, circular or oblong structure, as *a.* the central portion of the head in various composites; *b.* a flat, elevated receptacle about the base of a pistil; *c.* the flattened tip of a tendril.

**Disc(k) Floret.** A regular, tubular flower which is found in the centre of a capitulum when it contains two types of flowers.

**Disc Flower.** One of the tubular flowers comprising the central portion of the head in composites. Compare ray flower.

**Disciform.** Circular in outline and shallow, like a disc.

**Disclimax.** Used for describing the final stable state of equilibrium reached by succession in an area in which it becomes possible to prevent the ultimate growth of trees and shrubs in ultimate climatic climax due to interference in climate by biotic factors (often intensive grazing).

**Discoblastula.** A disc-shaped blastula; a germinal disc or blastoderm.

**Discoid**

1. Shaped like a disc.
2. Having only disc flowers, with reference to the head of composites.

**Discomycetes.** A class of the Ascomycotina containing those ascomycetes that produce an apothecium (the exception being the Tuberales, where the hymenium is enclosed). It contains over 3000 species in some 425 genera, which are distributed among the orders Phacidiales, Helotiales, Ostropales, Pezizales, and Tuberales. The majority of fungi that form lichens are Discomycetes.

**Discontinuous Variation** (qualitative variation). Clearly defined differences in a characteristic that can be observed in a population. Characteristics that are determined by different alleles at a single locus show discontinuous variation, *e.g.* garden peas are either wrinkled or smooth. Compare continuous variation.

**Disease Resistance** (resistance). Used for the ability of a plant to resist *i.e.*, remain unaffected by harmful effect of a disease causing pathogen. It may be specific *i.e.*, effective against a particular strain of pathogen or non-specific *i.e.*, effective against a variety of strains.

**Disinfectant.** Any substance that kills or inhibits the growth of disease-producing microorganisms and is in general toxic to human tissues. Disinfectants include cresol, bleaching powder, and phenol. They are used to cleanse surgical apparatus, sickrooms, and household drains and if sufficiently diluted can be used as antiseptics.

**Disjunction**

1. The act of disjoining or separating.

2. *genetics.* The separation of homologous chromosomes during meiosis.

**Disjunct Species.** A species which occurs in two or more widely separated regions but does not occur anywhere in between *e.g.*, magnolias grow in southeast Asia, eastern North America and Central America but nowhere in between.

**Disk.** A disc; a flat platelike structure.

**Displacement Activity.** An activity shown by an animal that appears to be irrelevant to its situation. Displacement activities are frequently observed when there is conflict between opposing tendencies. For example, birds in aggressive situations, in which there are simultaneous tendencies to attack and to flee, may preen their feathers as a displacement activity.

**Display Behaviour.** Stereotyped movement or posture that serves to influence the behaviour of another animal. Many displays in courtship and aggression are conspicuous and characteristic of the species; special markings or parts of the body may be prominently exhibited (for example, the male peacock spreads its tail in courtship). Other displays are cryptic and make it harder for a predator to recognize the displaying animal as potential prey. For example, geometer moth caterpillars, which look like twigs, hold themselves on plant stems with one end sticking into the air.

**Dissect.** To divide into separate parts, especially to cut into and expose and separate the various parts of a plant or animal for study purposes.

**Dissected.** Deeply cut into or divided into many lobes or divisions, as a dissected leaf.

**Dissepiment.** A septum or partition, as *a.* that separating the segments of an annelid; *b.* that separating the locules of the ovary of a flower.

**Dissociation**

1. The act of disunion or separation, as the breakdown of a substance into simpler substances or of a molecule into its ions.

2. *bacteriol.* A form of bacterial variation in which a change in the form of a colony occurs usually associated with a change in virulence or other physiological properties.

**Distal.** Describing the part of an organ that is farthest from the organ's point of attachment to the rest of the body. For example, hands and feet are at the distal ends of arms and legs, respectively. Compare proximal.

**Distant.** Not closely aggregated; remote; not approximate.

**Distely.** A special case of polystely in which the vascular system is divided into two separate steles. This condition is exhibited in certain species of Selaginella, *e.g.* S. kraussiana.

**Distichous.** Describing a form of alternate leaf arrangement in which successive leaves arise on opposite sides of the stem so that two vertical rows of leaves result. It is seen, for example, in grasses. The term also describes a form of opposite leaf arrangement in which the pairs of leaves all arise in the same plane, again giving two rows of leaves.

**Dithiocarbamate Fungicide.** Any fungicide based on the organic sulphur compound dithiocarbamic acid. Such compounds include the commonly used fungicides ziram, thiram, zineb, and maneb.

**Diurnal**

1. Pertaining to the day; occurring daily.
2. *zool.* Active during the day, as certain birds.
3. *bot.* Opening during the day and closing at night, as certain flowers. Compare nocturnal, crepuscular.

**Diurnal Rhythm.** Circadian rhythm.

**Divaricator.** A muscle which opens the beak of an avicularium or the valves of a brachiopod.

**Diver.** Water birds similar to the grebes, and also known as loons. Divers are excellent swimmers, with short tails, and pointed bills to catch fish. They can stay under water for minutes at a time but on land can only waddle clumsily. Examples are the great northern and red-throated divers, both of northern regions.

**Divergent Evolution** (divergence). The development of different forms from a single basic structure as a result of different selective pressures acting on that structure. These changes may be associated with a new function that is added to or replaces the original function. For example, the general form of the angiosperm stem is aerial and elongated. Its function is to support and space out the leaves and flowers as well as conducting food and water. However certain xerophytic plants with reduced leaves have expanded leaflike stems to increase photosynthetic capacity. Other plants have short swollen stems that serve as underground perennating organs.

**Diverticulum**. A saclike or tubular outgrowth from a tubular or hollow internal organ. Diverticula may occur as normal (RNA). The two chains are wound round each other and linked together by hydrogen bonds between specific complementary bases (base pairing) to form a spiral ladder-shaped molecule (double helix).

When the cell divides, its DNA also replicates in such a way that each of the two molecules is identical to the parent molecule. The hydrogen bonds between the complementary bases on the two strands of the parent molecule break and the strands unwind. Using as building bricks nucleotides present in the nucleus, each strand directs the synthesis of a new one complementary to itself. Replication is initiated, controlled, and stopped by means of polymerase enzymes.

**Diving Beetle**. The popular name for a number of carnivorous aquatic beetles which spend much of their time under water, particularly the great diving beetle and the whirligig beetles.

**Division**. A category used in the classification of plants that consists of one or several similar classes. Division names end inphyta. Examples are the Bryophyta (mosses and liverworts) and the Tracheophyta (vascular plants). The divisions are grouped in the kingdom Plantae. In animal classification, the term phylum is substituted for division.

**Division of Labour.** Specialization of function resulting from differentiation during development.

**Dizygotic.** Originating from two zygotes, as fraternal twins.

**Dizygotic Twins.** Fraternal twins.

**DNA** (deoxyribonucleic acid). The substance of which genes are made and that determines the inherited characteristics. In eukaryotes, it is mostly confined to the chromosomes, where it is found in association with basic proteins called histones. Bacterial, mitochondrial, and chloroplast DNA is naked and forms circles or loops. Typically a DNA molecule consists of two polynucleotide chains, forming a right-handed helix with one coil positioned more or less underneath the other (the double helix, diagram). There are only four types of nucleotides in the polynucleotide chains, although each chain can be thousands of nucleotides long. Each nucleotide is constructed from deoxyribose sugar, esterified to phosphate and a base. The base may be adenine or guanine (the purine bases), or cytosine or thymine (the pyrimidine bases). The sequence of nucleotides in a polynucleotide chain ultimately specifies the sequence of amino acids in proteins, *i.e*, forms the basis of the genetic code. The phosphate groups are on the outside of the helix. Each polynucleotide chain is established and held together by the formation of further ester bonds between the phosphate group of one nucleotide and the deoxyribose sugar of an adjacent nucleotide in the same chain. For this reason, each polynucleotide is sometimes described as having a 'sugar-phosphate' backbone (diagram). The two polynucleotide chain in a double helix are antiparallel, *i.e.*, in one chains the sugar—phosphate backbone is composed of 3′—5′ phosphodiester bonds, while in the other, it is composed of 5′—3′ phosphodiester bonds. The bases are on the inside of the helix, and each forms hydrogen bonds with a complementary base on the other helix. By the formation of these hydrogen bonds, the two helices are held together. The base pairing is highly specific, adenine : thymine and guanine : cytosine being the only permissible combinations.

DNA may be contrasted with RNA, the other main type of nucleic acid found in cells. The latter plays an important role in transcribing (copying) and translating (decoding) the genetic message during protein synthesis. In viruses the genetic material is much more variable and can be double-stranded DNA (*e.g.*, T-even bacteriophage), single-stranded DNA (*e.g.* $\phi$174 bacteriophage), double-stranded RNA (*e.g.*, $\phi$6 bacteriophage), or single-stranded RNA (*e.g.*, tobacco mosaic virus).

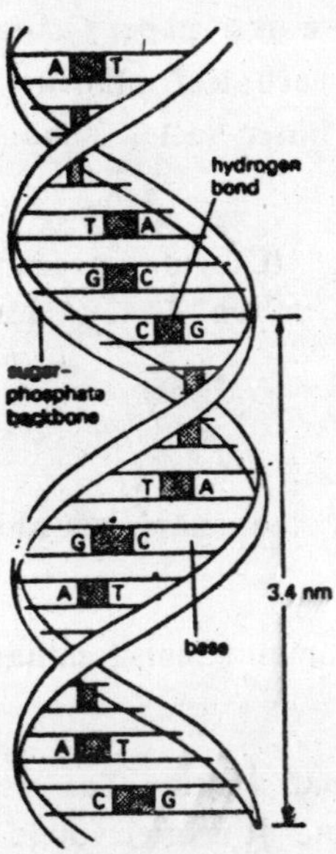

Double helical structure of DNA

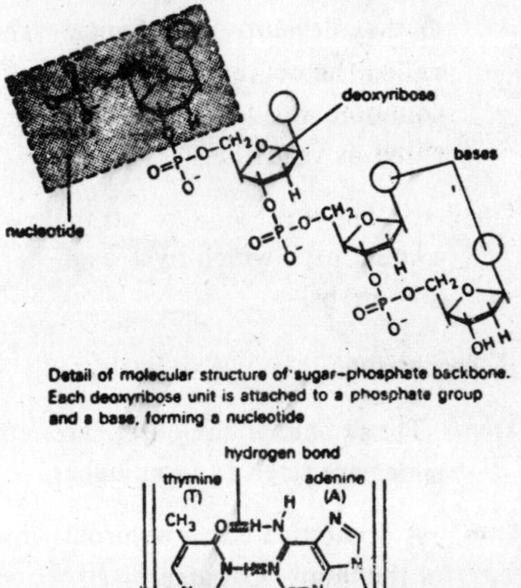

Detail of molecular structure of sugar–phosphate backbone. Each deoxyribose unit is attached to a phosphate group and a base, forming a nucleotide

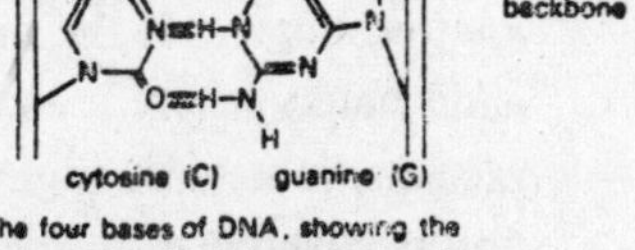

The four bases of DNA, showing the hydrogen bonding between base pairs

Molecular structure of DNA

**DNA Hybridization**. A method of determining the similarity of DNA from different sources. Single strands of DNA from two sources, *e.g.*, different bacterial species, are put together and the extent to which double hybrid strands are formed is estimated. The greater the tendency to form these hybrid molecules, the greater the extent of complementary base sequences, *i.e.*, gene similarity. The method is one way of determining the genetic relationships of species.

**Dolipore Septum.** A type of septum occurring in many basidiomycete fungi in which there is a narrow pore surrounded by a thickened rim and protected on both sides by caps.

**Dock.** Any of a group of plants with stout tapering roots, large flat leaves and greenish flowers which often turn red as they develop into fruits. There is a papery sheath, called the ochrea, at the base of each leaf. Docks are common weeds. Despite their bitter taste, some are eaten as vegetables.

**Dodder.** The love vine or strangleweed (Cuscuta), a leafless annual herb which lives as a parasite on various shrubs and herbs.

**Dodecamerous.** In twelve parts.

**Doe.** The female of the deer, hare, and other mammals whose males are referred to as bucks.

**Dog.** A domesticated carnivorous mammal (Canis familiaris) of the family Canidae.

**Dogfish.** Any of several species of small shark. The lesser spotted dogfish is the most common. It is often found on sand banks where it hunts small fishes, molluscs and crustaceans, mostly at night. It grows up to 1 metre long and is covered in brown spots. Also known as the rock salmon or rough hound.

**Dog's Mercury.** A poisonous plant with petalless green flowers. The flowers are single-sexed and are borne on separate plants, the males in slender spikes and the females in small clusters. The leaves grow in opposite pairs along the unbranched stem. Dog's mercury often carpets woodlands in the spring.

**Dolioform.** Barrel-shaped.

**Doliolaria.** The barrel-shaped, ciliated larva of crinoids and holothuroids.

**Dolphin**

1. One of several species of beaked cetaceans of the family Delphinidae, as the common dolphin (Delphinus delphis).
2. A slender marine fish (Coryphaena hippurus) of the family Coryphaenidae.

**Dolipore Septum.** A type of septum found in many basidiomycete fungi, in which there is a narrow pore surrounded by a thickened im and protected on both sides by caps.

**Dominance Hierarchy.** Dominant.

**Dominant**

1. Describing an allele that masks the expression of a different (recessive) allele at the same locus. Thus the phenotype of the heterozygote resembles that of a plant homozygous for the two dominant alleles. The dominant allele is usually the normal and more common form in natural populations, *i.e.*, the wild-type allele. Not all characteristics are governed by simple dominant/recessive relationships.
2. Describing the most abundant plant species in a community, *e.g.*, in the UK Quercus robur (pedunculate oak) is dominant in most deciduous woodlands on nonacid clays and loams.
3. In forestry, a tree whose crown is more than half exposed to full illumination.

**Domin Scale.** A variation of Braun-Blanquet scale having more subdivisions of the original scale and is more accurate than that.

**DOPA.** Dihydroxyphenylalanine, an intermediate product in the metabolism or tyrosine. It is the precursor of melanin.

**Dopamine.** A catecholamine that is a precursor in the synthesis of noradrenaline and adrenaline. It is also believed to function as a neurotransmitter in the brain.

**Dormancy.** Inactive state, during which no growth takes place. Certain animals and many plants and their seeds or spores have periods of dormancy during unfavourable conditions. In some instances dormancy is seasonal, *e.g.* animal hibernation or the dormancy of bulbs, and forms part of an annual rhythm. In others it only exists for as long as conditions remain unfavourable. A seed, for example, which needs water to germinate, will remain dormant until it is put in moist soil.

**Dormant**

1. *zool.* Quiescent, not active; in a state of suspended animation.
2. *bot.* In a resting or nonvegetative state, as in buds, seeds, spores.

**Dormin.** Abscisic acid.

**Dormouse.** A small rodent that looks similar to a mouse but behaves more like a squirrel. Dormice have long, often bushy tails and are good climbers. They are active at night and hibernate for several months during the winter. The common or hazel dormouse is the smallest species, no more than 9 cm long. In has a golden brown coat and is found in most of NW Europe except Ireland and the far north. It lives among bushes where it makes a small, ball-shaped nest. Its favourite food is hazelnuts.

**Dorsal.** Describing the surface of a plant or animal that is farthest from the ground or other support, *i.e.*, the upper surface. In vertebrates, the dorsal surface is that down which the backbone runs. Thus in upright (bipedal) mammals, such as man and kangaroos, it is the backward-directed (posterior) surface. Compare ventral.

**Dorsifixed.** Describing an anther that is jointed to the filament for some distance along its dorsal edge. Compare basi-fixed, versatile.

**Dorsiventral.** Having distinct dorsal and ventral surfaces, as the thallus of a liverwort, or distinct upper and lower surfaces, as a leaf.

**Dorsum**

1. The back or upper surface of an animal.
2. The upper surface of a part, as of the foot or tongue.

**Double Fertilization.** The process found in most flowering plants where two male gametes enter the embryo sac and both participate in fertilization. One male gamete fuses with the female gamete or egg nucleus to form a zygote, which develops into the embryo. The other male gamete fuses with either the polar nuclei or the definitive nucleus to form a triploid primary endosperm nucleus, which will give rise to the endosperm.

A form of double fertilization is also seen in some species of the gymnosperm genus Ephedra, in which one male gamete fuses with the egg cell and the other fuses with the ventral canal cell. However the product of the second fertilization does not undergo further development.

**Double Flower.** A flower having more than the usual number of petals usually due to the transformation by a mutation of stamens into petals. Extremely double flowers, in which the carpels have also become petals, are termed flore pleno. An example is Ranunculus aconitifolius 'flore pleno' (fair maids of France). The transformation of reproductive organs into petals is called petalody.

**Double Helix.** A molecule composed of two similar polymeric chains coiled in the same direction about the same axis, as in DNA. Actin, a fibrous protein found in most eukaryotic cells also takes the form of a double helix. Double helices are, however, relatively rare configurations. Much more common is the single helix (α-helix) characteristic of globular protein.

**Double Recessive.** An organism with two recessive alleles for a particular characteristic.

**Double Staining.** Staining.

**Down**

1. *zool.* *a.* The covering of soft plumage possessed by young birds, especially precocial birds. *b.* In adult birds, soft down feathers which underlie the contour feathers. *c.* Fine soft hair on the skin.

2. *bot.* A soft, fine pubescence, as on certain leaves and fruits : Pappus.

**Down Feathers** (plumules). Small soft feathers that cover and insulate the whole body of a bird. In nestlings they are the only feathers; in adults they lie between and beneath the contour feathers. Down feathers have a fluffy appearance as their barbs are not joined together to form a smooth vane.

**Down's Syndrome** (mongolism). A congenital form of mental retardation due to a chromosome defect in which there are three copies of chromosome no. 21 instead of the usual two. The affected individual has a short broad face and slanted eyes (as in the Mongolian races), short fingers, and weak muscles. Down's syndrome can be detected before birth by amniocentesis. It is named after the

British physician John Down (1828-96), who first studied the incidence of the disorder.

**Downy Mildew.** A plant disease caused by fungi of the family Peronosporaceae in the order Peronosporales. The pathogen penetrates the tissues more deeply than powdery mildews and produces a white or grey mealy growth on the leaves and stems of the host in humid conditions. This surface growth is composed of sporangiophores, which grow out from the stomata. Examples include downy mildew of vine (Plasmopara viticola), downy mildew of onion (Peronospora destructor), and downy mildew of lettuce (Bremia lactucae).

**DPD.** Diffusion pressure deficit.

**DPN.** NAD.

**Dragonet.** A small bottom-living fish whose name is derived from the enlarged dragon-like fins and spines of the brightly-coloured male. The female is inconspicuous by comparison and was once thought to be a separate species.

**Dragonfly.** A group of insects that are among the most efficient aerial hunters. Dragonflies catch other insects on the wing, usually near or over water. They can fly forwards of backwards and can also hover in mid-air. They have excellent eye-sight and many species are brightly coloured. The dragonfly nymph lives under water and is an equally fierce predator.

**Drill**

1. A small, carnivorous, marine gastropod which feeds on other mollusks by drilling a hole in their shell, especially Urosalpinx cinerea, the oyster drill.

2. An African baboon (Mandrillus leucophaeus).

**Drum**

1. The tympanic or middle ear cavity; the eardrum.
2. A drumfish.

**Drumfish.** A fish of the family Sciaenidae capable of producing grunts or booming sounds, as Pogonias chromis, the common drumfish; a grunt.

**Drupe** (pyrenocarp). A fleshy fruit that develops from either one or several fused carpels and contains one or many seeds. The seeds are enclosed by the hard protective endocarp (pericarp) of the fruit. Thus the stone of a peach is the endocarp containing the seed. Plums, cherries, coconuts and almonds are other examples of one-seeded drupes; holly and elder fruits are examples of many-seeded drupes.

**Drupelet.** A small drupe, as that in an aggregate fruit as the blackberry.

**Druse** (sphaeroraphide). A globular mass of needle-like crystals found either attached to the cell wall or free in the cytoplasm.

**Dryad's Saddle.** A bracket fungus, especially common or elm but also found on many other deciduous trees. The brackets are fan-shaped and scaly, sometimes up to 60 cm across. They often grow in overlapping tiers and may be high up on the trunk. The fungus weakens the tree and often causes the branches to snap off.

**Dryopithecus.** A genus of extinct apes, fossils of which have been found in India and dated as 30-46 million years old. Fossils of Dryopithecus and of the similar genus Proconsul are often referred to as dryopithecines. Dryopithecines are believed to be either the ancestors of the fossil hominids or ancestral to both the human and ape lines.

**Dry Rot.** A fungus that is a serious pest in old, dampbuildings where it attacks floor boards and other concealed timbers. The wood becomes clothed with a greyish blanket of fungal threads, and coarse dark strands spread out and carry the infestation to other areas. The fruiting body is a rust-coloured sheet. The whole fungus has a strong musty smell.

**Duck.** A group of birds found worldwide, always close to water. Ducks are related to geese and swans but are smaller with shorter necks and flat beaks. They have webbed feet for swimming and in most species the males and females have very different plumages. There are two main groups of ducks : those which feed on the surface of the water, and those which dive. Surface-feeding ducks, also called dabbling ducks, prefer shallow, inland [illegible] and can often be seen up-ended, feeding on water [illegible]ants. They include the Mallard, shoveler and Teal. The diving ducks prefer deeper water and several species can be found in coastal waters. They swim beneath the surface of the water to feed on water plants and animals. They swim beneath the surface of th[illegible] water to feed on water plants and animals. They [illegible] the Eider, Merganser and Pochard.

**Duckbill**

1. The duckbilled platypus (Ornithorhynchus anatinus), a primitive egg-laying mammal (monotreme) of Australia and Tasmania; duckmole or water mole.
2. A bipedal, beaked dinosaur of the order Ornithischia.

**Duckweed.** The name given to a group of very tiny flowering aquatic plants. Duckweed floats on the surface of ponds, and consists of a flat disc or frond with a long thin root. The flowers are almost invisible. Reproduction occurs mainly by producing detachable buds which grow directly into new discs.

**Duct**

1. *anat.* *a.* A small vessel which conveys a fluids, especially one from a gland. *b.* One of the main lymph vessels, as the thoracic duct.

2. *bot.* A vessel for conducting specialized substances as latex or various resins.

**Ductless Gland.** Endocrine gland.

**Dugong.** A seal-like mammal about 2.5 metres long, with flipper-like front limbs and a broad paddle for a tail. Dugongs live along swampy tropical coasts of the Indian Ocean, from Africa to northern Australia. They feed on eel grass and other aquatic vegetation. Dugongs are closely related to the manatees and both groups are often known as sea cows.

**Dulse.** A common red seaweed with a branching, fan-shaped frond. It often grows on other seaweeds instead of attaching itself to stones. Certain dulses are edible.

**Dung Beetle.** A group of beetles that live on animal dung, both eating it and laying their eggs on it to provide food for their larvae. They often bury the dung before laying their eggs in it. The Scarab Beetles are dung beetles.

**Duodenum.** The first section of the small intestine of vertebrates. It is the site where food from the stomach is subjected to the action of bile (from the bile duct) and pancreatic enzymes (from the pancreatic duct) as well as the enzymes secreted by digestive glands in the duodenum itself (succus entericus), which are required in the breakdown of proteins, carbohydrates, and fats. By neutralizing the acidic secretions of the stomach, the duodenum provides an alkaline environment necessary for the action of the intestinal enzymes.

**Duplicate Genes.** The existence of two genes each capable of producing the same phenotypic effect.

**Duplication**

1. A doubling of parts.
2. *genetics.* A type of chromosomal aberration in which a chromosome bears two groups of identical genes.

**Dura Mater.** The outermost and toughest of the three membranes (meninges) that surround the central nervous system in vertebrates. It lies adjacent to the skull and its purpose is to protect the delicate inner meninges (the arachnoid membrane and the pia mater).

**Duramen.** The hard central wood of a tree stem; the heartwood.

**Durango.** A poisonous scorpion (Centruroides) of the southwest United States.

**Dutch Elm Disease.** Disease attacking all species of elm. The presence of a certain fungus results in the sap-carrying vessels of the branches becoming blocked. The flow of water and minerals to the leaves is cut off and the tree dies. The fungus is carried from one tree to another by a small bark beetle, which tunnels under the bark to lay its eggs.

**Dwarf.** An abnormally small individual.

**Dwarfism.** Stunted growth, often due to a fault in genetic composition.

**Dysgenic.** Detrimental to the race from the standpoint of hereditary makeup or constitution.

**Dyspnea.** Difficult or labored breathing.

**Dystrophic Lake.** One of low productivity in which the content of organic matter is high and the amount of dissolved oxygen low.

Encyclopaedic Dictionary of

# BIOLOGICAL SCIENCES

# ENCYCLOPAEDIC DICTIONARY OF BIOLOGICAL SCIENCES

Vol. 4

K. NARANG
R. RANI
M. PRAKASH

**ANMOL PUBLICATIONS PVT LTD**
**New Delhi-110002**

**ANMOL PUBLICATIONS PVT LTD**
4374/4B, Ansari Road
Daryaganj, New Delhi-110 002

*Encyclopaedic Dictionary of Biological Sciences*



First Edition, 1991
ISBN 81-7041-462-8 (Set)
ISBN 81-7041-466-0 (Vol.4)
**Reprint 1994**
**Reprint ... 1998**

**PRINTED IN INDIA**
Published by J.L. Kumar for Anmol Publications Pvt. Ltd. New Delhi
and Printed at Mehra Offset Press.

# Preface

The *Encyclopaedic Dictionary of Biological Sciences* (set of six volumes) has been carefully compiled and edited to meet the long felt needs of increasingly large number of, those who have to deal with the different aspects of biological sciences in colleges, universities, and research institutes. These volumes provide a speedy means of reference to easily interpreted definitions of the terms selected from botany, zoology, environmental science, ecology, genetics, biochemistry, forestry, agriculture geomorphology, cell biology, plant pathology, anatomy, evolution and ecology.

This set of dictionary is more or less encyclopaedic in its contents and style of representation which is evident from the comprehensiveness of its coverage and contextual relevance of explanations with illustrations and chemical formulae wherever necessary.

The entries in this dictionary have been written in a clear and explanatory style to provide both straight forward definitions and invaluable background information. The presentation throughout has been aimed at sustaining the interest of readers while enriching their vocabulary and comprehension of technical terms and expressions.

Throughout the process of compilation and editing these volumes our sincere effort was to make the dictionary as a ready reference for undergraduate and post graduate biological, agricultural, environmental, medical, marine and biochemistry students and also for those appearing for competitive examinations, research scholars, teachers and authors.

The editors express their thanks to their friends and colleagues whose continuous inspiration have initiated them to bring out these volumes.

**The Editors**

# K

**Kainozoic.** Cenozoic.

**Kallidin.** Kinin.

**Kala-azar.** Disease of humans, found chiefly in tropical regions; symptoms include enlargement of the spleen, with anaemia, fever, and prostration. The causal agent is a protozoon, Leishmania donovani, which is transmitted by sandflies (Phlebotomus).

**Kangaroo.** A group of Australian marsupials with powerful hindlimbs, short forelimbs and a strong tail. Best known are the great grey kangaroo of eastern Australia and the red kangaroo found in most parts of the continent. The former can measure 2 metres in height and is a browsing animal of the open forests. The red kangaroo is similar in size and grazes on the open plains. Kangaroos can hop at speeds up to 40 km/h and have been known to leap 8 metres in a single bound.

**Kangaroo Rat.** A small, nocturnal, burrowing rodent of the genus Dipodomys of the western United States.

**Kapok.** The silky fibers which invest the seeds of the kapok tree (Ceiba pentandra) of tropical countries, also called Java cotton.

**Kappa Particles.** Cytoplasmic particles in certain paramecia (killers) which contain a substance (paramecin) which is toxic to other paramecia (sensitives).

**Karyallagy.** The union of two swarm cells in slime molds.

**Karyogamy.** The fusion of two nuclei during sexual reproduction. Fusion normally occurs between haploid nuclei and follows immediately after plasmogamy, resulting in the formation of a diploid zygote. In the higher fungi, especially the basidiomycetes, karyogamy may be delayed and occur separately from plasmogamy, resulting in a dikaryotic mycelium.

**Karyogram** (idiogram). A diagram representing the characteristic features of the chromosomes of a species.

**Karyokinesis.** Nuclear division, the phase of mitosis during which chromosomes are divided into equal portions.

**Karyolymph.** Nuclear sap; the fluid substance of a nucleus.

**Karyolysis.** Dissolution of a uucleus of a cell.

**Karyophore.** In protozoans, an apparatus consisting of a nucleus suspended by ectoplasmic fibrils, as in Isotricha.

**Karyoplasm.** Nuclear substance.

**Karyosome.** A dense mass of chromatin other than the nucleolus within the nucleus of a cell. Also called chromocenter of false nucleolus.

**Karyotype.** The physical appearance of chromosomes from an individual or species as seen at mitotic metaphase. Cells from the root meristem are commonly used, suitably stained, usually with acetic orcein or acetocarmine. The number, size and shape of chromosomes in a set is usually highly characteristic of a species and often also constant within a genus. The karyotype is most conveniently studied by forming a karyogram.

**Katabolism.** Catabolism.

**Katharobic.** Living in clear water, as that of mountain streams.

**Katydid.** A large, green orthopteran insect (Pteryophylla camellifolia) noted for its stridulatory sounds produced by the male.

**Keel** (carina). The projection of bone from the sternum (breastbone) of a bird or bat, to which the powerful fiight muscles are attached. The sterna of flightless birds (*e.g.* ostrich and emu) lack keels.

**Keel**

1. A ridge or ridgelike process; a carina.
2. *bot.* *a.* The edge of two united petals in a bean or pea flower; *b.* a ridge on a blade of grass.

**Kelp**. Also known as oarweed, these large brown seaweeds have broad fronds up to 3 metres long and form dense underwater forests. They are often found along the strand line of beaches.

**Kelt.** A salmon after it has spawned. It returns to the sea where it either dies, or remains until it is ready to spawn again.

**Kentrogon**. The nonmotile larval stage which follows the cypris stage in Sacculina, a parasitic crustacean.

**Keratin** Any of a group of fibrous proteins occurring in hair, feathers, hooves, and horns. Keratins have coiled polypeptide chains that combine to form supercoils of several polypeptides linked by disulphide bonds between adjacent cysteine amino acids. Aggregates of these supercoils form microfibrils, which are embedded in a protein matrix. This produces a strong but elastic structure.

**Keratinization** (cornification). The process in which the cytoplasm of the outermost cells of the mammalian epidermis is replaced by keratin. Keratinization occurs in the stratum corneum, feathers, hair, claws, nails, hooves, and horns.

**Kermes**. The dried bodies of scale insects from which a reddish-purple dye is obtained.

**Kernel**

1. The entire grain or seed of a cereal, as a kernel of corn.
2. The inner and usually the more edible portion of a seed contained within the integuments or hard outer wall, as the kernel of a nut.

**Kestrel.** A bird of the falcon family noted for its hovering flight. A small falcon, with a brownish plumage and a grey head and tail, the kestrel preys mainly on mice, voles and insects. Kestrels are frequently seen above roadside verges, hovering in mid air on the lookout for prey.

**α-ketoglutaric Acid.** A five-carbon dicarboxylic keto acid with the formula $HOOCCO(CH_2)_2COOH$. α-ketoglutarate is an intermediate in the TCA cycle. It is formed by the oxidation of isocitrate, with the concomitant reduction of NAD to NADH. In the next step of the TCA cycle

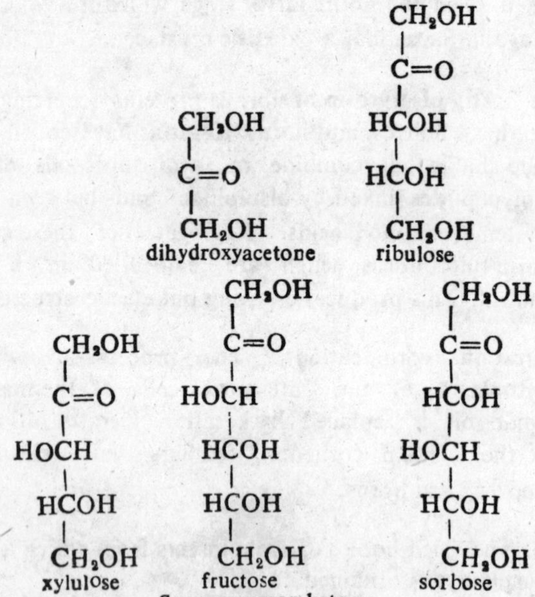

Some common ketoses

α-ketoglutarate undergoes oxidative decarboxylation to form succinyl CoA in a reaction similar to the formation of acetyl CoA from pyruvate.

α-Ketoglutarate is also involved in amino acid metabolism (transamination).

**Ketohexose.** Monosaccharide.

**Ketone.** A compound containing the characteristic group -CO, formed by the oxidation of a secondary alcohol, as acetone, $CH_3COCH_3$.

**Ketone Body.** Any of three compounds, acetoacetic acid (3-oxobutanoic acid, $CH_3COCH_2COOH$), β-hydroxybutyric acid, (3-hydroxybutanoic acid, $CH_3CH(OH)\,CH_2COOH$), and acetone (propanone, $CH_3COCH_3$), produced by the liver as a result of the metabolism of body fat deposits. Ketone bodies are normally used as energy sources by peripheral tissues. However, if carbohydrate supply is limited (*e.g.* during starvation or in diabetics), the blood level of ketone bodies rises and they may be present in urine, giving it a characteristic 'pear drops' odour. This condition is called ketosis.

**Ketopentose.** Monosaccharide.

**Ketose.** Any monosaccharide with the carbonyl (CO) group at a position other than on the terminal carbon atom, so forming a ketone group. The simplest ketose is the three-carbon dihydroxyacetone. Other ketoses include the five-carbon ribulose and xylulose and the six-carbon fructose and sorbose (diagram). Compare aldose.

**Key**

1. A list of characteristics drawn up to enable speedy identification of a specimen. Prominent contrasting features are given at each stage in the key so that by a process of elimination successively smaller groupings of organisms are split of until the specimen can be identified. Simple keys to flowering plants often rely solely on flower structure. For

example, the first step in the key may be to form a number of groups on the basis of petal number. The second stage could be to subdivide these groups on the basis of flower colour and further subdivisions could then be made by petal shape, flower symmetry, etc. The groupings derived from such a key are artifical rather than natural and this method of identification has the disadvantage that if a mistake is made at any stage identification will be completely wrong.

2. samara.

**Kid.** A young goat.

**Kidney.** The main organ of excretion of vertebrates, through which nitrogenous waste material (usually in the form of urine) is eliminated from the body. In mammals there is a pair of kidneys situated in the abdomen. They are made up of tubular units called nephrons, through which nitrogenous waste is filtered from the blood, with the formation of urine. The nephrons drain into a basin-like cavity in the kidney (the renal pelvis), which leads to the ureter and bladder.

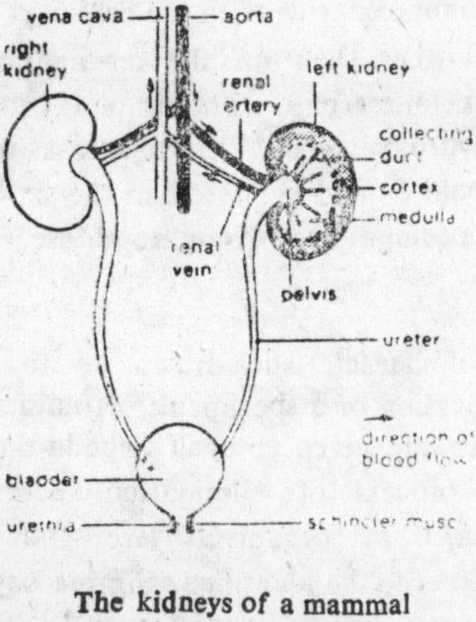


The kidneys of a mammal

**Kidney Worm.** One of two species of nematode worms which infest the kidneys and urinary ducts of certain vertebrates, as Dioctophyme renale, a large worm found in carnivores, and Stephanurus dentatus, found in swine.

**Killer.** An individual which kills, as *a.* a paramecium which contains kappa particles; *b.* a killer whale.

**Kinaesthetic Orientation.** Behaviour of an animal that moves through familiar terrain in the absence of sensory information (*e.g.* in total darkness) by the repetition of actions remembered from past experience of the terrain.

**Kinase** (phosphotransferase, phosphorylase). Any transferase enzyme that catalyses the transfer of phosphate to or from ATP or a related molecule. For example, hexokinase catalyses the phosphorylation of glucose and some other hexose sugars and is an impotant enzyme in the interconversion of hexose sugars, as most isomerases require a phosphorylated sugars as a substrate. Hexokinase is also one of three kinases in the glycolytic pathway.

**Kind.** A natural group, as a class, order, family, etc.

**Kinesiology.** The science which deals with muscular movement, especially in man.

**Kinesthesia.** The sense of movement or position; the proprioceptive or muscle sense.

**Kinesis.** Phenomenon in which a motile organism or cell changes its rate of locomotion in response to a particular stimulus. The direction of locomotion remains random and is unrelated to the direction of the stimulus Compare taxis.

**Kinetic.** Of or pertaining to motion or activity.

**Kinetodesma.** A fine fibril or a set of fibrils connected to a kinetosome.

**Kinetoplast.** A structure in trypanosomes consisting of a parabasal body and a blepharoplast.

**Kinetosome.** A basal body of a cilium or flagellum.

**Kinety** In ciliates, a ciliary row consisting of kinetosomes and kinetodesma.

**Kingfisher.** One of the most brightly coloured birds, with a glossy blue-green back and orange underparts. Kingfishers are shy birds that live by clear unpolluted streams and ponds. They dive into the water, either from a perch on in flight, to catch fish with their long sharp bills. They live in most of Europe, except the far north.

**Kinetin** (6-furfurylaminopurine). A synthetic cytokinin. It was first isolated from DNA extracts of animal origin but has now also been synthesized commercially.

**Kinetochore.** Two parallel brushlike filaments situated in the centromere of a chromosome. Kinetochores attach chromatids to the spindle fibres during nuclear division.

**Kinetosome** (basal body, blepharoplast). A cylindrical structure in the cytoplasm from which a flagellum or cilium arises in motile eukaryotic cells. It is composed of a cylinder of nine microtubules linked by fine crossbridges. It transfers ATP and possibly other materials to the fibres in the shaft of the flagellum or cilium. Striated fibrous extensions, termed rootlet fibres, may arise from the basal body and project backwards into the cytoplasm. These probably serve to anchor the flagellum.

**Kingdom.** The highest category into which organisms are classified. Traditionally two kingdoms have been recognized, the Plantae (plant) and the Animalia (animal). More recently a number of other kingdoms have been suggested. For example, the fungi are considered by some to be sufficiently distinct from green plants to merit being placed in a separate kingdom, Fungi. The differences between prokaryotes and eukaryotes have led some to recognize the two kingdoms Prokaryota and Eukaryota.

**Kingfish.** One of a number of marine fishes, as Menticirrhus, of the Atlantic coast; Genyonemus, of the California coast; Seriola, of the Australian region.

**Kinin**

1. One of a group of peptides, occurring in blood, that are involved in inflammation. Kinins are formed by the enzymatic splitting of blood plasma globulins (kininogens) at the site of inflammation. Kinins so far identified include bradykinin and kallidin. They cause local increases in the permeability of small blood vessels.

2. Cytokinin.

**Kinomere.** Centromere.

**Kin Selection.** Natural selection of genes that tend to cause the individuals bearing them to be altruistic to close relatives. These relatives therefore have a higher probability of bearing identical copies of those same genes

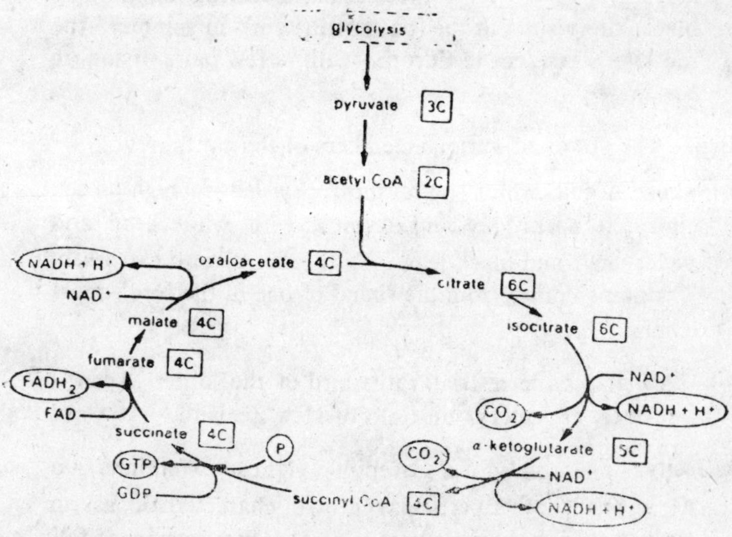


Krebs cycle

than do other members of the population. Thus kin selection for a gene that tends to cause an animal to share food with a close relative will result in the gene being spread through the population because it (unconsciously) benefits itself. The more closely two animals are related, the higher the probability that they share some identical genes and therefore the more closely their interests coincide. Parental care is a special case of kin selection.

**Kipper**

1. A male salmon, especially during the spawning season.

2. In commerce, a smoked herring or salmon.

**Kissing Bug.** One of several species of bloodsucking hemipterans, as Melanolestes picipes, the black corsair, which inflicts painful bites on the lips.

**Kite.** A bird of prey, about the same size as the buzzard. It is recognized by its forked tail and soaring flight. The black kite visits Europe (but not Britain) in summer; the red kite is resident in Europe, with a few pairs living in Britain.

**Kitten.** The young of various members of the cat family.

**Kittiwake.** A gull which nests on rocky ledges high on sea cliffs. It is a grey-winged bird, with white head and underparts, and black legs. Kittiwakes dive to catch fish. The name comes from the sound of one of the bird's most common cries.

**Kiwi.** A flightless, terrestrial, ratite bird of the order Apterygiformes, as Apteryx australis of New Zealand.

**Klendusity.** The ability of a susceptible plant to avoid infection as a result of a particular growth characteristic, as an early-maturing variety escaping a late summer or fall disease.

**Klinotaxis.** A group of reactions in which an organism moves its head from side to side as it is moving forward.

**Knapweed.** Several species of flowering plant related to the daisy and thistle. They have stiff hairy stems and purple-pink, thistle-like flowers. Unlike thistles, the plants are not prickly. They are common in fields and on waysides where some species may grow up to 1 metre high.

**Knee**

1. *zool.* A joint or articulation, as that *a.* in most tetrapods, between femur and tibia; *b.* in birds, the tarsal joint; *c.* in quadrupeds, the carpal or wrist joint of the forelimb.
2. *bot.* A sharp bend in a stem or branch.

**Kneecap.** The patella.

**[1]Knot**

1. A rounded swelling, knob, excrescence, or protuberance, as in a muscle, stem, or root.
2. *bot.* *a.* A hardened mass of wood formed at the base of a branch of a tree. *b.* A plant disease characterized by formation of excrescences.

**[2]Knot.** A large sandpiper (Calidris canutus).

**Kranz Structure.** A type of organization of the photosynthetic tissues found in the leaves of $C_4$ plants. In such plants the cells of the bundle sheath are large and contain specialized elongated chloroplasts with no grana but capable of forming starch grains. The mesophyll chloroplasts are similar in structure to those of $C_3$ plants but do not form starch grains. It is within the mesophyll chloroplasts that oxaloacetic acid is formed through the combination of carbon dioxide and phosphoenolpyruvate. This is then transported to the bundle sheath chloroplasts where the carbon dioxide is released and refixed ribulose bisphosphate carboxylase.

**Krebs Cycle** (citric acid cycle; tricarboxylic acid cycle; TCA cycle). A cyclical series of biochemical reactions that is fundamental to the metabolism of aerobic organisms, *i.e.* animals, plants and many microorganisms. The enzymes of the Krebs cycle are located in the mitochondria and are in close association with the components of the electron transport chain. The two-carbon acetyl coenzyme A (acetyl CoA) reacts with the four-carbon oxaloacetate to form the six-carbon citric acid. In a series of seven reactions, this is reconverted to oxaloacetate and produces two molecules of carbon dioxide. Most importantly, the cycle generates one molecule of guanosine triphosphate (GTP—equivalent to 1 ATP) and reduces three molecules of the coenzyme NAD to NADH and one molecule of the coenzyme FAD to $FADH_2$. NADH and $FADH_2$ are then oxidized by the electron transport chain to generate three and two molecules of ATP respectively. This gives a net yield of 12 molecules of ATP per molecule of acetyl CoA.

Acetyl CoA can be derived from carbohydrates (via glycolysis), fats, or certain amino acids. (Other amino acids may enter the cycle at different stages.) Thus the Krebs cycle is the central 'crossroads' in the complex system of metabolic pathways and is involved not only in degradation and energy production but also in the synthesis of biomolecules. It is named after its principal.

**Krill.** Shrimp-like, marine, euphausiid crustaceans, dense swarms of which occur in ocean waters. They feed on diatoms and themselves comprise the main food of filter-feeding whales. Krill are up to 5 cm in length and are found in both surface and bottom waters.

**Kronism.** The killing and eating of offspring.

**Kronosaurus.** During the Late Jurassic and Lower Cretaceous gigantic aquatic reptiles such as Kronosaurus were among the major predators in the marine environment. Krono-

is a short-necked, large-headed pliosaur. Individuals grew to 12-15 in long. Kronosaurus is recorded from the Upper Cretacmous of Australasia.

**Krummholz.** Elfin forest.

**K-selection.** Selection for maximizing competitive ability, the strategy of equilibrium species. Most typically this is a response to stable environmental resources. This implies selection for low birth rates, high survival rates among offspring, and prolonged development. K represents the carrying capacity of the environment for species populations showing an S-shaped population-growth curve.

**Kudu.** A large, spiral-horned, African antelope (Strepsiceros). Also called koodoo.

**Kumquat.** A dwarf evergreen tree, native to China. It is related to the Orange, and its fruits look like tiny round or oval oranges. The tree grows about 3 metres tall.

**Kupffer's Cells.** Fixed macrophages present in sinusoids of the liver.

**Kuru.** Human disease which occurs naturally only in a small area of Papua New Guinea. The disease involves a progressive degeneration of the central nervous system. It is caused by a virus.

**Kymograph.** A slowly-revolving drum, often covered with graph paper or smoked paper, on which a tracer records measurements of such activities as plant growth movements.

**Kyphosis.** Humpback, hunchback; excessive curvature of the spine with convexity of the curve being directed posterior, usually in the thoracic region.

# L

**Labelling.** The tagging of a compound with an isotopic tracer so that its fate within an organism can be followed.

**Labellum**

1. *bot*. The enlarged third petal in the corolla of an orchid.
2. *zool.* The expanded tip of the labium in certain insects, especially dipterans.

**Labia.** Plural of Labium.

**Labial.** Of or pertaining to lips or labia.

**Labiatae.** Family of herbs or low shrubs, comprising a natural group, whose members have quadrangular stems, and simple leaves without stipules in opposite pairs. Commonly there are apparently whorled spikes of flowers; actually branched cymes are borne in the axils of opposite pairs of bracts, but are usually very condensed. The flowers are strongly irregular, with a five-toothed or two-lipped calyx, and a tubular corolla which is often clearly two-lipped but may have only the lower lip developed; there are two or four stamens, and a four-lobed ovary with the style inserted between the four lobes. The fruit is composed of four, separating, one-seeded nutlets, a clear distinction from those genera of Scrophulariaceae which are superficially similar. Many genera and species are used as flavourings, as they contain aromatic, volatile, essential oils. Some of these oils (*e.g.* menthol and rhymol) are used as mild antiseptics. Many species are cultivated for their flowers, others beautify northern temperate woodlands in springtime. There are some 170 genera, with 3000 species, and their main distribution is in tropical and warmer temperate regions.

**Labile.** Capable of adapting, being changed, or modified; unstable.

**Labium**

1. A lip or liplike structure.
2. *zool.* *a.* The lower lip of an insect or crustacean. *b.* One of two pairs of folds, labia majora and labia minora, lying on each side of the vaginal orifice.
3. *bot.* The lower lip of a labiate flower.

**Labor**

1. Childbirth : Parturition.
2. Functional activity.

**Labrum.** Broad piece of cuticle which forms the upper lip in an insect. The labrum articulates with the clypeus. It is anterior to the mandibles, and can be moved away from them by a pair of muscles, or closed down on to them by another pair of muscles with a rocker-like action.

**Labyrinth**

1. A maze of canals, cavities, or passageways.
2. *anat.* The internal ear, consisting of the osseous or bony labyrinth (semicircular canals, vestibule, cochlea) within which lies the membranous labyrinth (semicircular ducts, utricle, saccule, and cochlear duct).

**Labyrinthine.** Pertaining to or of the nature of a labyrinth.

**Labyrinthine Receptors.** The maculae and cristae.

**Labyrinthodont.** A fossil amphibian of the subclass Stegocephalia.

**Lac.** One of a number of natural resins secreted by various species of scale insects used in the manufacture of waxes, varnishes and lacquers.

**Lace Bug.** A hemipterous insect of the family Tingididae, with a sculptured, lacelike pattern on the dorsal side of body.

**Lacerated**

1. Torn; mangled.
2. Irregularly cleft at the edge, as though torn, said of leaves.

**Laceration**

1. The act of tearing.
2. In sea anemones, a method of asexual reproduction in which a portion of the pedal disc is left behind when the animal moves; pedal laceration.

**Lacewing.** A neuropterous insect of the family Chrysopidae, with large, delicate, finely-veined wings, as Chrysopa oculata.

**Lachrimal Gland** (lachrymal gland). The tear gland, present in the eyelids of some vertebrates. The fluid (tears) produced by this gland cleanses and lubricates the exposed surface of the eye; it drains into the nose through the lachrimal duct.

**Lacinate.** Jagged, fringed, deeply incised.

**Lacinia**

1. *bot.* A narrow, incised portion of a leaf.
2. *zool.* The innermost of two processes on the stipes of the maxilla of an insect.

**Lac Insect.** One of a number of scale insects of the family Coccidae, especially Laccifer lacca, of Southeast Asia, the source of lac used in the manufacture of shellac.

**Lacrimal.** Of or pertaining to tears; lachrymal.

**Lacrimal Apparatus.** The organs involved in the production and flow of tears. Includes the lacrimal gland and excretory ducts, lacrimal canaliculi, lacrimal sac, and nasolacrimal duct leading to the nasal cavity.

**Lactase.** An enzyme in intestinal juice which hydrolyzes lactose to dextrose and galactose.

**Lactation.** The discharge of milk from the mammary glands. This generally only occurs after birth of the young and is stimulated by the sucking action of the infants. The production of milk is under the control of hormones, notably prolactin.

**[1]Lacteal.** Pertaining to or resembling milk.

**[2]Lacteal.** *anat.*

1. A minute lymph vessel in a villus of the intestine.
2. One of the larger lymph vessels of the intestine, containing chyle.

**Lactescent**

1. Resembling milk.
2. Producing or yielding milk or a milklike fluid, as latex.

**Lactic Acid** (2-hydroxypropanoic acid). An alpha hydroxy carboxylic acid, $CH_3CH(OH)COOH$, with a sour taste. Lactic acid is produced from pyruvic acid in active muscle tissue when oxygen is limited (oxygen debt) and subsequently removed for conversion to glucose by the liver. During strenuous exercise it may build up in the muscles, causing cramplike pains. It is also produced by fermentation in certain bacteria and is characteristic of sour milk.

**Lactic Acid Bacteria.** A group of gram-positive anaerobic bacteria that use pyruvic acid as the acceptor for the hydrogen produced in glycolysis, so forming lactic acid. Such organisms (*e.g.* Streptococcus lactis) are used on a large scale in the food industry, especially as starter cultures in cheese making. Most lactic acid bacteria are rod-shaped organisms belonging to the family Lactobacillaceae of the Eubacteriales.

**Lactiferous.** Secreting or conveying milk or a milklike substance.

**Lactogenic.** Stimulating the secretion of milk.

**Lactogenic Hormone.** Prolactin secreted by the anterior pituitary.

**Lactose** (milk sugar). A sugar comprising one glucose molecule linked to a galactose molecule. Lactose is manufactured by the mammary gland and occurs only in milk. For example, cows' milk contains about 4.7% lactose. It is less sweet than sucrose (cane sugar).

**Lacuna**

1. *anat.* A small space or cavity, especially one in cartilage or bone, containing a cell; also a pit or depression.
2. *bot.* An air space of cavity in the stems of certain plants.

**Lacunar.** Consisting of or containing spaces or cavities.

**Lacunose.** Containing cavities or lacunae; bearing pits, depressions, or perforations.

**Ladybird Beetle.** A small, brightly-colored, predaceous beetle of the family Coccinellidae, the larvae, and adults feeding principally upon aphids.

**Ladybug.** A ladybird beetle.

**Laevorotatory.** Designating a chemical compound that rotates the plane of plane-polarized light to the left (anticlockwise for someone facing the oncoming radiation).

**Laevulose.** Frucluose.

**Lagena.** A small diverticutm on the sacculus of lower vertebrates corresponding to the cochlear duct of mammals.

**Lagomorph.** Any mammal of the order Lagomorpha, principally terrestrial, short-tailed, gnawing herbivores as the pikas, rabbits, and hares; distinguished from rodents by presence of two pairs of incisors in upper jaw.

**Lag Phase.** The period, following the inoculation of a nutrient medium with microorganisms, in which there is much physiological activity but no increase in numbers. The rate of cell division accelerates when the organisms become adapted to the culture conditions and enters the logarithmic phase.

**LAI.** Leaf Area Index.

**Lake Forest.** Forest dominated by conifers, which occurs in the eastern half of N. America, in Minnesota, Michigan, N. Pennsylvania, S. Ontario, and northern New England. Although a distinct formation it is in many respects transitional between boreal coniferous forest and southern deciduous forest. Very little lake forest survives, having been cut in the latter part of the nineteenth century.

**Lamarck, Jean Baptiste Pierre Antoine de Monet, Chevalier de** (1744-1829). French naturalist who, in 1809, advanced the theory that evolutionary change may occur by the inheritance of characteristics acquired during the lifetime of the individual. For example, fossil evidence suggests that the ancestors of the giraffe had short necks : Lamarck proposed that competition for food encouraged them to stretch upward in order to browse among higher vegetation, causing their necks to lengthen, and that this lengthening was passed on to their descendants. Over millions of years the minute increases from each generation to the next culminated in the long-necked form. Compare Darwin, Charles Robert.

**Lamarckian Theory.** A theory of evolution proposed by Jean Baptiste Lamarck (1744-1829) that evolutionary changes result from changes in environment, use and disuse of organs, and that such changes (acquired characters) are inherited.

**Lamarckism.** One of the earliest superficially plausible theories of evolution, proposed by the French biologist Jean-Baptiste de Lamarck (1744-1829) in 1809. He suggested that changes in an individual are acquired during its lifetime, chiefly by increased use or disuse of organs in response to "a need that continues to make itself felt", and that these changes are inherited by its offspring. Thus the long neck and limbs of a giraffe are explained as having evolved by the animal stretching its neck to browse on the foliage of trees. This so-called inheritance of acquired characteristics has never unquestionably been demonstrated to occur and the theory was largely displaced by Darwinism. Lamarckism is also incompatible with the Central Dogma of molecular biology.

**Lamb.** A young sheep.

**Lamella**

1. A thin, platelike structure or layer.
2. *zool. a.* A layer of a gill in lamellibranchs. *b.* A layer of bone surrounding a haversian canal.
3. *bot. a.* A gill of a mushroom. *b.* A submicroscopic layer of a chloroplast. *c.* The original thin wall (middle lamella) separating two protoplasts.

**Lamellate.** Composed of thin plates or lamella.

**Lamellibranchia**. A class of aquatic molluces (the bivalves) that include the oysters, mussels, and clams. They are characterized by a laterally flattened body and a shell consisting of two hinged shells (*i.e.* a bivalved shell). The enlarged gills are covered with cilia and have the additional function of filtering microscopic food particles from the water flowing over them. Bivalves live on the sea bed or lake bottom and are sedentary, so the head and foot are reduced.

**Lamellose.** Lamellate.

**Lamina**

1. A thin layer or plate.
2. *anat.* A thin plate of bone, as that which forms the roof of a neural arch.
3. *bot. a.* The blade of a leaf. *b.* The flattened expanded part of a thallus, as in kelps.

**Laminariales** (kelps). An order of the Heterogeneratae, a subclass of the Phaeophyta. It contains the largest known algae, Macrocystis and Nereocystis. Most species occur below the lowtide mark. The sporophyte thallus is differentiated into a holdfast, stipe, and lamina. The gametophyte generation is much smaller and simpler and shows well developed oogamy. Certain species yield alginic acid, which is commercially important as an emulsifying agent.

**Laminarin.** The main assimilation product of algae belonging to the Phaecphyta. It is composed chiefly of glucose units though mannitol may also be present.

**Laminate.** Consisting of or bearing laminae.

**Laminate Placentation.** A form of placentation in which the placentae arise from all over the inner surface of the ovary. It is seen in the flowering rush (Butomus umbellatus) and the white water lily (Nymphaea alba).

**Lammergeier.** The bearded vulture (Gypaetus barbatus) of Europe.

**Lampbrush Chromosome.** One of the large chromosomes found in the eggs (primary oocytes) of amphibians, with paired loops which extent from most of their chromomeres, giving a furry, brush-like appearance under the microscope. They are particularly obvious at the diplotene stage of meiosis.

**Lamprey.** A jawless, eellike vertebrate of the class Marsipobranchii, as Petromyzon marinus, the sea lamprey, now established in the Great Lakes, where it has become a serious pest preying upon fishes, sucking their blood.

**Lamp Shell.** A brachiopod.

**Lanate.** Woolly; covered with long, fine hair.

**Lancelet.** An eel-like creature, also called amphioxus. It belongs to the chordate group, which also includes the vertebrates. Lancelets have no backbone but they have a flexible skeletal rod called a notochord and a nerve cord running down the back. The body is up to 8 cm long, pointed at both ends, and with a fin along the back. Whiskery tentacles strain food in through the mouth. Lancelets live on the sea bed, remaining buried by day with only the mouth showing. They swim by night.

**Lanceolate.** Narrow and tapering at both ends.

**Lancelet.** A marine chordate of the subphylum Cephalochordata; an amphioxus.

**Lanceolate.** Pointed; lance-shaped.

**Land Bridge.** A connection which formerly existed between two land masses now separated by water.

**Landlocked.** Confined to fresh water by being cut off from the sea by a barrier, said of certain fishes.

**Landrace.** An ancient or primitive cultivar of a crop plant. Landraces are often genetically very heterogeneous and contain numerous alleles that contributed to the survival of the organism under natural conditions. Since intensive plant breeding can result in the loss of these alleles, landraces are a source from which plant breeders can selectively reintroduce them into highly bred cultivars.

**Languet.** One of numerous filiform processes which extend from the hyperbranchial band into the branchial chamber in tunicates.

**Langur.** A slender-bodied, long-tailed monkey of the genus Presbytis of Southeast Asia; the sacred monkey of India.

**Lanolin.** Wool Fat.

**Lanose.** Woolly : Lanate.

**Lanuginous.** Covered with down; cottony : Woolly.

**Lanugo.** A downy coat of hair on a fetus, shed shortly before or after birth.

**Lapillus.** The utricular otolith in fishes.

**Lappet**

1. A small fold or flap, especially one hanging pendant, as those on the margin of a scyphozoan jellyfish.
2. In crinoids, a movable plate bordering an ambulacral groove.
3. *ornith.* A wattle.

**Larch.** A coniferous tree of the genus Larix, family Pinaceae.

**Large Intestine.** The portion of the alimentary canal of vertebrates between the small intestine and the anus. It consists of the caecum, colon, and rectum and its principal function is the absorption of water and formation of faces.

**Lark.** A small ground bird of the family Alaudidae, as Eremophila alpestris, the horned lark.

**Larkspur.** A plant (Delphinium) of the crowfoot family or its dried, ripe seeds used in a tincture for the treatment of pediculosis.

**Larva.** Stages in insect development that occur after hatching from the egg, and prior to the reorganizations involved in becoming adult. The term is applied loosely to all exopterygote and endopterygote insects at this stage of growth and feeding, although the term 'nymph' is frequently applied to exopterygotes.

**Larva Migrans.** A condition of the skin resulting form invasion by a foreign species of hookworms, usually Ancylostoma braziliense; creeping eruption.

**Larviparous.** A form of viviparity in which the young produced are larvae, as in blowflies.

**Larynx.** In tetrapods, a dilated region of the upper trachea at the junction with the pharynx, often possessing a folded membrane (vocal cords) which can be made to vibrate and so produce sound, the pitch of the sound being controlled by stretching or relaxing the cords.

**Lasso Cell.** A colloblast.

**Late Blight.** Blight.

**Latent Infection.** An infection in which no symptoms are visible during the first phase of the infection. Growth of the pathogen stops soon after penetration but resumes at some later stage. For example, banana anthracnose infection (caused by the fungus Colletotrichum musae) originates in the field on unripe fruit but after penetration the fungus becomes latent as a subcuticular hypha for up to five months. The fungus resumes activity as the fruit nears maturity and typical black lesions develop on the ripe fruit.

**Latent Period.** The interval between *a.* application of a stimulus and the response; *b.* exposure to radiation and appearance of effects. *c.* exposure to infection and appearance of symptoms.

**Laterad.** Toward the side.

**Lateral**

1. *zool.* Of, pertaining to, or directed to the side; away from the midline or median plane.
2. *bot.* Pertaining to, towards, or borne on the side of a structure, away from the central axis.

**Lateral Line.** System of receptors, often embedded in special grooves in the skin, capable of detecting movement and vibrations in the water surrounding the animal. In most fish, the lateral line runs along the sides of the body, but usually it forms a number of branches on the head. It is found in all lower aquatic vertebrates and some Amphibia.

**Lateral Line System.** A system of sense organs in cyclostomes, fishes, and aquatic amphibians located in the lateral line canal. It contains neuromasts which are sensitive to vibrations and pressure.

**Lateral Meristem.** A meristem arranged parallel to the sides of the organ in which it occurs and responsible for increase in girth usually by formation of secondary tissues. The cambia are lateral meristems. Occasionally the term is used of axillary meristems. Compare apical meristem.

**Lateral Root.** Any root that originates endogenously from the pericycle of another root.

**Laterigrade.** Running of walking sideways, as certain crabs.

**Laterite.** A hard crust that may develop on the soil surface in tropical regions with alternating wet and dry seasons. In the wet season the soluble mineral salts are washed down into the lower horizons. In the dry season the soil solution moves back to the surface by capillarity and the aluminium and irom oxides accumulate and combine together to form the crust. Laterization results in a sterile soil called a latosol.

**Latex.** A milky fluid of mixed composition found in some herbaceous plants and trees. Its function is not clear but it may assist in protecting wounds (compare gum) and it may be involved in the nutrition of the plant. The lates of some species, notably rubber trees, is collected for commercial purposes.

**Latex Tubes.** A system of branching and anastomosing tubes in plants which produce latex.

**Laticifer.** A cell or a linked complex of cells containing a milky liquid called latex and penetrating various tissues in certain plants. A laticifer consisting of a single cell is referred to as simple, whereas a jointed complex is termed compound. Laticifers may be further classified as articulated (branched) or nonarticulated (unbranched). Sometimes the end walls between the elements of a compound laticifer break down forming a continuous tube, sometimes referred to as a laticiferous vessel. A laticifer enclosed by a ray is termed a latex tube. Laticifers are present in many plants, such as the rubber tree, Hevea brasiliensis, rubber being the latex secreted by the laticifers and tapped by cutting through the bark.

**Latin Square.** An experimental design in which the number of treatments is the same as the number of replications, and each treatment occurs once in every column and row. It is analagous to a randomized block design in two directions. It is often used in fertilizer field trials and has the advantage of eliminating from the total variation environmental differences, such as soil fertility, that exist across and down the square experimental plot. The Latin square generally yields more useful information that would a randomized block design of similar size. However it has the limitation that with a large number of treatments there must consequently be a large number of replicates and beyond a certain point the labour involved is not worth the information obtained. Also, with small squares, the method is insensitive because the number of degrees of freedom is low. This can be overcome by replicating the squares.

**Laurer's Canal.** In flukes, a tube extending dorsally from the oviduct, usually ending blindly. When it opens tot he outside, it may serve as a vagina.

**Lauric Acid** (dodecanoic acid) A white crystalline fatty acid, $CH_3(CH_2)_{10}COOH$. Glycerides of the acid are present in natural fats and oils (*e.g.* coconut and palm kernel oil).

**Lavender.** A group of usually greyleaved, fragrant shrubs with mauve, blue or occasionally white flowers, attractive to butterflies.

**Laver.** A dried edible food prepared from algae, green laver from Ulva, purpile or red laver from Porphyra.

**Laxative.** An agent which induces activity of the bowel; a mild cathartic.

**Layer**

1. A stratum; one thickness of a substance, as a layer of cells.
2. A branch of a plant propagated by layerage.
3. A bird which lays eggs.

**Layerage.** A method of plant propagation in which a branch is bent downward, covered with soil at which point roots develop, then the branch is separated from parent plant.

**Layering.** A method of plant propagation involving the pegging down of runners and stolons to the soil surface. Adventitions roots develop where a node touches the soil and a shoot develops from the lateral meristem. New daughter plants eventually establish. Carnations are commonly propagated in this way.

**$LD_{50}$.** Lethar dose 50, or median lethal dose; the amount of a pharmacological or toxic substance (such as ionizing radiation) that causes death in 50% of a group of experimental animals. For each $LD_{50}$ the species and weight of the animal and the route of administration of the substance is specified. $LD_{50}$s are used both in toxicology and in the bioassay of therapeutic compounds.

**Leaching**. The washing out of soluble substances from the upper layers of the soil by water passing down the soil profile. The substances are either deposited lower down in the B horizon or removed completely. It takes place when the amount of rainfall exceeds the amount of water lost by surface evaporation. It may result in podsolization or the development of an impermeable layer of mineral salts at some point in the soil profile. Compare flushing.

**Leader.** The tip of the main stem of a plant. The form of the leader (whether erect or drooping) can aid identification of certain conifers. For example, the western red cedar, Thuja plicata, has an upright leader, which distinguishes it from the similar Lawson cypress, Chamaecyparis lawsonia, which has a drooping leader. The term may also be used of the terminal segment of any main branch in distinction to any lateral branches arising from it. In those conifers in which the leaves are borne in clusters on short side shoots, *e.g.* cedars (Cedrus) and larches (Larix), the side shoots are termed spurs while the main shoot is the leader.

**Leaf** pl. **Leaves.** A green, lateral outgrowth of a stem of a plant in which the functions of photosynthesis, transpiration, and respiration are concentrated, consisting typically of a blade, petiole, and stipules. Other functions may include protection, food and water storage, attachment, insect capture, and reproduction.

**Leaf-area Index** (**LAI**). Of a plant, the total leaf-surface area exposed to incoming light energy, expressed in relation to the ground surface area beneath the plant : *e.g.*, an LAI of 4 means that the leaf area exposed to light is four times the ground surface area.

**Leaf Area Ratio.** A value obtained by dividing the total leaf area of a plant by its dry weight. The ratio is useful in relating total photosynthetic to total respiratory material within the plant, thereby giving information concerning the plant's available energy balance.

**Leaf Arrangement.** Phyllotaxy.

**Leaf Beetle.** A beetle of the family Chrysomelidae, as the Colorado potato beetle, striped cucumber beetle.

**Leaf Bug.** A sucking hemipterous insect of the family Miridae, as the tarnished plant bug, apple red bug, and garden fleahopper; also called plant bug.

**Leaf Buttress.** A lateral prominence on the shoot apex, destined to differentiate into a leaf. It is the earliest stage in the development of a leaf primordium, and later forms the leaf base, the remainder of the leaf growing upwards and outwards from the buttress.

**Leaf Chafer.** A beetle of the family Scarabaeidae which feeds on the roots, flowers, and foliage of various plants, as the rose chafer, Japanese beetle.

**Leaf Curl.** A plant disease in which an increase in cells on either side of the midrib and extra growth of the palisade and spongy mesophyll cause curling and puckering of the leaves. In peach and almond this is caused by the fungus Taphrina deformans and in tobacco and cotton by tobacco and cotton leaf curl viruses respectively. These viruses are transmitted by whiteflies (Bemisia tabaci).

**Leaf-cushion.** A rhomboidal or circular area on the stem of a fossil lycopod.

**Leaf-cutter Bee.** A bee of the family Megachilidae which lines its nest with circular pieces of leaves.

**Leaf-cutting Ant.** A tropical ant of the genus Atta which cuts pieces of leaves used in the cultivation of fungus gardens.

**Leaf Disease.** Any disease in which leaves are the principal parts affected, as leaf blotch, mildew, curl, mold, rust, scald, scorch, smut, spot, streak, and others.

**Leaf Fall.** The shedding of leaves as a result of the formation of a zone of abscission at the base of the petiole. Leaves on dead branches do not fall as no such zone is produced. In deciduous plants there is a continual shedding of older leaves throughout the growing season but with the onset of the winter or dry season there is a conspicuous shedding of all the remaining leaves. In evergreens leaves are shed and replaced continually and there is no period when the plant is devoid of foliage. Leaf fall is associated with a drop in the auxin level of the lamina.

**Leaf Gap** (lacuna). A parenchymatous area in the stele of many vascular plants, associated with and positioned immediately above a leaf trace. Leaf gaps are characteristic of angiosperms but are also present in some gymnosperms and ferns.

**Leafhopper.** A group of sap-sucking bugs, some of which do considerable damage to farm crops. They are small relatives of the froghoppers, found mostly on the leaves of plants.

**Leaflet.** One of the divisions of a compound leaf.

**Leaf Miner** One of a number of insects whose larva feeds on the tissues between upper and lower surfaces of leaves, causing blotchlike or serpentine mines, as moths of the family Gracilariidae; also certain dipterans and hymenopterans.

**Leaf Mosaic.** A rosette arrangement of first-formed leaves with a minimum of leaf overlapping, as in mullein.

**Leaf Roller.** A lepidopterous insect of the families Olethreutidae and Tortricidae whose larvae roll or tie leaves and pupate within them.

**Leaf Scar.** A scar on a stem marking former attachment of a leaf.

**Leaf Sheath.** The basal portion of the blade of a leaf which surrounds the stem, as in leaves of the corn plant.

**Leaf Spot.** A plant disease in which the principal symptom is limited areas of necrosis on the leaves. There are numerous causes of leaf spots—mineral imbalance, insects, weather conditions, viruses, bacteria, and fungi. The leaf spots may be minor symptoms or a particular phase of a disease that develops other, more characteristic, symptoms. Bacteria and fungi are the usual causal agents of the diseases in which leaf spots are the main symptom. Angular leaf spot of cucumber is caused by the bacterium Pseudomonas lacrymans. Fungal leaf spots affect most crop plants and common pathogenic genera are Septoria, Botryodiplodia, Colletotrichum, Gloeosporium, Cercospora, Alternaria, and Helminthosporium.

**Leaf Stalk.** A petiole.

**Leaf Tier.** An insect which ties leaves together and feeds on the inner surface of the folded leaves, as the greenhouse (celery) leaf tier.

**Leaf Trace.** A vascular bundle which extends from the vascular tissue of the stem into the petiole of a leaf; foliar trace.

**Leafy**

1. Consisting principally of or having many leaves.
2. Of the nature of or resembling a leaf.
3. Laminate.

[1]**Lean.** Thin, not fat; having little flesh; deficient in quantity or quality.

**[2]Lean.** To bend or incline from a vertical position, usually necessitating support.

**Learned.** Acquired; not inherited, as learned behavior.

**Learning.** A process by which an animal's response to a particular situation may be permanently altered, usually in a beneficial way, as a result of its experience. Learning allows an animal to respond more flexibly to the situations it encounters; learning abilities in different species vary widely and are adapted to the species' environment. Numerous different categories of learning have been proposed, but there is no general agreement on how many different processes are involved. These categories include habituation, associative learning (through conditioning), and insight learning (which may include imprinting).

**Leather.** The skin of an animal, tanned and prepared for use.

**Leatherjacket**

1. The larva of a crane fly.
2. A carangid fish (Oligoplites saurus) of tropical waters.

**Lecanorales.** An order of the Ascolichenes or of the Discomycetes in which the majority of lichens (8—10,000 species) are placed. Such lichens bear apothecia on their upper surface from which ascospores are violently discharged. The Lecanorales includes such genera as Cladonia, Lecanora, Parmelia, Umbilicaria, and Usnea. The fungal partners in such lichens are closely related to the Helotiales. In certain lichens, *e.g.* Sphaerocarpus species, the asci and paraphyses of the apothecium disintegrate at maturity to form a mass of spores and hymenial tissues. Such lichens may be placed in a separate order, Caliciales. In order lichens the apothecium may be locular and elongate and contain pseudoparaphyses rather than true paraphyses. Such lichens may be placed in the order Hysteriales. Rocella tinctorum, a lichen from which the dye litmus is obtained, is an example of this group.

**Lecanorine.** Describing a lichen ascocarp in which the margin cannot be distinguished from the rest of the thallus. The margin is said to be thalline and consists of both algal and fungal cells. Lecanorine ascocarps are seen in Lecanora. Compare lecideine.

**Lecideine.** Describing a lichen ascocarp having a thin margin, termed a proper margin, composed solely of fungal cells, as in Lecidia. Most lichen ascocarps do have a proper margin but it is often hidden by the thalline margin (lecanorine) when this is present.

**Lecithin.** A choline-containing phospholipid universally present in animal and plant tissues, especially abundant in egg yolk and nervous tissue.

**Lectotype.** A specimen or other element (description, illustration, etc.) subsequently selected from the original material on which the name of a taxon was based. Very often these original elements will be syntypes. A lectotype is only necessary when the original author failed to designate a holotype.

**Leech.** A predatory or parasitic bloodsucking annelid worm of the class Hirudinea, as Hirudo medicinalis, the medicinal leech, formerly used for bloodletting.

**Leek.** A liliaceous plant (Allium porrum) which resembles the onion.

**Leg.** A limb or an appendage of the body used for support or for locomotion (walking or running); in tetrapods, the forelimb or the hindlimb; in bipeds, the hindlimb; in man, the portion of the lower extremity between the knee and the ankle.

**Leghaemoglobin.** A protein found in the centre of root nodules of leguminous plants infected with the nitrogen-fixing bacterium Rhizobium. It has been found that the haemoglobin is coded for by a legume gene but that synthesis only occurs in the presence of the bacterium. The haemoglobin is believed to transport oxygen to the bacterium (which respires aerobically) in such a way that the activity of the nitrogen-fixing enzyme, nitrogenase (which is destroyed on exposure to oxygen), is not affected. Haemoglobin is not found elsewhere in the plant kingdom.

**Legionnaires' Disease.** Human disease first recognized in 1976 when an outbreak occurred among people attending a convention of the American Legion in Philadelphia. The causal agent was found to be a bacterium which was named Legionella pneumophila. Symptoms of legionnaires' disease include fever and pneumonia; the disease may be fatal.

**Legume**

1. A dry, dehiscent fruit which develops from a single carpel or simple ovary, when ripe splitting along both sutures, as that of the bean or pea plant; a pod.
2. Any member of the Leguminosae, the pulse family, a large group of dicots which produce legumes as the characteristic fruit, as beans, peas, peanuts, alfalfa, clover, vetch.

**Leguminosae.** Third largest family of flowering plants, comprising trees, climbers, shrubs, and herbs, some of which are aquatic. Innumerable species are of great economic importance for timber, fodder, drugs, or food. The leaves have stipules, and are usually pinnate. Many species have root nodules containing nitrogen-fixing bacteria. The inflorescence is basically racemose. The flowers are regular or zygomorphic, basically with five sepals and petals, the sepals often united. Typically there are 10 stamens (but many in Mimosoideae) which are sometimes fused. The ovary is superior, with a single carpel. The fruit is a pod, usually several-seeded, and usually dehiscent. There are three subfamilies, distinguished by their different flower construction : Caesalpinoideae and Mimosoideae are mainly tropical; Papilionatae has many temperate species and many herbs. There are 700 genera, with 170 000 species, with cosmopolitan distribution.

**Leguminous**

1. Of, pertaining to, or producing legumes.
2. Belonging to the family Leguminosae, legume-producing plants.

**Leishman's Stain.** A neutral stain for blood smears devised by the British surgeon W. B. Leishman (1865-1926). It consists of a mixture of eosin (an acidic stain), and methylene blue (a basic stain) in alcohol and is usually diluted and buffered before use. It stains the different components of blood in a range of shades between red and blue. The similar Wright's stain is favoured by American workers.

**Lek.** Territory that is held and defended against rivals by males of certain species of animals during the breeding season. The male displays within its lek in order to attract females into the lek for mating. Females move among the leks, mating with males to whose displays they respond. Consequently, for a local population of a species leks are usually grouped together within a breeding area and dominant males tend to occupy the more central leks where their displays can be seen by the largest number of females.

**Lemma** (flowering glume). The lower of a pair of bracts beneath each floret (flower) in the inflorescence of a grass. The lemma is usually membranous to coriaceous, whereas the other bract, the palea (if present), is usually thinner and more delicate. Compare glume.

**Lemming**. One of several species of Arctic, mouselike rodents of the genera Lemmus and Dicrostonyx, noted for migrating in large numbers at irregular times.

**Lemniscus**

1. A band of nerve fibers in the brain.
2. One of a pair of glandular structures in acanthocephalans.

**Lemon** The yellow, acid fruit of the citrus tree (Citrus limon) or the tree which produces it.

**Lemur**. One of a number of primitive primates of the suborder Lemuroidea, solitary, arboreal, nocturnal mammals of Madagascar and neighboring islands. Most belong to the genus Lemur.

**Lenitic**. Describing a freshwater ecosystem in which there is not a continuous flow of water, such as a lake or pond. Compare lotic.

**Lens**

1. A piece of glass or other transparent material with one or both surfaces curved for bringing light rays to a focus.
2. *zool.* *a.* A transparent, biconvex structure present in an eye which focuses light rays on the retina or other light-sensitive structure, as the crystalline lens of the vertebrate eye. *b.* A comparable structure in the eye of a cephalopod.

**Lentic**. Of or pertaining to standing, inland waters, as lakes, ponds, swamps; lenitic.

**Lenticel**. Any of the raised pores in the stems of woody plants that allow gas exchange between the atmosphere and the internal tissues. The pore is formed by the cork cambium, which, at certain points, produces a loose bulky form of cork that pushes through the outer tissues to create the lenticel.

**Lenticellate.** Having lenticels.

**Lenticular**

1. *bot.* Resembling in shape the seed of a lentil.
2. *anat.* Having the shape of a double convex lens.

**Lenticularis.** From the Latin lenticularis meaning biconvex or lens-shaped, a form of cloud consisting of clearly defined, elongated lenses. The form is typical of lee-wave clouds and may affect such clouds as stratocumulus, altocumulus, and cirrocumulus.

**Lentil**

1. A leguminous plant (Lens culinaris) widely grown throughout Europe and Asia, whose seeds are used for food, the plant for fodder.
2. The lens-shaped seeds of this plant.

**Lenzites** (family Polyporaceae). Genus of fungi, which form bracket-like fruit bodies on the under-side of which are gills bearing hymenium. The spores are colourless, smooth, and cylindrical. There are many species. L. betulina forms semicircular or fan-shaped brackets, often in tiers, on deciduous trees and dead wood.

**Lepidodendrales.** An extinct order of the Lycopsida containing arborescent forms, such as Lepidodendron, that flourished during the Carboniferous. Species of Lepidodendron reached heights of up to 30 m. The trunks, some of which had a girth of over 3 m at their base, were unbranched for the main part but divided dichotomously at the top into numerous branches. The trunk was patterned with diamond-shaped leaf scars and from its base arose four dichotomously branching axes that gave rise to the root system. Strobili, similar, except in size, to those of

Selaginella, were borne on the ends of the branches and it appears that the method of fertilization was basically similar to that of Selaginella.

**Lepidoptera.** An order of insects comprising the butterflies and moths, found mainly in tropical regions. Adults possess two pairs of membranous wings, often brightly coloured and usually coupled together. The wings, body, and legs are covered with minute scales. Adult mouthparts are generally modified to form a long proboscis for sucking nectar, fruit juices, etc. Butterflies are typically small-bodied, active during daylight, and rest with their wings folded vertically; moths have larger bodies, are nocturnal, and rest with their wings in various positions. The larvae (caterpillars) have a prominent head and a segmented wormlike body, most segments bearing a pair of legs. They chew leaves and stems, sometimes causing considerable damage to crop plants. The larvae undergo metamorphosis via a pupa (chrysalis) to the adult form. In some groups, the pupa is enclosed in a cocoon of silk derived from silk glands (modified salivary glands); others use leaves, etc. to build a cocoon.

**Lepidopteran.** An insect of the order Lepidoptera which comprises the moths, butterflies, and skippers characterized by two pairs of wings covered by overlapping scales, sucking mouth parts, and complete metamorphosis, the larvae called caterpillars.

**Lepidopterous.** Adapted for pollination by moths or butterflies, said of flowers.

**Leporid.** A mammal of the family Leporidae which includes the hares and rabbits.

**Leprosy** (Hansen's disease). Chronic disease of humans caused by the bacterium Mycobacterium leprae. The disease occurs in various forms. There is a very long incubation period and the onset of symptoms is often very gradual.

Typically, the nerves are affected and skin becomes anaesthetized; this tends to allow damage of anaesthetized parts and hence leads to mutilation and deformity.

**Leptocephalus.** The larva of freshwater eels of the genus Anguilla, which develop from eggs laid in deep waters of the Atlantic.

**Leptocephalus Larva.** Type of larva found only in certain species of marine bony fish. The appearance of the leptocephalus larva is different from that of the adult. In the case of the eel (Anguilla) the larva has a small head with tiny eyes, and the body is shaped like a willow leaf and is virtually transparent; the dorsal and ventral portions of the body divided by the notochord and spinal cord are of approximately the same size. Only after metamorphosis does the fish begin to look like an adult eel.

**Leptodactylidae** (class Amphibia, order Anura (Salientia, suborder Procoela). Varied family of frogs including arboreal and burrowing forms. Their adaptations to arid conditions include rapid metamorphosis and a capacity to retain water. The family includes Sminthillus limbatus, the world's smallest frog (body length 1 cm), but many species are large and voracious. There are about 650 species occurring in Australia, tropical America, and southern Africa.

**Leptoid.** An elongated nutrient-conducting cell in the stems of Polytrichum (hair mosses) and related bryophytes, analogous to a sieve cell in vascular plants. Compare hydroid.

**Leptom** or **Leptome**. Phloem or bast.

**Leptóme.** The region in the exine of a pollen grain where the pollen tube makes its exit.

**Leptoscope.** An apparatus for measuring the thickness of thin membranes, as the plasma membrane of a cell.

**Leptosporangiate.** Originating from a single cell, as in most ferns, with reference to sporangium formation. Compare eusporangiate.

**Leptosporangium.** A type of sporangium that is derived from one initial cell. It is typical of ferns of the order Filicales (the leptosporangiate ferns). The wall of a leptosporangium is usually only one cell thick and does not contain tissue derived from the archesporium. Compare eusporangium.

**Leptotene.** The beginning of the first prophase of meiosis, when the chromatids can be seen and pairing begins.

**Lesion.** A structural alteration of an organ resulting from injury or disease processes.

**Lespedeza.** A bush clover (Lespedeza), an important forage legume.

**Lethal.** Deadly, fatal pertaining to or causing death.

**Lethal Gene.** A mutant allele that results in the death of an organism. The mutation commonly takes the form of a small chromosomal deletion, so that the genetic code for a key protein is missing or disrupted. Such mutations do not necessarily take effect at fertilization but may manifest themselves at any stage of development. The chlorophyll-less mutant ($chl^-$) of barley, which is typically recessive, only shows its lethal effects after the food reserves in the germinating seed have been used up.

**Leucine.** A nonpolar branched chain amino acid with the formula $(CH_3)_2CHCH_2CH(NH_2)COOH$ (illustration at amino acid). It is synthesized from pyruvate and is degraded by a complex pathway leading eventually to acetoacetate. Many of the enzymes involved in the synthesis and degradation of leucine are the same as those involved in the metabolism of isoleucine and valine.

**Leucocyte.** White blood cell, present in invertebrate and vertebrate animals. There are three types : lymphocytes, amoeboid, non-phagocytic cells that produce or convey antibodies; monocytes, phagocytic cells that ingest invading organisms, sometimes entering tissue to do so; and polymorphs (polymorphonuclear leucocytes, or granulocytes), also phagocytic cells, with granular cytoplasm and lobed nuclei.

**Leuconoid.** Pertaining to a type of canal system in sponges consisting of a complicated branching series of canals with choanocytes limited to small cavities.

**Leucoplast.** Any of various organelles in plant cells that contain no pigment and are therefore colourless. Leucoplasts are usually found in tissues not normally exposed to light and frequently contain reserves of starch, protein, or oil.

**Leuconostoc** (family Streptococcaceae). Genus of Gram-positive bacteria in which the cells are spherical or lenticular and usually occur in pairs or chains. Chemo-organotrophic, they can grow in the presence or absence of air. There are several species, found for example in fruit and vegetable matter, and dairy products; none is pathogenic. Some strains are used in the manufacture of certain dairy products, *e.g.* butter.

**Leucosin.** Chrysolaminarin, a storage carbohydrate present in certain algae.

**Leukemia.** A neoplastic disorder of blood-forming tissues characterized by formation of an excessive number of white blood cells.

**Leukoblast.** A cell which gives rise to a leukocyte.

**Leukocyte.** A colorless or white blood cell, nucleated, ameboid cells of the following types: granulocytes (neutrophils, eosinophils, basophils) and agranulocytes, lymphocytes, monocytes).

**Leukocytosis.** An increase in the number of white blood cells above normal numbers, as occurs in infections.

**Levator.** A muscle which raises or elevates a part.

**Leveret.** A hare or rabbit in its first year.

**Levorotatory.** Pertaining to rotation or turning to the left counterclockwise), with reference to a plane of polarized light.

**Levulose.** Fructose or fruit sugar, $C_6H_{12}O_6$, a levorotatory hexose present in fruit juices and honey.

**Leydig Cells.** Interstitial cells, 2.

**LH.** Luteinizing hormone.

**Liana** (liane). A long-stemmed woody climbing plant that grows from ground level to the canopy of trees. Lianas abound in tropical forest and individual stems can be as long as 70 m. The plants begin their growth in deep shade but by climbing up and over the top of very tall trees they benefit from full sunlight at maturity. They may bind the trees together so if one dies it is held in position until it decays.

**Lianous.** Vinelike, creeping.

**Lice.** Mallophaga (bird lice); Siphunculata (sucking lice).

**Lichen.** Type of 'composite organism', which consists of a fungus (the mycobiont) and an alga or cyanobacterium (the phycobiont) living in symbiotic association. A lichen thallus may be crust-like, scaly, leafy, or shrubby, according to the species. In the majority of lichen the fungal partner belongs to the Ascomycotina, and many lichens produce ascocarps which are important in classification. Asexual reproductive structures may also be produced (for example, soredium; and isidium). Many lichens are extremely sensitive to atmospheric pollution and have been used as pollution indicators.

**Lichenes** (lichens). A group consisting of organisms that are symbiotic associations (symbiosis) between a fungus (usually one of the Ascomycetes) and an alga (from the Chlorophyta or Cyanophyta). The fungus usually makes up most of the plant body and the cells of the alga are distributed within it. The alga photosynthesizes and passes most of its food to the fungus and the fungus protects the algal cells. The lichen reproduces by mean of fungal spores, which must find a suitable alga on germination. Lichens are slow growing but can live in regions that are too cold or exposed for other plants. They may form a flattened crust or be erect and branching. Many grow as epiphytes, especially on tree trunks. Some species are very sensitive to air pollution and have been used as indicator species.

**Lichenin**. Glucan found in lichens, containing 80—200 beta-glucose units. Of these, about 30% are glycosidically linked to the third carbon atom, and the remainder to the fourth carbon atom of the neighbouring sugar units.

**Lichen Zone.** Area with a characteristics lichen flora ranging from complete absence to a full complement of foliose and fruticose species, depending on the level and type of air pollution present in the area. The standardized lichen zones for England and Wales range from zone 0 (complete absence) typical of heavily polluted industrial areas, to zone 10 in which bearded lichens (*e.g.* Usnea and Ramalina species) are present in association with many other species. Zone 10 is typical of unpolluted areas in which virtually no sulphur dioxide, fluorine compounds, or other air pollutants are present.

**Lichi.** Litchi.

**Liebig's Law of the Minimum.** Concept first stated by J. von Liebig (1840) that the rate of growth of a plant, the size to which it grows, and its overall health depend on the amount of the scarcest of its essential nutrients that is available to it. This concept is now broadened into a general model of limiting factors for all organisms, including the limiting effects of excesses of chemical nutrients and other environmental factors.

**Life.** State of physical entities that utilize substances derived from outside themselves for the purposes of growth, the repair of their own structure, and the maintenance of their functional systems, and that reproduce. The oldest known fossils are from rocks about 3300 million years old, and the Earth is estimated to be about 4600 million years old. If it is accepted that life began on Earth (rather than being introduced from elsewhere), then it must have done so during the intervening 1300 million years. There is disagreement on the mechanism by which this happened. The classic view is that lightning discharges in a reducing atmosphere produced prebiotic substances which became dissolved in the oceans where, protected from ultraviolet light, they were somehow assembled into the first organisms. Recently evidence has been advanced that suggests that life may have originated in small freshwater pools in an atmosphere of carbon dioxide with just traces of ammonia

**Life Cycle.** Series of developmental changes undergone by the individuals comprising a population, including fertilization, reproduction, and the death of those individuals and their replacement by a new generation. The life 'cycle' in fact is linear with respect to individuals, but cyclical with respect to populations. In many animals and plants there is a succession of individuals in the entire cycle with sexual or asexual production linking them. In vertebrates, the life cycle is confined to the period from fusing of the gametes to the death of the resulting individuals.

**Life Expectancy**

1. The average length of life of all individuals born at a certain time.

2. The probable number of years that a person of a particular age group will survive.

**Life-form.** The structure, form, habits, and life history of an organism. In plants, especially, characteristic life-forms, in particular morphological features, are associated with different environments. This observation has formed the basis of several attempts at life-form classifications of vegetation. Raunkiaer's scheme (1934) is the best-known and most widely applied life-form scheme.

**Life History.** The complete series of changes in an organism beginning with its origin from an ovum, zygote, spore, or other primary stage and continuing to its natural death.

**Lifeless.** Without life; devoid of vital activity.

**Life Plant.** A tropical plant (Bryophyllum) which reproduces by the development of plantlets on the margins of its leaves.

**Life Span.** The extreme limit of life for an individual of a given species.

**Ligament.** A resilient but flexible band of tissue (chiefly collagen) that holds two or more bones together at a movable joint. Ligaments restrain the movement of bones at a joint and are therefore important in preventing dislocation.

**Ligase.** Any of a class of enzymes that catalyse the formation of covalent bonds using the energy released by the cleavage of ATP. Ligases are important in the synthesis and repair of many biological molecules, including DNA.

**Ligate.** To tie off a vessel, as an artery, vein, or duct.

**Ligature**

1. The act of tying off a vessel or duct.
2. A cord or band used in tying off a vessel.
3. Any structure which binds.

**Light** (visible radiation). Electromagnetic radiation with wavelengths ranging from roughly 400 nm (extreme violet) to 770 nm (extreme red). Light from the sun provides the energy to fuel the photosynthetic fixation of carbon dioxide by green plants and is thus the basis of life on earth.

**Light Green.** Fast green.

**Light Microscope** (optical microscope). An optical instrument that contains one or more lenses and is used in the laboratory to enlarge objects that are too small to be examined in detail by the naked eye. Its maximum resolution (the capacity to observe fine detail clearly), is about 0.3 $\mu$m (*i e.* it can distinguish points only 0.3 $\mu$m apart) as compared to about 80 $\mu$m for the average humam eye (resolving power). Light is passed through a condenser, which converges the light rays onto the specimen, and then through one or more lenses. The earliest instruments were simple microscopes with a single lens (*i.e.* basically magnifying glasses). Such instruments are little used today as they have to be positioned close to the eye and have a limited field of vision. Also the illumination and mounting of the specimen is very tricky. The compound microscope has two lenses, one at either end of the body tube. The objective lens is at the base of the tube close to the specimen and the eyepiece or ocular at the other end close to the eye. The image is focused either by moving the body tube or by moving the microscope stage to which the specimen is secured. Most modern compound microscopes have several objective lenses of different magnifications, fitted to a revolving nosepiece. Some microscopes have a built-in light source while others are fitted with a mirror to reflect light from a lamp. The adjustment of an iris diaphragm reduces glare by limiting the part of the specimen that is illuminated. The modern compound microscope is used extensively for observing fine detail of microorganisms and thin sections through tissues and organs. Sections are often stained to increase contrast. The stereoscopic binocular microscope is used for work requiring lower magnifications, such a dissection, or for viewing detail of comparatively large specimens. It has two eyepieces that give a three-dimensional image, and the specimen is usually placed on a contrasting background.

**Light Reactions.** The light-dependent sequence of photosynthetic reactions that, taking place on the thylakoid membranes of chloroplasts, produce the ATP and NADPH used in the carbon dioxide fixation of the subsequent dark reactions. Incident light is absorbed by pigments, distributed between two separate photosystems, I and II. The energy absorbed causes excitation of chlorophyll *a* molecules, which emit high-energy electrons that are passed down an electron transport chain, their energy being used to produce ATP and the reduced form of $NADP^+$. Unlike respiration, the transfer of electrons in photosynthesis is from less electronegative molecules to more electronegative molecules. The energy needed to achieve this reversal of normal electron flow is provided by light.

**Ligneous.** Of the nature of or resembling wood; woody.

**Lignicolous.** Describing organisms that live on or in wood, such as bracket fungi.

**Lignification.** The impregnation of cellulose with lignin, resulting in formation of wood.

**Lignin.** A complex organic polymer that is deposited within the cellulose of plant cell walls during secondary thickening. Lignification makes the walls woody and therefore rigid.

**Lignite.** Wood coal or brown coal, a variety of coal intermediate between peat and soft coal.

**Lignosae.** In John Hutchinson's system of classification, a subgroup of the dicotyledons into which the predominantly woody families are placed. The predominantly herbaceous plants are placed in the Herbaceae. The division is considered unnatural by most taxonomists as it separates certain families generally thought of as closely related, *e.g.* the woody Verbenaceae from the herbaceous Labiatae.

**Ligula**

1. *zool. a.* The terminal, lobed portion of the labium of an insect. *b.* The thickened line of attachment of the tela choroidea to the medulla oblongata. *c.* A lobe of a parapodium of certain polychaetes.
2. *bot.* A ligule.

**Ligulate.** Strap or tongue shaped as, for example, the outer ray florets of the inflorescences of plants in the family Compositae.

**Ligule**

1. A membranous scalelike outgrowth from the leaves of certain flowering plants. Many grasses have a ligule at the base of the leaf blade.

2. A small membranous structure that develops on the upper surface of a young leaf base in certain pteridophytes, for example Selaginella. It withers as the plant matures.

3. A strap-shaped extension from the corolla tube in certain florets of a capitulum. They are termed ligulate (or ray) florets.

**Lilac.** A common garden shrub (Syringa vulgaris) of the family Oleaceae.

**Liliaceae.** A large monocotyledonous family, commonly known as the lily family, containing about 3500 species in about 250 genera. Many of the Liliaceae possess swollen underground perennating organs, such as bulbs, corms, and rhizomes. The only important food plant in the family is the onion (Allium cepa). Minor food plants include garlic, leek, and asparagus. However horticulturally the Liliaceae are one of the most important families and the flowers display a wide range of form and colour. They may be solitary, as in the tulips (Tulipa), in a raceme, as in hyacinths (Hyacinthus), or in a cyme, as in the umbellike cymes of onion. Ornamental genera include Lilium, Aloe, Hosta, Muscari, and Scilla.

**Liliidae.** A subclass of the monocotyledons containing mainly herbaceous plants often with relatively large flowers. It may contain, depending on the classification scheme referred to, two to five orders. The differences arise because the Zingiberales and Triuridales (sometimes placed in the Liliidae) are alternatively classified in the Commelinidae and Alismatidae respectively, and the family Iridaceae (order Liliales) is sometimes raised to the status of an order, Iridales. The order Liliales contains some 14—18 families including : the Iridaceae (which contains the horticulturally important Crocus, Iris, Freesia, and Gladiolus); the Liliaceae; the Amaryllidaceae (which contains the genera Narcissus and Galanthus); Agavaceae (which includes sisal—hemp, Agave sisalana); and the Dioscoreaceae (yam family). The order Orchidales contains the Burmanniaceae and the Orchidaceae.

**Lily**. A large family of mostly herbaceous plants which includes, along with the true lilies, familiar species such as the bluebell, ramsons, meadow saffron and lily of the valley. True lilies are rarely found in NW Europe. Members of the family appear to have six-petalled flowers, but in fact the flowers have only three petals, with three petal-like sepals. Most of the plants grow from bulbs.

**Limb**

1. *zool. a.* One of a pair of appendages as an arm, leg, or wing, used for locomotion or grasping *b.* A limb-like structure, as one of the parts of the internal capsule of the brain or of the loop of Henle of a nephron.

2. *bot. a.* A large branch of a tree. *b.* The expanded portion of a gamopetalous corolla. *c.* The broad expanded portion of a leaf or petal.

**Limbate**. Bordered, as when the margin of a petal or leaf differs in color from the central portion.

**Limbus**

1. An edge or border, especially one with a distinct color or structure.

2. In anthozoans, a constricted region near the base.

[1]**Lime**. A tropical tree or shrub (Citrus aurantifolia) or its small, yellowish-green, acid fruit.

[2]**Lime**. *chem.* Calcium oxide (CaO) or quicklime, prepared by heating (calcining) calcium carbonate thus driving off carbon dioxide.

**Limen.** A boundary line or threshold.

**Limicoline**

1. Shore-inhabiting.

2. Of or pertaining to shorebirds.

**Limicolous.** Inhabiting mud.

**Liminal.** Of or pertaining to a limen or threshold.

**Liming.** The application of lime (calcium hydroxide) to soils to increase levels of calcium and decrease acidity.

**Limiting Factor** (ecological factor). Defined originally as whichever essential material is available in an amount most closely approaching the critical minimum needed, but now used more generally to describe any environmental condition or set of conditions that approaches most nearly the limits (maximum or minimum) of tolerance for a given organism.

**Limits of Tolerance.** The upper and lower limits to the range of particular environmental factors (*e.g.* light, temperature, availability of water) within which an organism can survive. Organisms with a wide range of tolerance are usually distributed widely, while those with a narrow range have a more restricted distribution.

**Limivorous.** Swallowing mud containing food.

**Limnetic.** Pertaining to organisms inhabiting open waters of ponds, lakes, and inland seas.

**Limnetic Zone.** The area in more extensive and deeper freshwater ecosystems that lies above the compensation level and beyond the littoral (lake-edge) zone. This zone is mainly inhabited by plankton and nekton with occasion neuston species. The limnetic and littoral zones together comprise the euphotic or well-illuminated zone. In very small and shallow lakes or ponds the limnetic zone may be absent.

**Limnobiology.** Limnology.

**Limnology.** The science which deals with life in inland waters and all factors which influence it.

**Limnoplankton.** Lake plankton.

**Limpet.** A sessile, marine gastropod with a low conical shell.

**Limpid.** Clear, transparent, translucent.

**Limpkin.** A large tropical, marsh bird (Aramus guarauna) of the family Aramidae; courlan.

**Linden.** Any tree of the genus Tilia, especially T. americana, the American basswood.

**Linea.** A line or linelike mark or structure.

**Lineage.** A line of descent with reference to *a.* the offspring or progeny of a single ancestor; *b.* the succession of ancestors from which an individual has descended.

**Lineal**

1. In a straight line.
2. In the direct line of ancestry : Hereditary.

**Linear.** Describing leaves, such as those of grasses, that are elongated and parallel sided for much of their length.

**Lineate.** Bearing parallel lines or stripes.

**Linen.** Thread or fabric made from the fibers of flax.

**Lineolate.** Possessing or marked by fine, parallel lines; minutely lineate.

**Ling**

1. A marine food fish (Molva molva) of the North Atlantic.
2. Burbot.

**Lingua.** A tongue or tonguelike structure.

**Lingual**

1. Of or pertaining to the tongue.
2. Produced by or resulting from action of the tongue, as certain sounds.

**Linin.** Term formerly applied to a light-staining reticulum connecting the chromatin particles of a nucleus.

**Linkage.** The association of genes that results from their being on the same chromosome. Linkage is detected by the greater association in inheritance of two or more non-allelic genes than would be expected from independent assortment. The nearer such genes are to each other on a chromosome, the more closely linked they are, and the less often they are likely to be separated in future generations by crossing-over. All the genes in one chromosome form one linkage group.

**Linkage Disequilibrium.** In genetics, the continued association of characters known to be determined by separate genes. Such genes are said to be co-adapted with the others with which they are associated. In natural populations, linkage disequilibrium is observed as unusually small or zero recombination frequencies; it is most common between loci already known to be closely linked. A likely explanation is that a section of the chromosome has been inverted and/or translocated, making this section (and perhaps some other section) non-homologous with the sister chromosome of the pair. Recombination is thus precluded, and genes along this section behave as a single 'supergene'.

**Linkage Map.** A diagrammatic representation of the order of genes on a chromosome. Linkage maps can be constructed by crossing appropriate strains carrying different alleles on homologous chromosomes. Results show that the arrangement of genes is linear, although the distance between the genes is expressed not in units of length but in crossover units or Morgan units (named after T. H. Morgan who discovered linkage). Infrequent crossing over is interpreted to mean that genes are near each other (closely linked), and is expressed quantitatively by a small cross-over value (% crossing over). Conversely, genes are regarded as being further apart if the frequency of crossing over is higher, as indicated by a large crossover value.

**Linnaean.** Pertaining to Carolus Linnaeus (Carl von Linne), a Swedish naturalist, the author of Systema Naturae, the 10th edition (1758) of which became the basis of the binomial system of nomenclature employed in the classification of animals and plants.

**Linnaean System.** Binomial nomenclature.

**Linoleic Acid.** A liquid polyunsaturated fatty acid with two double bonds, $CH_3(CH_2)_4CH : CHCH_2CH : CH(CH_2)_7COOH$. Linoleic acid is abundant in many plant fats and oils, *e.g.* linseed oil, groundnut oil, and soya-bean oil. It is an essential fatty acid.

**Linolenic Acid.** An eighteen-carbon triunsaturated fatty acid. It occurs in many plant lipids but is especially prevalent in the chloroplast, where it is the predominant fatty acid. Like linoleic acid it is essential in animal diets.

**Lion.** A large, carnivorous mammal (Panthera (Felis) leo) of the family Felidae found principally in Africa and South-east Asia.

**Lioness.** A female lion.

**Lip**

1. One of two fleshy structures which surround the mouth opening in man and other vertebrates.
2. A corresponding structure in other animals, as the labium or labrum of an insect.

3. The rim or a projecting edge of a tube or cavity, as the glenoid lip of the acetabulum.
4. The edge of a valve in a bivalve mollusk.
5. *bot.* *a.* The labellum of an orchid. *b.* One of the two divisions of a bilabiate calyx or corolla.

**Lipase.** An enzyme secreted by the pancreas and the glands of the small intestine of vertebrates that catalyses the breakdown of fats into fatty acids and glycerol.

**Lip Cells.** In ferns, two thin-walled cells in the wall of a sporangium which mark the point of rupture.

**Lipid.** Any of a diverse group of organic compounds, occurring in living organisms, that are insoluble in water but soluble in organic solvents, such as chloroform, benzene, etc. Lipids are broadly classified into two categories: complex lipids, which are esters of long-chain fatty acids and include the glycerides (which constitute the fats and oils of animals and plants), glycolipids, phospholipids. and waxes; and simple lipids, which do not contain fatty acids and include the steroids and terpenes.

Lipids have a variety of functions in living organisms. Fats and oils are a convenient and concentrated means of storing food energy in plants and animals. Phospholipids and sterols, such as cholesterol, are major components of cell membranes. Waxes provide vital waterproofing for body surfaces. Terpenes include vitamins A, E, and K, and phytol (a component of chlorophyll) and occur in essential oils, such as menthol and camphor. Steroids include the adrenal hormones, sex hormones, and bile acids.

Lipids can combine with proteins to form lipoproteins, *e.g* in cell membranes. In bacterial cell walls, lipids may associate with polysaccharides to form lipopolysaccharides.

**Lipoblast.** A cell which is capable of developing into a fat cell.

**Lipochrome.** Any of a number of fat-soluble pigments as carotene, xanthophyll, or lutein present in yellow vegetables, egg yolk, and corpora lutea.

**Lipoic Acid** (6,8-dithio-*n*-octanoic acid). Compound that functions as a coenzyme in the oxidative decarboxylation of pyruvic acid to alpha-ketoglutaric acid and of the latter to succinic acid. It is sometimes classed as a vitamin as it is an essential requirement for some micro-organisms.

**Lipoid.** Resembling fat or oil.

**Lipolysis.** The breakdown of storage lipids in living organisms. Most long-term energy reserves are in the form of triglycerides in fats and oils. When these are needed, *e.g.* during starvation, lipase enzymes convert the triglycerides into glycerol and the component fatty acids. These are then transported to tissues and oxidized to provide energy.

**Lipophore.** A chromatophore containing red, yellow, or orange pigment.

**Lipopolysaccharide.** Any molecule containing both lipid and carbohydrate elements. Lipopolysaccharides are the principal components of gram-negative bacterial cell walls. Such molecules have a repeating trisaccharide backbone, to which are attached side chains of oligosaccharides and the fatty acid 3-hydroxymyristic acid.

**Lipoprotein.** A conjugated protein consisting of a simple protein and a lipid.

**Lirella.** A long, narrow apothecium of a lichen.

**Litchi.** A tree (Litchi chinensis) of Southeast Asia or the fruit it produces.

**Lithocyst.** A cell that contains a cystolith.

**Lithocyte.** A cell containing a statolith; present in the statocysts of various invertebrates.

**Lipoprotein.** An association of lipids and proteins in a system that combines aspects of the properties of both types of molecule. Most membrane systems (plasma membrane) are composed primarily of lipoprotein. The major lipids in plant membranes are phosphoglycerides and glycolipids. (Glycolipids are especially abundant in the chloroplast membranes.) The protein component is not limited to any one type of protein but membrane proteins often have a slightly modified structure to improve their interaction with lipids. For example, there are relatively few disulphide bridges in membrane proteins.

The forces binding lipid and protein together in a lipoprotein system are not conventional chemical bonds. The most important binding forces are hydrophobic interactions but polar and electrostatic forces are also important.

**Liposome.** A microscopic spherical membrane-enclosed vesicle or sac (2 -30 nm in diameter) made artificially in the laboratory by the addition of an aqueous solution to a phospholipid gel. The membrane resembles a cell membrane and the whole vesicle is similar to a cell organelle. Liposomes can be incorporated into living cells and are used to transport relatively toxic drugs into diseased cells, where they can exert their maximum effects. For example, liposomes containing the drug methotrexate, used in the treatment of cancer, can be injected into the patient's blood. The cancerous organ is heated to a temperature higher than body temperature, so that when the liposome passes through its blood vessels, the membrane melts and the drug is released. The study of the behaviour of liposome membranes is used in research into membrane function, particularly to observe the behaviour of membranes during anaesthesia with respect to permeability changes.

**Lithophyte**

1. A plant that grows on rock outcrops or on rocky or stony ground. An example is the fern Asplenium ruta-muraria (wall-rue).
2. An organism partly composed of siliceous or calcareous material, *e.g.* the stoneworts (Charophyta).

**Lithosere**. A sere which develops upon a rock surface.

**Lithostyle**. A club-shaped static organ in certain medusae; sense club : Tentaculocyst.

**Lithotroph**. Organism that obtains energy from the oxidation of inorganic compounds or elements (compare organotroph). Sometimes the term is inaccurately used as a synonym of 'autotroph'.

**Litmus**. Dye obtained from lichens of the genus Roccella. Litmus is used as a pH indicator, being red under acidic conditions and blue under alkaline conditions.

**Lithosphere**. The outer, rigid part of the Earth's crust, including the continental and oceanic crust and the upper part of the mantle, and that part of the surface of the planet that is derived from rock, in contrast to the hydrosphere and atmosphere. The lithosphere is approximately 80 km thick under the oceans and 100-150 km thick beneath the continents.

**Litmus**. A purple dyestuff obtained from lichens used as an indicator, with a pH range of 4.5 to 8.3., that turns red in acid solutions and blue in alkaline.

**Litter**. Collectively, the young of a multiparous animal at one birth.

**Littoral**. Designating or occurring in the marginal shallow-water zone of a sea or lake, especially (in the sea) between high and low tide lines. In this zone enough light penetrates to the bottom to support rooted aquatic plants. Compare profundal; sublittoral.

**Littoral Fringe.** The uppermost reaches of the littoral zone of marine ecosystems. On rocky shores it is the main area for Littorina species (periwinkles), and the black lichen, Verrucaria, and is distinguished from the lower, eulittoral zone by the absence of barnacles, *e.g.* Balanus species and Chthamalus species. On sandy shores crabs, beach amphipods, and some land insects are characteristic.

**Littoral Zone**

1. The area in shallow fresh water and around lake shores where light penetration extends to the bottom sediments, giving a zone colonized by rooted plants.

2. In marine ecosystems the shore-area or intertidal zone whete periodic exposure and submersion by tides is normal. Since the precise physical limits of tidal range vary constantly a biological definition of this zone, which essentially reflects typical physical conditions rather than rarely experienced events, is generally more useful. Thus in Britain the littoral zone is defined as the region between the upper limit of species of the seaweed Laminaria, and the upper limit of Littorina species (periwinkles), or of the lichen Verrucaria.

**Live.** Alive; viable, not dead.

**Live-bearing Fish.** Fish in which the fertilized eggs are retained initial y within the body of the female, but are subsequently released as newly-hatched larvae (*e.g.* some Scorpaenidae) or born as free-swimming postlarvae in which the yolk has been fully utilized and the yolk sac has disappeared (*e.g.* some sharks, and Poeciliidae).

**Liver**

1. In vertebrates, a large, glandular organ which secretes bile and performs a number of other functions as glycogenesis, glycogenolysis, deamination of amino acids and formation of urea, storage of vitamins and minerals, detoxication, denaturization of hormones, hemopoietic and phagocytic functions.
2. In various invertebrates, any of a number of glandular, digestive organs which perform comparable functions.

**Liver Fluke.** A parasitic trematode inhabiting the liver and bile ducts of vertebrates, as Fasciola hepatica, infesting sheep, and cattle, and Opisthorchis (Clonorchis) sinensis, the Chinese liver fluke, infesting cats and dogs. Both may infest man.

**Liverwort.** A simple plant of the phylum Bryophyta, class Hepaticae, with a flattened gametophyte, as Marchantia.

**Living Fossil** Any organism whose closest relatives are extinct and that was once itself thought to be extinct. An example is the coelacanth, a primitive fish that was common in the Devonian era, the first recent living specimen of which was discovered in 1938.

**Lizard**

1. In common usage, any small to moderate-sized, four-legged, long-tailed reptile.
2. Specifically, any reptile of the suborder Sauria (Lacertilia), which includes the geckos, chameleons, skinks, monitors, and some limbless forms.

**Loam.** A type of soil in which there is an even mixture of fine clay particles and coarser sand particles. It is the best type of soil for cultivation as the sand helps drainage and aeration but the clay prevents excessive water loss and binds the organic material.

**Lobar.** Of or pertaining to a lobe or lobes.

**Lobate.** Composed of or possessing lobes or divisions resembling lobes.

**Lobe.** A rounded division or projection of an organ.

**Lobed.** Describing a leaf that is divided into curved or rounded parts connected to each other by an undivided central area.

**Lobopodium.** A blunt, fingerlike pseudopodium; lobopod.

**Lobule.** A subdivision of a lobe, a small lobe.

**Lobulus.** A lobule.

**Local.** Limited to or occupying a particular place or location; not general or widespread.

**Localization.** The limitation of function or activity to a specific location or area.

**Localized.** Confined to or restricted to a limited area, not general or widespread.

**Lock-and-key Theory.** Theory to explain the mechanism of enzymatic reactions, in which it is proposed that the enzyme and substrate(s) bind temporarily to form an enzyme-substrate complex. The binding site on the enzyme is known as the 'active site' and is structurally complementary to the substrate (s). Thus the enzyme and substrate(s) are said to fit together as do a lock and a key.

**Lockjaw.** Tetanus.

**Loco Disease.** A disease of livestock resulting from eating locoweeds.

**Locomotion.** The act of moving from place to place.

**Locoweed.** One of a number of plants of the genera Astragulus and Oxytropis which contain unknown poisons or selenium taken up from the soil. Eating the plants causes poisoning of sheep, cattle, and horses.

**Locular.** Loculate.

**Loculate.** Possessing compartments or cells (loculi).

**Locule** (loculus). A cavity within which specialized organs may develop, most usually the ovules or pollen grains. In an anther there are normally four locules. In a simple ovary there is one locule while in a compound ovary there may be one or many locules depending on how the carpels are fused.

**Loculocidal.** A form of dehiscence in which the splitting occurs along a dorsal suture directly into each locule of the ovary.

**Loculicidal.** Describing fruit dehiscence in which the slits in the pericarp arise along the dorsal suture of each carpel.

**Loculoascomycetes.** A class of the Ascomycotina in which the asci are two-walled (bitunicate) and are contained in perithecia enclosed in a stroma. It includes some 530 genera and over 2000 species, some of which are important plant parasites, *e.g.* Venturia inaequalis, which causes apple scab.

**Loculus** pl. **Loculi**

1. A compartment, cavity, or chamber.
2. *bot.* A cavity of a compound ovary, pollen sac, or certain ascocarps.
3. *zool.* *a.* A chamber in the shell of a foraminiferan protozoan. *b.* A pocket between the septa at the base of an anthozoan polyp.

**Locus** (pl. loci). Specific place on a chromosome where a gene is located, In diploids, loci pair during meiosis and unless there have been translocations, inversions, etc., the homologous chromosomes contain identical sets of loci in the same linear order. At each locus is one gene; if that gene can take several forms (alleles), only one of these will be present at a given locus).

**Locust**

1. *zool.* *a.* A short-horned grasshopper of the family Acrididae, as Melanoplus mexicanus, the Rocky Mountain locust, a migrating species. *b.* Common name for the cicada.
2. *bot.* A tree, Robinia pseudoacacia, the black locust, or Gleditsia triacanthus, the honey locust, of the family Leguminosae.

**Lodicule.** Either of the minute scales between the stamens and the glume of a grass flower. They are believed to represent the reduced perianth parts and may, through changes in turgor, be involved in the opening of the flower. Rarely there are three lodicules, while in a few species they are absent.

**Loess.** A fine-textured yellowish azonal soil that is widespread in central Europe, southern Russia, northern China and Argentina. It consists of clay and silt particles that were deposited at the edge of the ice sheets during the last ice age. It is a fertile, often calcareous, soil and is the parent material of chernozem soils.

**Logarithmic Phase.** The period during the growth of micro-organisms in culture when the cells are dividing rapidly and there is a huge increase in cell number. If the logarithm of cell numbers is plotted against time then a straight line is obtained on the graph. This period usually ends quite abruptly when nutrient levels fall, the pH of the medium changes, or toxic wastes build up. The logarithmic phase may be maintained by transferring cells to a fresh culture medium or by adding more nutrients to the existing medium. Compare lag phase.

**Loggerhead Sponge.** A massive sponge (Spheciospongia) sometimes reaching a diameter of several meters.

**Logistic Equation** (logistic model). Mathematical description of growth rates for a simple population in a confined space with limited resources. The equation summarizes the interaction of biotic potential with environmental resources, as seen in populations showing the S-shaped growth curve, as : $dN/dt = rN(N-K)/k$ where N is the number of individuals in the population, $t$ is time, $r$ is the biotic potential of the organism concerned, and K is the saturation value or carrying capacity for that organism in that environment. The resulting growth rate or logistic curve is a parabola, while the graph for organism numbers over time is sigmoidal. Compare J-shaped growth curve.

**Logwood.** The heartwood of a tree (Hematoxylon campechianum) from which a dye, hematoxylin, is obtained. A native of Central America, it is now grown throughout the West Indies.

**Loin.** The region of the body between the pelvis and false ribs.

**Lomasome.** A complex invagination of the plasma membrane into the cytoplasm. Lomasomes have been identified in some fungal hyphae and spore-producing structures, algal cells, and in some cells of higher plants. In the prokaryotic cells of blue-green algae, lomasomes, like the mesosomes of bacteria, are thought to be the site of biochemical processes that in eukaryotic cells are associated with the membranebound organelles.

**Loment.** An indehiscent legume with constrictions between the seeds which, at maturity, breaks into one-seeded portions.

**Lomentum.** A type of dry dehiscent fruit formed from a single carpel but divided into one-seeded compartments by constrictions between the seeds. Legumes (*e.g.* those of Acacia) and siliquas (*e.g.* those of wild radish) can be divided in this way.

**Long-day Plant.** Plant in which flowering is favoured by long days and correspondingly short dark periods. There are two groups of such plants, species in which there is an absolute requirement for these conditions (such that flowering will not begin without them) and others in which flowering is merely hastened by them.

**Longitudinal.** Lengthwise; extending along the long axis.

**Long-sightedness.** Hypermetropia.

**Longspur.** A sparrowlike bird of the genera Rhynchophanes and Calcarius, of the family Fringillidae.

**Loop.** A bend or fold of a cordlike structure.

**Looper.** A moth of the family Phalaenidae (Noctuidae) whose larvae have a reduced number of prolegs and move like measuring worms.

**Loop of Henle.** A U-shaped portion of a renal tubule connecting proximal and distal convoluted portions.

**Loose Smuts.** Smuts.

**Lophodont.** Designating a type of dentition in which molar teeth bear prominent transverse ridges and are adapted for grinding, as in ungulates and rodents.

**[1]Lophophorate.** Possessing a lophophore, as animals of the phyla Phoronida, Ectoprocta (Bryozoa), Entoprocta, and Brachiopoda.

**[2]Lophophorate.** Any animal which possesses a lophophore.

**Lophophore.** A circular or U-shaped, food-getting structure bearing ciliated tentacles present in certain invertebrates.

**Lophotrichous.** Describing a bacterium that has a group of flagella at one end of the cell. Compare monotrichous, peritrichous.

**Loquat.** A small evergreen tree (Eriobotrya japonica) widely grown in the Orient, or the fruit it produces.

**Lorate.** Strap-shaped.

**Lore.** In birds, the space between the eye and the bill or the corresponding space in other vertebrates, as reptiles.

**Lorica**

1. A protective case or covering.
2. *zool. a.* A case or shell enclosing certain ciliate protozoans. *b.* The thin, chitinlike covering of rotifers.
3. *bot.* The covering of a protoplast in certain algae.

**Loris.** A small nocturnal lemur of Southeast Asia, as Nycticebus coucang, the slow loris, and Loris tardigradus, the slender loris.

**Lotic.** Describing a freshwater ecosystem in which there is a continuous flow of water, such as a river. Compare lenitic.

**Lotka—Volterra Equations.** Mathematical models of competition between resource-limited species living in the same space with the same environmental requirements. They have been modified subsequently to simulate simple predator-prey interactions. The competition model predicts that coexistence of such species populations is impossible; one is always eliminated, as was vertified experimentally by G. F. Gause. The predation model predicts cyclic fluctuations of predator and prey populations. Reduction of predator numbers allows prey to recuperate, which in turn stimulates the population growth of the predator.

Increasing predator numbers depress the prey population, leading eventually to a reduction in the predator population. This was also tested experimentally by Gause (1934) and more recently and more convincingly by S. Utida (1950, 1957).

**Lotus Fruit.** Zizyphus.

**Lotus**

1. A flowering water plant of the Far East, of religious significance, as the sacred lotus of India (Nelumba nucifera).
2. A leguminous plant of the genus Lotus, the bird's-food trefoil.

**Loxodont.** With shallow grooves between the ridges of molar teeth, as in those of the African elephant.

**Loxsomaceae.** Family of ferns in which the much-divided fronds arise from creeping rhizomes and have their sori, which are of gradate type, in cup-like indusia terminally on the leaf veins on the leaf margins. The sporangia have a complete oblique annulus. The are two genera : Loxsoma, with only one species, in New Zealand, and Loxsomopsis, with three species, in C. and S. America.

**Low-temperature Scanning Electron Microscopy.** The preparation of specimens for the scanning electron microscope, and their subsequent examination, at very low temperatures. The specimen is frozen with liquid nitrogen (the melting point of nitrogen is −210°C), coated at liquid nitrogen temperatures, and examined in a special specimen chamber similarly cooled. In this way frozen hydrated material can be examined. The results are similar to those obtained by critical point drying but with fewer artefacts. The technique is particularly useful for delicate plant specimens.

**Lubricous.** Smooth, slippery, slimy.

**Luciferase.** An enzyme which catalyzes the oxidation of luciferin.

**Luciferin.** A substance present in light-producing organs of bioluminescent organisms which, when oxidixed, yields light energy, as in fireflies.

**Lugworm.** A burrowing mar'ne polychaete (Arenicola marina).

**Lumbar.** Of or pertaining to the region of the loin.

**Lumbar Vertebrae.** The vertebrae in the region of the lower back. They occur below the thoracic vertebrae and above the sacral vertebrae. In mammals they bear processes for the attachment of back muscles.

**Lumen**

1. *zool.* A passageway within a tube, vessel, or duct.
2. *bot.* A cavity within the cell wall after the protoplast has disappeared, as in tracheids.
3. *physics.* A unit of luminous flux, that is the quantity of visiblc radiation per unit of time.

**Luminescene.** The emission of light without appreciable production of heat or incandescence, as in bioluminescent organisms.

**Luminous.** Bright or shining; reflecting, emitting,or producing light; phosphorescent.

**Luminons Organ.** An organ which emits light; a photophore.

**Luna Moth.** A large, pale green, saturnid moth (Tropaea) (Actias) luna) called the "pale empress of the night".

**Lunar.** Of, pertaining to, or caused by the moon.

**[1]Lunate.** Crescent-shaped.

**²Lunate.** The semilunar bone, a carpal bone.

**Lung**

1. In terrestrial Mollusca, a highly vascular part of the mantle involved in respiration.
2. In air-breathing vertebrates, the respiratory organ. It is probably derived from an accessory respiratory organ of aquatic vertebrates inhabiting oxygendepleted fresh water : this developed into the swim-bladder of many fish. The lung is present embryonically as a diverticulum of the gut. It contains many alveoli across whose walls oxygen and carbon dioxide diffuse.

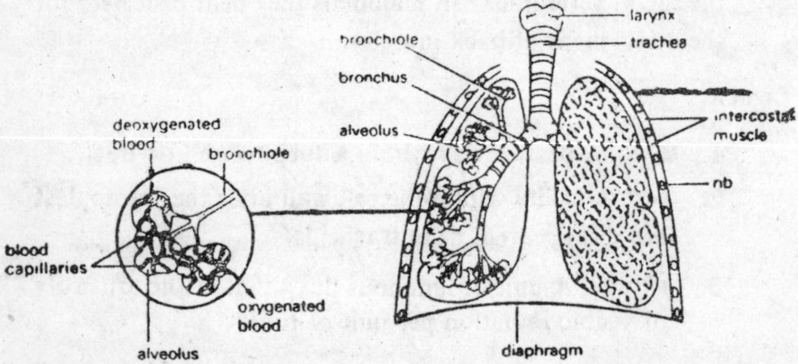


The lungs and air passages of a mammal (right lung cut open to show internal structure)

**Lungfish.** One of three genera of dipnoian fishes in which the swim bladder functions as a lung, as Neoceratodus of Australia, Lepidosiren of South America, and Protopterus of Africa.

**Lung Fluke.** A fluke which inhabits the lungs, as Paragonimus westermanii in man and other mammals.

**Lungworm.** One of a number of parasitic nematodes living within the lungs, especially Metastrongylus elongatus, the lungworm of swine.

**Lunula.** A narrow, crescent-shaped area of structure, as *a.* the clear area at the base of a nail; *b.* a slit above the base of the antenna in certain insects, especially dipterans; *c.* a notch or opening in the test of certain sand dollars.

**Lutein**

1. Xanthophyll, a yellow pimpent in plants.
2. A yellow pigment present in cells of the corpus luteum, egg yolk, and other lipochromes.
3. A dried powdered preparation of corpora lutea from hogs.

**Luteinzing Hormone** (LH; interstitialcell-stimulating hormone; ICSH). A hormone, secreted by the anterior pituitary gland in mammals, that stimulates in males the production of sex hormones (androgens) by secretory cells in the testes (known as interstitial cells) and in females ovulation, progesterone synthesis, and corpus luteum formation.

**Luteotrophic Hormone.** Prolactin.

**Lutescent.** Turning or becoming yellow.

**Luxation.** A dislocation, as at a joint.

**Luxuriant.** Rank, exuberant, profuse in growth.

**Lyase.** Any enzyme that catalyses the nonhydrolytic cleavage of its substrate. An example is pyruvic decarboxylase, which catalyses the formation of acetaldehyde and carbon dioxide from pyruvic acid.

**Lycopene.** A carotene pigment present in the chromoplasts of ripe fruits.

**Lycoperdales.** An order of the Gasteromycetes containing the puff balls and earth stars. It includes about 275 species in some 48 genera. The basidiocarp remains closed until maturity and its contents become dry and powdery. In the earth stars (*e.g.* Geastrum triplex) the outer wall of the basidiocarp splits into a number of rays, which peel back to surround the spores still enclosed by the thin inner wall. The whole fruiting body thus fancifully resembles a flower or star. The puff balls (*e.g.* Lycoperdon pyriforme) and earth stars discharge their spores in a series of puffs when disturbed.

**Lycopod.** A club moss.

**Lycopodiales.** An order of the Lycopsida containing two genera, Lycopodium (club mosses) and Phylloglossum, both homosporous. There are some 200 species of Lycopodium distributed worldwide. They are all herbs and have long dichotomously branching stems bearing numerous small leaves with no ligules (compare Selaginellales). The unilocular sporangia are borne singly in the axils of sporophyllus, which in many species occur together in distinctive club-shaped strobili. The free-living gametophyte may, depending on species, be either photosynthetic or saprophytic. It is always found in association with an endotrophic mycorrhiza. The antheridia, which produce may biflagellate antherozoids, are located in the centre of the apex of the prothallus and are surrounded by a ring of archegonia.

Phylloglossum contains the single species P. drummondii, which is very different from Lycopodium in habit, consisting of a basal whorl of leaves and a single strobilus borne on a long stalk.

**Lycopsida.** A subdivision of the Tracheophyta or a class of the Pteridophyta containing the clubmosses (Lycopodium) and related genera (including Selaginella) as well as numerous extinct forms, which reached their peak in the Carboniferous period with giant coal-forming tree species. Lycopsids have roots and their stems are covered with numerous small leaves.

**Lydekker's Line.** Defines the easternmost extension of Oriental animals into the zone of mixing between the Oriental and

Australian faunal regions or zoogeographic kingdoms. The corresponding western limit of the zone is known as Wallace's line, and marks the maximum extent of marsupials in that direction.

**Lymph.** The colourless liquid found within the lymphatic system, into which it drains from the spaces between the cells. Lymph (called tissue fluid in the intercellular spaces) resembles blood plasma, consisting mostly of water with dissolved salts and proteins. Fats are found in suspension and their presence varies with food intake. The lymph eventually enters the bloodstream near the heart.

**Lymphatic System.** The network of vessels that conveys lymph from the tissue fluids to the bloodstream. Tiny lymph capillaries drain into larger tubular vessels that converge to form the right lymphatic duct and the thoracic duct, which connect with the venous blood supply to the heart. Associated with the lymphatic vessels at intervals along the system are the lymph nodes. The lymph capillary walls are very permeable, so lymph bathing the body's tissues can drain away molecules that are too large to pass through blood capillary walls. Lymph is pumped by cycles of contraction and relaxation of the lymphatic vessels and also by the action of adjoining muscles.

**Lymphatic**

1. Of, pertaining to, or conveying lymph.
2. A small lymph vessel.

**Lymphatic Organ.** An organ composed principally of lymphatic tissue, as Peyer's patch, lymph node, hemolymph node, tonsil, thymus, spleen.

**Lymphatic System.** A system of vessels and associated organs consisting of lymphatic vessels and ducts and lymphatic organs which function in the return of tissue fluid to the blood stream, filtration of lymph, manufacture of leukocytes, and formation of antibodies.

**Lymphatic Tissue.** The tissue which comprises lymphatic organs, consisting of a stroma of reticular tissue and free cells (macrophages and lymphocytes) within the meshes of the fibers. It functions in filtration of lymph and formation of lymphocytes.

**Lymph Node.** A mass of lymphoid tissue, many of which occur at intervals along the lymphatic system. Lymph in the lymphatic vessels flows through the lymph nodes, which filter out bacteria and other foreign particles, so preventing them from entering the bloodstream and causing infection. The lymph nodes also produce lymphocytes. In humans, major lymph nodes occur in the neck, under the arms, and in the groin.

**Lymphocyte.** A type of white blood cell (leucocyte) that has a large nucleus and little cytoplasm. Lymphocytes are formed in the lymph nodes and provide about a quarter of all leucocytes. They are important in the bod'y defence and are responsible for immune reactions as the presence of antigens stimulates them to produce antibodies.

**Lymphoid.** Resembling or of the nature of lymph. Term is sometimes used as a synonym for lymphatic.

**Lymphoid Tissue.** The type of tissue found in the lymph nodes, tonsils, spleen, and thymus. It is responsible for producing lymphocytes and antibodies and therefore contributes to the body's defence against infection.

**Lynx.** A wildcat of the genus Lynx characterized by short stubby tail and usually tufted ears, as Lynx canadensis, the Canada lynx and L. rufus, the wildcat or bobcat.

**Lyophilization.** Rapid freezing of a substance followed by dehydration under high vacuum. Also called freeze-drying or gelsiccation.

**Lyrebird.** An Australian bird of the family Menuridae, the males possessing a beautiful, lyre-shaped tail when spread. Common genera are Menura and Harriwhitea.

**Lyriform Organs.** Lyre-shaped organs in certain spiders thought to have an olfactory function.

**Lysenkoism.** The official Soviet science policy governing the work of geneticists in the USSR from about 1940 to 1960. It was named after its chief promoter, the agriculturalist Trofim Lysenko (1898-1976). Lysenkoism dismissed all the advances that had been made in classical genetics, denying the existence of genes, and held that the variability of organisms was produced solely by environmental changes. There was also a return to a belief in the inheritance of acquired characteristics (Lamarckism). This state of affairs continued, despite overwhelming conflicting evidence from Western scientists, because it provided support for communist theory.

**Lysigeny** The localized disruption of plant cells to form a cavity (surrounded by remnants of the broken cells) in which secretions accumulate. Examples are the oil cavities in the leaves of citrus trees. Compare schizogeny.

**Lysigenous.** Originating by the dissolution of cells, with reference to secretory cavities or glands of plants, as oil cavities in the rinds of citrus fruits.

**Lysigeny.** The formation of a space by the destruction of cells. This is often achieved by enzymatic dissolution. Compare schizogeny.

**Lysimeter.** Device for the direct estimation of evapotranspiration. Typically it comprises a vegetated block of soil 0.5-1 $m^3$, to which the amount of water added is known, and from which the amount lost as run-off or percolation may be measured. Recording the changing weight of the soil-vegetation system (keeping vegetation change due to growth static or monitored) reveals the amount of water retained by the system, and thus by difference the amount lost as evaporanspiration. For geographic comparisons, easily standardized, short, grass vegetation cover is used. For water-budget experiments, vegetation cover may be varied to simulate different crop types or seminatural communities.

**Lysine.** A basic amino acid with the formula $NH_2(CH_2)_4CH(NH_2)COOH$ (illustration at amino acid). Lysine is synthesized from aspartic and pyruvic acids via an aldol condensation reaction; control of synthesis is through feedback inhibition of this condensation reaction by lysine. Degradation of lysine occurs via acetyl CoA and the TCA cycle.

Lysine is a precursor in the synthesis of the pyridine and piperidine alkaloids, *e.g.* the nicotine derivative anabasine.

**Lysogenic**

1. Inducing the production of lysins.
2. Inducing lysis.

**Lysis.** The destruction of a living cell. This may be effected by lysosomes or phagocytes, either as part of the normal metabolic process (as when cells are damaged or worn out) or as a reaction against invading cells (*e.g.* bacteria). Bacteriophages eventually cause lysis of their host cells.

**Lysogeny.** Stable, non-destructive relationship between a bacteriophage and its host bacterium; the genome of the bacteriophage may become integrated with that of its host. Under certain conditions the stable relationship breaks down and the phage may then destroy the bacterium.

**Lysosome.** A membrane-bound sac within the cytoplasm of animal cells that contains enzymes responsible for the digestion of material in food vacuoles, the dissolution of foreign particles entering the cell (such as bacteria) and, on the death of the cell, the breakdown of all cell structures. A similar structure is present in plant cells.

**Lysosome.** A cytoplasmic body rich in hydrolytic enzymes, present in certain cells, especially phagocytes.

**Lysozyme.** Bacteriolytic enzyme found in a number of biological fluids, including tears, saliva, and egg white. It facilitates the hydrolysis of structural polysaccharides in the cell walls of bacteria.

**Lytic.** Inducing or bringing about lysis.

**Lytic Response.** Rupture and death (lysis) of a bacterial cell following infection by a phage which then reproduces inside the cell, as opposed to a lysogenic response in which the infecting phage does not multiply but instead behaves as a prophage.

# M

**Macaque.** The common rhesus monkey (Macaca mulatta), a short-tailed monkey of Southeast Asia. Also called bandar.

**Macaw.** A noisy, brightly-colored parrot of Central and South America, most species belonging to the genus Ara.

**Mace.** An aromatic spice obtained from the shell of the nutmeg.

**Macerate**

1. To soften, as by boiling, to bring about the separation of parts.
2. In microtechnique, to treat tissues so as to cause dissociation of cells.

**Maceration.** In microscopical preparation, the chemical dissolution, often by the application of strong acids, of the matrix binding parts of specimen. The isolated pieces of the specimen may then be examined or subjected to further preparation.

**Macrandrous.** Having large male plants or structures; producing antheridia on large filaments.

**Macrobiota** (macrofauna, macroflora). General term for the larger soil organisms which may be hand-sorted from a soil sample. 'Macrofauna' in particular refers to burrowing vertebrate animals (*e.g.* rabbits and moles), while 'macrobiota generally also includes larger plant material (*e.g.* tree roots). Some workers also include larger insects and earthworms in this category, but others consider them part of the mesobiota. Compare mesobiota; and microbiota.

**Macrocarpous.** Bearing or producing large fruit.

**Macrocyst.** A reproductive body formed in certain slime bacteria within which develop microcysts.

**Macrodont.** Possessing abnormally large teeth.

**Macroevolution.** Evolution in which marked alterations occur in the genetic makeup of an organism, thus accounting for the origin of larger groups as classes and phyla. Compare microevolution.

**Macrofibrils.** Fibrils within the cell wall but are large enough in some cases to be visible under the light microscope. They are formed from microfibrils lying parallel to each other.

**Macrogamete.** The larger of two gametes which undergo conjugation, as in certain algae and protozoans, considered the female gamete as it is usually passive and nonmotile. Compare microgamete.

**Macromere.** One of the four large blastomeres at the vegetal pole of a telolecithal ovum undergoing cleavage, as in the eggs of amphibians.

**Macromolecule.** A large molecule composed of smaller units or monomers linked together, as a protein composed of amino acids.

**Macromutation.** A pronounced, abrupt change which results in an individual differing markedly from its parents, in contrast to a small or point mutation.

**Macronucleus.** The vegetative nucleus, the larger of two nuclei present in certain protozoans, as Paramecium.

**Macronutrient.** Organic or inorganic element or compound, that is needed in relatively large amounts by living organisms. Organic macronutrient organic groups include amino acids, carbohydrates, and fats. Compare micronutrient.

**Macrophage.** Large, phagocytic, white blood cell, which occurs in large numbers at sites of infection where it is instrumental in removing foreign cells and cell debris. Macrophages are derived from monocytes as a result of the monocytes' participation in phagocytic activity.

**Macrophagous.** Feeding on large particles of food.

**Macrophyll.** A megaphyll.

**Macrophyllous.** Having large leaflets or leaves.

**Macroplankton.** Organisms in plankton which can be recognized by the unaided eye.

**Macropterous.** Having large wings or winglike structures; having large fins.

**Macrosclereid.** A relatively short sclerenchyma cell (sclereid), somewhat columnar in shape. Macrosclereids form the outer layer of the seed coat in many plants.

**Macroscopic.** Visible to the unaided eye.

**Macrosmatic.** Having a well-developed olfactory sense.

**Macrosporangium.** Megasporangium.

**Macrospore.** A megaspore.

**Macrosporophyll.** Megasporophyll.

**Macrostylous.** With long styles.

**Macroszoospore.** A large, asexual spore, as in Ulothrix.

**Macrurous.** Having a long tail, with reference to crustaceans, as the lobster.

**Macula**

1. One of a number of patches of sensory cells in the utriculus and sacculus of the inner ear that are involved in maintaining balance and may also assist in assessing the degree of acceleration and deceleration when the body is moving.
2. An area of the retina of the vertebrate eye with increased visual acuity. Maculae occur in some animals that lack foveae and often surround foveae in those animals that possess them.

**Macula Lutea.** A yellow spot on the retina of the eye in the center of which is the fovea centralis upon which light rays are focused. It is the point of keenest vision.

**Macula Sacculi.** An area of sensory epithelium in the saccule of the ear containing hair cells which are stimulated by the movement of otoliths in the otolithic membrane on its surface. It is concerned with static equilibrium.

**Macula Utriculi.** A sensory area similar to the macula sacculi but located in the utriculus.

**Madrepore.** A coelenterate of the order Madreporaria (Scleractinia) which includes the stony corals, reef-building corals of tropical waters.

**Madreporite.** A porous, calcareous plate on the aboral surface of various echinoderms through which wates enters the watervascular system.

**Madtom.** A small catfish of the genus Noturus.

**Maggot**

1. The soft-bodied, legless larva of various dipterous insects, commonly found in decaying matter.
2. A parasitic copepod.

**Magnesium** (Mg). Element found in high concentrations in plants. It plays an important role in the chemical structure of chlorophyll and of membranes and is involved in many enzyme reactions, especially those catalysing the transfer of phosphate compounds. Deficiency can produce various symptoms, including chlorosis and the development of other pigments in leaves.

**Magnification.** The apparent enlargement of an object when seen through a series of lenses, as a microscope.

**Magnoliidae** (Ranales). A subclass of the dicotyledons containing plants in which the flower parts are numerous and often inserted spirally, and the gynoecium is apocarpous. The number of orders recognized varies considerably between classifications. The Magnoliales, including the Magnoliacear, Annonaceae, and Myristicaceae; the Laurales, including the Monimiaceae and Lauraceae; the Aristolochiales, including the Aristolochiaceae and (sometimes) the Nepenthaceae; and the Nymphaeales, including the Nymphaecaeae (water lilies), are usually all included in the Magnoliidae The following orders may also be placed in the Magnoliidae or may be allocated to a second subclass, the Ranunculidae : the Illiciales: the Ranunculales, including the Berberidaceae, Ranunculaceae (buttercup family), and Menispermaceae (which includes curare); the Papaverales, including the Papaveraceae (poppy family) and Fumariaceae; and the Sarraceniales, including the Sarraceniaceae. Other orders sometimes recognized include the Nelumbonales, which contains one family Nelumbonaceae. However lotus (Nelumbo) is often placed in the Nymphaeaceae or Berberidaceae. The Rafflesiales may also be placed in the Magnoliidae but are sometimes allocated to the Rosidae.

In those classifications that recognize the subclass Ranuncilidae, this is separated from the Magnoliidae on the basis that its members are mostly herbaceous rather than woody plants and generally more advanced than the Magnoliidae. They lack the oil cells common to many members of the Magnoliidae and have tricolpate pollen as compared to the monocolpate pollen of the Magnoliidae. Their stomata usually lack subsidiary cells whereas those of the Magnoliidae often have two subsidiary cells.

**Magnoliophyta.** In certain classifications, a division containing the flowering plants. It is divided into the two classes Magnoliopsida (dicotyledons) and Liliopsida (monocotyledons).

**Magpie.** A long-tailed corvine bird (Pica pica) of the Northern Hemisphere.

**Mahalanobis' $D^2$.** Measure of generalized distance between samples based on the means, variances, and covariances of various properties of replicate samples in multivariate analysis. The larger is $D^2$, the greater is the difference between the samples (or the properties measured).

**Mahogany**

1. A tree (Swietenia mahogani) in the Meliaceae family, of tropical America noted for its hard, reddish wood used in the manufacture of furniture.
2. One of a number of trees producing similar wood, especially S. macrophylla of Mexico and Central America.

**Maidenhead.** The hymen.

**Maintenance Evolution** (stabilizing selection, normalizing selection). The stabilizing influence of natural selection in an environment that changes little in space and time. It tends to inhibit evolutionary innovation, and accounts for the fact that many fossil groups changed very little over long periods of time.

**Maize.** Indian corn (Zea mays), a cereal grain.

**Major Gene.** A gene whose effects are readily identifiable in the phenotype. The existence of different allels of such genes results in instances of qualitative variation in the phenotypes. All Mendelian genes are examples of major genes. Compare polygenes.

**Malaceous.** Of or pertaining to apples.

**Malacology.** The branch of biology which deals with mollusks.

**Malaise.** A general feeling of not being well, accompanied by restlessness, loss of appetite, and decreased activity.

**Malar**

1. Of or pertaining to the cheek.
2. The zygomatic bone.

**Malaria.** Disease of humans caused by various species of the protozoan genus Plasmodium. The disease is transmitted by mosquitoes. (Anopheles species), and varies in severity according to the species of Plasmodium responsible. Symptoms typically involve cyclical periods of fever and chills. Recurrence of the disease is common.

**Malate Shuttle.** A method that has been proposed to explain the transfer of educing power across the chloroplast membranes. NADPH, produced by the light reactions of photosynthesis, is not able to pass through the chloroplast membranes. However there is evidence that reducing power produced by photosynthesis is nevertheless used in the cytosol. It is suggested that oxaloacetate in the chloroplast stroma is reduced by NADPH to malate, which is readily transported across the chloroplast membranes. In the cytosol malate is oxidized to oxaloacetate with the concomitant production of NADH from NAD. The oxaloacetate then passes back into the chloroplast stroma to begin the cycle again.

**Male.** Describing either the reproductive parts or a whole organism that bears the microspore-producing apparatus and does not nurture the developing embryo. Compare female.

**Male Fern.** Aspidium, the rhizome and stipes of Dryopteris filix-mas, which contains filicin, formerly used for expelling tapeworms.

**Maleic Hydrazide.** A growth inhibitor often used as a herbicide or to inhibit sprouting. In some species it promotes flowering by inhibiting vegetative growth.

**Male-sterile.** Producing no visible pollen, said of plants.

**Male Sterility.** A condition in which pollen production is prevented by mutation of one or more genes governing its formation. Male sterility has been employed by plant breeders as a method of ensuring cross pollination and hence $F_1$ hybrid production. Male-sterile cultivars can be maintained by crossing as (female parent) × SS (male parent) giving 50% ss and 50% Ss offspring (where s = male sterile).

**Malic Acid** (2-hydroxybutanedioic acid). A crystalline solid, $HOOCCH(OH)CH_2COOH$. L-malic acid occurs in living organisms as an intermediate metabolite in the Krebs cycle and also (in certain plants) in photosynthesis. It is found especially in the juice of unripe fruits, *e.g.* green apples.

**Malignant.** Virulent; inducing harm or injury; threatening life.

**Mallard.** A common wild duck (Anas platyrhynchos), a surface-feeding, freshwater duck, considered to be the ancestor of all domestic verieties of ducks.

[1]**Malleate.** Shaped like a hammer.

[2]**Malleate.** A type of mastax in rotifers adapted for grinding, grasping, and pumping.

**Malleolus.** One of the two processes on either side of the ankle joint, one on the tibia, the other on the fibula.

**Malleus**

1. The hammer, the first of the three ear ossicles.
2. A portion of the trophi of a rotifer.

**Malpighian Body** (Malpighian corpuscle). The part of a nephron in the kidney that consists of its cup-shaped end together with the glomerulus that in encloses. It is named after its discoverer, the Italian anatomist M. Malpighi (1628-94).

**Malpighian Cell.** An alternative term for a macrosclereid when present in the testa of a leguminous seed.

**Malpighian Layer** (stratum germinativum). The innermost layer of the epidermis of mammalian skin, separated from the underlying dermis by a fibrous basement membrane. It is only in this layer of the epidermis that active cell division (mitosis) occurs. As the cells produced by these divisions age the mature, they migrate upwards through the layers of the epidermis to replace the cells being continuously worn away at the surface.

**Malpighian Tubule.** One of the numerous, blind, threadlike, excretory tubules opening into the anterior end of the hindgut of insects.

**Malonyl ACP.** The three-carbon dicarboxylic acid malonic acid bound to acyl carrier protein (ACP). Malonyl ACP, with malonyl CoA, is central to fatty acid synthesis. It is formed from malonyl CoA and ACP and then reacts with enzyme-bound acetate to form acetoacetly ACP, with concomitant release of carbon dioxide. Acetoacetyl ACP is then reduced to butyryl ACP before the addition of another molecule of malonyl ACP to form a six-carbon chain. Malonyl ACP thus provides the two-carbon building blocks with which long-chain fatty acids are progressively synthesized.

**Malonyl CoA.** The coenzyme A derivative of the dicarboxylic acid malonic acid. It is synthesized from acetyl CoA and bicarbonate in a reaction catalysed by the enzyme acetyl CoA carboxylase. Malonyl CoA provides the carbons for the synthesis of fatty acids—the malonyl moiety reacts with acyl carrier protein (ACP) to form malonyl ACP, which in turn combines with the growing fatty acid molecules, with elimination of carbon dioxide, to add two more carbons to the chain.

**Mallophaga.** An order of wingless insects comprising the bird lice. Bird lice are minute with dorsoventrally flattened ovoid bodies, reduced eyes, and biting mouthparts. They are ectoparasites of birds, feeding on particles of dead skin, feather fragments, and sometimes blood. The eggs hatch to form nymphs resembling the adults.

**Mallophagan.** An insect of the order Mallophaga which includes the biting or chewing lice, external parasites of birds and mammals.

**Malt.** Grain, usually barley, which has softened by soaking in water, then allowed to germinate; used in the brewing and distilling industry.

**Maltase.** An enzyme which converts maltose to dextrose, present in germinating grains, saliva, and intestinal juice.

**Malting.** The production of malt.

**Maltose** (malt sugar). A sugar consisting of two linked glucose molecules that results from the action of the enzyme amylase on starch. Maltose occurs in barley seeds following germination and drying, which is the basis of the malting process used in the manufacture of beer and malt whisky.

**Malt Sugar.** Maltose.

**Malvaceous.** Of or pertaining to plants of the mallow family, Malvaceae, including cotton, hemp, jute, okra, hibiscus, and hollyhock.

**Mamba.** The tree cobra (Dendraspis), a poisonous snake of Africa.

**Mamma** (mammatus). From the Latin Mamma meaning 'udder', a cloud feature consisting of projections from the basal surface of altocumulus, altostratus, stratocumulus, cumulonimbus, cirrus, and cirrocumulus.

**Mammal.** Any vertebrate of the class Mammalia, characterized by possession of hair and mammary glands. They are airth-breating, possessing lungs, have a four-chambered heart and are warm-blooded. All are viviparous except the egg-laying monotremes.

**Mammalia** (kingdom Animalia, subkingdom Metazoa, phylum Chordata, superclass Gnathostomata). Class of homoiothermic animals in which the head is supported by a flexible neck, typically with seven vertebrae, articulating through two occipital condyles; the side wall of the skull is formed by the alisphenoid bone; the lower jaw if formed from the dentary bone and articulates with the squamosal; the quadrate and articular bones form auditory ossicles and the angular bone forms the tympanic bone; typically teeth are present and are thecodont, heterodont, and diphyodont; the buccal cavity; is separated by a hard palate from the cavity; and epihpyses are present on many of the bones.

**Mammalian.** Of, pertaining to, characteristic of, or belonging to the class Mammalia.

**Mammalogy.** The study of mammals.

**Mammary Glands.** The milk-producing organs (possibly modified sweat glands) of female mammals, which provide food for the young (milk; colostrum). Their number (2 to 20) and position (on the chest or abdomen) very according to the species. In most mammals the gland openings project as a nipple or teat. Nipples have a number of milk-duct openings; teats have one duct leading from a storage cavity.

**Mammiform.** Shaped like a breast; conical with a nipplelike or rounded tip.

**Mammilla**

1. *zool.* A small prominence or papilla; a nipple or teat.
2. *bot.* A rounded protuberance, as that on a spore wall.

**Mammillate.** Having nipples or nipplelike protuberances.

**Mammoth.** An extinct elephantlike mammal (Elephas (Mammuthus) primigenius) with long, recurved tusks and long, thick hair, the remains of which have been found in the frozen tundra of Siberia and Alaska.

**Mammotrophic.** Inducing the development of the mammary gland.

**Man**

1. A human being, especially an adult male of the human race.
2. Any member of the genus Homo, all present-day individuals considered as belonging to a single species (Homo sapiens).
3. The human race or mankind; all human beings considered collectively.

**Mandible.** In Crustacea, insects, and Myriapoda one of the pair of mouth-parts most commonly used for seizing and cutting food. In birds, specifically the lower jaw but the term is also used to denote the two parts of the bill of a bird, as upper and lower mandibles.

**Mandibular.** Of or pertaining to the mandible.

**Mandibular Arch.** The first visceral arch.

**Mandibulate.** Any member of the Mandibulata, a subphylum of the Arthropoda characterized by possession of antennae and the first pair of jaws as mandibles. Includes the classes Crustacea, Insectx, Chilopoda, Diplopoda, Symphyla, and Pauropoda.

**Mandrill.** A fierce, tailless baboon (Mandrillus sphinx) of West Africa, with brilliantly colored face and buttocks.

**Mane.** The long, thick hair growing along the sides and back of the neck, as in lions, or along the back of the neck, as in horses.

**Manganese.** Symbol : Mn. A metallic element, atomic number 25, atomic weight 54.94, needed in trace amounts by plants for successful growth. Manganese ions are required as cofactors by certain enzymes, *e.g.* kinases and IAA oxidase. Certain deficiency diseases, *e.g.* blight of sugar cane and grey speck of oats, are attributed to manganese deficiency. More general symptoms inclde dwarfing and mottling of the upper leaves. Manganese is often added to the soil as manganous sulphate to treat such problems.

**Mange.** A skin condition characterized by inflammation, exudation, and scab formation resulting from infestation by parasitic mites, as Demodex, the follicle mite and Sarcoptes, the itch or mange mite.

**Mango.** A well-known tropical tree (Mangifera indica) or the fruit it produces, used extensively for food. Its seeds and bark are used medicinally.

**Mangrove.** A tropical tree or shrub of the genus Rhizophora, with leaves and bark which are rich in tannin. It prop roots form dense interlacing masses.

**Manikin also Mannikin** or **Manakin.**

1. A model of the human body showing various organs in their normal positions.
2. A sheet or series of sheets of drawings of the human body showing organs in their relative positions.

A model of a full-term fetus used for instruction in obstetrics.

4. A man of small structure; a dwarf.

**Manioc.** Cassava.

**Manna.** A sweet exudate of the manna ash (Fraxinus ornus) of Europe, used as a mild laxative.

**Mannan.** A polysaccharide in which the major monosaccharide subunit is mannose. Galactose and glucose are also often present, forming galactomannans, glucomannans, and galactoglucomannans. Mannans frequently occur in hemicellulose. They are also found as reserve polysaccharides in some higher plants, *e.g.* the ivory palm (Phytelephas macrocarpa,) in which the extremely hard endosperm (known as vegetable ivory) is composed of mannans.

**Mannitol.** Mannite or manna sugar, a carbohydrate widely distributed in nature, present in manna, brown algae, and certain fungi.

**Mannose.** A monosaccharide $C_6H_{12}O_6$, stereoisomeric with glucose, that occurs naturally only in polymerized forms called mannans. These are found in plants, fungi, and bacteria, serving as food energy stores.

**Manta Ray.** A large ray Manta biostris) of the suborder Batoidea. Also called devilfish or sea devil.

**Mantid** or **Mantis,** A carnivorous, orthopteran insect of the family Mantidae with greatly enlarged front legs adapted for grasping and holding prey. Also called the praying mantid or soothsayer.

**Mantle.** The fold of skin covering the dorsal surface of the body of molluscs, which extends into lateral flaps that protect the gills in the mantle cavity (the space between the body and mantle). The outer surface of the mantle secretes the shell (in species that have shells).

**Manubrium.** A tubular structure, a number of which arise on the inner walls of the antheridium of algae in the Charophyta. A mass of filaments form from specialized cells at the tip of the manubrium. The cells of the filaments subsequently form antherozoids.

**Manure.** Animal excreta, usually mixed with other material, especially straw, used to improve soil fertility. The term may be used in a wider sense to mean any sort of fertilizer.

**Manus.** The distal portion of the forelimb in vertebrates. In man it comprises the hand; in tetrapods, the forefoot.

**Manypiles.** The omasum or psalterium, the third portion of the stomach of a ruminant.

**Maple.** A tree of the genus Acer, important as a source of wood, maple syrup and sugar, and as an ornamental tree.

**Maquis.** A stunted form of woodland (scrub woodland) found in semiarid regions that have been deforested for agricultural purposes or by fire. The poor soil supports a mass of tangled bushes and shrubs growing to about three metres, with scattered twisted dwarfed trees. The species include rockroses (Cistus), broom (Cytisus scoparius), gorse (Ulex), etc., together with herbs, such as thymes (Thymus), and heathers (Erica). Maquis is widespread in countries around the Mediterranean. In Italy it is called macchia, and in Spain, mattoral. Similar vegetation in California is called chaparral.

**Mara.** A large South American cavy (Dolichotis patagona) called Patagonian hare because of its long hind legs.

**Marattiales.** An order of the Filicinae consisting entirely of large fleshy tropical ferns, commonly known as giant ferns. There are about 100 species in 6 genera. In most species the sporophyte consists of a broad short stem giving rise to large compound fronds. The sporangia are formed on the abaxial surface of fertile fronds that otherwise resemble the sterile fronds. The spores germinate to form a thallose gametophyte, somewhat similar to a liverwort, which may be quite long lived. The Marattiales have a rich fossil record going back to the Carboniferous.

**Marcescent.** Withering, but persistent, that is, not falling off, as leaves.

**Marchantiopsida.** Hepaticae.

**Mare.** The mature female of the horse and related equines.

**Margin.** A border or an edge.

**Marginal Effect.** A phenomenon exhibited by the plants at the edge of a stand of vegetation whereby they grow more vigorously than those in the centre. It has been well documented in advancing areas of bracken (Pteridium), where the fronds at the edge are significantly taller than those behind them. This is believed to be due to increasing rhizome age at the centre rather than to depletion of soil nutrients. Marginal effects may play a part in the hummock and hollow cycle of vegetation.

**Marginal Meristem.** A region of meristematic tissue located along the edges of a leaf primordium. Repeated divisions of initials in this area give rise to the mesophyll and epidermal tissues of the blade.

**Marginal Placentation** (ventral placentation). A form of placentation in which the placentae develop along the ventral suture of a simple ovary. It is seen in the pods of the Leguminosae.

**Marginate** Possessing a margin, especially one of a distinctive nature.

**Margo**

1. Pit.
2. In a pollen grain, the zone of thickened sexine around a colpus.

**Mariculture.** Intensive fish-farming in marine or estuarine waters, involving additions of nutrients, energy, and stock. It is the marine equivalent of aquaculture, and provides an important food supplement for humans in some areas, notably Japan and Indonesia. It is little practised elsewhere, although it has considerable potential. The organisms farmed are predominantly shellfish, especially clams, muscles and oysters.

**Marigold.** A yellow- or orange-flowered plant of the genus Tagetes.

**Marihuana** or **Marijuana.** Cannabis, the dried flowering tops of pistillate plants of hemp (Cannabis sating).

**Marine.** Of, pertaining to, living in, or related to the seas or oceans.

**Marita.** A sexually mature fluke.

**Mark-recapture Technique.** Technique for estimating the population density of more elusive or mobile animals. A sample of the population is captured, marked, and released. Given that these marked individuals become randomly distributed through the wild population, and that subsequent trapping is random, any new sample should contain a representative proportion of marked to unmarked individuals. From this, the size of the population (P) may be estimated, most simply by dividing the number in the sample recaptured ($n_r$) by the product of the number of marked individuals in the recaptured sample ($n_{rm}$) multiplied by the number of individuals originally marked ($n_{om}$). This calculation (the Lincoln index) $P = n_r \div n_{rm} \times n_{om}$, is appropriate only when the population is fairly static or where changes—due to migration, natality, or mortality—are known. When a population is fluctuating rapidly, as is common in insect populations, more sophisticated indices, which allow for the probabilities of change, are preferable.

**Marl.** Lime-rich clay, usually found as an alluvial deposit and containing a high proportion of soft calcium carbonate.

**Marrow.** The soft, myeloid tissue filling the spaces in bone, yellow marrow, consisting principally of fat, filling the medullary cavities of long bones; red marrow, composed of hemopoietic tissue, filling the spaces af cancellous bone.

**Marsh.** A region of vegetation where the water table is at or just beneath the soil surface. The soil is neither highly acid nor alkaline (compare bog, fen). Common marsh plants are water lilies, reeds, sedges, and various grasses. A marsh is a stage in the development of a climax vegetation from a hydrosere.

**Marsh Grass.** Any of a number of coarse grasses which grow in marshes, especially those of the genus Spartina.

**Marsupial.** Any member of the Marsupialia, an order of mammals which Includes the kangaroos, wallabies, wombats, and opossum. Females bear immature young which are nourished in a marsupiam which encloses the nipples.

**Marsupium**

1. *zool.* A pouch or cavity in which young develop, as *a.* that in marsupials and certain monotremes; *b.* the gill of a bivalve mollusk when containing embryos or larvae; *c.* the brood pouch of various crustaceans or the sea horse.
2. *bot.* The pendant perigynium of various bryophytes.

**Masculine**

1. *zool.* Of the male sex; belonging to or having qualities of a male.
2. *bot.* Staminate.

**[1]Mask.** To cover, hide, conceal, or prevent from showing.

**[2]Mask.** A structure which conceals, as the distal end of the labium of a dragonfly nymph.

**Mass Flow Hypothesis.** The theory that translocation of sugars in the phloem is brought about by a continuous flow of water and dissolved sugars between sources and sinks. (A source is the site of production of sugar, usually leaves, and the sink is the site of their utilization, for example the root system.) At the source osmotic pressure is high due to the continuous formation of sugars and at the sink osmotic pressure is low as the sugars are used up. Thus water from the xylem enters the phloem at the source and leaves it at the sink, returning to the source via the xylem. This tends to drive the contents of the phloem towards the sink. The hypothesis has been challenged, notably by those who believe there is a metabolic component, *i.e.* that active diffusion plays a part in phloem translocation.

**Mass Provisioning.** The provision of all the food required for larval development by wasps and bees. The food, either insect or spider prey (for wasps) or honey and pollen (for bees) is stored in a specially prepared space (cell) within the nest. An egg is laid on or in the food, and the cell is sealed. Mass provisioning is very largely found in solitary (non-social) species, but is also practised by the highly social stingless bees.

**Massulae.** Mucilaginous extensions of the tapetum that surround the microspores and megaspores of water ferns of the genus Azolla. Four massulae surround the megaspore and are believed to aid buoyancy. A variable number of massulae are developed in the microsporangium, each of which contains a number of microspores.

**Mast.** The fruit of various forest trees, especially beechnuts, which is utilized as food by hogs and other animals.

**Mast Cell.** Connective tissue cell that on becoming injured at a site of tissue damage releases certain chemicals. Some of these cause a restriction of lymph vessels, thus allowing localized swelling to occur. Another, called histamine, increases capillary permeability, allowing leucocytes to leave the circulatory system more readily and to congregate at the site of injury.

**Mastic.** A resin which exudes from the mastic tree (Pistacia lentiscus), used medicinally and as an ingredient of varnishes.

**Masticate.** To grind, chew, and crush the food in preparation for swallowing.

**[1]Masticatory.** Adapted for or pertaining to the chewing of food.

**[2]Masticatory.** A substance that is chewed but not swallowed, as chewing gum.

**Mastigate.** Having one or more flagella.

**Mastigium.** A protrusible, whiplike anal organ in certain caterpillars.

**Mastigobranch.** A slender, fringed extension of the epipodite of the maxillipeds of decapod crustaceans.

**Mastigomycotina.** A subdivision of the Eumycota consisting predominantly of aquatic fungi or fungi that flourish under particularly damp conditions. It contains about 190 genera and some 1280 species. Its members characteristically produce motile cells and are thus called zoosporic fungi. The number and type of flagella possessed by the zoospores is used to divide the Mastigomycotina into three classes : the Chytridiomycetes, whose zoospores have one posterior whiplash flagellum; the Hyphochytridiomycetes, whose zoospores have one anterior flimmer flagellum; and the Oomycetes, whose zoospores have an anterior flimmer flagellum and a posterior whiplash flagellum. The diversity of zoospore structure implies the Mastigomycotina are polyphyletic and hence not a natural group.

**Mastigonema.** Any of numerous fine hairlike rodlets attached to a flimmer flagellum. Mastigonemata are arranged in longitudinal row and are orientated at an angle, giving the flagellum a feathery appearance at high magnification.

**Mastigoneme.** A flimmer, one of the numerous minute lateral processes on the sides of the tinsel type of flagellum.

**Mastigophoran.** Any protozoan of the class or superclass Mastigophora characterized by possession of one or more flagella, as Euglena, Trypanosoma; a flagellate.

**Mastigote.** Mastigate.

**Mastigure.** A lizard of the genus Uromastix of Southern Asia and Africa.

**Mastitis.** Inflammation of the breast.

**Mastoid.** Nipplelike.

**Mastoid Cells.** Air cells of the mastoid portion of the temporal bone which communicate with the tympanic cavity.

**Mastoid Process.** An outgrowth from the temporal bone of the skull containing air cavities that communicate with the cavity of the middle ear. In man it is a route through which infection may spread from the middle ear.

**Mat**

1. A thick, dense, tangled mass of fibers, hair, weeds, or other filamentous structures.
2. A thin crust formed by the stolons of stoloniferous corals.

[1]**Mate.** One of a pair of animals which associate together for mating.

[2]**Mate.** To join together for breeding.

**Mate**

1. A South American holly (Ilex paraguariensis).
2. A beverage, Paraguay tea, prepared from the leaves of this holly.

**Maternal.** Pertaining to, produced by, or derived from the female parent or mother.

**Mating.** The joining of individuals of different sexes for reproductive purposes.

**Mating Strain.** A group of organisms within a species that are characterized by not being able to interbreed with each other. However they are able to breed with members of other physiologically different but morphologically identical groups. Different mating strains are usually denoted by the symbols + and − since male and female forms cannot be distinguished as such. The differences are genetically determined. Compare physiological race.

**Mating Type.** Equivalent in lower organisms (particularly micro-organisms) of sexes in higher organisms. Micro-organisms may be sub-divided into mating types on the basis of their physiology and mating behaviour. Different mating types are usually identical in physical form although individuals of one mating type possess on their surfaces proteins that will bind to complementary proteins or polysaccarides found only on the coats of individuals of the opposite mating type. In this way, only individuals of different mating types will undergo conjugation.

**Matric Potential ($\psi_m$).** That component of the water potential of plants and soils that is due to capillary and imbibitional forces. Thus the water potential of cell walls and intercellular spaces is largely due to matric potential. Values of matric potentials are always negative and range from 0 bar in fully turgid tissues to −10 bar in slightly wilted plants.

**Matrix**

1. The intercellular substance of cartilage or bone.
2. A mass of cells (germinal matrix) from which a hair develops.
3. The posterior portion of the nail bed from which a nail develops.

**Matroclinous.** Resembling the female parent more than the male, with reference to hereditary traits.

**Mattoral.** Maquis.

**Maturation**

1. The process of coming to a full state of maturity or development.
2. The processes involved in the formation of functional gametes, as in spermatogenesis and oogenesis.

**Mature.** Fully grown or developed; ripe.

**Mature Phase.** Stage in the cyclical pattern of community change in grasslands and heathlands. In grasslands, the mature phase is the stage in which the grass hummocks attain their maximum height (about 4 cm) and begin to be colonized by lichens. In heathlands, it is the stage at which Calluna vulgaris bushes, about 12-18 years old, start to become less dense, allowing other species, especially bryophytes, to grow. Compare building phase; pioneer phase; hollow phase; and degenerate phase.

**Maturity.** The state or quality of being mature.

**Matutinal.** Of, pertaining to, or occurring in the morning.

**Maw.** The portion of the digestive tract into which food is taken, as *a.* the mouth and throat of a carnivore; *b.* the crop of a bird; *c.* the stomach.

**Maw Seed.** The seed of the opium poppy, used for bird feed.

**Maxilla**

1. In vertebrates, the posterior bone of the upper jaw, which bears the teeth other than the incisors. The term is sometimes applied to the whole of the upper jaw.
2. In some arthropods, one of a pair of mouthparts used in eating.

**Maxilliped**

1. One of a pair or several pairs of appendages located posterior to the maxillae in crustaceans.
2. The poison claw of a centipede.

**Maxillulla.** One of the first pair of maxillae in arthropods having two pair.

**Mayapple.** Mandrake.

**Mayfly.** A soft-bodied insect of the order Ephemeroptera; adults are short-lived nymphs are aquatic living 1 to 3 years.

**Maze.** A confusing, interconnected series of lines or pathways including blind alleys or compartments used extensively in intelligence tests.

**M Chromosome.** A very small chromosome, a number of which may be found in the nuclei of mosses. Their function is obscure.

**MCPA** (2-methyl-4-chlorophenoxyacetic acid). A synthetic auxin of the phenoxyacetic acid group that is used as a selective weedkiller.

**Meadow.** A region of moist grassland maintained at the subclimax stage by moving. Similar areas maintained at the subclimax stage by grazing are often termed pastures.

**Mean.** Intermediate or occupying a median position; average; midway between extremes.

**Mean** (arithmetic mean). The average of a series of quantities, obtained by adding up all the observed values and dividing by the total number of observations. If a normal curve were plotted from an infinitely large number of observations, then the mean (and the median and mode) would be the distance from the origin of the axes to the centre point of the curve, represented by the symbol $\mu$. However when sample size is limited, as always occurs in practice, then the estimated mean, rather than the median or mode, gives the best estimate of the true mean.

**Mean Deviation.** The average magnitude of deviations from the centre of a normal curve. Compare standard deviation.

**Mean Square.** The estimated square of the standard deviation.

**Meatus.** A small canal or passage in the body. An example is the external auditory meatus of the outer ear in mammals, which connects the exterior opening to the eardrum.

**Measles** (morbilli, rubeola). Acute, infectious disease which affects mainly children; other primates can also be affected. Symptoms begin with cough and cold-like symptoms, and these are followed by fever and skin rash. In healthy children the disease is usually mild and self-limiting, but in undernourished children it can be fatal. It is caused by a paramyxovirus.

**Measly Meant.** Meat infested with the larvae (bladderworms or cysticerci) of tapeworms.

**Measuring Worm.** The larva or caterpillar of a moth of the family Geometridae, which moves in a characteristic, looping fashion; a looper or inchworm; a geometer.

**Meat**

1. The flesh of an animal which is used for food.
2. The edible part of anything, as the meat of a nut.

**Meatus.** A natural opening, passageway, or canal.

**Mechanical**

1. Of or pertaining to a mechanism or a machine.
2. Of or pertaining to the action of physical force on matter as distinguished from chemical, vital, mental, or spiritual forces.

**Mechanical Tissue** (strengthening tissue, supporting tissue). Any tissue consisting of cells with thickened cell walls, such as collenchyma and sclerenchyma.

**Mechanism.** The doctrine that all phenomena in nature are the result of natural processes and explicable by the laws of chemistry and physics. Compare vitalism.

**Mechanoreceptor.** A receptor that responds to such mechanical stimuli as touch, sound, and pressure. The skin is rich in mechanoreceptors.

**Meconium**

1. The intestinal contents of a fetus which accumulates before birth.
2. The intestinal contents of an organism which accumulates during its dormant state, as that of the pupa of an insect.

**Mecopteran.** An insect of the order Mecopteran which includes the scorpion flies.

**[1]Media.** Plural of Medium.

**[2]Media**

1. The middle coat of a blood or lymph vessel, as the tunica media.
2. A vein in the wing of an insect.

**Mediad.** Toward the median plane or midline of the body.

**Medial.** Located in or toward the median plane.

**Median**

1. Located in the middle of the body or a part of it, as the median plane.
2. In statistics, in a series of numerical values, the point above which the number of individuals in the series equals the number below it.

**Median Eye** (pineal eye). An eyelike structure, with a lens and retina, found on the top of the head of some lizards, Sphenodon, and the Cyclostomata (lampreys) as well as in many fossil vertebrates. Its function is unknown.

**Mediastinum**

1. A membrane in the midline of the thorax of mammals that separates the lungs.
2. The space between the two lungs, which is occupied by the heart and oesophagus.

**Mediate.** To serve as an intermediary or a medium by which an effect is produced, as a sensory receptor which mediates a sensation.

**Medicinal**

1. Having therapeutic or healing properties.
2. Pertaining to or caused by a medicine, as a medicinal rash.

**Medicine**

1. Any substance used in the diagnosis, treatment, or prevention of disease.
2. Medical science; the science and art of diagnosing, treating, and preventing disease, especially internal diseases requiring the services of a physician.

**Medium.** The surrounding substance in which an organism exists, such as air or water, or (in an experimental situation) a mounting medium, staining medium, culture medium, etc.

**Medulla**

1. In cylindrically-stemmed plants, the pith or central part.
2. The central part of an organ or bone (*i.e.* the marrow).

3. In vertebrates the term is often used as an abbreviation of medulla oblongata, the most posterior part of the brain linked directly to the spinal cord. It is primitively concerned with the processing of sensory information and contains centres controlling many involuntary functions.

**Medulla Oblongata.** Part of the vertebrate brainstem, derived from the hindbrain, that is continuous with the spinal cord. Its function is to regulate the reflex responses controlling respiration, heart beat, blood pressure, and other involuntary processes. It gives rise to many of the cranial nerves.

**Medullary**

1. *anat.* Of or pertaining to a medulla, marrow, or myelin.

2. *bot.* Of or pertaining to the medulla or pith.

**Medullary Ray** (ray). Any of the vertical plates of parenchyma cells running radially through the cylinder of vascular tissue in the stems and roats of plants. Each may be one to many cells in width. Primary medullary rays occur in young plants and in those not showing secondary thickening; they pass from the cortex through to the pith. Secondary medullary rays are produced by the vascular cambium and terminate in xylem and phloem tissues. Medullary rays store and transport food materials.

**Medullary Sheath**

1. *anat.* The myelin sheath.

2. *bot.* A layer of cells surrounding the pith in the stem of certain plants.

**Medullated.** Myelinated; possessing a myelin sheath.

**Medullated Nerve fibre.** A nerve fibre that is characterized by a myelin sheath, which insulates the axon.

**Medullated Protostele.** A protostele in which the central core of xylem consists mainly of tracheids interspersed with numerous parenchyma cells. It thus resembles the medulla (pith) of a siphonostele (hence the name). The medullated proto stele shows how the siphonostele may have evolved from a protostele, with the pith originating in the xylem itself. Medullated protosteles are exhibited in some primitive ferns, *e.g.* Gleichenia.

**Medusa.** The free-swimming stage in the life-cycle of the Coelenterata. Medusae are umbrella-shaped, with tentacles round the edge and the mouth in the centre underneath. They swim by pulsations of the body and reproduce sexually. In the Hydrozoa (*e.g.* Hydra) they alternate in the life cycle with polyps, from which they are produced by budding. In the Scyphozoa, which includes all the common jellyfish, the medusa is the dominant form and the polyp is reduced or absent.

**Medusoid**

1. Resembling a medusa.
2. In colonial coelenterates, designating a type of zooid which gives rise to medusae.

**Megacephalic.** Possessing an abnormally large head.

**Megagamete.** A macrogamete.

**Megagametophyte.** The female gametophyte; the plant which develops from a megaspore.

**Megakaryocyte.** A large, multinucleated cell of red bone marrow, the source of blood platelets.

**Megalocephalic.** Megacephalic.

**Megalopteran.** Any insect of the order Megaloptera which includes the alderflies and dobsonflies.

**Megalospheric.** Having a large first chamber, with reference to the shell of a foraminiferan.

**Megaphyll.** A type of foliage leaf in ferns and seed plants that has branched or parallel vascular bundles running through the lamina. The megaphylls of ferns are large pinnate leaves called fronds. A megaphyll was formerly called a macrophyll. Compare microphyll.

**Megasporangiophore.** A stalklike structure that bears megasporangia. The ovule-bearing structures (megasporophylls) making up the female cones of cycads are termed megasporangiophores.

**Megasporangium.** A sporangium which produces macro-or megaspores.

**Megaspore.** The larger of two kinds of spore produced by heterosporous ferns, or the first cell of the female gametophyte generation of such ferns and seed plants (angiosperms and gymnosperms). In angiosperms it is one of four haploid cells formed from a megasporocyte during meiosis, the other three degenerating. The megaspore of angiosperms divides to produce the female gametophyte or embryo sac.

**Megaspore Mother Cell.** A diploid cell that gives rise by meiosis to four megaspores. Often only one develops and the rest abort. Compare microspore mother cell.

**Megasporocyte.** A cell from which a megaspore develops.

**Megasporophyll** (macrosporophyll). A leaflike structure that bears the megasporangia. In angiosperms and gymnosperms it is represented by the carpel and ovuliferous scale respectively. Compare microsporophyll.

**Mehlis' Gland.** A group of unicellular glands surrounding the ootype in trematodes and cestodes. Formerly called shell gland.

**Meiocyte.** A cell that divides to produce haploid spores. The microspore mother cells (pollen mother cells) in anthers and the megaspore mother cells in nucellar tissue are the meiocytes of flowering plants.

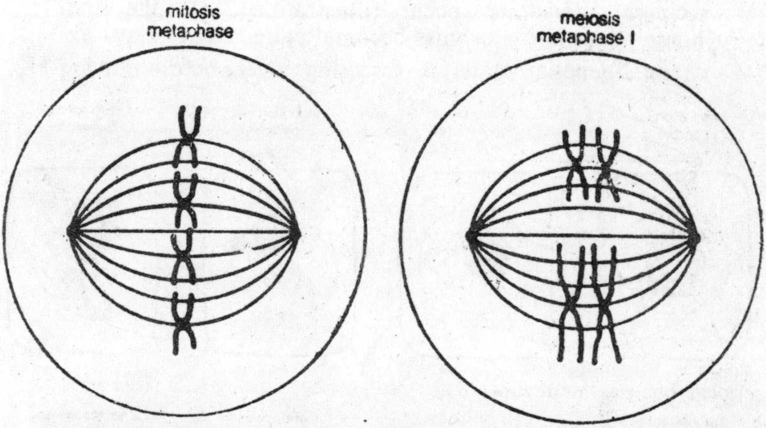


The basic differences in chromosome behaviour in mitosis and meiosis.

**Meiotic Drive.** A process occurring during meiosis that results in the two kinds of gametes produced by a heterozygote not being equally common. It is more often seen in the formation of megaspores than microspores. An example is seen in maize plants that are heterozygous for a chromosome mutation, in which one of the homologues of chromosome. 10 has an abnormal terminal knob. The knob acts as a centromere and causes the abnormal chromosomes to move the poles of the spindle earlier in both the first and second divisions of meiosis. The product of meiosis is a linear tetrad in which the abnormal chromosomes are more likely to be in the outer two cells. Since all four cells of a tetrad normally develop into pollen grains, the abnormal chromosome is recovered in equal numbers among the microspores. Howeve only the basal cell of the tetrad develops into the megaspore. Thus the abnormal chromosome is recovered at higher frequencies (about 70%) among the megaspores.

**Meiosis** (reduction division). A type of cell division that gives rise to four reproductive cells (gametes) each with half the chromosome number of the parent cell. Two consecutive divisions occur (illustration). In the first, homologous chromosomes become paired and may exchange genetic material (crossing over) before moving

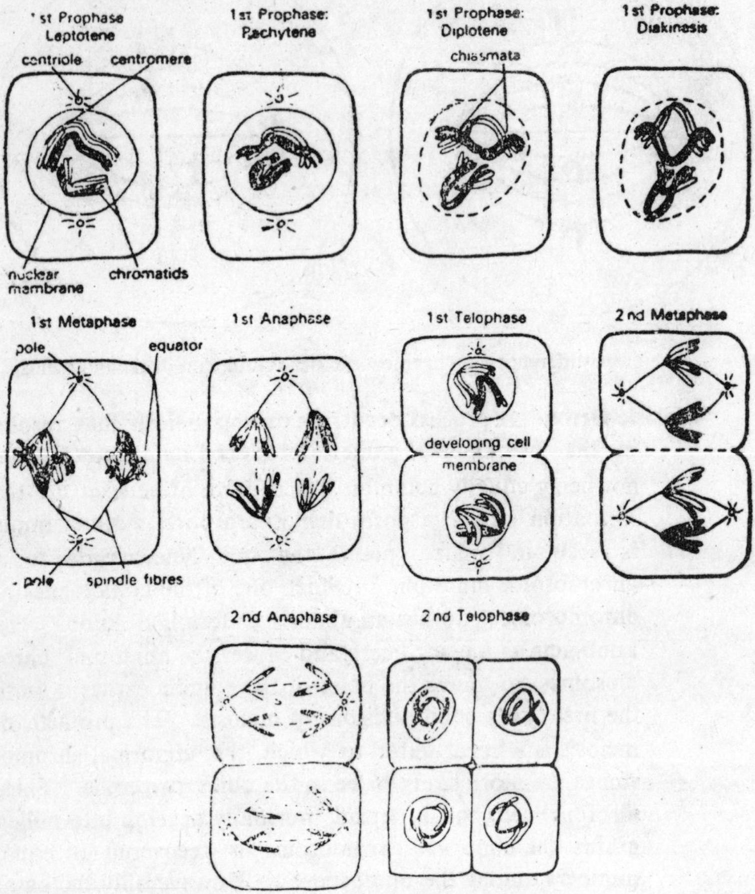


The stages of meiosis in a cell containing two pairs of homologous chromosomes

away from each other into separate daughter nuclei. This is the actual reduction division because each of the two nuclei so formed contains only half of the original chromosomes. The daughter nuclei then divide by mitosis and four haploid cells are produced.

**Meiospore.** A haploid spore produced by meiosis.

**Meissner's Corpuscle.** A sensory receptor which mediates the sense of light touch; a tactile corpuscle.

**Melanconiales.** An order of the Coelomycetes containing many fungi parasitic on plant stems and leaves, *e.g.* Gloeosporium and Colletotrichum, both causal agents of anthracnose. It numbers about 1000 species in some 120 genera. The conidiophores erupt in a mass through the host epidermis forming an acervulus.

**Melanin.** Any of a group of polymers, derived from the amino acid tyrosine, that cause pigmentation of eyes, skin, and hair in vertebrates. Melanins are produced by specialized epidermal cells called melanocytes. Certain invertebrates, fungi, and microorganisms also produce melanin pigments. The 'ink' of the octopus and squid is a notable example. Hereditary albinism is caused by the absence of the enzyme tyrosinase, which is necessary for melanin production.

**Melanism.** Black coloration of the body caused by overproduction of the pigment melanin, often as a reaction to the environment. There are several species of melanic moths in industrially polluted areas (industrial melanism) and the panther is a nielanic form of leopard.

**Melanoblast.** A cell in the skin of neural crest origin which produces melanin.

**Melanocyte.** A branched, melanin-containing cell present in the basal layer of the epidermis.

**Melanophore.** A branched, pigment cell (chromatophore) which contains granules of melanin present in many animals; responsible for pigmentation and color changes.

**Melelanosome.** A pigment mass in the ocellus of a dinoflagellate.

**Melatonin.** A substance isolated from the pineal body which causes the concentration of melanin in melanophores.

**Melon.** A muskmelon or watermelon.

**Membranaceous**

1. Membranous.
2. *bot.* Like a thin, soft, delicate, and usually transparent or translucent membrane.

**Membrane.** Sheet-like structure, 7-10 nm wide, that forms the boundary between a cell and its environment and also between various compartments within the cell. It is composed mainly of lipids, proteins, and some carbohydrates, the structural arrangement of which is still subject to speculation. Membranes function as selective barriers and also as a structural base for enzymes, which may form an integral part of the membrane itself.

Mendel (1822-84). The first law, of segregation, is that the two members of a gene pair segregate from each other during meiosis, each gamete having an equal probability of obtaining either member of the gene pair. The second law, of independent assortment, is that different segregating gene pairs behave independently. This second law is not universal as was originally thought, but applies only to unlinked or distantly liked pairs. At the time of Mendel, genes had not been identified as the units of inheritance : he considered factors of a pair of characters segregating and members of different pairs of factors assorting independently.

**Membrane.** A sheetlike tissue that covers, connects, or lines biological cells and their organells, organes, and other structures. Membranes consist of polar lipids (predominantly the phospholipids lecithin and cephalin) and protein : the lipids form a double layer (bilayer) with protein molecules suspended within it. Membranes are permeable to water and fat-soluble substances but impermeable to polar substances (*e.g.* sugars). Movement of ions across a membrane occurs by carrier-mediated processes, including active transport and facilitated diffusion. Large molecules may be taken up by phagocytosis.

**Membrane Bone** (dermal bone). Bone formed directly in connective tissue, rather than by replacing cartilage (compare cartilage bone). Some face bones, skull bones, and part of the clavicle are membrane bones. Small areas of membrane become jelly-like and attract calcium salts. Bone-forming cells break down these areas forming a bone lattice, which eventually fills in.

**Membranous.** Of, pertaining to, consisting, of, originating in, or resembling a membrane.

**Membranous Labyrinth.** The soft tubular sensory structures that form the inner ear of vertebrates and are housed within the bony labyrinth.

**Menarche.** The onset of menses at puberty.

**Mendelism.** The theory of heredity that forms the basis of classical genetics, proposed by Gregor Mendel (1822-84) in 1866 and formulated in two laws (Mendel's laws; particulate inheritance). Mendel suggested that individual characteristics were determined by inherited 'factor', and when improved microscopes revealed detail's of cell structure the behaviour of Mendel's factors could be related to the behaviour of chromosomes during meiosis.

**Mendel's Laws.** Two laws summarizing Gregor Mendel's theory of inheritance (also Mendelism). The Law of Segregation states that each hereditary characteristic is controlled by two 'factors' (now called alleles) which segregate (separate) and pass into separate germ (reproductive) cells. The Law of Independent Assortment states that pairs of 'factors' segregate independently of each other when germ cells are formed (also independent assortment). These laws are the foundation of genetics.

**Meninges sing. Meninx.** The three membranes, dura mater, arachnoid, and pia mater, which enclose the brain and spinal cord.

**Menopause.** The time of cessation of menstrual cycles and ovarian function occurring normally in women between the ages of 45 and 50; climacteric, change of life.

**Menotaxis.** A light-compass reaction in which an animal moves at a fixed angle to the source of light.

**Menses.** Menstruation; the cyclic discharge of blood or bloody fluid from the vagina.

**Menstrual Cycle.** The approximately monthly cycle of events associated with ovulation that replaces the oestrous cycle in most primates (including humans). The lining of the uterus becomes progressively thicker with more blood vessels in preparation for the implantation of a fertilized egg cell (blastocyst). Ovulation occurs during the middle of the cycle (the fertile period). If fertilization does not occur the uterine lining breaks down and is discharged from the body (menstruation). In women the fertile period is 11-15 days after the end of the last menstruation.

**Menstruate.** To undergo menstruation.

**Menstruation.** The discharge of menstrual fluid consisting of blood, necrotic tissue, and secretions of glands, occurring monthly from puberty to menopause.

**Menstrum.** A solvent, especially one used in crude drug extraction.

[1]**Mental.** Of or pertaining to the mind.

[2]**Mental.** Of or pertaining to the chin.

**Mentum**

1. *zool. a* The chin. *b.* The distal portion of the postmentum of the labium of an insect. *c.* The basal portion of the gnathochilarium of a diplopod.

2. *bot.* An extension of the column in the flower of an orchid; a perula.

**Meraspis.** The second larval stage of a trilobite

**Mercuric Chloride.** Bichloride of mercury, $HgCl_2$, used in biology as an antiseptic and fixing agent; corrosive sublimate.

**Mericarp.** Any of the one-seeded portions that result when a compound fruit divides at maturity. Mericarps may be dehiscent or indehiscent.

**Meristele.** One of a number of amphicribal vascular bundles constituting a dictyostele.

**Meristem.** Group of plant cells that are capable of dividing indefinitely, and whose main function is the production of new growth. They are found at the growing tip of a root or stem (apical meristem); in the cambium (lateral meristem); and, in grasses, also within the stem and leaf sheaths (intercalary meristem).

**Meristem Culture** (shoot-tip culture). The culture of excised meristems on suitable nutrient media under aseptic conditions. The stem apex is usually used though axillary meristems may also be taken. Often gibberellic acid must be added to the medium to promote normal growth into a plantlet. Once a suitable medium has been found for the regeneration of plantlets, the technique can be used as a means of rapid propagation since the plantlets can be divided at intervals into segments that can be grown on individually. Meristem culture may be used to propagate infertile plants, nursery stock, or $F_1$ hybrids that do not breed true. As few virus diseases affect the plant apex, the technique can be used to produced virus-free stock.

**Meristic.** Divided into segments or metameres.

**Meristoderm.** The outer region of the stipe of certain members of the Phaeophyta (brown algae) in which meristem-like activity occurs. Continued division in the region below the lamina serves to replace tissues that are worn away by tide action.

**Mermaid's Purse.** The horny egg capsule of certain elasmobranchs.

**Meroblastic.** Undergoing partial cleavage in which cell divisions are limited to region of the animal pole, as in telolecithal ova.

**Merocrine.** Designating a type of gland in which the gland cells remain intact during the process of secretion, as the parotid.

**Merocrine Secretion.** Secretion.

**Merogon.** An embryo or larva resulting from merogony.

**Merogony**

1. The development of a part of an egg or an egg fragment.
2. The splitting of schizont into merozoites, as occurs in sporozoans.

**Meromixis.** Sexual phenomena in bacteria which involve the unidirectional transfer of genetic material as in transformation and transduction.

**Meromyarian.** Having only two or a few muscle cells in each quadrant, as in certain nematodes.

**Meronephridium.** A multiple nephridium arising from a single embryonic cord of cells, as in oligocheltes.

**Meroplankton.** Plankton organisms which exhibit daily vertical movements.

**Merosome.** A segment, somite, or metamere.

**Merostomate.** An arachnid of the subclass Merostomata which contains the king or horseshoe crab (Xiphosura or Limulus).

**Merozoite.** One of the divisions or segments of a schizont seen in asexual reproduction of certain sporozoans, as Plasmodium.

**Mesarch.** Describing xylem maturation in which the older cells (protoxylem) are in the centre of the xylem strand because maturation has progressed both centrifugally and centripetally. Compare endarch, exarch.

**Mesaxonic.** Designating a type of foot in which the midaxis passes through the middle digit, as in the horse.

**Mescal.** An intoxicating drink of Mexico distilled from the leaves of maguey (Agave).

**Mescaline.** An alkaloid with hallucinogenic properties obtained from mescal buttons, used by American Indians during religious ceremonies.

**Mesectoderm.** Mesenchyme derived from neural crest cells.

**Mesencephalon.** The midbrain, one of the three primary vesicles of a vertebrate brain located between forebrain and hindbrain.

**Mesenchyme.** A form of embryonic connective tissue derived principally from mesoderm consisting of a diffuse network of stellate cells which gives rise to connective tissue, cartilage, bone, blood and blood vessels, cardiac and smooth muscle.

**Mesenteron.** Old term for midgut.

**Mesentery.** A thin sheet of tissue, bounded on each side by peritoneum, that supports the gut and other organs in the body cavities of animals. Vertebrates have a well-developed dorsal mesentery that anchors the stomach and intestine and contains blood vesels and nerves supplying the gut. The reproductive organs and their ducts are also supported by mesenteries.

**Mesial.** Of, in, or toward the middle.

**Mesic.** Characterized by moderately moist conditions; neither too moist nor too dry.

**Mesobiota** (mesofauna, mesoflora). General term for soil organisms of intermediate size. 'Mesofauna' in particular refers to small, invertebrate animals found in the soil, characteristically annelids, arthropods, nematodes, and molluscs. These organisms are readily removed from a soil sample using a tullgren funnel or similar device. Compare macrobiota and; microbiota.

**Mesoblast.** Old term for mesoderm.

**Mesocarp.** The middle layer of the pericarp of an angiosperm fruit, positioned between the exocarp and endocarp. In many fruits, such as the peach (Prunus persica), the mesocarp is the fleshy part of the fruit. However, in some fruits no mesocarp is present, the pericarp consisting only of exocarp and endocarp.

**Mesocolon.** The mesentery which supports the colon.

**Mesoderm.** The layer of cells in the gastrula that lies between the ectoderm and endoderm. It develops into the muscles, circulatory system, and sex organs and in vertebrates also into the excretory system and skeleton.

**Mesodont**

1. With medium-sized teeth.
2. With medium-sized mandibles, with reference to insects.

**Mesogenous.** Describing an angiosperm stomatal complex in which the subsidiary cells are derived from the same initial as the guard cells. Compare perigenous.

**Mesoglea.** The gelatinous noncellular layer between the endoderm and ectoderm in the body wall of coelenterates. It may be thin, as in Hydro, or tough and fibrous, as in the larger jellyfish and sea anemones. It often contains cells that have migrated from the two body layers but these do not form tissues and organs and the mesoglea is not homologous with the mesoderm of triploblastic animals.

**Mesome** or **Mesom.** The region of a plant axis between successive branches.

**Mesomere.** The intermediate mesoderm; a nephrotome.

**Mesonephric Duct.** The duct of a mesonephros terminating caudally at the cloaca : Wolffian Duct.

**Mesonephros.** A type of embryonic kidney in amniotes consisting of a number of paired tubules which open into a mesonephric duct. It is transitory, following the pronephros and preceding the metanephros. Also called Wolffian body, middle kidney.

**Mesophil.** An organism which grows best at modera te temperatures (23°–40°C.)

**Mesophilic.** Describing microorganisms that require moderate temperatures (30–40°C) for optimal growth. Compare thermophilic, psychrophilic.

**Mesophyll.** The internal tissue of a leaf blade (lamina), consisting of parenchyma cells. There are two distinct forms. Palisade mesophyll lies just beneath the upper epidermis and consists of cells elongated at right angles to the leaf surface. They contain a large number of chloroplasts and their principal function is photosynthesis. Spongy mesophyll occupies most of the remainder of the lamina. It consists of spherical loosely arranged cells containing fewer chloroplasts than the palisade mesophyll. Between these cells are air spaces leading to the stomata.

**Mesophyte.** A plant whose water requirement is intermediate between that of xerophytes and hydrophytes, as most plants growing in watered land of the temperate zone. Compare hydrophyte, xerophyte.

**Mesorchium.** The mesentery which supports the testis.

**Mesophyte.** Any plant adapted to grow in soil that is well supplied with water and mineral salts. Such plants wilt easily when exposed to drought conditions as they are not adapted to conserve water. The majority of flowering plants are mesophytes. Compare hydrophyte; xerophyte.

**Mesosaprobic.** Living in waters in which active oxidation and decomposition of organic matter is occurring, said of protozoans.

**Mesosoma**

1. The preabdomen of curypterids.
2. The first portion of the abdomen (opisthosoma) of an arthropod.

**Mesosome.** The middle portion of the body of a deuterostome, as in hemichordates.

**Mesothelium.** A single layer of thin platelike cells covering the surface of the inside of the abdominal cavity and thorax and surrounding the heart, forming part of the peritoneum and pleura (serous membrane). It is derived from the mesoderm. Compare endothelium; epithelium.

**Mesothelium.** Simple squamous epithelium of mesodermal origin which lines the serous cavities of vertebrates.

**Mesothorax.** In insects, the middle region of the thorax usually bearing the first pair of wings and second pair of legs.

**Mesovarium** The mesentery which supports the ovary.

**Mesozoan.** One of a group (phylum?) of animals of uncertain affinities intermediate between protozoans and true multicellular animals, as Dicyema, Rhopalura.

**Mesozoic.** The middle of three eras that constitute the Phanerozoic period of time. The Mesozoic (literally 'middle life') was preceded by the Palaeozoic Era and followed by the Cenozoic Era. It lasted 160 million years, beginning with the Triassic 225 million years ago and ending 65 million years ago the start of the Tertiary. The Mesozoic comprises the Triassic, Jurassic, and Cretaceous Periods.

**Mesquite**

1. A spiny shrub, of the genus Prosopis, especially P. glandulosa and P. juliflora of arid regions of Southwest United States and Mexico, its pulpy pods a source of food.
2. The algaroba or keawe (Prosopis chilensis), a leguminous tree of the West Indies, Mexico, and Central America; an important food source.

**Messenger RNA (mRNA).** A linear single-stranded polynucleotide of uridine, adenine, guanidine, and cytidine monophosphates. mRNA is synthesized on DNA by mRNA polymerase enzyme, and the sequence of bases in it is a complementary copy (transcript) of the bases in one strand of DNA, the sense strand. The molecule initially manufactured on DNA now undergoes modification prior to its involvement in protein synthesis. This modification, called post-transcriptional processing, occurs in the nucleolus and involves the addition of adenine polynucleotide (poly A) to one end and a guanine derivative to the other end. In eukaryotic cells; post-transcriptional processing may also include excision of introns. Sometimes the term heterogeneous RNA (hnRNA) is given specifically to newly formed intron-containing mRNA, and the term mature mRNA is reserved for the molecule produced as a result of post-transcriptional processing. Mature mRNA moves to the ribosomes in the cytoplasm, where the triplets of bases in it act as a template and correspond to amino acids in proteins.

**Mestom Sheath** (mestome sheath) A thin-walled type of bundle sheath present in some grasses.

**Metabolic.** Of or pertaining to metabolism.

**Metabolic Rate.** The rate of metabolism as determined by the amount of food consumed, heat produced, or oxygen utilized. Basal metabolic rate (BMR) is the energy output as determined under special conditions.

**Metabolism.** The sum of the chemical reactions that occur within living organisms. The various compounds that take part in or are formed by these reactions are called metabolites. In animals many metabolites are obtained by the digestion of food, whereas in plants only the basic starting materials (carbon dioxide, water and minerals) are externally derived. The synthesis (anabolism) and breakdown (catabolism) of most compounds occurs by a number of reaction steps, the reaction sequence being termed a metabolic pathway. Some pathways (*e.g.* glycolysis) are linear; others (*e.g.* the Krebs cycle) are cyclic. The changes at each step in a pathway are usually small and are promoted by efficient biological catalysts—the enzymes. In this way the amounts of energy required or released at any given stage are minimal, which helps in maintaining a constant internal environment. Various feedback mechanisms exist to govern metabolic rates.

**Metabolite**

1. A product of metabolic activity, especially one formed in intermediary metabolism.
2. A substance utilized in a metabolic process, as certain vitamins.

**Metaboly.** Squirming, undulating movements, as in Euglena.

**Metacarpal.** One of the bones in the metacarpus.

**Metacarpus.** The hand (or corresponding part of the forelimb) in terrestrial vertebrates, consisting of a number of rod-shaped bones (metacarpals) that articulate with the bones of the wrist (carpus) and those of the fingers (phalanges). The number of metacarpals varies between species : in the basic pentadactyl limb there are five, but this number is reduced in may species.

**Metacentric.** Describing a chromosome in which the chromatid arms are of a similar length either side of the centromere so that the centromere appears to be near the centre of the chromosome. Compare acrocentric, telocentric.

**Metacercaria.** A stage in development of a digenetic fluke between cercaria and adult during which the tail is lost and encystment usually occurs.

**Metachromatic.** Assuming a color different from that usually resulting from a specific stain or dye.

**Metachromatic Granules.** Babes-Ernst bodies; inclusion bodies present in certain bacteria, yeasts, and algae.

**Metachromatic Stain.** A stain that dyes certain tissues a different colour to the dye solution. Examples are methyl violet and thionine. Thionin violet produces colours in sections ranging from blue to reddish violet and is particularly useful for distinguishing chromatin and mucin.

**Metachronism.** The orderly succession in the initiation of beat of cilia, resulting in a wavelike action on a ciliated surface.

**Metachrosis.** The ability to change color, as seen in fishes, amphibians, reptiles, and other animals.

**Metacoel.** The cavity of a metasome.

**Metagenesis.** Alternation of Generations.

**Metamere.** A somite or segment; one of a linear series of more or less similar divisions or parts which make up the body of a segmented animal.

**Metamarism.** The state or condition or being composed of segments or metameres.

**Metameric Segmentation** (metamerism; segmentation). The division of an animal's body (except at the head region—cephalization) into a number of compartments (segments or metameres) each containing the same organs. Metameric segmentation is most strongly marked in annelid worms (*e.g.* earthworms), in which the muscles, blood vessels, nerves, etc. are repeated in each segment. In these animals the segmentation is obvious both externally and internally. It also occurs internally in arthropods and in the embryonic development of all vertebrates, in which it is confined to parts of the muscular, skeletal and nervous systems and does not show externally.

**Metamorphosis**

1. *zool.* A change in shape or form which an animal undergoes in its development from egg to adult as seen in annelids (trochophore to adult worm); insects (egg, nymph, adult; egg, larva, pupa, adult); crustaceans (egg, nauplius, zoea, mysis, adult); amphibians (egg., tadpole, adult).
2. *med.* A retrogressive change of one type of tissue to another, as fatty degeneration of the liver.

**Metanauplius.** In crustaceans, a larval stage preceding the nauplius, as in the shrimp.

**Metandrous.** Maturing before male flowers, said of female flowers.

**Metanephric.** Of or pertaining to a metanephros.

**Metanephridium.** A nephridium with an internal opening or nephrostome opening into the coelom and a nephridiopore opening to the outside.

**Metanephros.** An embryonic type of kidney in amniotes which develops posterior to the mesonephros. It becomes the functional kidney in reptiles, birds, and mammals.

**Metaphase.** The second stage of cell division, during which the membrane around the nucleus breaks down, the spindle forms, and centromeres attach the chromosomes to the equator of the spindle. In the first metaphase of meiosis pairs of chromosomes (bivalents) are attached, while in mitosis and the second metaphase of meiosis, individual chromosomes are attached.

**Metaphloem.** Late primary phloem. The metaphloem completes its elongation after the surrounding tissues have ceased elongating and therefore, unlike the protophloem, is not obliterated. However, in plants exhibiting secondary growth, the growth of the secondary phloem often results in obliteration of the metaphloem. Unlike those in the protophloem, these obliterated cells do not usually differentiate into fibres, although they may undergo sclerification. The sieve elements of the metaphloem are usually wider and longer than those of the protophloem, and their sieve plates are usually more distinct. Compare metaxylem.

**Metaphysis.** In the development of a bone, the region between diaphysis and epiphysis; the epiphyseal plate.

**Metaphyta.** Kingdom that includes all the plants. The earliest true plants were probably unicellular green algae, which first appeared in the Precambrian. The bryophytes (mosses, liverworts, and hornworts) are known from the Devonian, and the first recorded vascular plants date from the Silurian.

**Metaphyte.** Any plant of the Metaphyta, a major category of living things comprising the bryophytes and tracheophytes complex multicellular plants.

**Metaplasia.** The transformation of a tissue into a different type. This is an abnormal process; for example, metaplasia of the epithelium of the bronchi may be an early sign of cancer.

**Metaplasm.** The nonliving constituents of protoplasm; cell inclusions.

**Metapleural Folds.** Two ventrolateral folds in lancelets which meet in the region of the atriopore and continue posteriorly as the caudal fin.

**Metapterygium.** Basalia.

**Metarteriole.** A minute blood vessel which lies between an arteriole and a true capillary.

**Metasoma**

1. The posterior portion of the abdomen of an arthropod : Opisthosoma.
2. The postabdomen of a eurypterid.

**Metasomatism.** Kind of metamorphism that involves the introduction of chemical constituents into a rock, or their removal from it (or both), via a volatile phase. Complete mineral transformations may occur, but the rock texture may remain (resulting in a 'pseudomorph').

**Metasome**

1. The midbody of a copepod.
2. The third portion of the body of a deuterostome.

**Metastasis.** The spread from one part of the body to another of a pathological state or condition resulting from the dispersal by way of blood or lymphatic channels of the causative agents or cells from the primary focus of infection, as the spread of a malignant neoplasm.

**Metasternum**

1. In insects, the sternum of the metathorax.
2. In vertebratrs, the posterior portion of the sternum; the xiphisternum.

**Metastoma**

1. The lower lip of certain crustaceans, usually divided into two paragnatha.
2. A pregenital plate in eurypterids.

**Metatarsal.** One of the bones in the metatarsus.

**Metatarsus.** The foot (or corresponding part of the hindlimb) in terrestrial vertebrates, consisting of a number of rod-shaped bones (metatarsals) that articulate with the bones of the ankle (tarsus) and those of the toes (phalanges). The number of metatarsals varies between species : in the basic pentadactyl limb there are five, but this number is reduced in some species.

**Metatheria.** A subclass of mammals containing the marsupials. The female bears an abdominal pouch (marsupium) into which the newly born young, which are in a very immature state, move to complete their development. They obtain nourishment from the mother's mammary teats. Modern marsupials are restricted to Australasia (where they include the kangaroos, koala bears, phalangers, and bandicoots) and America (the opossums). Marsupials evolved during the late Cretaceous period, 80 million years ago. In Australia, where the marsupials have been isolated for millions of years, they show the greatest diversity of form, having undergone adaptive radiation to many of the niches occupied by placental mammals elsewhere. Compare Eutheria; Prototheria.

**Metatherian.** Any mammal of the Metatheria which includes the marsupials.

**Metathorax.** The third and most posterior division of the thorax in insects, usually bearing the second pair of wings and the third pair of legs.

**Metatroch.** A girdle of cilia located just below the mouth in a trochophore.

**Metatrochophore.** A larval stage between trochophore and nectochaeta in certain polychaetes.

**Metatrophic.** Saprophytic or saprozoic.

**Metaxenic.** *bot.* Pertaining to the influence of the male parent on maternal tissue outside the embryo and endosperm.

**Metazoa.** The subkingdom of animals in which the body is composed of many cells grouped into tissues and coordinated by a nervous system. It comprises all vertebrates and invertebrates except the Protozoa and Porifera (sponges).

**Metazoan**

1. A multicellular animal.
2. Any member of the Metazoa, a major category of the animal kingdom comprising all animals except the Protozoa.

**Metazoea.** In certain decapod crustaceans, a stage in development between the zoea and megalops stages.

**Metencephalon.** The anterior portion of the hindbrain which gives rise to the pons and cerebellum.

**Metestrus.** The stage in the estrous cycle which follows estrus during which corpora lutea develop; in the vagina the cornified lining is shed and leukocytes appear in its lumen.

**Methanobacteriaceae.** Family of bacteria which have a specialized type of energy-yielding metabolism in which methane is an end-product. The organisms can grow only in the absence of air. They are found in anaerobic habitats, *e.g.* sewage sludge, the intestines of animals, sediments in natural waters, and waterlogged soils.

**Methanol.** Methyl or wood alcohol.

**Methionine** A nonpolar sulphur-containing amino acid with the formula $CH_3S(CH_2)_2CH(NH_2)COOH$ (illustration at amino acid). Methionine is synthesized from aspartate via the nonprotein amino acid homoserine. Control of methionine synthesis is by feedback inhibition. Methionine is broken down to succinyl CoA, which can be further oxidized in the TCA cycle.

The methyl group of methionine is important in the formation of a large number of methylated biomolecules. The actual methyl transferring molecule is not methionine itself but its ATP-activated derivative, S-adenosyl methionine. Methionine has also been implicated in the formation of the growth substance ethylene.

**Methylene Blue.** A blue dye used in optical microscopy to stain nuclei of animal tissues. It is als suitable as a vital stain and a bacterial stain.

**Methylomonadaceae.** Family of Gram-negative bacteria which can use as nutrients only methane, methanol, or similar ('one.carbon') compounds. The cells may be motile or non-motile. They are chemo-organotrophic, and can grow only in the presence of air. There are two genera.

**Mevalonic Acid.** A precursor in the formation of terpenoids and steroids. It has the formula $CH_2OHCH_2C(OH)(CH_3)CH_2COOH$. Biosynthesis of gibberellins, cytokinins, and abscisic acid is from mevalonic acid. Certain growth retardants, *e.g.* Amo-1618 and CCC (chlorcholine chloride), are believed to act by blocking the step from geranylgeranylpyrophosphate to kaurene in the mevalonic acid synthesis pathway, so preventing gibberellin synthesis.

**Mice.** Plural of mouse.

**Micelle.** An aggregate of molecules in a colloid. For example, phospholipids in aqueous solution form micelles—small clusters of molecules in which the nonpolar hydrocarbon groups are in the centre and the hydrophilic polar groups are on the outside.

**Microaerophilic.** Growing in minute quantities of free oxygen.

**Microclimate.** The atmospheric characteristics prevailing within a small space, usually in the layer near the ground that is affected by the ground surface. Special influences include the impact of vegetation cover on humidity (by evapotranspiration) and on temperature and winds.

**Microascales.** An order of fungi belonging to the Plectomycetes whose members, numbering about six genera, characteristically have a beaked cleistothecium. It contains the species Ceratocystis ulmi, which causes Dutch elm disease.

**Microbe.** Any minute living thing; a microorganism, especially a disease-causing bacterium.

**Microbiology.** The scientific study of microrganisms (*e.g.* bacteria, viruses, and fungi). Originally this was directed towards their effects (*e.g.* in causing disease and decay), but during the 20th century the emphasis has shifted to their physiology and biochemistry. Microbes are now recognized as important vehicles for the study of biochemical processes common to all living organisms, and their rapid growth enables their laboratory culture in large numbers for studies in genetics.

**Microbiostasis.** A condition in which microorganisms, although alive or viable, do not multiply.

**Microbody.** A small organelle in the cytoplasm, about 0.5 $\mu$m in diameter and surrounded by a single membrane. Microbodies contain oxidative enzymes.

**Microbiota.** The microscopic fauna and flora of a region or locality.

**Microcercous.** Having a minute tail, said of cercaria.

**Microclimate.** The climate immediately about an organism in its microhabitat.

**Micrococcaceae.** Family of bacteria in which the cells are Gram-positive and spherical, and occur in regular or irregular groups. They may be motile or non-motile. Resting stages are unknown. They are chemo-organotrophic. There are several genera, found in a wide range of habitats—in soil, in aquatic environments, on the bodies of animals (including humans), etc.

**Microconjugant.** The smaller of two conjugating protozoans.

**Microcyst.** One of the numerous ranging cells in the fruiting body of a myxobacter.

**Microdissection** (micromanipulation). A technique used for the dissection of living cells under the high power of an optical microscope. It utilizes minute mechanically manipulated instruments, such a needles, scalpels, and pipettes. For example, the instruments may be used to remove a single nucleus from one cell and to implant it an another.

**Micro evolution.** Evolutionary change within species, which results from the differential survival of the constituent individuals in response to natural selection. The genetic variability on which selection operates arises from mutation and sexual reshuffling of gene combinations in each generation.

**Microfauna.** The microscopic animals present in a particular habitat.

**Microfibril.** A ribbon-like structure about 10—45 nm in width and visible only under the electron microscope. Microfibrils form the basic structural units of the cell wall. Each microfibril is formed from many long-chain cellulose molecules lying approximately parallel to each other. Hydrogen bonds between hydrogen and oxygen atoms in adjacent chains bind them together. The intermolecular spaces and the interfibrillar spaces are partly occupied by structural substances, *e.g.* pectic compounds and hemicellulose. As a result of imbibitional and capillary effects, these spaces are also filled with water so that the cell wall is normally heavily hydrated. In primary walls (cell wall) water may account for up to 70% of the volume. In secondary walls, more efficient packing of the microfibrils leaves less room for water between them.

**Microfilariae.** The minute larvae of parasitic nematodes of the order Filarioidea found in the bloodstream or tissues.

**Microflora.** Small plants, such as certain algae and fungi, found in a given area, *e.g.* on a leaf surface.

**Microfossil.** A fossil that is so small that it can only studied under a microscope. Microfossils include bacteria, diatoms, and Protozoa and parts of organisms, such as plant pollen and skeletal fragments. Microfossils are important in the correlation of rocks where only small samples are available. The study of microfossils, particularly pollen, is known as palynology.

**Microgamete.** In a heterogamous organism, the smaller of the two types of gametes, usually the male gamete.

**Microgametocyte.** A cell which gives rise to a microgamete

**Microgametophyte.** *bot.* A male gametophyte; the plant which develops from a microspore and produces microgametes.

**Microglia.** Neuroglial cells of the central nervous system of mesodermal origin. They are ameboid and capable of phagocytic activity.

**Micrograph.** A photograph of a specimen taken through a microscope. Photomicrographs and electron micrographs are produced using light microscopes and electron microscopes respectively.

**Microhabitat.** The local conditions which immediately surround an organism.

**Microincineration.** The subjection of a glass slide bearing a thin slice of tissue to a high temperature resulting in combustion of all organic materials. The remaining ash gives information as to quantity and distribution of minerals before incineration.

**Micromanipulation.** Microdissection.

**Micromanipulator.** A micropositioner, an apparatus by which microtools (needles, pipettes, electrodes, etc.) can be moved about with extreme precision.

**Micromere.** One of the smaller blastomeres in an egg undergoing unequal cleavage.

**Micrometazoa.** Microscopic multicellular animals.

**Microniscus.** A larval stage of an isopen of the suborder Epicaridea parasitic upon copepods.

**Micronucleus.** A small nucleus, especially the smaller of two nuclei present in certain protozoans, as Paramecium. It functions in the processes of reproduction and rejuvenation. Compare macronucleus.

**Micronutrient.** A nutrient required by organisms in relatively small quantities. Micronutrients are typically found in cofactors and coenzymes. They include vitamins and trace elements (essential element). Compare macronutrient.

**Micro-organism.** Literally, a microscopic organism. Usually taken to include only those organisms studied in microbiology—*i.e.* bacteria, fungi, microscopic algae, protozoa, viruses—and thus excluding other microscopic organisms such as eelworms and rotifers.

**Microphyll.** A type of foliage leaf seen in certain pteridophytes (*e.g.* Selaginella, Lycopodium) that has a single unbranched midrib. Such leaves are generally no more than a few millimetres long. Compare megaphyll.

**Microphyllous.** Having small leaves (microphylls).

**Micropterous.** Possessing small wings.

**Micropyle** (adj. micropylar)

1. Canal in the coverings of the nucellus, through which the pollen tube passes during fertilization. Later, when the seed matures and starts to germinate, it serves as a minute pore through which water enters.
2. Pore in the egg membrane of an insect oocyte, which allows sperm to enter and fertilize the egg.

**Microseptum.** An incomplete septum in an anthozoan.

**Microsere.** A successional series in a microhabitat.

**Microsome.** Small, membrane-bound vesicle formed from the endoplasmic reticulum in large numbers following the homogenization of cells. Microsomes may or may not bear ribosomes, depending upon the type of endoplasmic reticulum from which they are derived.

**Microspheric.** Designating a foraminiferan in which the first chamber of the shell is small.

**Microsporangiophore.** A stalklike structure bearing microsporangia.

**Microsporangium.** A sporangium which produces micro- or meiospores.

**Microspore.** The smaller of the two types of spore formed after meiosis in heterosporous species and usually designated male. In seed plants it is the pollen grain.

**Microspore Mother Cell.** A cell that gives rise by meiosis to four haploid cells that develop into microspores. Unlike the tetrad formed by meiosis of the megaspore mother cell, all four cells usually develop into microspores. Pollen mother cells are examples of microspore mother cells.

**Microsporophyll.** A modified leaf which bears microsporangia, as *a*. the scalelike leaves of the carpellate cone of a gymnosperm; *b*. the stamen of a flower.

**Microsurgery.** Micrurgy or surgery on extremely small organisms or individual cells, usually performed under a microscope or by means of a micromanipulator; includes microdissection, microinjection, microisolation, and various other procedures.

**Microtome.** A machine used to cut thin sections (3-5 $\mu$m thick) of plant or animal tissue for microscopical observation. There are various designs of microtome, each basically consisting of a steel knife, a block for supporting the specimen, and a device for moving the specimen towards the knife. The specimen is usually supported by being embedded in wax; if a freezing microtome is used, the specimen is frozen. An ultra-microtome is used to cut much thinner sections (20-100 nm thick) for electron microscopy. The biological material is embedded in plastic or resin, sectioned with a glass or diamond knife, and the cut sections are allowed to float on the surface of water in an adjacent water bath.

**Microtubule** Tubular structure, 15-25 nm in diameter, of indefinite length, and composed of subunits of the protein tubulin. It occurs in large numbers in all eukaryotic cells, either freely in the cytoplasm, or as a structural component of organelles (*e.g.* centrioles, cilia, and flagella). Microtubules appear to function in the motility of cells, the maintenance of cell shape, and the transport of materials within cells. In addition, they form part of the structure of the mitotic spindle (responsible for the movement of chromosomes during cell division), and have been implicated in sensory transduction in some receptor cells.

**Microtubule Organizing Centre** (MTOC). A general term for kinetosomes, centrioles, and other structures involved in the formation and organization of microtu ules or their derivatives.

**Microvilli.** Extremely minute cylindrical processes which form the striated border of columnar epithelium or brush border of cuboidal epithelium.

**Microvillus.** Small, finger-like projection. Microvilli are found in large numbers on the free surfaces of many cells. They serve to increase the surface area of a cell and are a particular feature of those with an absorptive function, *e.g.* the epithelial cells of the intestine, and renal tubules.

**Microzoa.** Microscopic multicellular animal.

**Micrurgy.** Microsurgery.

**Mictic.** Of or pertaining to the haploid egg of rotifers which, if fertilized, forms a thick-shelled, dormant egg which after a time hatches into a female; if not fertilized, it develops parthen-ogenetically into a male.

**Micturition.** Urination or the act of passing urine; voiding.

**Midbrain** (mesencephalon). One of the three sections of the brain of a vertebrate embryo. Unlike the forebrain and the hindbrain, the midbrain does not undergo further subdivision to form additional zones.

In mammals it becomes part of the brain-stem but in amphibians, reptiles, and birds the roof of the midbrain becomes enlarged as the tectum, a dominant centre for integration, and may include a pair of optic lobes.

**Middle Ear.** In tetrapods, except for Urodela, Apoda, and snakes, the central chamber of the ear, derived from a gill pouch, lying between the tympanic membrane and the inner ear, linked to the pharynx by the eustachian canal, and containing the ear ossicles. In most mammals it is encased in the bulla.

**Midgut**

1. The middle section of the alimentary canal of vertebrates, which is concerned with digestion and absorption. It comprises most of the small intestine.

2. The middle section of the alimentary canal of arthropods.

**Middle Lamella.** A thin layer of material, consisting mainly of pectins, that binds together the walls of adjacent plant cells.

**Midge.** One of a number of small, dipterous insects, as *a.* chironomids of the family Chironomidae whose aquatic larvae are called bloodworms; *b.* biting midges, blood-sucking insects of the family Ceratopogonidae, commonly called punkies or no-see-ums; *c.* phantom midges of the family Culicidae; *d.* gall midges or gnats of the family Cecidomyiidae, some of which form galls, others live as inquilines in galls produced by other insects.

**Midget.** A dwarf or undersized human; an adult who has not attained full growth.

**Midgut**

1. The midintestine or mesenteron, the middle portion of the digestive tract in a vertebrate embryo.

2. In arthropods, the portion of the digestive tract between stomach and intestine.

**Midrib**

1. The vein running down the middle of a leaf from the petiole or leaf base to the leaf tip, often dividing the leaf into similar halves or mirror images.

2. Any thickened region of cells running down the centre of a thallus or lamina, such as the midrib of wracks (Fucus).

**Midriff**

1. The diaphragm.
2. The upper portion of the abdomen.

**M[illegible]**

1. Movement of individuals or their propagules (seeds, spores, larvae, etc.) from one area to another. Three cases may be distinguished : (a) emigration, which is outward only; (b) immigration, which is inward only; (c) migration, which in this stricter sense implies periodic two-way movements to and from a given area and usually along well-defined routes. Such migratory movement is triggered by seasonal or other periodic factors (*e.g.* changing day-length), and occurs in many animal groups.

2. In plant succession, specifically the arrival of migrating propagules (migrules) at a newly denuded area.

**Migration Route.** Link between two biogeographical regions that permits the interchange of plants and/or animals. Various types are recognized in the literature : for example, G. G. Simpson's (1940) 'corridors', 'filters', and 'sweepstakes routes' are widely referred to in connection with mammalian, and more recently reptilian, migrations.

**Migratory.** Having a tendency to migrate; migrating periodically.

**Mildew**

1. A white, powdery growth which appears on plants or organic matter produced by phycomycete fungi.

2. A fungus which causes mildew to develop. Downy mildew, powdery mildew.

3. A plant disease caused by a fungus whose mycelial growth forms a white coating on infected parts.

**Milk.** The fluid secreted by the mammary glands of mammals. It provides a balanced and highly nutritious food for offspring. Cows' milk comprises about 87% water, 3.6% lipids (triglycerides, phospholipids, cholesterol, etc.), 3.3% protein (largely case-in), 4.7% lactose (milk sugar), and, in much smaller amounts, vitamins (especially vitamin A and many B vitamins) and minerals (notably calcium, phosphorus, sodium, potassium, magnesium, and chlorine). Composition varies among species; human milk contains less protein and more lactose.

**Milk Snake.** A harmless snake (Lampropeltis doliata), so called because of the erroneous belief that they milk cows; also celled king snake.

**Milk Sugar.** Lactose.

**Milk Teeth.** The temporary or deciduous teeth of a mammal; baby teeth.

**Milky Disease.** A bacterial disease of insects caused by Bacillus popilliae, used in the control of grubs of the Japanese beetle.

**Millipedes.** Myriapoda.

**Millet.** One of a number of small-grained, rapidly-growing grasses, especially Panicum miliaceum, grown extensively for hay and forage. It seed is also used extensively for human, poultry, and bird feed.

**Millon's Test.** A technique used to demonstrate the presence of the amino acid tyrosine. Million's A, a mixture of sulphuric acid and mercury (II) sulphate is added to the test solution. A yellow colour indicates the presence of protein. A drop of Millon's B, a sodium nitrite solution, is then added. A red colour indicates a positive reaction.

**Millipede.** Any arthropod of the class Diplopoda which includes the thousand-legged worms, terrestrial animals with many segments each bearing two pairs of appendages, as Julus terrestris.

**Milt**

1. The testes of fishes or the seminal fluid produced by them.
2. Breeding males of fishes, as milt salmon.

**Mimesis.** Mimicry.

**Mimetic.** Mimicking, imitating.

**Mimic**

1. An organism which imitates or mimics.
2. A bird of the family Mimidae which mimics the songs of other birds, as a mockingbird.

**Mimicry.** The resemblance of one animal to another, which has evolved as a means of protection. In one form of mimicry the markings of certain harmless insects closely resemble the waring coloration of another insect (the model). Predators that have learnt to avoid the model will also avoid good mimics of it. This phenomenon is often found among butterflies. A second form of mimicry involves, the mutual resemblance of a group of animals, all harmful, such as the wasp, bee, and hornet, so that a predator, having experienced one, will subsequently avoid them, all.

**Mine.** To form a burrow or excavate a tunnel.

**Mineral.** An inorganic compoud, usually a solid, having a definite chemical composiation and usually formed as a result of inorganic processes. When in crystalline form, each has a characteristic molecular structure. Water and mercury are minerals which are liquid at ordinary temperatures.

**Mineralocorticoid.** One of a group of adrenal cortical hormones which regulate salt and water balance, a 11-deoxycorticosterone.

**Mineral Salts.** Inorganic constituents of the body which, upon combustion, yield ash, as salts, of sodium, calcium, and potassium.

**Minimum.** The least, smallest, or lowest in strength, effectiveness, or intensity.

**Mink.** A weasellike, fur-bearing mammal (Mustela vison) of the family Mustelidae.

**Minnow** A small fish, especially any of the small, freshwater fishes of the carp family, Cyprinidae.

**Minor.** Lesser or smaller; of little consequence or importance.

**Mint** Any plant of the mint family, Labiatae, especially those of the genus Mentha, as peppermint.

**Miocene Epoch.** An epoch of the Tertiary period preceding the Pliocene and following the Oligocene.

**Miosis.** Meiosis.

**Miracidium.** The first larval stage of a fluke, a ciliated, free-swimming form which, upon hatching from the egg, enters a snail or bivalve in which it transforms into a sporocyst.

**Mirror**

1. A glass or polished surface which reflects light.
2. A tense, shining membrane in the sound-producing apparatus of a cicada.
3. A resonating structure in the stridulatory apparatus of a male cricket.
4. A speculum.

**Miscarriage.** Expulsion of the fetus before the age of viability.

**Miscegenation.** The mixing of races, especially the intermarriage of individuals of white and colored races.

**Miscible.** Capable of being mixed or dissolved.

**Mite.** Any of a large number of arachnids of the order Acarina, including free-living and parasitic forms, as the itch mite, follicle mite, harvest mite.

**Mitochondrion.** Oval, or occasionally round or thread-shaped, organelle, whose length averages 2$\mu$m, and that occurs in large numbers in the cytoplasm of eukaryotic cells. It is a double membrane-bound structure in which the inner membrane is thrown into folds (the cristae) that penetrate the inner matrix to varying depths. It is a semi-autonomous organelle containing its own DNA and ribosomes, and reproducing by binary fission. It is the major site of ATP production and thus of oxygen consumption in cells, and houses the enzymes involved in the citric acid cycle and in oxidative phosphorylation.

**Mitosporangium.** A sporangium which produces spores by mitosis. Spores may be haploid or diploid.

**Mitospore.** A spore produced by mitosis.

**Mitosis.** Normal process of nuclear division (occuring at cell division) by which two daughter muclei are produced, each identical to the parent nucleus. Before mitosis begins each chromosome replicates; these daughter chromosomes then separate during mitosis so that one duplicate goes into each daughter nucleus. The result is two daughter nuclei, each with an identical complement of chromosomes and hence of genes. Mitosis is generally divided into four phases : prophase, metaphase, anaphase, and telophase. During prophase, chromosomes become visible within the nucleus because they shorten, thicken, and coil up as a spiral. Each chromosome is longitudinally double except in the region of the centromere, and each single strand of the chromosome is called a chromatid. The nucleolus and nuclear membrane disappear. In metaphase the chromosomes move within the spindle connecting the two centrosomes (formed by division of the centriole into two at the start of prophase, and the subsequent moving apart of these two daughter centrioles).

**Mitosis.** The division of a cell to form two daughter cells each having a nucleus containing the same number and kind of

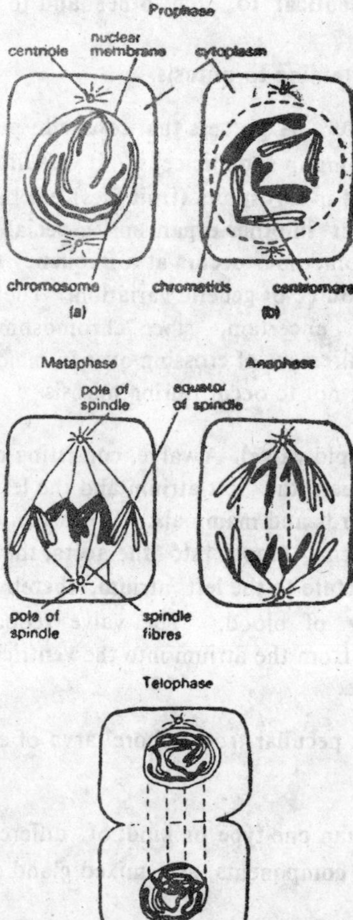


The stages of mitosis in a cell containing two pairs of homologous chromosomes

chromosome as the mother cell. The changes during divisions are clearly visible with a light microscope. Each chromosome divides lengthwise into two chromatids, which separate and form the chromosomes of the resulting daughter nuclei. The process is divided into four stages, prophase, metaphase, anaphase, and telophase, which merge into each other (illustration). Mitotic divisions ensure that all the cells of an individual are genetically identical to each other and to the original fertilized egg.

**Mitotic**. Of or pertaining to mitosis.

**Mitotic Crossing Over**. A process that results in genetic recombination occuring in somatic cells. It was first discovered as a rare event in Drosphila (fruit flies) but has since been found to occur in other organisms, especially fungi. In the latter, it sometimes occurs at a frequency that suggests it is a major source of genetic variation. The mechanisms involved are uncertain, since chromosomal pairing (a supposed requirement of crossing over in meiosis) is normally believed not to occur during mitosis.

**Mitral Valve** (biscuspid valve). A valve, consisting of two flaps, situated between the left atrium and the left ventricle of the heart of birds and mammals. When the left ventricle contracts, forcing blood into the aorta, the mitral valve closes the aperture to the left atrium, thereby preventing any backflow of blood. The valve reopens to allow blood to flow from the atrium into the ventricle. Compare tricuspid valve.

**Mitraria Larva**. A peculiar trochophore larva of certain polychaetes.

**Mixed**. Of more than one type or kind; of different or dissimilar parts or components, as a mixed gland or a mixed bud.

**Mixed Lactic Fermentation** (heterolactic fermentation). A from of anaerobic respiration found in certain microorganisms, *e.g.* Lactobacillus brevis, in which the end products are a molecule each of lactic acid, ethanol, and carbon dioxide.

**Mixonephridium.** A combined nephridium and coelomoduct.

**Mixotrophic.** Nourished by more than one method, with reference to nutrition in protozoans.

**Mode.** The class of observations that occurs most frequently, for example the number 3 in the series 9, 3, 3, 1. Compare mean, median.

**Model.** In mimicry, the organism or the structure mimicked.

**Modern Synthesis** (neo-Darwinism). Darwin showed that evolution involves selection interacting with variation within populations, but he did not know that the bases of this variation are discrete units of heredity, or genes. This was discovered by Mendel. The fusion of Mendelian genetics and Darwin's natural selection is referred to as the modern synthesis. A further synthesis has been achieved in recent years with the incorporation of knowledge of evolution at the molecular level.

**Modifier.** A modifying gene.

**Modifying Gene.** A gene which influences the expression of another nonallelic gene, as that which affects the degree and extent of spotting.

**Modiolus.** The central axis or pillar of the cochlea of the ear.

**Molar**

1. A molar tooth.
2. Of or pertaining to molar teeth.
3. *chem.* Pertaining to or expressed is gram-molecules.

**Molasses.** A thick, viscid syrup obtained from sugar in the process of refining.

**Mold**

1. A slimy, cottony, or filamentous growth which develops on moist organic material as the result of a growth of saprophytic fungi.
2. Any mold-producing Fungus, as a black mold, blue-green mold.

**[1]Mole.** *zool.* A small, burrowing, insectivorous mammal of the family Talpidae, as Scalopus aquaticus, the common North American mole.

**[2]Mole**

1. *med.* A small growth on the skin, usually pigmented and sometimes hairy.
2. A benign tumor of the uterus which develops from a fetus or fetal membranes following cessation of growth or degeneration.

**Molecular Biology.** Thy study of the structure and function of large molecules associated with living organisms, in particular proteins and the nucleic acids DNA and RNA.

**Molecular Evolution.** Substitution of one amino acid for another in protein synthesis as a result of mutation of the genetic code. According to the neutral-mutation theory of molecular evolution, the variability at the molecular level which results from mutation is caused by random drift of the mutant genes rather than by selection.

**Mollusc.** A mollusk.

**Mollusca.** A phylum of soft-bodied invertebrates characterized by an unsegmented body differentiated into a head, a ventral muscular foot used in locomotion, and a dorsal visceral hump covered by a fold of skin—the mantle—which secretes a protective shell in many species. Respiration is by means of gills or a lunglike organ and the feeding organ is a radula. Molluscs occur in marine, freshwater, and terrestrial habitats and there are six classes, including the Gastropoda (snails, slugs, etc.), Lamellibranchia (bivavles), and Cephalopoda (squids and octopuses).

**Mollusk.** Any invertebrate of the phylum Mollusca, unsegmented animals with a body consisting of a ventral foot and a dorsal visceral mass. Most possess a mantle which secretes a calcareous shell. Common representatives are chitons, tooth shells, snails, slugs, mussels, clams, oysters, squids, octopuses, and nautili.

**Molly.** A small, freshwater fish of the genus Mollienisia, commonly kept in aquaria.

**Molt.** To shed and develop anew the outer covering of the body, as the cuticle, exoskeleton, skin, hair, or feather.

**Molt Cycle.** A cycle in crustaceans which includes four periods; premolt, molt, postmolt, and intermolt.

**Molting.** The act or process of shedding the outer covering of the body or a part of it : Ecdysis.

**Molting Gland.** The prothoracic gland of insects and the Y-organ of crustaceans, both of which secrete hormones which control molting.

**Molting Hormone.** A hormone, MH, which promotes growth and differentiation to the adult stage, produced by the prothoracic glands of insects. Also called growth and differentiation hormone : Ecdysone.

**Molybdenum.** Symbol : Mo. A metal element, atomic number 42, atomic weight 95.94, needed (under certain conditions) in trace amounts for plant growth. It is involved in nitrate reduction being a part of the flavoprotein enzyme nitrate reductase. Plants absorbing nitrogen as ammonium ions do not need molybdenum. The nitrogenase system involved in nitrogen fixation also requires molybdenum since one of the two proteins forming the nitrogenase complex is a molybdenum-iron-sulphur protein.

**Monad.** A simple, one-called organism, especially a flagellate of the genus Monas.

**Monadelphous.** *bot.* With stamens united to form a single tube or column. Compare didelphous.

**Monandrous.** Having one stamen.

**Monanthus.** Having a single flower.

**Monarch**

1. *bot.* Having a single protoxylem.
2. *zool.* The milkweed butterfly (Danaus plexippus), a migratory butterfly of the family Danaidae. It is mimicked by the viceroy butterfly.

**Monaxon.** A single, needlelike spicule of sponges.

**Monera.** In some systems of classification, the kingdom that includes the bacteria, blue-green algae, and other microorganisms with prokaryotic cells.

**Moneran.** Any organism of the Monera, a major taxon which includes the bacteria and blue-green algae, characterized by the absence of true nuclei and chromosomes.

**Monoculture.** The growing over a large area of a single crop species (*e g.* Triticum aestivum bread wheat), or of a single variety of a particular species. Monocultures are especially vulnerable to pest and disease infestation, but uniformity of height, development, etc., in a crop facilitates management, especially harvesting. The economic and ecological wisdom of monoculture is widely debated.

**Monogoose.** One of several species of ferretlike, carnivorous mammals of the family Viverridae distributed throughout Asia and Africa Most belong to the genus Herpestes; their food, snakes and rodents.

**Mongrel.** An individual resulting from the interbreeding of two different strains or races; a hybrid; an animal of unknown ancestry.

**Moniliales.** A group of imperfect fungi comprising the Blastomycetes and Hyphomycetes.

**Moniliform.** Constricted at intervais, resembling a string of beads.

**Monitor.** A large lizard of the genus Varanus found in Southeast Asia, Africa, and Australia some reaching a length of eight feet.

**Monkey**

1. In a general sense, any mammal of the order Primates except the lemurs, tarsiers, and man.
2. More specifically, one of the smaller, long-tailed primates as distinguished from the apes, as the macaques, langurs, marmosets.

**Monocarpic.** Bearing fruit once and then dying.

**Monocarpous.** Having a single carpel.

**Monocephalous.** Bearing a single head or capitulum, said of flowers.

**Monochasium** (monochasial cyme). A cymose inflorescence in which only one axillary bud develops into a lateral branch at each node. Laterals may arise on alternate sides of the stem (a scorpioid monochasium) or may arise on one side only (a helicoid monochasium), which gives an asymmetrical appearance to the inflorescence. Compare dichasium.

**Monoclinous.** Hermaphroditic; having stamens and pistil in one flower.

**Monoclonal Antibody.** A specific antibody produced by one of numerous identical cells derived from a single parent cell. (The population of these cells comprises a clone and each cell is said to be monoclonal). The parent cell is obtained by the fusion of a normal antibody-producing cell (a lymphocyte) with a cell derived from a malignant tumour of lymphoid tissue of a mouse. This hybrid cell then multiplies rapidly and yields large amounts of antibody. Monoclonal antibodies are used to identify a particular antigen within a mixture and can therefore be used for identifying blood groups; they also enable the production of highly specific, and therefore effective, vaccines.

**Monocolpate.** Describing a pollen grain having one colpus, as is commonly found in most petaloid monocotyledon species.

**Monocot.** A monocotyledon.

**Monocotyledon.** Any plant of the Monocotyledoneae, a class of the Angiospermae which includes vascular plants characterized by an embryo with a single cotyledon, flower parts usually in threes or sixes, not in fives; leaves with parallel veins, and a stem with scattered vascular bundles. Comprises over 75,000 described species, as the grasses, palms, arums, lilies, irises, and orchids.

**Monocotyledonae.** One of the two classes or subclasses of plants within the Angiospermae, distinguished by having one seed leaf (cotyledon) within the seed. The monocotyledons generally have parallel leaf veins, scattered vascular bundles within the stems, and flower parts in threes or multiples of three. Monocotyledon species include some crop plants (*e.g.* cereals, onions, fodder grasses), ornamentals (*e.g.* tulips, orchids, lilies), and a very limited number of trees (*e.g.* the palms). Compare Dicotyledonae.

**Monocular**

1. Having a single eye.
2. In optics, having a single ocular or eyepiece.

**Monocyclic.** Arranged in one whorl or circle, said of floral parts.

**Monocyte.** A large, agranular leukocyte with a large, oval or slightly indented nucleus.

**Monodactylous.** Having a single digit or claw.

**Monodont.** Having a single tooth, as the narwhal.

**Monodynamous.** Having one stamen longer than the others.

**Monoecious.** Applied to an organism in which separate male and female organs occur on the same individual: for example to a plant which bears male and female reproductive organs in the same flower, or separate male and female flowers on the same plant; or to a hermaphrodite animal.

**Monocyte.** The largest form of white blood cell (leucocyte) in vertebrates. It has a kidney-shaped nucleus and is actively phagocytic, ingesting bacteria and cell debris.

**Monogamous.** Having only one mate.

**Monogamy.** Mating of a male with a female involving no extra individuals of either sex. Usually the bond operates through the breeding season and in some cases it may extend through the adult life of the two individuals. Examples may be found amongst several bird species, such as mute swan, sparrowhawk, and great tit.

**Monogenetic**

1. Of or pertaining to direct development in which there is no alternation of generations.
2. Of or pertaining to flukes of the subclass Monogenea.

**Monogolism.** Down's syndrome.

**Monogonoporous.** Having a single opening for both male and female sex cells.

**Monogynous**

1. *bot.* Having a single pistil.

2. *zool.* Mating with one female only.

**Monohybrid.** The offspring of a cross between parents that differ in the alleles they possess for one particular gene, one parent having two dominant alleles and the other two reccssives. All the offspring have one dominant and one recassive allele for that gene (*i e.* they are hybrid at that one locus). Crossing between these offspring yields a characteristic 3 : 1 (monohybrid) ratio in the following generation of dominant; recessive phenotypes.

**Monokaryotic.** Having a single haploid nucleus, with reference to the hyphae of certain fungi.

**Monolete.** Describing a spore that has a simple linear scar marking the point at which it was joined in the tetrad. The microspores of members of the Isoetales are monolete which sets them apart from other lycopsids. However their megaspores are trilete.

**Monolocular.** Unilocular or one-called, with reference to the ovaries of flowers.

**Monomerous.** Designating flowers with only one member in each whorl.

**Monomorphic.** Having only one form. Compare dimorphic, polymorphic.

**Mononucleotide.** Nucleotide.

**Monopetalous.** Having a single petal : Gamopetalous.

**Monophagous.** Subsisting on a single type of food, with special reference to insects.

**Monophyletic.** Applied to a group of species that share a common ancestry, being derived from a single interbreeding (or Mendelian) population, as opposed to a polyphyletic group, which is derived from many such populations. If the members of a given taxon are descended from a common ancestor they are said to be 'monophyletic', *e.g.* the families within a class would be monophyletic if they were all descended from the same family or lower taxonomic unit. Under the strictest definition they would all have to be descended from a single species.

**Monophyllous.** Possessing or composed of a single leaf.

**Monophyodont.** Describing a type of dentition that consists of a single set of teeth that last for the entire lifespan of an animal. Compare diphyodont; polyphyodont..

**Monopodium.** The primary axis of growth in such plants as pine trees. It consists of a single main stem that continues to grow from the tip and gives rise to lateral branches. Compare sympodium.

**Monoplanetic.** Describing fungi that produce only one type of zoospore (planospore). Compare diplanetic.

**Monoploid.** Haploid.

**Monopodial.** Having a single main axis of growth from which lateral branches arise. Compare sympodial.

**Monopodial Branching.** A type of growth exhibited by many plants in which secondary shoots or branches arise behind the growing point but remain subsidiary to the main stem, which continues to grow indefinitely. The largest secondary shoots are furthest from the apex of the main stem and the size of the shoots decreases regularly towards the top of the plant. This results in the pyramidal form of growth typical of many conifers, *e.g.* the spruce (Picea). The secondary shoots also tend to show the same pattern of branching along their length. Compare sympodial branching.

**Monorchid.** Having a single testis.

**Monosaccharide** (simple sugar). A carbohydrate that cannot be split into smaller units by the action of dilute acids.

Monosaccharides are classified according to the number of carbon atoms they possess : trioses have three carbon atoms; tetroses, four; pentoses, five; hexoses, six; etc. Each of these is further divided into aldoses and ketoses, depending on whether the molecule contains an aldehyde group (–CHO) or a ketone group (—CO—). For example glucose, having six carbon atoms and an aldehyde group, is an aldohexose whereas fructose is a ketohexose. These aldehyde and ketone groups confer reducing properties on monosaccharides; they can be oxidized to yield sugar acids. They also react with phosphoric acid to produce phosphate esters (*e.g.* in ATP), which are important in cell metabolism. Monosaccharides can exist as either straight-chain or ring-shaped molecules. They also exhibit optical activity.

**Monosepalous.** Having one sepal.

**Monosomic.** An organism deficient in one chromosome from an otherwise diploid set, *i.e.*, $2n-1$. Monosomy typically arises by fertilization occurring between a normal gamete ($n$), and one deficient in the said chromosome ($n-1$). Monosomics are more common in polyploids where the deleterious consequences of missing a chromosome can be masked by chromosomes in other genomes.

**Monospermous.** Producing only one seed.

**Monospermy.** Fertilization of an egg by only one sperm.

**Monospondyly.** The condition in which a vertebra possesses a single centrum, as in amniotes. Compare diplospondyly.

**Monosporangium.** A vegetative cell that produces a single spore, as in certain red algae.

**Monospore.** A spore formed by certain red algae of the Bangioideae as a means of asexual reproduction.

**Monostichous**

1. *bot.* Arranged along one side of an axis.

2. *zool.* Arranged in a single row.

**Monostachous.** Having a single spike.

**[1]Monostome.** A fluke with a single sucker.

**[2]Monostome.** Possessing a single sucker.

**Monostylous.** Having a single style.

**Monotocous.** Producing one young at birth.

**Monotreme.** An egg-laying mammal of the order Monotremata, as the duckbill platypus and the spiny anteater.

**Monotrichous.** Describing a bacterium that has a single polar flagellum. Compare lophotrichous, peritrichous.

**Monotrophic.** Monophagous.

**Monotypic.** Describing any taxon that includes only one subordinate taxon. Thus a family with just one genus or a genus with a single species, are examples of monotypic taxa. An extreme case of monotypy occurs in the classification of the maidenhair tree, Ginkgo biloba. This species is the sole representative of the genus Ginkgo, the family Ginkgoaceae, and the order Ginkgoales—each being monotypic taxa.

**Monoxenous.** Having a single species as a host, said of parasites.

**Monozoic.** Lacking segmentation, with reference to tapeworms.

**Monozygotic.** Derived from a single fertilized ovum or zygote, as identical twins.

**Mons.** *anat.* An eminence, as the mons pubis, an elevated area over the pubic symphysis covered with pubic hair; in the female, sometimes designated mons veneris.

**Monster**

1. A huge living thing.

2. *embryol.* A fetus which, as a result of maldevelopment differs markedly from the normal, usually having a grotesque appearance and with reduced viability. A double monster is one consisting of conjoined twins.

**[1]Montane.** Pertaining to the fauna and flora of the mountains.

**[2]Montane.** In mountainous regions, a zone extending downward from the timberline, a vertical distance of about 1500 feet.

**Moor.** A region of land that is found in wet exposed conditions where the soil water can seep laterally very slowly but is not stagnant as in bogs. It has an acid peaty soil and common plant species found there include mat grass (Nardus stricta) and purple moor-grass (Molinia caerulea). The top soil loses water in summer but the subsoil is permanently waterlogged. The peat layer is rarely more than 30 cm deep and most of the plants have their roots in the mineral soil horizon.

**Morass.** A swamp or marsh.

**Morel.** An edible ascomycete fungus (Morchella esculenta).

**Morphactin.** Any of a group of synthetic compounds, all derivatives of fluorene-carboxylic acid, that affect many aspects of plant growth and differentiation. Morphactins have little effect on mature tissuas but in seedlings and growing shoots apical dominance is removed and internode elongation inhibited, giving a dwarfed bushy appearance. Expansion of the leaf lamina is also prevented and flowers, if produced, may be deformed. Seeds from morphactintreated plants may contain abnormal embryos. Morphactins applied to seeds slow down germination and inhibit lateral root formation from the radicle. In legumes, root nodule formation is prevented. Other diverse effects of morphactions include the inhibition of phototropism and geotropism, the induction of parthenocapy, and an alteration in sex expression in dioecious plants.

Morphactin is thought to induce dwarfism by affecting the orientation of the spindle in dividing cells. It also disrupts the formation of a middle lamella between daughter cells. Although morphactins superficially resemble gibberellins is structure their effects are not thought to be brought about by interaction with gibberellin or any of the other natural growth substances.

Morphactins may be used commercially to slow growth of, for example, mixed plant populations at roadsides.

**Morphallaxis.** Regeneration of a structure through the remodeling or transformation of parts of the parent, with only limited production of new tissue.

**Morphine.** An alkaloid present in opium. It is an analgesic and narcotic, used medically for the relief of severe pain.

**Morphogenesis.** The development of specific organs and structures which result in an organism having its characteristic size, from, and structure.

**Morphology.** The study of the form and structure of organisms, especially their external form. Compare anatomy.

**Mortality.** The death of individuals of a population, especially death in large numbers.

**Mortality Rate.** The death rate, especially the specific-cause-of-death rate, the number of deaths from a certain cause in a unit of population in a certain time unit, as the number of deaths from typhoid fever per 100,000 per annum.

**Morula.** *embryol* A solid mass of cells resulting from cleavage of the zygote preceding the formation of the blastula.

**Mosaic**

1. An irregular pattern of small light and dark green areas on the foliage of a plant. Infection with a virus is the usual cause. Examples include tobacco mosaic and cucumber mosaic.
2. A leaf mosaic.

**Mosaic Development.** Determinate development in which the fate of the blastomeres is determined at an early stage, destruction of a single blastomere resulting in a defective embryo. Compare regulative development.

**Mosaic Disease.** Any of a number of virus-caused plant diseases characterized by irregularly distributed light and dark spots on the leaves, as tobacco mosaic.

**Mosaic Evolution.** Differential rates of development of various adaptive attributes within the same evolutionary lineage. For example, a particular taxon might show greatly different rates of change with respect to the head, body, and limbs. This is a common phenomenon and makes the reconstruction of transitional fossil types very difficult.

**Mosaic Image.** An apposition image or that formed from the functioning of the numerous ommatidia of a compound eye.

**Mosasaur.** A carnivorous, marine lizard of the Cretaceous period.

**Mosquito.** One of several species of small dipterous, blood-sucking insects of the family Culicidae. Important genera are Cluex, the house mosquito; Anopheles, malaria mosquito; Aedes, yellow-fever mosquito.

**Moss**

1. A small, leafy, nonvascular land plant of the class Musci, division Bryophyta, with sex organs borne at

the tip of the gametophyte plant, as Polytrichum, the hairy-cap moss.

2. A clump or mass of these plants.
3. Any of a number of plants which resemble moss in appearance, as club moss, Irish moss, reindeer moss, Spanish moss.

**Moss Animal.** An ectoproct.

**Mossbunker.** The menhadden.

**Moth** A lepidopterous insect of the suborder Frenatae. Most are nocturnal insects with a siphoning proboscis, blunt abdomen, antennae not clubbed, and wings held together when in flight. Their larvae (caterpillars) are often serious pests, as those of the codling moth, clothes moth, gypsy moth.

**[1]Mother**

1. The female parent, especially of a human.
2. The source from which something arises or is formed.
3. Designating a cell from which other cells arise, as a spore mothercell.

**[2]Mother.** A thick, gelatinous or slimy membrane which forms on the surface of a liquid undergoing fermentation, as mother-of-vinegar.

**Mother Cell.** A cell that divides other differentiated cells and hencesses, its identity, for example, the cell that gives rise to a sieve element and companion cell.

**Moths.** Lepidoptera.

**Motile.** Capable of spontaneous movement; exhibiting motility.

**Motility.** Having the ability to move or to change position spontaneously.

**Motivation.** The internal conditions responsible for temporary reversible changes in the responsiveness of an animal to external stimulation. Thus an animal that has been deprived of food will accept less palatable food than one that has not been deprived : the difference is attributed to a change in feeding motivation. Changes in responsiveness due to maturation, learning, or injury are not usually readily reversible and are therefore not considered to be due to changes in motivation. Early attempts to describe motivation in terms of a numbe of separate 'drives' (*e.g.* food drive, sex drive) have not found general favour, partly because 'drives' interact with one another; for example, water deprivation often affects an animal's willingness to feed.

**Motoneuron.** A motor neuron.

**Motor.** *physiol.* Of or pertaining to muscles or muscular activity.

**Motor Area.** An area in the cerebral cortex from which impulses initiating voluntary movement arise.

**Motor Cells.** *bot.* Large, thin-walled cells in the upper epidermis of the leaves of grasses and other plants which, when turgid, keep the leaf blade flat, but in dry weather, on loosing their turgidity, cause the leaf margins to turn inward.

**Motor End Plate.** The termination of the axon of a motor neuron in a striated muscle fiber; myoneural junction, neuromuscular junction.

**Motor Nerve.** A nerve composed entirely of the axons of motor neurons.

**Motor Neurone.** A neurone that transmits nerve impulses from the central nervous system to an effector organ (such as a muscle or gland) and thereby initiates a physiological response (*e.g.* muscle contraction).

**Mould.** A fungus that produces a distinct mycelium or spore mass, which often resembles a velvet-like pad, on the surface of its host. Moulds frequently occur on dead or decaying vegetable matter, such as food or stored fruits. Common examples are white bread mould (Mucor) and blue and green moulds of citrus fruit (Penicillium italicum and P. digitatum).

**Moult.** Molt.

**Moulting.** Periodic, often seasonal, shedding of hair or feathers by animals. In birds, it is the process by which feathers are periodically renewed, at least once a year, sometimes twice or (rarely) three times. Feather shedding is usually a gradual process and does not affect flight or other functions but Anatidae lose their flight feathers simultaneously, becoming temporarily flightless. The usual sequence of moult begins with the loss of primaries, followed by secondaries, tail feathers, and then body feathers.

**Mounting.** The final stage in the preparation of permanent slides for microscopical examination. The mount, which may be a section, wholemount, squash, or smear, is immersed in a mounting medium, usually a liquid that later solidifies. The medium permeates entirely through the specimen, leaves no air spaces, and does not support the growth of bacteria and fungi. Examples are glycerol, Canada balsam, and osmium tetroxide.

**Mouse pl. Mice**

1. Any of a large number of species of small rodents of the family Muridae, as the house mouse (Mus-musculus).
2. Any of a number of mouselike mammals of other families.
3. One of a number of animals which superficially resembles a mouse, as a mousefish, sea mouse.

**Mouth**

1. The opening through which food is ingested.
2. In vertebrates, the first portion of the alimentary canal in which food is masticated; the oral or buccal cavity.
3. In a restricted sense the opening between the lips.
4. In general, the opening or orifice of any tube, canal, or cavity.

**Mouthparts.** Modified paired appendages on the head segments of arthropods, used for feeding. A typical insect has a labium (lower lip), one pair each of mandibles and maxillae, and a labrum (upper lip), although in many the mouthparts are modified to form piercing stylets or a sucking proboscis. Crustaceans, centipedes, and millipedes have one pair of mandibles and two pairs of maxillae used for cutting and holding the food. Crustaceans also have several pairs of maxillipedes.

**Movement.** Motion or any activity which results in change of shape, form, place, or position. Various types include ameboid Brownian, ciliary, cytoplasmic.

**MTOC.** Microtubule Organizing Centre.

**Mucigenic Bodies.** Organelles in ciliates which produce a mucoid material utilized in the formation of cysts and protective coverings.

**Mucilage.** Any substance that swells in water to form a slimy solution. Mucilages are usually concerned with water retention; for example, the pentosan mucilages produced in the interior of succulent xerophytes serve to increase the water-holding capacity of the cells and hence reduce the transpiration rate. Many seeds have a mucilaginous coating that aids water uptake during germination.

Structurally, mucilages are very complex : linseed mucilage is a mixture of a complex polyuronide, proteinaceous matter, and cellulose. Mild hydrolysis of the polyuronide yields xylose and galactose residues and a more resistant fraction consisting of galacturonic acid and rhamnose residues.

**Mucilage Canal.** An elongated cell in certain brown algae and cycads which conducts mucilaginuos substances.

**Mucilage Cell.** A cell which secretes mucilage, as the cells in the gemmae of certain bryophytes.

**Mucilaginous.** Of the nature of or pertaining to mucilage; slimy; sticky.

**Mucin.** A glycoprotein or a mixture of glycoproteins secreted by mucous cells or glands which is responsible for the high viscosity of mucus.

[1]**Mucoid.** Resembling mucus.

[2]**Mucoid.** One of a group of glycoproteins resembling mucin present in connective tissue, egg white, and other substances.

**Mucor** (family Mucoraceae). Genus of fungi in which colourless, branched or unbranched sporangiophores arise from the substrate mycelium and bear at their tips spherical sporangia containing many spores. Zygospores are brown to black with warty surfaces. Species are common on soil, dung, fruit, vegetables, etc. and distribution is cosmopolitan. They may cause spoilage of bread, fruit, and other foods.

**Mucoraceae** (order Mucorales). Family of fungi in which the sporangia typically are all alike : spherical or pear-shaped, columellate, thin-walled, and containing numerous spores. There are 20 genera, with many species, most of which are saprotrophic in soil, dung, organic debris, etc. Some can parasitize plants and some can cause disease in animals and humans.

**Mucorales.** An order of the Zygomycetes containing about 360 species (55 general) of mostly saprobic fungi, many of which cause spoilage of stored food. Its members generally form a dense mycelium from which arise sporangiophores or conidiophores. The tips of these may become pigmented, hence the common name 'pin mould' for Mucor mucedo. In the coprophilous fungus Pilobolus a specialized mechanism has developed to disperse the sporangia. Zygospores are formed by sexual reproduction and many species show heterothallism.

**Mucous Cell.** Any cell which secretes mucin, as a goblet cell of the intestine or the mucous cells of mixed glands.

**Mucous Membrane.** A layer of tissue comprising an epithelium supported on connective tissue. Within the epithelium are special goblet cells, which secrete mucus onto the surface, and the epithelium often bears cilia. Mucous membranes line body cavities communicating with the exterior, including the alimentary and respiratory tracts. Compare serous membrane.

**Mucron.** An anchoring device possessed by certain acephaline gregarines.

**Mucronate.** Having a small fine point (a mucro) arising abruptly, usually at the tip.

**Mucus.** The slimy substance secreted by goblet cells onto the surface of a mucous membrance to protect and lubricate it and to trap bacteria, dust particles, etc. Mucus consists of water, the glycoprotein mucin, cells, and salts.

**Mulch.** Organic material, such as peat, leaf mould, or shredded bark, that is spread on the ground to suppress annual weeds. It is also applied around the base of trees and shrubs to help absorb and retain water and add nutrients.

**Mule**

1. The hybrid and usually sterile offspring of a cross between a male ass or jack and a mare, noted for its strength, endurance, and stubbornness.
2. Any sterile hybrid.

**Mull.** Humus.

**Mullerian Duct.** One of a pair of ducts present in the embryos of vertebrates which gives rise to the uterine tubes, uterus, and a portion of the vagina.

**Mullerian Mimicry.** The similarity in appearance of one species of animal to that of another, where both are distasteful to predators. Both gain from having the same warning coloration, since predators learn to avoid both species after tasting either one or the other. The phenomenon is named after H.J. Muller who described it in relation to insects in S. America. Compare Batesian mimicry.

**Muller's Larva.** The free-swimming larva of certain polyclad turbellarian worms, with eight ciliated arms or lobes directed posteriorly.

**Multicellular.** Describing tissues, organs, or organisms that are composed of a number of cells. Compare unicellular.

**Multi factorial Inheritance.** The determination of a particular characteristic, *e.g.* height or skin colour, by many genes, each having a small effect individually. Characteristics controlled in this way show continuous variation.

**Multifid.** Divided into many lobes or divisions.

**Multifoliate.** Having many leaves.

**Multilocular**

1. Containing many cells or compartments.
2. Containing many cysts, as a hydatid cyst; polycystic.

**Multipartite.** Divided into many parts.

**Multiple**

1. Consisting of or involving more than one.
2. Having several or many units or parts.
3. Affecting many parts simultaneously.

**Multiple Alleles.** A series of alleles of a particular gene. In theory probably all genes can exist in more than two alternative forms since mutations can occur at any number of points along their length. In practice, natural selection may eliminate all but one or two of these in wild populations. Examples of naturally occurring multiple allelism are found in the incompatibility systems of plants. For example, in Brussels sprouts (Brassica oleracea var. bullata) there are some 35–40 different incompatibility alleles, termed S alleles.

**Multiple-factor Inheritance.** The determination of an inherited characteristic by polygenes, so that it shows approximately continuous variation from one extreme to another. The size of beans, ear-length in maize, and many other characteristics show multiple-factor inheritance, and do not, at first sight, behave like Mendelian characters. Compare single-factor inheritance.

**Multiple Fruit** (composite fruit). A fleshy fruit that incorporates a complete inflorescence and is thus derived from the ovaries of many flowers. It may also incorporate other floral parts and the receptacles. The coenocarpium, sorosis, and syconus are multiple fruits.

**Multiple Genes.** A condition in which two or more sets of genes produce more or less equal and cumulative effects on the same character. Such genes are primarily involved in the inheritance of quantitative characters as weight, size, yield, etc.

**Multivalent.** An association of three or more homologous chromosomes observed during meiosis in polyploid or polysomic organisms.

**Multivoltine.** Having more than two broods or generations a year.

**Mummified.** Dried, shrunken, withered; converted into a mummy.

**Mummy**

1. *zool.* The embalmed, preserved body of a human or other animal.
2. *bot.* A dried, shrunken fruit, as that resulting from fungus infections, as brown rot.

**Mural.** Of, pertaining to, or resembling a wall.

**Mural Plates.** Those forming the carina and rostrum of a sessile barnacle.

**Murex.** A carnivorus, marine snail of the genus Murex.

**Muricate** .Having a surface covered by sharp points or prickles or hard short projections.

**Muriculate.** Finely muricate.

**Murine**

1. Of or pertaining to the family Muridae.
2. Of, pertaining to, or resembling a mouse or rat.

**Muscarian.** Having a putrid odor which attracts flies, with reference to flowers.

**Muscarine.** A poisonous alkaloid present in certain mushrooms, as Amanita muscaria.

**Musci.** A class of plants within the Bryophyta comprising the mosses, which are found in both damp (including fresh-water) and drier situations. Mosses-possess erect or prostrate leafy stems, which give rise to leaf less stalks bearing capsules. Spores formed in the capsules are released and grow to produce new plants. A common moss is Funaria.

**Muscle**

1. A spectalized organ or tissue whose special function is contraction by means of which change of shape or movements of parts is accomplished.
2. A specific contractile structure, as the biceps muscle of the arm or an adductor muscle of a bivalve.
3. A contractile layer or structure, as the circular muscle of an earthworm or a sphincter muscle.

**Muscle Sense.** The kinesthetic or proprioceptive sense; the perception of movement or position of parts of the body.

**Muscle Tissue.** A specialized type of contractile tissue composed of elongated cells or fibers. In vertebrates, there are three types: striated (striped, voluntary, skeletal), smooth (non-striated, involuntary, visceral), and cardiac.

**Muscular**

1. Of, pertaining to, or composed of muscles or muscle tissue.
2. Due to or resulting from the activity of muscles.

**Muscularis.** A layer of muscle in the wall of a visceral organ, as the intestine.

**Musculature.** The muscles of the body or a portion of it.

**Musculocutaneous.** Pertaining to the muscles and the skin, with special reference to nerves and blood vessels which supply both structures.

**Mushroom.** The usually umbrella-like fruiting body or sporophore of fungi, in the Agaricales. It is a pseudoparenchymatous structure composed of numerous fused hyphae, and is differentiated into a stalk or stipe and a circular cap, the pileus. In immature mushrooms these structures are united by a membrane, the universal veil, but this breaks as the stalk elongates leaving a cuplike structure, the volva, around the base of the stalk. In some mushrooms the edge of the cap is united with the stalk by a second membrane, the partial veil. This ruptures to expose the underside of the cap leaving a ring, the annulus, towards the top of the stem. The lower side of the cap is composed either of gills or pores, which are lined by the hymenium tn which the basidiospores are produced. Mushroom is often used in a wide sense to mean any macroscopic fungal fruiting body. The term toadstool is essentially synonymous with mushroom in both the narrow and broad senses, but is more often used of inedible species.

**Musk**

1. An odiferous substance obtained from the musk sac or gland of the male musk deer; used in the manufacture of perfumes.
2. A substance secreted by the musk glands of a number of animals, as turtles and crocodiles.

**Musk Bag.** A sac containing musk located under the skin of the abdomen of the male musk deer.

**Muskeg.** A beat bog characteristic of the northern coniferous forest of North America. Plants commonly found are pitcher plants, sundews, and black spruce (Picea mariana), which thrives in the moist conditions.

**Musk Gland.** A musk-secreting gland, as *a.* that of certain mammals, especially the musk deer; *b.* that of various reptiles, as the musk turtle and alligator.

**Must.** The expressed juice of grapes or other fruits before fermentation occurs. For red wines, it contains the skins and seeds.

**Musk Hog.** The collared peccary.

**Mustard**

1. A powder prepared from the ground seeds of the mustard plant used as a condiment; in paste form it is used medicinally in poultices.
2. A plant (Brassica) of the mustard family, Cruciferae.

**Musth.** In sexually mature male elephants, a physiological and behavioural condition associated with sexual activity It lasts 2-3 months, during which testosterone levels are high; the temporal glands become enlarged and temporin secretion becomes copious; urine is discharged continally, and behaviour becomes more aggressive. Musth occurs annually or biennially, but at any time of year rather than within a particular season. Its occurrence is not synchronized among groups of males.

**Mutable.** Capable of mutation; having the capacity of undergoing change.

**Mutagen.** An agent that causes an increase in then umber of mutants (mutation) in a population. Mutagens operate either by causing changes in the DNA of the genes, so interfering with the coding system, or by causing chromosome damage. Various chemicals (*e.g.* colchicine) and forms of radiation (*e.g.* X-rays) have been identified as mutagens.

**Mutagenic.** Capable of causing or inducing a mutation.

**Mutant.** An organism or a gene which has undergone mutation.

**Mutation**

1. Process by which a gene or chromosome set undergoes a structural change.
2. Gene or chromosome set that has undergone a structural change. The majority of mutations are changes within individual genes (*e.g.* the substitution

of a different nucleotide at some point in the DNA so that the amino-acid sequence is altered), but some are gross structural changes of chromosomes (for example inversion or translocation) or changes in the number of chromosomes per nucleus (*e.g.* polyploidy). Mutations are the raw material for evolution : they provide the source of all variation. For mutations to affect subsequent generations, though, they must occur in gametes or in cells destined to be gametes, since only then will they be inherited. A mutation that occurs in a body-cell is called a 'somatic mutation' : it is transmitted to all cells derived, by mitosis, from that cell. Most mutations, however, are deleterious; evolution progresses through the few that are favourable. Some mutations are recurrent—the occur repeatedly within a population, or over long periods of time (as does haemophilia, for example).

**Mutation Rate.** Number of mutation events per gene per unit of time (*e.g.* per cell generation). The term is also applied to the frequency with which mutation events occur in a given species or to the frequency with which a specified mutation event or mutational class occurs in a given population. Normally mutations occur at a constant, very low, rate : this rate can be greatly increased by irradiation with X-rays, gamma rays, neutrons, etc., or by treatment with carcinogens.

**Muton.** A unit of mutation; the smallest portion of a chromosome or gene which, by mutation, can give rise to a new trait.

**Mutualism.** Interaction of species populations that benefits both populations. Strictly, the term may be confined to obligatory mutualism, in which neither species can survive under natural conditions without the other. Sometimes the term is used more generally to include facultative mutualism (protocooperation).

**Mutation Theory**. The theory, first proposed by Hugo de Vries in 1903, that suggests that new forms of organisms (mutations) arise suddenly in a population, and that evolution proceeds by natural selection operating on these. The theory was based on de Vries' observations of the relatively frequent occurrence of markedly different forms of Oenothera erythrosepala (evening primrose). (It was later demonstrated that the different forms were triploids or tetraploids and hence gave an exaggerated idea of the rate and effects of mutations). The theory was first validated experimentally when it was found that x-ray induced heritable mutations occurred in Drosophila. It is now recognized that although new allelic forms can only arise by mutation much of the variation on which natural selection acts is generated by crossing over and recombination during meiosis.

**Muzzle**

1. The projecting portion of the head of an animal, especially the mouth, jaws, and nose as the muzzle of a cow.
2. A restraining device covering the jaws to prevent them from being opened.

**Mycelioid**. Resembling a mycelium; having the structure of a mold, said of bacterial colonies.

**Mycelium**. A network of hyphae that forms the body of a fungus. It consists of feeding hyphae together with reproductive hyphae which produce sporangia and gametangia.

**Mycetangium**. A tube- or baglike structure which functions in fungus storage and transmission, as in the ambrosia beetle.

**Mycetocyte.** A hypertrophied cell in the gut of insects which houses symbiotic fungi.

**Mycetome.** A structure in larval or adult insects which houses symbionts.

**Mycetozoan**

1. A myxomycete or slime mold.
2. Any member of the Mycetozoa (Mycetozoida), regarded by some as an order of the phylum Protozoa.

**Mycobiont.** The fungal partner in a lichen, which is usually an ascomycete fungus, especially one of the class Discomycetes. Compare phycobiont.

**Mycobionta.** Eumycota.

**Mycocecidium.** A gall caused by a fungus.

**Mycoid.** Funguslike.

**Mycology.** The division of botany which deals with fungi.

**Mycoplasmatales** (pleuropneumonialike organisms, PPLO). An order containing extremely small parasitic microorganisms some of which are only 108 nm in diameter. Mycoplasmas are gram-negative, mostly nonmotile, and lack a rigid cell wall. Most species require sterols for growth. They are thought to be responsible for certain yellows diseases of plants and have been implicated in witches broom of alfalfa and maize stunt. They cause various serious diseases in animals, *e.g.* pleuropneumonia, bovine mastitis, and puerperal septicaemia.

**Mycorrhiza.** A symbiotic association between a fungus and the roots of a plant.

**Mycosis.** A pathological condition resulting from infection by a fungus, as tinea capitis, ringworm of the scalp.

**Mycostatic.** Inhibiting the growth of molds.

**Mycotrophic.** Describing a symbiotic association between a fungus and the whole of a plant. Such an association occurs when a mycorrhizal fungus extends into the aerial parts of a plant, as in certain heathers and orchids.

**Myelencephalon.** The caudal portion of the hindbrain from which the medulla oblongata develops.

**Myelin.** A complex mixture of lipids present in the myelin sheath of nerve fibers.

**Myelinated.** Possessing a myelin sheath; medullated.

**Myelin Sheath** (medullary sheath). The layer of fatty material that surrounds and electrically insulates the axons of most vertebrate and some invertebrate neurones. The myelin sheath enables a more rapid transmission of nerve impulses (at speeds up to 120 m $s^{-1}$), It consists of layers of membrane derived from Schwann cells. The sheath is interrupted at intervals along the axon by nodes of Ranvier; myelinated sections of axon are called internodes.

**Myelocyte.** A cell in red bone marrow which gives rise to a granular leukocyte.

**Myeloid.** Of or pertaining to bone marrow; marrowlike.

**Myeloid Elements.** Blood cells (erythrocytes and granular leukocytes) formed in red bone marrow.

**Myeloid Tissue.** Tissue within red bone marrow that produces the blood cells. It is found around the blood vessels and contains various cells that are precursors of the blood cells.

**Myelon.** The spinal cord.

**Myenteric.** Of or pertaining to the muscle layers of the intestine.

**Myiasis.** Infestation by maggots or the larvae of flies, as by screwworms, wool maggots, bots, or warbles. The larvae may localize in the skin (cutaneous myiasis) or invade cavities or passageways.

**Myna** also **Mynah** or **Mina.** A starlinglike bird (Gracula religiosa) the talking myna or Indian grackle, commonly caged and taught to talk.

**Myoblast.** A cell which develops into a muscle cell or fiber.

**Myocardium.** The muscular layer of the heart located between the outer epicardium and the inner endocardium.

**Myochordotonal Organ.** A sensory receptor on the walking legs of decapod crustaceans.

**Myocoel.** The cavity within a myotome.

**Myocomma.** A myoseptum.

**Myocyte**

1. A contractile cell, especially one in sponges.
2. A muscle cell.

**Myoepithelial Cell.** A cell of ectodermal origin which possesses contractile processses, present in the secreting portions and ducts of various glands. Also called basal or basket cell.

**Myofibril.** A minute, contractile element in the cytoplasm of a contractile cell, as a muscle cell.

**Myofilament.** A minute element of a myofibril.

**Myogenic.** Originating within muscle.

**Myoglobin.** Haemoprotein consisting of a single polypeptide chain surrounding a haem group that is capable of reversibly binding oxygen. It has a higher affinity for oxygen than has haemoglobin and releases it only when the oxygen supply becomes limiting. Myoglobin is found in the muscles of vertebrates and certain invertebrates, where it serves to store oxygen.

**Myology.** The study of muscles.

**Myomere**

1. A V-shaped muscle segment in the body wall of lancelets and fishes.
2. A myotome.

**Myometrium.** In mammals, the muscular layer of the uterus.

**Myoneme.** A contractile fibril present in certain ciliates and in the epithelial-muscular cells of coelenterates.

**Myoneural Junction.** A motor end plate.

**Myopia.** Short-sightedness. It results from the lens of the eye refracting the parallel rays of light entering it to a focus in front of the retina generally because of an abnormally long eyeball. The condition is corrected by using diverging spectacle lenses to move the image back to the retina.

**Myoseptum.** A sheet of connective tissue between two myotomes.

**Myosin.** A protein of high molecular weight present in striated muscle tissue.

**Myosotis** (forget-me-not; family Boraginaceae). Genus of hairy herbs with simple, alternate leaves, and curved (scorpioid) cymes of small flowers each with a five-lobed calyx. The five-lobed, wheel-shaped corolla may be pink at first, then blue. Forget-me-nots are much cultivated for their flowers. There are some 405 species, occurring in temperate regions.

**Myotome**

1. *embryol.* The portion of a somite which gives rise to striated or skeletal muscles.
2. A myomere.

**Myriapod**

1. An arthropod with an elongated, segmented body each segment bearing one or two pairs of jointed legs, as a centipede, millipede, pauropod, or symphylan.
2. Any member of the Myriapoda, formerly a class of the Arthropoda which included the centipedes and millipedes.

**Myriapoda**. A group of terrestrial arthropods generally found in damp conditions, comprising centipedes (class Chilopoda), millipedes (class Diplopoda), pauropods (class Pauropoda), and symphylids (class Symphyla). Myriapods characteristically possess a distinct head with a single pair of antennae and a wormlike body with numerous similar segments, each bearing one or two pairs of legs. Young myriapods may hatch with fewer segments than the adult, gaining more with each successive moult. Centipedes are fast-moving predators with 15-177 body segments, relatively long antennae, and the first pair of appendages specialized as poison fangs; the remaining segments each bear a single pair of legs. Millipedes are slow moving and feed on decaying leaves are antennae are short and the body consists of 20 to over 60 segments, each bearing two pairs of legs.

**Myriapodous**. Having many pairs of legs.

**Myrmecochory**. The distribution of seeds or other reproductive structures by ants. For example, the seeds of Helleborus species are distributed by ants, which are attracted to the plant by an oil-containing swelling on the raphe.

**Myrmecophagous**. Feeding upon ants.

**Myrmecophile**. An ant guest; an organism, especially an insect which regularly inhabits an ant's nest.

**Myrmecophilous.** Ant-loving, with reference to plants which are regularly inhabited by or pollinated by ants.

**Myrmecophily.** The condition when an organism (a myrmecophile) lives with a colony of ants. It is often seen in the animal kingdom but some flowering plants have specialized inflated organs in which to house ant colonies. For example, various tropical American Acacia species have specialized thorns, which provide shelter for the ants, and extrafloral nectaries, which provide food. The ants in turn control insect pests that would otherwise feed on the Acacia leaves. Similarly epiphytes belonging to the genera Myrmecodia and Hydnophytum in the Rubiaceae have large swellings on their roots, which house ants in a network of cavities.

**Myrrh.** A gum resin occurring in two forms : *a.* nerabol myrrh, from Commiphora myrrha, a shrub of the Middle East, used for medicinal purposes; *b.* bisabol myrrh, from C. erythraea, common in Arabia, used in perfumes, incense, and embalming fluids.

**Mysis Larva.** A schizopod larva of various crustaceans, so called because of its resemblance to the adult crustacean, Mysis.

**Myxamoeba.** A swarm cell that has lost its flagella. Myxamoebae may increase by division before acting as gametes.

**Myxedema.** A pathological condition resulting from inadequate secretion of the thyroid hormone.

**Myxobacter.** A bacterium of the order Myxobacteriales which comprise the slime bacteria.

**Myxobacteriales** (slime bacteria). An order containing flexible creeping bacteria that lack a rigid cell wall and flagella, and move by gliding across the substrate. Most of its members are terrestrial. Myxobacters differ from other bacteria in producing resting cells, termed microcysts, that are often borne in fruiting bodies. Many are soil saprophytes, some species (*e.g.* of Cytophaga and Sporocytophaga) producing cellulase enzymes.

**Myxobionta.** Myxomycota.

**Myxoid.** Of the nature of or resembling mucus.

**Myxoma.** A tumor of connective tissue consisting of stellate cells embedded in a matrix of mucoid material.

**Myxomycetes** (slime moulds). A class of the Myxomycota containing fungus-like organisms that consist of a naked mass of protoplasm termed a plasmodium. They number about 500 species divided among some 70 genera and are usually found growing on decaying vegetation. The various forms encountered in the life cycle (swarm cell, myxamoeba, plasmodium) show certain animal-like characteristics, notably the ingestion of solid particles of food, and this has led some authorities to place them in the animal kingdom as Mycetozoa.

In some classifications the Myxomycetes contains the orders Acrasiales and Plasmodiophorales but these are now usually elevated to class status as the Acrasiomycetes and Plasmodiophoromycetes.

**Myxomycota** (Myxobionta). A division of the Fungi containing those species that have amoeboid, plasmodial, or pseudoplasmodial thalli. It contains some 475 species in about 90 genera and is divided into the four classes Acrasiomycetes, Hydromyxomycetes, Myxomycetes, and Plasmodiophoromycetes.

**Myxophyceae.** The older and hence, strictly, the correct name for the blue-green algae. It is not however in such common use as Cyanophyta.

**Myxosporidian.** A sporozoan of the order Myxosporidia which includes a number of parasites of fishes, amphibians, reptiles, and some invertebrates.

**Myxovirus.** One of a group of RNA-containing viruses associated with various diseases of man and other vertebrates. Orthomyxoviruses produce diseases of the respiratory tract, *e.g.*, influenza; paramyxoviruses include the causal agents of mumps, measles, and fowl pest.

**Myzostome.** An invertebrate of the taxon Myzostomida generally regarded as an order of polychaete annelids, members of which live as commensals or parasites in echinoderms, especially crinoids, as Myzostoma.

# N

**Nacreous**. Composed of mother-of-pearl.

**NAD** (nicotinamide adenine dinucleotide, coenzyme I). A pyridine-based nucleotide that functions as a coenzyme in many oxidation—reduction reactions, according to the general reaction : $NAD^+ +$ reduced substrate$\rightleftharpoons NADH +$ $H^+ +$ oxidized substrate. An example of such a reaction is the oxidation of citrate to α-ketoglutarate in the TCA cycle.

Reduced NAD can act as a reducing agent or it may be reoxidized in the respiratory chain with coupled ATP formation. NAD is not usually tightly bound to the enzyme with which it is acting, but instead acts as a second substrate, binding only during the reaction and being released into the medium with the reaction products.

**NAD**. is sometimes called DPN, an abbreviation for the trivial name diphosphopyridine nucleotide.

**NADP** nicotinamide adenine dinucleotide phosphate, coenzyme II). A pyridinebased nucleotide that functions as a coenzyme to several different oxidoreductases. NADP usually acts as an electron donor in enzymatic reduction reactions; in this it differs from its counterpart NAD, which acts principally as an electron acceptor in biological oxidations. NADP is sometimes called TPN, an abbreviation for its trivial name triphosphpyridine nucleotide.

**Nagana**. An infectious disease of horses and cattle in East Africa caused by Trypanosoma brucei transmitted by the tsetse fly.

**Naiad**. An aquatic, gill-bearing nymph of an insect.

**Nail**

1. A flattened, horny, epidermal structure on the tips of the digits of primates.
2. A horny structure or scale on the upper mandible (maxilla) of ducks, geese, and swans.

**Naked**

1. Nude, bare, uncovered.
2. *zool.* Lacking hair, feathers, or a shell.
3. *bot. a.* Lacking pubescence, said of leaves. *b.* Lacking enveloping structures, as a naked bud.

**Namaycush**. A large lake trout (Cristivomer namaycush) of North America.

**Name**. *biol.* The term applied to an individual or the group to which it belongs.

**Nanander**. *bot.* A dwarf male.

**Nannandry**. The existence in a species of male individuals that are considerably smaller than the females. For examples, within the moss genus Homaliadelphus there is a species in which the male gametophyte is sufficiently small to grow as an epiphyte upon the leaves of the female gametophyte. The dawrf male filaments of certain members of the Oedogoniales are further examples. Species in which the male plants are of normal size are termed macrandrous.

**Nanandrous**. Produced on dwarf-sized filaments, as antheridia of algae.

**Nanism**. Abnormal smallness; dwarfism.

**Nannoplankton**. Microplankton; organisms in plankton less than 40 microns in length or diameter.

**Nape**. The back part of the neck.

**Naphthalene Acetic Acid (NAA).** A synthetic auxin that has proved of great use in stimulating the rooting of cuttings and promoting flowering.

**Napiform.** Turnip-shaped.

**NAR.** Abbreviation of net assimilation rate.

**Narcosis.** A state of stupor or unconsciousnes induced by a drug.

**Narcotic.** Any drug that induces stupor and relieves pain, especially morphine and other opiates. Such narcotics are addictive and cause dependence, and their medical use is strictly controlled.

**Narcotize**

1. To subject to the influence of a narcotic.
2. In microtechnique, to render immobile or, incapable of contracting preparatory to examination, fixing, or preserving.

**Nares** sing. **Naris.** The openings of the nasal cavity.

**Nares** (nostrils). The paired openings of the nasal cavity in vertebrates. All vertebrates have external nears, which open to the exterior; in some species these are situated on a nose. Internal nares (or choanae) are present only in air-breathing vertebrates (including lungfish) and open into the mouth cavity. In mammals they open posteriorly, beyond the secondary palate.

**Narwhal.** A cetacean of northern waters (Monodon monoceros), males possessing a single, long, twisted tusk projecting forward from the upper jaw.

[1]**Nasal.** Of or pertaining to the nose or nasal cavity.

[2]**Nasal.** The nasal bone.

**Nasal Cavity.** The cavity in the head of a vertebrate that is lined by a membrane rich is sensitive olfactory receptors (olfaction). It is connected to the exterior by external nostrils and (in air-breathing vertebrates) to the respiratory system by internal nares.

**Nasanov's Gland.** Pheromone-producing gland in the abdomen of a worker honeybee (Apis species). It opens at the base of the last tergite via a partially eversible membrane, and is functional only in bees of foraging age (10 days old). During emission, the bee adopts a characteristic stance, with abdomen raised, gland exposed, and the wings beating to waft away a plume of scent. The gland secretes a mixture of scents (geraniol, nerolic and geranic acids, and citral) whieh have several functions according to the context in which they are released. Thus in combination with 'queen substance' the Nasanov's gland scents recruit additional workers to a settled swarm; in the presence of disorientated bees the scent attracts them back to the hive. The scents are also emitted by foragers at a food source that does not have a characteristic scent of its own, and additional workers are recruited. Thus the Nasanov's gland scents may augment information conveyed by the round dance and waggle dance. The scents are also used to recruit workers to sources of water.

**Nascent** Being formed or coming into existence.

**Nastic Movements.** Movements of plant organs in response to external stimuli that are independent of the direction of the stimuli. Examples are the opening of scrocus and tulip flowers in response to a rise in temperature (thermonasty), the opening of evening primrose flowers at night (photonasty), and the folding up and drooping of leaves of the sensitive plant (Mimosa pudica) when lightly touched (seismonasty). Compare tropism.

**Nasties** Paratonic or stimulus movements in plants.

**[1]Nasute**

1. Having a large, prominent nose.

2. *entomol.* With a large beaklike snout.

[2]**Nasute.** A soldier in a termite colony, with an elongated snout from which a sticky secretion is exuded which repels invaders.

**Natal.** Of or pertaining to birth.

**Natatory.** Of, pertaining to, or adapted for swimming.

**Nates.** The buttocks.

[1]**Native**

1. Occurring in a region at the time of its discovery : Indigenous.

2. Occurring or produced naturally, as a native protein; not denatured.

[2]**Native.** A plant or animal raised or produduced in a particular region.

**Natural.** Term that is applied to a community of plants and animals. 'Future-natural' describes the community that would develop were human influences to be removed completely and permanently, but allows for possible changes in climate or site. 'Original-natural' describes a community as it existed in the past, with no modification by humans. 'Past-natural' describes the condition in which the present features are derived directly from those existing originally, with relatively little modification by humans. 'Potential-natural' describes the community that would develop were human influence removed, but the consequent succession completed instantly—future changes in climate or site are not taken into account. 'Present-natural' describes the community that would exist now had there been no human modification. Because of the dynamic nature of any ecosystem,* this condition may not be identical to the last original-natural state before human intervention began.

**Natural Classification.** A classification of organisms in which there is a high level of predictivity, as opposed to artificial classifications, which tend to be very unpredictive. Most taxonomists strive towards the production of natural classifications, although their approaches and interpretations of the data may vary greatly. Natural classifications can best be achieved by exploring the fields of cytogenetics, microanatomy, and phytochemisty in addition to morphology, anatomy, and plant geography, thus broadening the base on which classifications are founded.

Many phylogenists believe that only those classifications based on monophyletic taxa are natural.

**Natural Group.** A group of organisms of any taxonomic rank that are believed to be descended from a common ancestor (monophyletic). For example, man and the apes are often regarded as a natural group, descended from fossil ancestors, the dryopithecines (or their near relatives). In an ideal natural classification all taxa should be natural groups.

**Natural History.** Formerly, the study of animals, plants, and minerals in a general and more or less unsystematized manner. Now, generally restricted to the general study of a limited group, as the natural history of mammals, in which various aspects of mammalian life, as the classification, ecology, geographic distribution, life cycles, and economic importance, are considered.

**Natural Immunity.** Immunity that has been inherited in contrast to one that has been acquired. If an individual acquires immunity by having the disease in question, as opposed to acquiring it as the result of vaccination, then that individual is said to have natural acquired immunity.

**Naturalist.** A student of or one versed in natural history.

**Naturalize.** To introduce and cause to grow in a region to which an organism is not native.

**Natural Order.** In the classification of plants, the former name for a family.

**Natural Selection.** The process that, according to Darwinism, brings about the evolution of new species of animals and plants. Darwin noted that the size of any population tends to remain constant despite the fact that more offspring are produced than are needed to maintain it. He also saw that variations existed between individuals of the population and concluded that disease, competition, and other forces acting on the population, eliminated those individuals less well adapted to their environment. The survivors would pass on any inheritable advantageous characteristics (*i.e.* characteristics with survival value) to their offspring and in time the composition of the population would change in adaptation to a changing environment. Over a long period of time this process could give rise to organisms so different from the original population that new species are formed.

**Nature**

1. The entire physical universe.
2. All the processes and activities which take place in or occur within the universe.
3. In a limited sense, the outdoors, especially the plants and animals which comprise the natural scenery.
4. The physical and physiological makeup of an organism, its mode of life, and its manner of responding to stimuli.

**Nature and Nurture.** Synonyms for heredity and environment as they affect a character. Both may affect observed variation amongst individuals; only variations due to 'nature' are inherited, and it is these that form the subject of quantitative genetics.

**Nauplius.** A free-swimming larva, the first stage in the development of certain crustaceans, as shrimps and prawns.

**Nauplius Eye.** Single median eye comprising three or four pigment cup ocelli, sometimes with a lens, probably enabling the organism to determine the direction of a source of light for orientation. The median eye is typical of crustacean nauplius larvae. It may degenerate as the larva develops, or it may persist into the adult form.

**Nauplius Larva.** The first, free-swimming, planktonic larva of most marine and some freshwater crustaceans. It has no evident segmentation. There is a single, median, 'nauplius' eye at the front of the head. There are only three pairs of appendages, the first and second antennae, and the mandibles. The second antennae and mandibles bear swimming setae. Additional trunks segments and appendages appear with successive moults, the increments proceeding from anterior to posterior. The late nauplius stages are often called metanauplii. The term 'postlarva' is applied to all immature crustaceans when the full complement of segments and appendages have developed. Some or all larval stages are absent in certain groups of Crustacea, and in others they may be considerably modified.

**Nautilus.** A cephalopod mollusk of the genus Nautilus.

**Navel.** The umbilicus.

**[1]Navicular.** Boat-shaped.

**[2]Navicular**

1. A tarsal bone.
2. The scaphoid bone of the wrist.

**Neanderthal Man.** A form of fossil man that appeared in Europe and Western Asia about 100 000 years ago. He was thought to be different species (Homo neanderthalensis) from modern man but is now generally regarded as a subspecies of H. sapiens. The fossil remains indicate that Neanderthals were fairly short and had low brows but that the brain size was the same as modern man's. They were nomadic hunters and are thought to have had a language. Cromagenon began to replace Neanderthal man about 35 000 years ago. The name is derived from the site in the Neander valley, West Germany, where fossils were found in 1856.

**Nearctic Realm.** A biogeographical realm which includes Greenland and all of North America from Mexico northward. Characteristic animals are the mountain goat, caribou, muskrat, raccoon, and pronghorned antelope.

**Near Point.** The nearest point at which the human eye can focus an object. As the lens becomes harder with age, the extent to which accommodation can bring a near object into focus decreases. Therefore with advancing age the near point recedes—a condition known as presbyopia.

**Neck.** The slender portion of the archegonium through which the male gamete has to travel to reach the female gamete prior to fertilization.

**Necrosis.** The death of a plant cell or group of cells while the rest of the plant is still alive, particularly when the dead tissue becomes dark in colour. Necrosis is a common symptom of fungus infection and the shape of necrotic areas is often characteristic of the particular disease.

**Nectar.** A sugary liquid produced in plants by nectaries, regions of secretory cells on the receptacle or other parts of a flower. It attracts pollinating insects or other animals.

**Nectar Guides.** Honey guides.

**Nectary.** A sugar secreting gland. Nectaries are usually present at the base of a flower, sometimes in a spur, to attract pollinators. Often scents are also secreted by the nectary as additional attractants. Nectaries may also be extrafloral, for example the gland spines of certain cacit. Here they may serve to attract seed dispersal agents, such as ants.

**Negative Staining.** A staining technique that trelies on the property of certain components of the specimen not to take up the dye or negative siain. Thesa then show up light against a dark background. For example, in light microscopy, bacteria can be made visible by mixing them with a dark dye such as nigrosin or Indian ink. The method is used widely in electron microscopy to study viruses and certain large molecules. The material is mixed with negative electron-dense stains, such as potassium molybdate or phosphotungstic acid (PTA). Any proteinaceous material present in the specimen does not take up the stain. In the resulting electron micrograph the electron-transparent proteinaceous material will appear dark against a light background.

**Nekton.** Pelagic organisms that actively swim through the water. Examples are fish, jellyfish, turtles, and whales. Compare plankton.

**Nematoblast.** Thread cell.

**Nematocyst.** In Cnidaria, a pear-shaped sac with a lid (operculum), the outer end of the sac being extended to form a long, hollow thread which is stored coiled within the sac, immersed in a fluid. On stimulation the thread is expelied, as a weapon or to capture or hold prey, depending on the type of nematocyst. Some nematocysts are barbed and some inject venom.

**Nematoda** (eelworms, roundworms, threadworms; phylum Aschelminthes). Class of aschelminth worms (a phylum in some classifications) which vary greatly in size, from about 1 mm to 5 cm. The cuticle has flanges, and may also have ridges or spines. Morphologically they are all similar, but they occur as parasites in plants and animals, and as free-living forms. They are first known from rocks of Carboniferous age.

**Neo-darwinism** (modern synthesis). The current theory of the process of evolution, formulated between about 1920 and

1950, that combines evidence from classical genetics with the Darwinian theory of evolution by natural selection (Darwinism). It makes use of modern knowledge of genes and chromosomes to explain the source of the genetic variation upon which selection works. This aspect was unexplained by traditional Darwinism.

**Neo-Lamarckism.** The Chevalier de Lamarck (Jean Baptiste Pierre Antoine de Monet, 1744—1829) believed that evolution proceeds because characteristics acquired in one generation are transmitted to the next. His original ideas are no longer accepted, but variants of them have continued to appear right up to the present. These newer versions are referred to as 'neo-Lamarckism'.

**Neolithic.** The New Stone Age, beginning in the Middle East approximately 9000 BC and lasting until 6000 BC, during which man first developed agriculture. Grinding and polishing of stone tools was also practised.

**Neoplasm.** Any new abnormal growth of cells, forming either a harmless (benign) tumour or a malignant one (cancer).

**Neoteny.** Slowing down of somatic development, so that sexual maturity is achieved while the organism still looks like a juvenile; this leads to paedomorphosis. Since the juvenile stages of many organisms are less specialized than the corresponding adult stages, such shifts allow the organisms concerned to switch to new evolutionary pathways. The word comes from the Greek neos (meaning 'youthful'). Neoteny is common among urodeles (class Amphibia).

**Neoteny.** The retention of the juvenile body form, or particular features of it, in a mature animal. For example, the axolotl, a salamander, retains the gills of the larva in the adult. Neoteny is thought to have been an important mechanism in the evolution of certain groups, such as man, who is believed to have developed from the juvenile form of apes.

**Nephrocyte.** A phagocytic cell present in arachnids, crustaceans, and insects.

**Nephroid.** Kidney-shaped : Reniform.

**Nephromixium.** A combined coelomoduct and nephridium functioning as an excretory organ and genital duct, as in certain polychaetes.

**Nephorn.** The excretory unit of the vertebrate kidney (illustration). Many constituents of the blood are filtered from the glomerulus into the Bowman's capsule at one end of the nephorn. The glomerular filtrate passes along the length of the nephorn and most of its water, plus some salts, glucose, and amino acids, are reabsorbed into the surrounding blood capillaries. The resulting concentrated

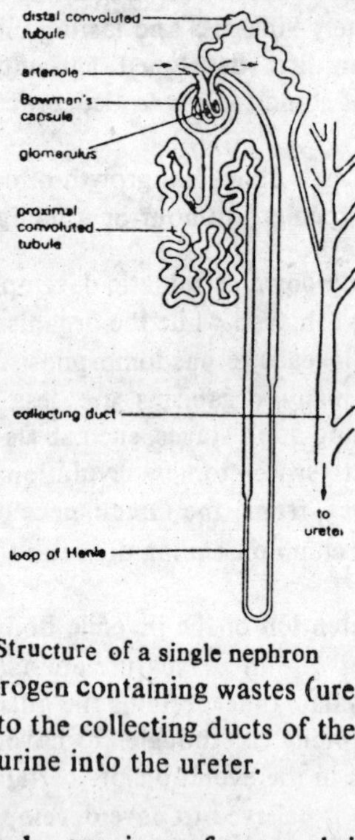


Structure of a single nephron

solution of nitrogen containing wastes (urea) plus inorganic salts passes into the collecting ducts of the nephrons and is discharged as urine into the ureter.

**Nephrostome**

1. The ciliated, opening of a nephridium into the coelom.

2. *embryol.* The opening of a pronephric tubule into the coelom.

**Nephrotome.** In vertebrate embroys, a narrow longitudinal band of mesoderm connecting a somite to the lateral mesoderm from which the urinary tubules develop; intermediate cell mass : Mesomere.

**Nepionic.** Postembryonic; infantile.

**Nereid.** A marine polychaete annelid of the family Nereidae, as Nereis.

**Neritic Zone.** The region of the sea over the continental shelf, which is less than 200 metres deep (approximately the maximum depth for organisms carrying out photosynthesis). Compare oceanic zone.

**Nervate.** *bot.* Having veins, said of leaves.

**Nervation.** Venation; the manner in which the nerves or veins of a leaf or wing of an insect are arranged. Alos called neuration.

**Nerve.** A strand of tissue comprising many nerve fibres plus supporting tissue, enclosed in a connective-tissue sheath. Nerves connect the central nervous system with the organs and tissues of the body. A nerve may carry only motor nerve fibres (motor nerve) or only sensory fibres (sensory nerve) or it may be mixed and carry both types (mixed nerve). Although the nerve fibres are in close proximity within the nerve, their physiological responses are independent of each other.

**Nerve Cell.** A neuron.

**Nerve Center.** A group of neurons within the central nervous system which controls a specific activity, as the respiratory center.

**Nerve Cord.** In Metazoa, a bundle of nerve fibres along the longitudinal axis of the body. In most invertebrates there are two solid nerve cords, located ventrally, with ganglia corresponding to each segment. In Chordata the nerve cord is located dorsally and in vertebrates it is the spinal cord.

**Nerve Fibre.** The axon of a neurone together with the tissues associated with it (such as a myelin sheath). The length and diameter of nerve fibres are very variable, even within the same organism.

**Nerve Impulse.** A wave of excitation initiated by a stimulus which passes along a nerve fiber.

**Nerve Net.** A network of nerve cells connected with each other by synapses or fusion. The nervous system of certain invertebrates (*e.g.* coelenterates and echinoderms) consists exclusively of a nerve net in the body wall.

**Nerve Ring.** A nerve cord which passes around a structure, as that encircling the esophagus in echinoderms.

**Nerve Root.** The connection of a spinal nerve with the spinal cord comprising a dorsal sensory root composed of afferent fibers and a ventral motor root composed of efferent fibers.

**Nervous**

1. Of, composed of, or related to nerves or nerve cell.
2. Excessively excitable, as a nervous individual.
3. Caused by or brought about by nervous impulses, as nervous control of the heart.

**Nervous System.** The system of cells and tissues in multicellular animals by which information is conveyed between sensory cells and organs and effectors (such as muscles and glands). It consists of the central nervous system (in vertebrates the brain and spinal cord; in invertebrates the nerve cord and ganglia) and the peripheral nervous system. Its function is to receive, transmit, and interpret information and then to formulate appropriate responses for the effector organs. It also serves to coordinate responses that require more than one physiological process. Nervous tissue consists of neurones, which convery the information in the form impulses, and supporting tissue.

**Nervous Tissue.** Tissue composed of neurons and neuroglia which comprise the organs of a nervous system (brain, ganglia, nerves, nerve cords, and sensory portion of sense organs).

**Nervure**

1. *bot.* A vein in a leaf.
2. *zool.* A vein in the wing of an insect.

**Nest**

1. A structure or a place prepared by a bird for receivins eggs, for their incubation and hatching, and for the rearing of the young.
2. In general, any place where an animal deposits its eggs and rears its young, as a turtle nest.
3. A place for concealment or retreat or for rearing young, as a rabbit nest.
4. embryol, and histol. An isolated mass of cells.

**Nestling.** A young bird that has not left the nest.

**Net Assimilation Rate.** (NAR). A value that relates plant productivity to plant size. It is obtained by dividing the rate of increase in dry weight by leaf size (usually leaf area).

**Netted.** Reticulated.

**Nettle**

1. A plant, especially one of the genus Urtica which possesses glandular stinging hairs.

2. A scyphozoan medusa which inflicts painful stings.

**Nettle Cell.** A nematocyst.

**Network.** A reticulum; an interlacing arrangement of vessels or fibers.

**Neural.** Of or pertaining to a nervous system or nervous tissue.

**Neural Arch.** The portion of a vertebra which forms the roof and sides of a vertebral foramen, consisting of two pedicles, two lamina, and their processes.

**Neural Canal**

1. *embryol.* The neurocoel or cavity of the neural tube.
2. The vertebral canal formed by the arches of successive vertebrae.

**Neural Crest** A band of cells of ectodermal origin located along each side of the neural tube following its formation.

**Neural Fold.** One of two folds which develop from the neural plate and, upon fusion, form the neural tube.

**Neural Groove.** A median, longitudinal groove which lies between the neural folds prior to their closing.

**Neural Lobe.** A portion of the posterior lobe of the pituitary gland.

**Neural Plate**

1. A median, dorsal sheet of ectoderm from which the neural tube and neural crest cells develop; medullary plate.
2. In turtles, one of a set of plates overlying, or in some cases, fused with the vertebrae.

**Neural Spine.** The spine of a neural arch; the spinous process of a vertebra.

**Neural Tube.** A longitudinal ectodermal tube which forms in the middorsal region of a vertebrate embryo from which the brain and spinal cord develop.

**Neuration.** Nervation.

**Neurenteric Canal.** In vertebrate embryos, the connection between *a.* the neurocoel and the tail gut, as in the frog; *b.* the amniotic cavity and the yolk sac, as in mammals.

**Neurilemma.** A delicate sheath composed of Schwann's cells which forms the outermost covering of a nerve fiber. Also neurolemma.

**Neurobiotaxis.** *embryol.* The migration of nerve cell bodies in the brain in the direction from which they receive their impulses.

**Neuroblast.** An embryonic cell which gives rise to a neuron.

**Neurocoel.** The cavity of the neural tube.

**Neurocranium.** The portion of the skull which encloses and protects the brain; the cranium.

**Neuroendocrine.** Pertaining to both nervous and endocrine systems.

**Neuroendocrine System.** Any of the systems of dual control of certain activities in the body of some higher animals by nervous and hormonal stimulation. For example, the posterior pituitary gland and the medulla of the adrenal gland receive direct nervous stimulation to secrete their hormones, whereas the anterior pituitary gland is stimulated by factors (neurosecretions) released from the hypothalamus.

**Neuroepithelial Cells.** Highly specialized receptor cells, as olfactory, gustatory, rod and cone cells, and hair cells of the internal ear.

**Neurofibrids.** Minute fibrils in the cell body and processes of a neuron.

**Neurogenic**

1. Of nervous origin.
2. Under nervous control.

**Neuroglia.** The non-nervous, interstitial tissue of the nervous system which includes ependyma, neuroglia proper (astrocytes, oligodendrocytes, microglia), satellite cells, and cells of Schwann.

**Neurohormone.** Any hormone that is product not by an endocrine gland but by a specialized nerve cell and is secreted from nerve endings into the bloodstream or directly to the tissue or organ whose growth of function it controls. Examples of neurohormones are noradrenaline, vasopressin, and hormones associated with metamorphosis and moulting in insects (ecdysone, juvenile hormone).

**Neurohemal Organ.** An organ which stores and liberates neurohormones, as *a.* invertebrates, the corpus cardiacum, sinus gland, pericardial and postcommissural organs; *b.* in vertebrates, the pars nervosa of the pituitary gland.

**Neurohormone.** A hormone secreted by a neurosecretory cell, as vasopressin.

**Neurohumor.** A transmitter substance produced at the termination of an axon, as acetylcholine and norepinephrine; a local hormone.

**Neurohypophysis.** The posterior lope of the pituitary gland which includes the neural stalk (infundibulum) and neural lobe.

**Neurolemma.** Neurilemma.

**Neurology.** The science which deals with the nervous system.

**Neuromast.** In fish and some Amphibia, the basic receptor units of the acoustico-lateralis system. The receptor cells are surrounded by a clump of supporting cells, the units being covered by a gelatinous capsule or cupula. Physical changes in the environment are relayed to the brain by means of electrical discharges through special nerve fibres.

**Neuromotor Apparatus.** A complicated fibrillar system in ciliates through which the movement of cilia in various part of the organism is coordinated.

**Neuromuscular Spindle.** A proprioceptor which is stimulated by changes in length and tension of muscle fibers.

**Neuron.** A nerve cell, the structural and functional units of the nervous system, typically consisting of a cell body (perikaryon) and its processes (axon and dendrites).

**Neurone** (nerve cell). An elongated branched cell that is the fundamental unit of the nervous system, being specialized for the conduction of impulses. A neurone consists of a cell body, containing the nucleus and Nissl granules; dendrites, which receive incoming impulses and pass them towards the cell body; and an axon, which conducts impulses away from the cell body, sometimes over long distances. Impulses are passed from one neurone to the next via synapses. Sensory neurones transmit unformation from receptors to the central nervous system. Motor neurones conduct information from the central nervous system to effectors (*e.g.* muscles).

**Neurone Theory.** The hypothesis, now accepted, that the nervous systems consists of nerve cells (neurones), which are functionally linked at synapes but are physically separate. This theory has superseded the idea that the cytoplasm of the cells of the nervous system is continuous.

**Neuropil.** A network of nerve fibers, as *a.* that between terminations of axons and dendrites in an axo-dendritic synapse; *b.* that in a ganglion of an invertebrate consisting of fibers of sensory, association, and motor neurons.

**Neuroplasm.** The interfibrillar substance in the cell body of a neuron.

**Neuropodium.** The ventral portion of a parapodium.

**Neuropore.** The anterior or posterior aperture of the neurocoel before complete closure of the neural tube.

**Neuropteran.** Any insect of the order Neuroptera, which comprises the nerve-winged insects as the lacewings, ant lions, and dobsonfly.

**Neurosecretion.** The elaboration and discharge of neurohormones or neurohumors by neurosecretory cells; the product produced.

**Neurosecretory Cell.** A neuron or nerve cell which produces and discharges a neurohormone or neurohumor.

**Neurotransmitter.** Substance that functions in the transmission of nervous impulses. Although numerous substances have been implicated in neurotransmission, the two most widespread and best understood systems involve acetylcholine and noradrenaline, the so-called cholinergic and adrenergic systems respectively.

**Neurotrophic.** Pertaining to the influence of nerves or impulses conducted by them upon the normal integrity of tissues.

**Neurotropic.** Having an affinity for, turning towards, or affecting nervous tissue, as neurotropic virus.

**Neurula.** An embryo during the period in which it possesses a neural plate.

**Neurulation**. *embryol.* The formation of a neural plate with the subsequent formation of the neural groove and its closure to form a neural tube.

**Neuston**. All organisms present in a surface film of water, those in the upper layer comprising the supraneuston, those in the lower layer the infraneuston.

**Neuter**. An organism that does not possess either male or female reproductive organs. Cultivated ornamental flowers that have neither pistils not stamens are called neuters.

**Neutral**

1. Lacking definite characteristics of one type or the other.
2. *biol.* Sexless; neither male nor female : Neuter.
3. *chem.* Neither acid nor alkaline; with a pH of 7.0.

**Neutrality Theory of Evolution** (neutral-mutation theory). This assets that many genetic mutations are adaptively equivalent (effectively neutral), and do not affect significantly the fitness of the carrier. Thus they can become fixed in the genome at a random rate. Changes in their frequencies are due more to chance than to natural selection. The theory applies only to protein evolution and does not deny the role of natural selection in shaping morphological and behavioural attributes.

**Neutral Theory of Molecular Evolution**. The theory that evolutionary change at the molecular level is caused by random drift of selectively equivalent mutant genes rather than by selection.

**Neutrophil**

1. A cell or part of a cell which stains readily with neutral dyes.

2. A polymorphonuclear leukocyte with cytoplasmic granules which stain with neutral dyes; a heterophil leukocyte.

**Nevus.** A small, congenital growth or pigmentary area on the skin.

**Newt.** One of a number of small, tailed salamanders especially those of the genus Triturus (Diemictylus).

**Nexine.** The inner layer of the exine in a pollen grain.

**Nexus**

1. An interconnection or bond between members of a group or series.
2. A connected group or series.

**Niacin.** A vitamin of the B complex which serves as an essential component of certain coenzymes concerned with hydrogen transport in cellular respiration; nicotinic acid, niacinamide.

**Nib.** A pointed structure, as a bill or beak; a prong.

**Niche** (ecological niche). Functional position of an organism in a community, together with its environmental position with respect to factors such as acidity, and temperature, etc., and the particular spatial habitat that the organism occupies.

**Nicotinamide Adenine Dinucleotide** (NAD, diphosphopyridine nucleotide, DPN). Derivative of the vitamin nicotinic acid, which functions as a coenzyme for various dehydrogenase enzymes involved in cellular respiration. It acts as an electron carrier in respiratory-chain phosphorylation.

**Nicotinamide Adenine Dinucleotide Phosphate** (NADP). Phosphorylated derivative of NAD, which functions as a hydrogen acceptor in the light stage of photosynthesis and is subsequently involved in the reduction of carbon dioxide in the dark reactions. It is a coenzyme in the reaction involving the oxidation of ferrodoxin by NADP reductase.

**Nicotine.** A poisonous alkaloid, $C_{10}H_{14}N_2$, obtained principally from tobacco, widely used as an agricultural insecticide, usually as a 40% solution of nicotine sulfate.

**Nicotinic Acid** (niacin). A vitamin of the vitamin B complex. It can be manufactured by plants and animals from the amino acid tryptophan. The amide derivative, nicotinamide, is a component of the coenzymes NAD and NADP. These take part in many metabolic reactions as hydrogen acceptors. Deficiency of nicotinic acid causes the disease pellagra in humans. Apart from tryptophan-rich protein, good sources are liver and groundnut and sunflower meals.

**Nictitating.** Lid-like membrane attached to the anterior corner of the eye. When drawn across the eye it reduces illumination of the retina. It is common in Reptilia and Aves, and present in some Mammalia and in many sharks, *e.g.* those of the family Carcharhinidae, which includes the tope (Galeorhinus galeus) and the blue shark (Prionace glauca).

**Nictitating Membrane.** A thin, transparent membrane which functions as a third eyelid in many vertebrates; vestigial in man.

**Nidamental Glands.** Four accessory reproductive organs in a squid which function in the formation of the eggshell.

**Nidation.** Implantation.

**Nidicole.** A nest parasite, especially a mite which parasitizes nestor burrow-dwelling vertebrates.

**Nidicolous**

1. Remaining in the nest for some time : Altricial.

2. Living in or inhabiting a nest.

**Nidification.** Nest construction or the manner of building a nest.

**Nidifugous.** Leaving the nest soon afterh atching : Precocial.

**Nidulariales.** An order of the Gasteromycetes containing some 60 species (9 genera) known as the bird's-nest fungi. The wall of the basidiocarp is nestlike and contains a number of separate spore masses (the 'eggs', which are exposed when the covering membrane dies back. An example is Crucibulum laeve.

**Nidus**

1. A nest.
2. A breeding place or place of origin.
3. A source or focus of infection.

**Night Blindness.** Reduced ability to see in dim light, usually resulting from a deficiency in vitamin A.

**Night-break Effect.** A phenomenon exhibited by many plants whereby a period of light, administered artificially during the night, even if only of short duration or low intensity, will interfere with the normal flowering rhythm of the plant. The precise effects vary with the time that has elapsed since the light phase but generally, under short-day conditions, a light treatment inhibits flowering in short-day plants and promotes it in long-day plants.

**Night-blooming Cereus.** An American cactus of the genera Hyalocereus and Selenicereus whose flowers open at night.

**Cr awler.** A large earthworm, as Lumbricus terrestris.

**Nighthawk.** A night-flying, insectivorous bird of the goatsucker family, Caprimulgidae, as the eastern nighthawk (Chordeiles minor).

**Nightingale**

1. An Old World thrush of the genus Luscinia.
2. Common name applied to the ovenbird or hermit thrush.

**Nightshade.** A plant of the family Solanaceae, as Atropa belladonna, the deadly nightshade, the source of atropine and belladonna.

**Night Temperature.** The temperature prevailing during the period of darkness, which can greatly affect the growth of many plants. For example, tomatoes have been shown to grow better if the night temperature is significantly lower than the day temperature. It is thought that low night temperatures inhibit respiration.

**Nilgai.** A large antelope of India (Boselaphus), tragocamelus), commonly called the blue cow or blue bull.

**Ninhydrin.** A colourless compound that is used in chromatography to locate amino acids and proteins on the chromotogram. Amino acids with a free amino group turn blue on heating with ninhydrin whereas those with a substituted amino group (proline and hydroxyproline) turn yellow.

**Nipple**

1. A conical protuberance of the mammary gland which bears the openings of the lactiferous ducts.
2. Any protuberance which resembles the nipple of the breast.

**Nissl Bodies.** Clumps or granules of chromophil substance present in the cell body and dendrites of a neuron.

**Nissl Granules** (Nissl bodies). Particles seen within the cell bodies of neurones. They are rich in RNA and stain strongly with basic dyes. They are named after F. Nissl

(1860—1919), the German neurologist who discovered them.

**Nit.** Name given to the eggs of lice (order Phthiraptera), particularly to those of the human body and head lice, Pediculus humanus and P. capitis. Eggs are cemented to the hair or feathers of the host and are very difficult to dislodge. Before hatching they are brownish-yellow, but afterwards air enters and they become silvery-white; it is in the latter form that eggs of P. capitis are generally recognized. The hatched eggs of some bird lice are used by mites, which enter them to shed their skins.

**Nitrification.** A chemical process in which nitrogen (mostly in the form of ammonia) in plant and animal wastes and dead remains is oxidized at first to nitrites and then to nitrates. These reactions are effected mainly by the bacteria Nitrosomonas and Nitrobacter respectively. Unlike ammonia, nitrates are readily taken up by plant roots; nitrification is therefore a crusial part of the nitrogen cycle. Nitrogen-containing compounds are often applied to soils deficient in this element, as fertilizer. Compare denitrification.

**Nitrifying Bacteria.** Soil bacteria which oxidide *a.* ammonia to nitrite, as Nitrosomonas; *b.* nitrite to nitrate, as Nitrobacter.

**Nitrogen** Symbol N. A colourless gaseous element that occurs in air (about 78% by volume) and is an essential constituent of proteins and nucleic acids in living organisms.

**Nitrogenase.** The enzyme system isolated from certain bacteria and shown to be responsible for nitrogen fixation. In the presence of ATP and a suitable electron donor it reduces molecular nitrogen ($N\equiv N$) to ammonia. It can also reduce other compounds with triple bonds, such as acetylene ($HC\equiv CH$). The enzyme is destroyed by free oxygen and is inhibited by high concentrations of ammonia.

**Nitrogen Cycle.** The circulation of nitrogen between living organisms and the environment. Atmospheric nitrogen is returned to the soil by nitrogen-fixing microorganisms (nitrogen fixation) and by electrical discharges in storms, which cause nitrogen and oxygen to combine. The oxides so formed dissolve in rain to form nitrous and nitric acids, which, in the soil, combine with mineral salts to form nitrites and nitrates. The nitrites and the ammonia in the soil derived from animal excretion and the decay of organic matter, are converted to nitrates by nitrification. Plants usually assimilate nitrogen as nitrates and the activities of nitrifying bacteria are thus essential to plant growth. The oxidation of ammonia to nitrite is carried out by Nitrosomonas species and the oxidation of nitrite to nitrate by Nitrobacter. The reverse process, denitrification, is mediated by different bacteria. Nitrates may also be lost by leaching.

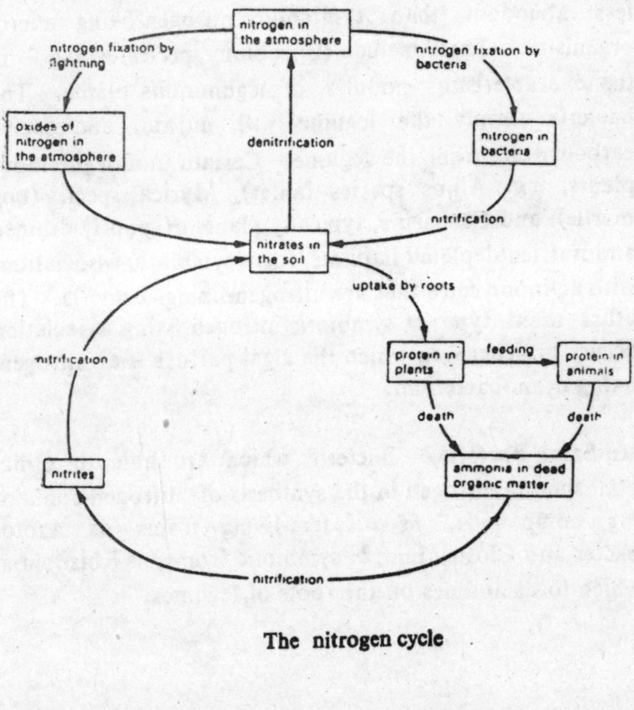


**The nitrogen cycle**

Man also affects the nitrogen cycle in various ways. He fixes nitrogen industrially by combining it with hydrogen in the Haber process and adds nitrogen to the soil in fertilizers. He removes nitrogen by overcultivation, by installing efficient sewage systems thus preventing urine and faces from reaching the soil, and by factory farming, which often results in animal wastes not being returned to the land in manageable form.

**Nitrogen Fixation.** The incorporation of gaseous molecular nitrogen into nitrogenous compounds. In nature this occurs during thunderstorms by means of the electrical energy released as lightning, by photochemical fixation in the atmosphere, and by the action of nitrogen fixing micro-organisms, especially bacteria and algae. Free living nitrogen-fixing soil micro-organisms include Azotobacter species, Clostridium species, and in wet and aquatic habitats cyanobacteria, *e.g.* Nostoc, which generally are less abundant than symbiotic nitrogen-fixing micro-organisms. These include Rhizobium species, which form the characteristic nodules of leguminous plants. The bacteria supply the legume with nitrate, and receive carbohydrate from the legume. Certain non-leguminous plants, *e.g.* Alnus species (alder), Myrica species (bog myrtle), and Casuarina, typically plants of poorly drained and nutrientdepleted habitats, form symbiotic associations with actinomycetes that are nitrogen-fixing bacteria. The other main type of symbiotic nitrogen-fixing association occurs in lichens, in which the algal partner is a nitrogen-fixing cyanobacterium.

**Nitrogen-fixing Bacteria.** Bacteria which are able to utilize atmospheric nitrogen in the synthesis of nitrogen-containing compounds, as *a.* free-living froms as Azotobacter and Clostridium; *b.* symbiotic froms, as Rhizobium, which form nodules on the roots of legumes.

**Nitrogenous Base.** A basic compound containing nitrogen. The term is used especially of organic ring compounds; such as adenine, guanine, cytosine, and thymine, which are constituents of nucleic acids.

**Nitta.** A leguminous tree (Parkia biglobosa) with large, edible pods, of West Africa.

**Nociceptive.** Pertaining to the sense of pain; injurious, as nociceptive stimuli.

**Noctilucous.** Shining at night; phosphorescent.

**Nocturnal**

1. Of, pertaining to, or occurring during the night.
2. Active at night, as animals which move about and seek their food principally at night.

**Nodal.** Of or pertaining to a node or nodes.

**Node**

1. (in botany). The part of a plant stem from which one or more leaves arise. The nodes at the stem apex are very close together and remain so in species of monocotyledons that form bulbs. In older regions of the stem they are separated by areas of stem called internodes.
2. (in anatomy). A natural thickening or bulge in an organ or part of the body. Examples are the sinoatrial node that controls the heartbeat (pacemaker) and the lymph nodes.

**Node of Ranvier.** One of a series of constrictions in the myelin sheath of a myelinated nerve fiber.

**Nodose.** Possessing nodes; swollen at intervals.

**Nodular.** Pertaining to, possessing, or composed of nodes or nodules.

**Nodule.** A small rounded mass, node, or lump; a tubercle.

**Nodulus.** A swelling in the middle of a seta, as in oligochaetes.

**Nodus**

1. A node or knot.
2. *entomol.* A notch marking the position of a prominent crossvein near the middle of the anterior margion of the front wings of odonatans.

**Nomad** (in cytology). A cell that migrates or wanders from its site of formation. Certain types of phagocytes are nomads.

**Nomenclature.** A system of names used in a particular field of knowledge, as the binomial system of nomenclature employed in naming animals and plants.

**Non-competitive Inhibition.** Irreversible inhibition of the activity of an enzyme, brought about by the presence of an inhibitor that is generally structurally unrelated to the normal substrate.

**Non-cyclic Phosphorylation.** The light-requiring part of photosynthesis in higher plants, in which oxygen is consumed and an electron donor is required. It consists of two photoreactions, resulting in the synthesis of ATP and $NADPH_2$.

**Nondisjunction.** The failure of paired (homologous) chromosomes to separate during anaphase 1 of meiosis. As a consequence, one daughter cell, and hence the two gametes formed from this, will receive both homologues. By corollary, the other daughter cell, and the gametes formed from this, will be deficient for the chromosome in question. Cells containing abnormal numbers of chromosomes are called aneuploids (aneuploidy).

**Nonmedullated.** Unmyelinated; lacking a myelin sheath.

**Nonmotile.** Lacking the power of spont neous movement.

**Nonpersistent.** Describing pesticides that break down and become inactive relatively quickly. Such pesticides should be used if spraying soon before harvest. Examples are the natural insecticides derris and pyrethrum.

**Nonsense Triplet.** A name given originally to triplets of bases that do not specify any amino acid and were thus once considered as having no function. There are three such triplets, UAG, UGA, and UGG, all of which have subsequently been found to act as 'stop-signals', *i.e.* they define the end of a polypeptide chain. Polypeptide initiation also requires a 'start signals', the signals being AUG or GUG, which also code for valine or methionine (or a methionine derivative) respectively.

**Nonsense Mutation.** Mutation that alters a gene so that a nonsense codon is inserted. Such a codon is one for which no normal tRNA molecule exists : the codon therefore does not code for an amino acid. Usually a nonsense codon causes the termination of translation (*i.e.* the end of the polypeptide chain). Three nonsense codons are recognized, and are called the amber, ochre, and opal codons.

**Nonstriated**. Lacking striations or cross margings, with reference to smooth muscle.

**Noolbender.** The honey mouse (Tarsipes spencerae), an Australian marsupial; also called honey possum.

**Noradrenaline** (norepinephrine). A hormone produced by the adrenal glands and also secreted from nerve endings in the sympathetic nervous system as a chemical transmitter of nerve impulses (neurotransmitter). Many of its general actions are similar to those of adrenaline, but it is more concerned with maintaining normal body activity than with preparing the body for emergencies.

**Norepinephrine.** A hormone secreted by the adrenal medulla; also produced at the terminations of sympathetic nerve fibers; a heart stimulant and general vasoconstrictor. Also called noradrenaline; sympathin E.

**Nori.** Purple laver, a food product prepared from a red alga (Porphyra).

**Norm.** A standard, usually the average or median.

**Normal**

1. *biol.* Typical, regular, standard, conforming to type.
2. *chem.* Containing one gram equivalent of the reagent or one gram of replaceable hydrogen ions per liter, with reference to solutions.

**Normal Analysis** Groupings based on analysis of the attributes describing individuals—*e.g.* in plant ecology, the grouping of sample sites by analysis of their species composition. The term is particularly applied to numerical vegetation classification, and sometimes implies a plot, as distinct from species, classification.

**Normal Curve** (normal curve of errors). The bell shaped curve obtained when a series of observations that shows a normal (Gaussian) distribution is plotted on a graph. The mean, median, and mode all occupy the same high middle point of the curve, which is perfectly symmetrical around this point.

**Normal Deviate** Symbol *c*. The ratio of the deviation, *d*, to the standard deviation, $\sigma$. It is used to asses experiments where the results to not fall into a limited number of classes but show a continuous range, for example the recording of corp yield in response to various fertilizer levels. To find whether any deviation is significant its probability is looked up in a table of normal deviates.

**Nose.** The protuberance on the face of some vertebrates that contains the nostrils (nares) and part of the nasal cavity. It therefore forms part of the olfactory system (olfaction) and the external opening of the respiratory system.

**No-see-um.** A biting midge or punkie.

**Nostril.** One of the external openings of the olfactory sac or nasal cavity of a vertebrate; an external naris.

**Notochord** (chorda dorsalis). Somewhat flexible, rod-like structure, composed on dis-like turgid cells, which extends virtually the entire length of the body of adult and/or larval members of the phylum Chordata. Lying below the nerve cord, but dorsal to the intestine, the notochord provides a form of flexible support to the body. In vertebrates the notochord is replaced wholly or partly by the vertebral column, but it is retained throughout life in Acania and Agnatha.

**Notonectal.** Swimming upside-down or with ventral side up.

**Notopodium.** The dorsal portion of a parapodium of a polychalte worm.

**Notum.** *entomol.* The dorsal portion of a body segment, especially in the thoracic region.

**Noxious.** Harmful, injurious, deleterious.

**Nurse**

1. An individual that nurses or takes care of another.
2. To nourish the yound at the breast.
3. *zool. a.* In social insects, a worker which takes care of the young. *b.* In ascidians, an asexual zooid which acts as a nurse to other zooids, as in Doliolum.

**Nuptial.** *biol.* Pertaining to mating or the breeding season, as nuptial plumage.

**Nucleus**

1. The double membrane-bound organelle containing the chromosomes that is found in most non-dividing eukaryotic cells : it is essential to their long-term survival. It is variously shaped, although it is normally spherical or ovoid. It disappears temporarily during cell division. It is absent from viruses. The chromosomes, though probably intact, are not visible when the cell is in a resting stage (*i.e.* not dividing). The nucleus also contains nucleoli, small spherical dense bodies made up of ribosomal RNA and protein, which gives it its integrity.

2. A small, solid particle, *e.g.* of dust, salt or smoke. Such particles are 'condensation nuclei' whose hygroscopic properties encourage condensation, often in unsaturated air. Other nuclei, *e.g.* some clay particles such as kaolinite, probably act as 'freezing nuclei' in the initial stage of ice-crystal formation.

**Nurse Cell.** A cell which provides nourishment or protection to other cells, especially developing germ cells, as archeocytes of sponges or nurse cells in insect ovarioles.

**Nucleotide**. An organic compound consisting of a nitrogen-containing purine or pyrimidine base linked to a sugar (ribose or deoxyribose) and a phosphate group. DNA and RNA are made up of long chains of nucleotides (*i.e.* polynucleotides). Compare nucleoside.

**Nyctinasty** (sleep movements). Nastic movements of plant organs in response to the changes in light and temperature that occur between day and night (and vice versa). Examples are the opening and closing of many flowers and the folding together of the leaflets of clover and other plants at night.

**Numbat**. A small, ant-eating marsupial of the genus Myrmecobius, of Australia.

**Nurse Tissue.** Metabolically active tissue that is used in tissue culture work to stimulate the growth of single cells that cannot be grown using defined media. The nurse tissue, which is often callus tissue, may be separated by a piece of filter paper through which growth substances and nutrients can diffuse. Pollen grains have been induced to grow into haploid plant by culturing them on filter paper in contact with intact anthers acting as nurse tissue. It may not be necessary to separate the nurse tissue if it is first treated, for example with x-rays, to prevent cell division.

Growth media may be enriched with growth substances by adding nurse tissue enclosed in a semipermeable membrane. Using such conditioned media it is possible to achieve satisfactoy growth using a much lower inoculum density than would normally be necessary. This is important in cloning work because cells can be plated out at much lower densities so increasing the chances that any resulting group of cells is derived from a single cell.

**Nurse Tree.** *forestry.* A tree planted to protect young and growing trees.

**Nurture.** That which encompasses the breeding, nourishment, care, education, and training of an individual.

**Nut.** , dry single-seeded fruit that develops from more than one carpel and does not shed its seed when ripe. The fruit wall is woody or leathery. Many nuts are enclosed in a hard or membranous cup-shaped structure, the cupule. The term nut is often loosely used of any hard fruit. For example, the walnut and coconut are in fact drupes and the Brazil nut is a seed.

**Nutant.** Nodding, drooping; with head bent forward.

**Nutation.** The spiral movement of a plant organ during growth, also known as circumnutation. It is seen in climbing plants and helps the plant find a suitable support to twine around. Examples are the coiling movements of the shoot tips of runner beans and of the tendrils of sweet peas.

**Nutgall.** A nutlike excrescence or gall which develops on the twigs of oaks.

**Nuthatch.** A small, square-tailed passerine bird of the family Sittidae which creeps over the trunks of trees with head pointed downward, as Sitta carolinensis, the white-tailed nuthatch.

**Nutlet.** A small, nutlike fruit or seed, as those produced by heliotrope.

**Nutmeg.** A tree (Myristica fragrans) cultivated in the East Indies for its seed sold commercially as a culinary spice.

**Nutria.** The coypu or its fur.

**Nutrient.** A nutritious or nourishing substance; any substance which promotes growth or provides energy for physiological processes.

**Nutrient Medium.** Culture Medium.

**Nutrition**

1. *zool.* The total of the processes involved in the absorption and utilization of foods and food accessories.

2. *bot.* The taking in of mineral substances and their utilization in plant metabolism, excluding the processes of photosynthesis and fat and protein synthesis.

**Nutritive.** Providing food or nourishment.

**Nutshell.** The hard external covering (pericarp) enclosing the meat of a nut.

**Nut Shell.** A small, marine bivalve of the genus Nucula.

**Numercial Taxonomy** (taxometrics). A classification method besed on the numerical analysis of the variation of a large number of characters in a group of organisms. It is assumed that a classification will be more predictive the more characters on which it is based. It is also assumed that, to begin with, each character is of equal weight (weighting) although some characters may later be weighted. Initially, a matrix of data is compiled of operational taxonomic units (OTUs) against characters so that for every OTU the state of each of perhaps 50 or more characters is recorded. This matrix can be subjected to a variety of mathematical analyses, which provide a measure of the similarity or dissimilarity between all the OTUs. The end product is usually one or more dendrograms.

**Nux Vomica.** The dried, ripe seed of an Asiatic tree (Strychnos mux·vomica), the source of strychine, brucnine, and other poisonous alkaloids.

**Nuzzle**

1. To work with the nose, as to dig, push, rub, or poke with the nose or snout.

2. To lie close together; to snuggle up to.

**Nucellus.** A rounded or oval mass of parenchymatous tissue in an ovule, containing the embryo sac. Its size and shape may be used as a diagnostic character. It is almost totally surrounded by the integuments except for a small channel, the micropyle, through which the pollen tube may grow prior to fertilization At fertilization the nucellus may by reabsorbed as the embryo develops or it may persist to form a nutritive perisperm in some seeds.

**Nuchal.** Of or pertaining to the nape of the neck.

**Nuchal Organs.** A pair of ciliated, sensory pits on the head of most polychaetes.

**Nuciferous.** Bearing nuts.

**Nuclear.** Of, pertaining to, within, or forming a part of a nucleus.

**Nuclear Body.** One or more bodies composed of a single strand of DNA present in a bacterium.

**Nuclear Division.** Karyokinesis.

**Nuclear Envelope** (nuclear membrane). The structure that separates the nucleus of eukaryotic cells from the cytoplasm. It comprises two unit membranes each 10 nm thick, separated by a perinuclear space of 10—40 nm. At intervals, the two membranes are fused around the edges of circular pores which allow for the selective passage of materials into and out of the nucleus.

**Nuclear Membrane** (nuclear envelope). A double membrane surrounding the nucleus. Each layer has a typical membrane, structure (plasma membrane) and is 4 nm to 6 nm in width. The outer membrane is studded with ribosomes on the cytoplasm side while the surface of the inner membrane next to the nucleus is smooth. Electron micrographs of many cells reveal connections between the outer membrane and the endoplasmic reticulum. Between the membranes there is a clear space, the perinuclear cisterna. At various points the two membranes fuse and pores are formed. The number of pores varies with the degree of nuclear activity. Extensions of the outer granular or fibrous region of the nucleus form cylindrical complexes within the pores. Their precise function is obscure but they appear to be involved in the transfer of information from nucleus to cytoplasm.

**Nuclear Sap.** Karyolymph.

**Nuclease.** One of a large group of enzymes which catalyze the hydrolysis of nucleic acids or their products (nucleotides, nucleosides).

**Nucleated.** Possessing a nucleus.

**Nucleic Acid.** A complex organic compound in living cells that consists of a chain of nucleotides. There are two types : DNA (deoxyribonucleic acid) and RNA (ribonucleic acid).

**Nulecocaspid.** A caspid and its enclosed nucleic acid.

**Nucleoid** (nuclear region). The part of a cell of a bacterium or a blue-green alga (*i.e.* a prokaryotic cell) that contains the genetic material DNA and therefore controls the activity of the cell. It corresponds to the nucleus of the more advanced eukaryotic cells but is not bounded by a membrane.

**Nucleolar.** Of or pertaining to a nucleolus.

**Nucleohistone.** A complex formed between the polynucleotides or DNA and basic proteins called histones, which only occur in the nuclei of eukaryotic organisms. Nucleohistone complexes are visible as nucleosomes.

**Nucleolar Organizer.** The region of chromosomal DNA that codes for ribosomal RNA. Such regions can be identified as secondary constrictions (the centromere being the primary constriction) often located towards the end of the chromosome. Like centromeres, nucleolar organizers are uncoiled regions of the chromosome and stain poorly. Nucleoli in the interphase nucleus have been shown to be associated with these regions.

**Nucleolus.** Structure within the nucleus that stains densely with basic dyes and consists of proteins associated with RNA. The number and distribution of nucleoli varies but is usually characteristic for any one cell type. Electron micrographs show a central area of short fibres surrounded by a matrix of protein material with granules embedded in the peripheral region. Nucleoli are closely associated with the regions of chromosomal DNA that code for ribosomal RNA (nucleolar organizer). The transcription of the code is dependent on a specific RNA polymerase found only in the nucleolus. A long precursor molecule is formed initially and is processed to produce two shorter molecules. The longer of these associates with proteins in the nucleolus to form the larger ribosomal subunits. The smaller molecules similarly associate with proteins to form the smaller subunits, possibly in the nucleolus or surrounding nucleoplasm. The formation of complete ribosomes from the subunits only occurs when the latter reach the cytoplasm.

**Nucleoplasm.** The protoplasm of a nucleus.

**Nucleoprotein.** Any compound present in cells of living organisms that consists of a nucleic and (DNA or RNA) combined with a protein. Chromosomes consist of nucleoprotein (DNA and proteins, mostly histones), as do ribosomes (RNA and protein).

**Nucleoside.** A general term for the category of substances formed when a purine or pyrimidine base combines with carbon—1 of a pentose sugar. Such base—sugar complexes are much less common than base—sugar—phosphate complexes, which are known as nucleotides.

**Nucleosome** (nu body). A nodule, some 7 – 10 nm in diameter, consisting of histones, around which is wrapped a strand of DNA about 150 base pairs long. One type of histone, HI, is positioned between adjacent nucleosomes and may serve to clamp the DNA in position. By wrapping around histone beads, the total length of DNA is condensed by a factor of some seven times. Supercoiling of the string of nucleosome beads results in a further condensation. Nucleosomes are thus of considerable importance in packaging enormous lengths of DNA into minute chromosomes.

**Nucleoside Diphosphate Sugars** (NDP-sugars) Compounds formed by the reaction of a phosphorylated hexose sugar with a nucleoside triphosphate (NTP) in the general reaction :

$$\text{NTP}+\text{sugar 1-phosphate}\rightleftharpoons \text{NDP-sugar}+\text{pyrophosphate}$$

NDP sugars are important as high-energy glycosyl donors in the synthesis of most polysaccharides, for example the enzyme starch synthase utilizes uridine diphosphate glucose (UDP-glucose) and adenosine diphosphosphate glucose (ADP-glucose) s substrates.

UDP-glucose it the most important of the NDP-sugars. It can be synthesized both from glucose 1-phosphate using the reaction shown above, or from sucrose using the enzyme sucrose synthase (sucrose). Besides their importance as glycosyl donors NDP-sugars are important intermediates in the interconversi of monosaccharides and their derivatives. For many enzymes catalysing sugar interconversions, notably the epimerases, NDP-sugars are substrates rather than the sugars themselves or their phosphate esters.

**Nucule.** The female fructification (oogonium of certain green algae, as Chara.

**Nude.** Naked, bare, uncovered.

**Nudibranch.** A sea slug, a gastropod mollusk of the order Nudibranchia characterized by lack of a mantle and shell, as Aeolis, Doris.

**Nullisomic.** Aneuploidy.

**Nyctitropism.** A turning in response to darkness; a sleep movement.

**Nyala.** A South African antelope of the genusg Traelaphus.

**Nystagmus.** Involuntary oscillatory movements of the eyeballs.

**Nymph**

1. The young of an insect which undergoes simple metamorphosis, having a body form resembling the parent but with undeveloped structures, as wings and reproductive organs, as in the grasshopper.
2. In the Acarina, the eightlegged immature form which follows the six-legged larva and precedes the adult stage.

**Nymphochrysalis.** In water mites, the larval exoskeleton within which transformation of the parasitic larva to the nymph takes place.

**Numerical Method** (numerical taxonomy). Any numerical description of an individual or community, or comparisons of these (such as similarity indices), or data-structuring methods (such as principal-components analysis and classification). The essential point is that numerical methods make no assumptions about the data, *e.g.*, the sampling approach used, the distribution of the data, or the probability of particular patterns or frequencies. In contrast, statistical methods do make certain assumptions about the form of the data, on which the validity of significance testing depends. Compare statistical method.

**Nyctalopia.** Hight Blindness.

# O

**Oak.** A tree or shrub of the genus Quercus, family Fagaceae, the fruit of which is the acorn; a valuable lumber tree.

**Oak Apple.** An applelike gall which develops on oak leaves caused by a gall insect of the genus Amphibolips.

**Oak Apple Gall** (King Charle's apple). Gall formed by the agamic (unisexual) generation of the wasp Biorrhiza pallida (family Cynipidae). Apterous, agamic females arise from root galls of Quercus robur and climb the trunk of the tree in spring to lay many eggs in the bases of leaf buds. These eggs cause the formation of the familiar multilocular, pale pink, spongy galls that have the appearance of small apples. The galls mature by mid summer, and give rise to the sexual generation whose males and females emerge in June to July and mate. Mated females penetrate the soil around the oak tree and lay eggs on rootlets, giving rise to small, brown, rounded galls whose occupants emerge at the end of their second winter. May 29 is Oak Apple Day, and commemorates the restoration of the English monarchy in 1660 (and the birthday of Charles II).

**Oarfish.** The ribbon fish, a long, slender, marine fish of the genus Regalecus, sometimes reaching a length of 25 feet.

**Oat**

1. The seed or grain of a cereal grass (Avena sativa).
2. The oat plant.

**Oat Coleoptile Test.** A test for determining the relative quantities of auxins present in an unknown material by affixing a block of agar containing the auxin unilaterally to a detipped oat coleoptile. The amount of curvature resulting from asymmetric growth is proportional to the amount of auxin in the block.

**Ob.** A prefix meaning inverted; hence obcordate describes a leaf shaped like an inverted heart.

**Obclavate.** Inversely clavate; attached at club-shaped end.

**Obcordate.** Inversely cordate or heart-shaped; attached at apex.

**Obdiplostemonous.** Describing stamens that are inserted in two whorls with the outer opposite the petals and the inner opposite the sepals. Obdiplostemonous stamens are seen in some members of the Caryophyllaceae. Compare diplostemonous.

**Obese.** Extremely fat or corpulent.

**Objective.** The lens or system of lenses nearest to the object being examined through an optical instrument.

**Oblanceolate.** Inversely lanceolate; with broadest portion towards the apex.

**Oblate.** Flattened at the poles.

**Obligate.** Having a specific requirement for a particular environmental factor and being unable to survive if it is not available. For example, obligate parasites cannot grow in the absence of their host.

**Oblong.** Elongated, with sides nearly parallel and corners rounded, as an oblong leaf.

**Obovate.** Inversely ovate, with distal end broader than basal end, with reference to leaves.

**Obsolete.** Indistinct not evident, rudimentary, vestigial.

**Obtect.** With appendages adfixed to the body surface, with reference to the pupae of insects, as in lepidopterans.

**Obturator.** Closing an opening, as the obturator membrane of the pelvic girdle.

**Obtuse.** Having a blunt or rounded leaf apex.

**Occipital.** Of or pertaining to the occiput.

**Occipital Bone.** The bone forming the posterior portion of the skull bearing one or two occipital condyles which articulate with the atlas. It contains the foramen magnum.

**Occipital Condyle.** A single or paired bony knob that protrudes from the occipital bone of the skull and articulates with the first servical vertebra (the atlas). In humans there is a pair of occipital condyles, one on each side of the foramen magnum. Occipital condyles are absent in most fish, which cannot move their heads.

**Occiput**

1. In vertebrates, the back or posterior region of the head.

2. *entomol.* The dorsal, posterior region of the head.

**Occlude.** To block, obstruct, or close a passageway.

**Occlusion**

1. *anat. a.* The state of being closed or blocked, said of vessels. *b.* The coming into contact of the teeth of the upper and lower jaws.

2. *bot.* The closing of a wound in a tree.

**Oceanic.** Of or pertaining to the seas or oceans.

**Oceanic Islands.** Those formed by volcanic action in waters of great depth, as the Hawaiian and Galapagos Islands.

**Oceanic Zone.** The region of the open sea beyond the edge of the continental shelf, where the depth is greater than 200 metres. Compare neritic zone.

**Ocellar.** Of or pertaining to an ocellus.

**Ocellar Bulb.** An enlargement at the base of a tentacle in a medusa : Tentacular Bulb.

**Ocellated**

1. Bearing an ocellus or ocelli.
2. Bearing an eyelike marking.
3. Resembling an ocellus in appearance.

**Ocellus.** A simple eye occurring in insects and other invertebrates. It typically consists of light-sensitive cells and a single cuticular lens.

**Ochrea.** A tube around the stem formed by sheathing stipules at the leaf base. Ochreas are characteristic of the Polygonaceae giving the familiar swollen joints on the stems of such plants.

**Ocrea**

1. *bot.* A tubular structure consisting of one or a pair of stipules which ensheaths the base of a petiole.
2. *zool.* A sheath, as that in the booted tarsus of a bird.

**Ocreated.** Possessing a sheath or ocrea.

**Octamerous.** Having parts which are eight in number or occur in multiples of eight.

**Octandrous.** Having eight stamens.

**Octopus.** A dibranchiate, cephalopod mollusk of the order Octopoda, as Octopus vulgaris with a globular body bearing eight long, sucker-bearing arms encircling a parrotlike beak; commonly called devilfish.

[1]**Ocular.** Pertaining to or of the nature of an eye.

[2]**Ocular.** The eyepiece of an optical instrument, as a micros-cope.

**Ocular Plate.** One of a series of ossicles in an echinoid.

**Oculomotor.** Of or pertaining to eye movements.

**Oculomotor Nerve.** The third cranial nerve (III), fibers of which innervate all eye muscles except the superior oblique and lateral rectus.

**Oculus**

1. *anat.* An eye.

2. *bot.* An eye or bud of a tuber.

**Odd-pinnate.** Pinnate but terminating in a single leaflet, said of leaves.

**Odonate.** An insect of the order Odonata which includes the dragonflies and damselflies.

**Odontoblast**

1. A cell in the outer layer of dental pulp which is involved in the formation of dentin.

2. A tooth-forming cell in the buccal mass of a mollusk.

**Odour.** A scent, fragrance, or smell; a sensation resulting from the stimulation of olfactory receptors.

**Odoriferous.** Having a pronounced odor or smell.

**Odorous.** Having a distinctive odor or smell : Odoriferous.

**Oedogoniophyceae.** A class of the Chlorophyta containing one order, the Oedogoniales, comprising three genera of filamentous algae. These algae are characterized by an unusual kind of cell division, which results in parallel rings of closely spaced 'caps' of old cell wall material being formed at the anterior end of dividing cells. Prior to cell division a ring of wall material forms at the anterior end of the cell. Nuclear division then occurs and the two resulting nuclei become separated by a septum, which however, is not contiguous with the outer wall at this stage. Meanwhile the ring of wall material at the top of the cell enlarges and the old cell wall to the outside of the ring ruptures. The new wall material is then free to extend and forms the outer walls of the new cell. Part of the old wall remains as a 'cap' at the upper end of this cell. The septum between the daughter nuclei moves up to fuse with the base of the new wall material and cell division is completed.

The zoospores of the Oedogoniophyceae are also peculiar in having numerous flagella forming an apical ring.

**Odonata.** An order of insects containing the dragonflies and damselflies, most of which occur in tropical regions. Adult dragonflies have a pair of prominent compound eyes, a compact thorax bearing two pairs of delicate membranous wings, and a long slender abdomen. They are strong fliers and prey on other insects, either in flight or at rest. The eggs are laid near or in water, and the newly hatched nymphs are aquatic and resemble the adults, with rudimentary wings. They breathe through gills and feed on small aquatic animals. The nymph leaves the water for its final moult into the terrestrial adult.

**Odontoblast.** A cell that is responsible for producing the dentine of vertebrate teeth. Odontoblasts are found around the lining of the pulp cavity and have processes that extend into the dentine.

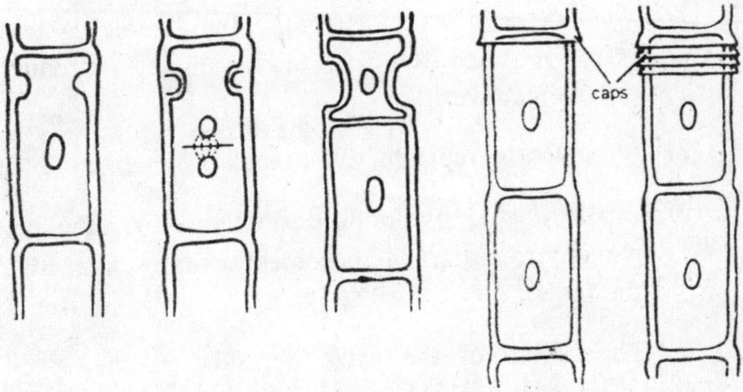


Stages of cell division in Oedogonium

**Oenocyte.** A large cell found in clusters about the tracheae and fat body of most insects.

**Oesophagus.** The section of the alimentary canal that lies between the pharynx and the stomach. It is a muscular tube whose function is to transfer food to the stomach by means of wavelike contractions (peristalsis) along its length.

**Oestrogen.** One of a group of female sex hormones, produced principally by the ovaries, that promote the onset of secondary sexual characteristics (such as breast enlargement and development in women) and control the oestrous cycle. Oestradiol is the most important. Oestrogens are secreted at particularly high levels during ovulation, stimulating the uterus to prepare for pregnancy. They are used in oral contraceptives (with progestogens) and as treatment for various disorders of the female reproductive organs. Small amounts of oestrogens are produced by the adrenal glands and testes.

**Oestrous Cycle.** The cycle of reproductive activity shown by most sexually mature nonpregnant female mammals except most primates (compare menstrual cycle). There are three phases :

(1) *anoestrus*—no sexual activity, the female is neither receptive nor attractive to the male, reproductive organs inactive;

(2) *pro-oestrus*—reproductive organs become active;

(3) *oestrus* (*heat*)—ovulation normally occurs, the female is ready to mate and becomes sexually attractive to the male.

The length of the cycle depends on the species: large mammals typically have a single annual cycle with a well-defined breeding season (monoestrus). The males have a similar cycle of sexual activity. Other species may have many cycles per year (polyoestrus) and the male may be sexually active all the time.

**Oestrus** (heat). Oestrous cycle.

**Offset.** A short shoot that arises from an axillary bud near the base of the stem and gives rise to a daughter plant at its apex. Examples of offsets are those produced by the houseleek (Sempervivum tectorum). The offset is a type of short runner and, like runners, is a means of vegetative reproduction. The term is also applied to bulbils and cormlets that form at the side of the parent bulb or corm.

**Offshoot.** A lateral branch of the main stem.

**Oidiophore.** A hyphal branch which produces oidia.

**Oidium** (arthrospore). A spore that forms by the organized fragmentation of a hypha as seen, for example, in Endomyces.

**Oil.** A triacylglycerol that is liquid at room temperature. The major fatty acids in oils are the unsaturated oleic and linolenic acids. Most oils function as energy storage compounds and are especially important in some oil-bearing seeds such as the castor bean.

**Oil Gland.** A gland which secretes oil, as the uropygial gland of birds or the sebaceous gland of mammals.

**Oil Immersion.** A technique used in light microscopy in which a special oil-immersion objective lens is employed to increase the resolving power of the microscope. A specimen mounted on a glass slide is covered by a drop of clear oil placed on the coverslip. The oil has the same refractive index as the glass lens. When the lens is immersed in the oil, the amount of light entering the objective increases (*i.e.* the effective aperture is increased). Such a technique is particularly useful at high magnifications. Oil is traditionally used but other liquids (*e.g.* sugar solution) may also be suitable.

**Oleaceous.** Of or belonging to the olive family, Oleaceae.

**Oleaginous.** Fatty, oily, unctuous; producing oil.

**Oleic Acid.** An eighteen-carbon monounsaturated fatty acid. It is the predominant unsaturated fatty acid in plant cells, except in some specialized organelles such as the chloroplast, where linolenic acid predominates. Oleic acid is formed from stearic acid in a desaturation reaction involving molecular oxygen, a reducing agent, and ferredoxin.

**Olfaction.** The sense of smell or the process of detecting smells. This is achieved by receptors in olfactory organs (such as the nose) that are sensitive to air- or water-borne chemicals. Stimulation of those receptors results in the transmission of information to the brain via the olfactory nerve.

**Olfaction.** Smelling; the sence of smell.

**Olfactory Brain.** The rhinencephalon.

**Olfactory Bulb.** The expanded anterior portion of the olfactory tract.

**Olfactory Cells.** Bipolar receptor cells present in olfactory epithelium which respond to olfactory stimuli, their axons forming the olfactory nerves.

**Olfactory Epithelium.** The epithelium covering the olfactory areas of the nasal cavity, containing olfactory, sustentacular, and basal cells.

**Olfactory Lobe.** The anterior portion of the telencephalon : Rhinencephalon.

**Olfactory Nerve.** The first cranial nerve (I), a sensory nerve composed of the unmyelinated axons of olfactory cells.

**Olfactory Pit**

1. A depression which contains olfactory receptors, as that of a lancelet.

2. *embryol.* In vertebrate embryos, a depression which develops from an olfactory placode which gives rise to the olfactory sac or nasal cavity.

**Olfactory Sac.** A blind pouch in lower vertebrates which contains olfactory receptors. Its opening is the nasal aperture.

**Olfactory Tract.** A bundle of nerve fibers which connects the olfactory bulb with the cerebral hemisphere.

**Oligandrous.** Possessing few stamens.

**Oligocarpous.** With few carpels or fruits.

**Oligocene.** The third geological epoch of the Tertiary period. It began about 38 million years ago, following the Eocene epoch, and extended for about 12 million years to the beginning of the Miocene epoch. The epoch was characterized by the continued rise of mammals; the first pigs, rhinoceroses, and tapirs made their appearance.

**Oligocene Epoch.** An epoch of the Tertiary period characterized by the rise of flowering plants and archaic mammals. It follows the Eocene epoch.

**Oligochaeta.** A class of hermaphrodite annelid worms that bear only a few bristles (chaetae). Oligochaetes are very abundant in freshwater and terrestrial habitats. The most familiar members of the class are the earthworm (Lumbricus) and the freshwater bloodworm (Tubifex).

**Oligodendroglia.** Small neuroglia cells with few branches, usually located close to the cell bodies of neurons.

**Oligolectic.** Visiting few food plants or flowers, said of insects.

**Oligophagous.** Having food restricted to a single food plant, with reference to insects.

**Oligopneustic.** Having few functional spiracles, said of insects.

**Oligopod Larva.** An insect larva which lacks abdominal appendages, as the larva of scarab beetles.

**Oligosaccharide.** A carbohydrate composed of between two and ten polymerized monosaccharide units. Most oligosaccharides contain two (disaccharides), three (trisaccharides) or four tetrasaccharides) sugar units. The most important plan sugar, sucrose, is a disaccharide. Cellobiose is another common disaccharide, being the basic repeating unit of cellulose. Other disaccharides include trehalose and gentiobiose. The commonest trisaccharide is raffinose and the commonest tetrasaccharide stachyose.

Oligosaccharides may be intermediates in polysaccharide metabolism or may serve as storage compounds.

**Oligosaprobic.** Pertaining to an aquatic habitat rich in minimum matter and high in oxygen content with decomposition and purification processes reduced to a minimum.

**Oligospermia.** Deficient production of sperm or semen.

**Oligospermous.** Producing few seeds.

**Oligotrophic.** Applied to waters poor in nutrient and with low primary productivity. Typically, oligotrophic lakes are deep, with the hypolimnion much more extensive than the epilimnion. Plankton density is low and littoral plants are scarce. The low organic content means that dissolved-oxygen levels are high, favouring fish species such as trout. By comparison with eutrophic lakes, oligotrophic lakes are considered geologically young, or little modified by weathering and erosion products.

**Oligotrophication.** The process of nutrient depletion, or reduction in rates of nutrient cycling, in aquatic ecosystems. It arises as a consequence of acidification, typically the result of pollution and most notably associated with air pollution and acid rain.

**Oligotrophic Lake.** A deep lake with clear water containing little organic matter.

**Oligoxenous.** Having a limited host range, with reference to parasites.

**Olive**

1. *bot.* A small, slow-growing tree (Olea europaea) of the Mediterranean region or its fruit, the latter a source of olive oil.

2. *anat.* The oliva or olivary body, a rounded eminence on the medulla oblongata.

**Olive Shell.** A cylindrical-shaped, marine gastropod with a smooth, highly polished shell, as Oliva sayana, the lettered olive.

**Olynthus.** A developmental stage in certain sponges in which the body is vase-shaped with a sycon type of canal system.

**Omasum.** The third compartment in the stomach of a ruminant; manyplies; psalterium.

**Omental Bursa.** The lesser peritoneal sac, a cavity within the greater omentum which communicates with the peritoneal cavity via vestibule and epiploic foramen.

**Omentum pl. Omenta.** A fold of peritoneum which connects and protects certain visceral organs consisting of the greater omentum, which hangs like an apron over the intestines and the lesser omentum which lies between the stomach and the liver.

**Ommachrome.** A brown pigment present in ommatidia.

**Ommatidium.** One of the numerous elongated units which make up a compound eye of an arthropod.

**Omnivore.** An animal that eats both animal and vegetable matter, Pigs, for example, are omnivorous. Compare carnivore; herbivore.

**Omnivorous.** Feeding on both animal and plant food.

**Omosternum.** A bone in the sternum of an amphibian which lies anterior to the junction of the clavicles and the epicoracoid cartilages.

**Omphalos.** The umbilicus or navel.

**Onchomiracidium.** The ciliated larva of a monogenetic fluke; also oncomiracidium.

**Onchosphere.** A hexacanth, a six-hooked embryo which develops within the egg of various tapeworms, especially those of the genus Taenia. Also oncosphere.

**Oncogenic.** Describing a chemical, organism, or environmental factor that causes the development of cancer. Some viruses are oncogenic to vertebrates, including the Rous sarcoma virus of thickens, and some are suspected of being oncogentic (*e.g.* some of the adenoviruses and papovaviruses). Many of these viruses contain genes (known as oncogenes) that are responsible for the transformation of a normal host cell into a cancerous cell.

**Oncology.** The study of tumors.

**One Gene : One Enzyme Hypothesis.** The theory that the principal function of a gene is to determine the structure of an enzyme molecule. This was based on evidence showing that the presence or absence of an enzyme in a biochemical pathway was a genetically determined characteristic, inherited as a single gene. The theory was extended to include proteins other than enzymes. Subsequent analysis showed that where a protein consists of several polypeptide chains, it is more correct to say that one gene codes for one polypeptide chain. The genes coding for the component polypeptides of an enzyme need not be closely linked.

**One-gene-one-polypeptide Hypothesis.** The hypothesis that a large class of structural genes exists in which each gene encodes a single polypeptide, which may function either independently or as a subunit of a more complex protein. Originally it was thought that each gene encoded the whole of a single enzyme, but it has since been found that some enzymes and other proteins derive from more than one polypeptide and hence from more than one gene.

**Onion** A liliaceous plant (Allium cepa) or its succulent bulb, with a characteristic taste and odor due to a volatile oil, allyl sulfide.

**Onisciform.** With a flattened body; platyform.

**Ontogeny.** The developmental course of an organism from the fertilized egg through to maturity. It has been suggested that "ontogeny recapitulates phylogen", *i e.* the stages of development, especially of the embryo, reflect the evolutionary history of the organism. This idea is now discredited.

**Onychium.** A pulvillus.

**Onychophoran.** Any member of the Onychophora, a phylum or a subphylum or class of the Arthropoda, which contains a small number of wormlike forms mostly of the genus Peripatus which possess characteristics of both annelids and arthropods.

**Oocyst**

1. A cyst containing sporozoites of Plasmodium which develops in the wall of the stomach of a mosquito.

2. The encysted zygote of various protozoans, as coccidia.

**Oocyte.** The cell that, following meiosis, forms the ovum. Most of the cytoplasmic growth involved in ovum formation is accomplished by the primary oocyte : this undergoes the first meiotic division, giving rise to two cells, the polar body, with very little cytoplasm, and the secondary oocyte, which has a large amount of cytoplasm. This latter oocyte undergoes the second meiotic division to give rise to another polar body and an ovum. Fertilization often takes place at one of the two oocyte stages.

**Oogamy.** An extreme expression of anisogamy, in which fertilization occurs with the fusion of a large nonmotile female gamete or egg and a small usually motile male gamete. Compare isogamy.

**Oogenesis.** The production and growth of the ova (egg cells) in the animal ovary. Special cells (oogonia) within the ovary divide repeatedly by mitosis to produce large numbers of prospective egg cell (oocytes). When mature, these undergo meiosis, which halves the number of chromosomes. During the first meiotic division a polar body and a secondary oocyte are produced. At the second meiotic division the secondary oocyte produces an ovum and a second polar body. Oocytes may be present in the ovaries at birth and may represent the total number of eggs to be produced.

**Oogonium**

1. *bot.* A single-celled organ or structure in algae or fungi which produces the female gamete.

2. *zool.* A cell which in oogenesis gives rise to a primary oocyte.

**Ookinete.** The active, motile zygote of certain parasitic protozoans, as Plasmodium; vermicule. In a mosquito, it develops into an oocyst.

**Oology.** The study of eggs, especially the eggs of birds.

**Oomycetes.** A class of the Mastigomycotina containing fungi that typically produce zoospores with an anterior flimmer flagellum and a posterior whiplash flagellum. It contains about 580 species in some 70 genera. The mycelium is coenocytic and, unlike other fungi, has no chitin in its walls. Sexual reproduction involves the formation and fusion of oogonia and antheridia. The oospheres within the oogonia form thickwalled oospores after fertilization. The Oomycetes contains the four orders Lagenidiales. Saprolegniales, Leptomitales, and Peronosporales.

**Oosperm.** A fertilized ovum; a zygote.

**Oosphere.** A large nonmotile gamete that is rich in nutrients and is normally designated as female. One or several oospheres may be formed within an oogonium. They may be released unfertilized from the plant, as in the brown alga Fucus, or they may be retained within the oogonium and there form a zygote or oospore following fertilization. The oosphere is equivalent to the egg cells formed in the archegonia or embryo sacs of land plants.

**Oospore.** A zygote this is produced as a result of oogamy in certain algae and fungi. It contains food reserves, develops a protective outer covering, and enters a resting phase before germination. Compare zygospore.

**Oostegite.** One of several flattened structures borne on the coxae of thoracic appendages of certain crustaceans which form a brood pouch for the eggs and young, characteristic of the Pericarida.

**Ootheca.** An egg case, as that produced by certain insects, mollusks, and elasmobranchs.

**Ootid.** A mature ovum following the second maturation division.

**Ootype.** A dilated region of the oviduct in flatworms in which yolk from the vitellaria is added to the fertilized ovum and a shell formed before passage of the ovum to the uterus.

**Oozooid.** In tunicates, an individual which develops from an ovum.

**Opah.** A large, brillian, colored, marine fish (Lampris regius). Also called moonfish or Jerusalem haddock.

**Open Cell.** A cell in the wing of an insect which extends to the margin; one net entirely surrounded by veins.

**Operational Taxonomic Units (OTUs).** The entities whose affinities are studied by numerical taxonomy. Depending on the level and the type of investigation an OTU may be of any taxonomic rank or an individual organism.

**Operator.** A controlling gene located close to or forming a part of the structural genes it regulates.

**Operator Gene.** A site on the DNA adjacent to a structural gene that acts as part of a molecular 'switch' anddetermines whether or not transcription of the structcral gene will occur. The switch may be turned 'off by a repressor molecular binding to the operator, so preventing mRNA polymerase reaching the DAN. Conversely, absence of a repressor allows mRNA polymerase to bind to the DNA, *i.e.* the switch is 'on'. Other methods by which the operator genes function are also known.

**Operculate.** Having a lid, covering, or operculum.

**Operculum**

1. A lid or convering.

2. *bot. a.* The lid covering the discharge pore in the sporangium of certain fungi. *b.* The lid of a spore capsule in mosses. *c.* The lid of a pyxis.

3. *anat.* A cerebral fold which conceals the insula.

4. *zool.* A flap or plate which *a.* closes the opening of a hydrotheca in coelenterates; *b.* closes the aperture of the shell in gastropods; *c.* closes the opening of an egg through which an embryo or larva makes its exit, as in trematodes and insects; *d.* closes a burrow when occupant is retracted, as in serpulid polychaetes; *e.* covers the cavity containing sound-producing structures in cicadas; *f.* covers the book gills and genital openings of the king crab;. *g.* forms a respiratory structure in terrestrial isopods; *h.* covers the gill chamber of fishes, *i.* covers the gills and developing legs in amphibian larvae; *j.* is the second ear ossicle in urodeles and some anurans.

**Operon.** A group of adjacent genes coding for a set of enzymes in a particular biochemical pathway. The act as a single unit in that they are either all transcribed together or none are transcribed at all. In order for transcription to occur, mRNA polymerase, which catalyses mRNA synthesis, must first bind with the DNA at a site called the promoter. mRNA polymerase activity is prevented (negative control) or promoted (positive control) by the binding of a regulator protein between the promoter and the structural genes (the genes that actually code for the enzymes) at a site called the operator. The regulator protein is itself the product of a gene, the regulator, which may be some distance from the operon. A classic case of negative control is the lac (lactose) operon in the bacterium Escherichia coli. Here the regulalor protein prevents transcription in the absence of an inducer (a substrate molecule, *i.e.* lactose, or some derivative). However, if an inducer is present, it complexes with the regulator, the protein formed by the latter no longer binds to the operator, mRNA polymerase activity is permitted, and the enzymes are synthesized.

[1]**Ophidian**. Of or pertaining to snakes.

[2]**Ophidian**. A snake

**Ophioglossales.** An order of the Filicinae containing a small group of morphologically distinct ferns. The spores are not borne on the undersurface of the frond but in a separate stalked spike, and unlike all other ferns the fronds do not show circinate vernation. The order contains three genera : Ophioglossum (adder's tongues) containing about 30 species; Botrychium (moonworts) containing about 25 species; and Helminthostachys.

**Ophiuroid**. An echinoderm of the class Ophiuroidea which includes the brittle stars, basket stars, and serpent stars.

**Ophthalmic**. Of or pertaining to the eyes; ocular.

**Opiate.** One of a group of drugs derived from opium, an extract of the poppy plant Papaver somniferum that depresses brain function (a narcotic action). Opiates include morphine, codeine, and their synthetic derivatives, such as heroin. They are used in medicine chiefly to relieve pain, but the use of morphine and heroin is strictly controlled since they can cause drug dependence and tolerance.

**Opisthocoelous.** Concave behind, with reference to vertebrae in which the posterior end of centrum is concave, anterior end convex, as in the garpike.

**Opisthoglyph.** Having one or more pairs of rear teeth or fangs attached to the posteior portion of the maxillary bones of the upper jaw.

**Opisthognathous.** Having a receding lower jaw.

**Opisthohaptor.** A haptor located at the posterior end, as in monogenetic flukes.

**Opisthonephros.** The functional kidney of lampreys, most fishes, and amphibians.

**Opisthosoma.** The abdomen or posterior portion of the body, as in chelicerates.

**Opium.** A narcotic drug prepared from the dried juice of the unripe capsules of the opium poppy (Papaver somniferum). It contains a number of alkaloids, including morphine.

**Opposite.** Describing a form of leaf arrangement in which the leaves arise in pairs at each node. If each pair is at right angles to the pairs above and below it, as is usually the case, the arrangement is termed decussate. If the leaf pairs all arise in the same plane a distichous arrangement results. Compare alternate, whorled.

**Opossum**

1. A marsupial (Didelphis virginiana) of the United States, noted for feigning death (playing possum).

2. One of a number of related marsupials of Australia.

**Opossum Shrimp.** A mysid, a crustacean of the order Mysidacea, females of which possess a brood pouch or marsupium.

**Opsiblastic.** Undergoing a period of dormancy before developing, with reference to eggs.

**Opsonin** An antibody or antibodylike substance which renders bacteria more susceptible to phagocytosis.

**Optic.** Of or pertaining to the eyes or vision.

**Optical Activity.** Term that refers to the ability of certain compounds to rotate the plane of polarized light when in solution; rotation of light to the right is designated dextrotatory, D, or (+), and to the left laevorotatory, L, or (−). Carbohydrates and amino acids are common organic compounds that exhibit this activity. This phenomenon arises in compounds that possess asymmetric carbon atoms and therefore exist as optical isomers which are mirror images of one another. The symbols 'D' and 'L' are used to distinguish two such isomers.

**Optical Fibre.** A glass fibre through which light can be transmitted with very little leakage through the sidewalls. In the stepindex fibre a pure glass core, with a diameter between 6 and 250 micrometres, is surrounded by a glass or plastic cladding of lower refractive index. The cladding is usually between 10 and 150 micrometres thick. The interface between core and cladding acts as a cylindrical mirror at which total internal reflection of the transmitted light takes place. This structure enables a beam of light to travel through many kilometres of fibre. In the graded-index fibre, each layer of glass, from the fibre axis to its outer wall, has a slightly lower refractive index than the layer inside it. This arrangement also prevents light from escaping through the fibre walls by a combination of refraction and total internal reflection, and can be made to give the same transit time for rays at different angles.

Fibre-optic systems use optical fibres to transmit information, in the form of coded pulses or fragmented images (using bundles of fibres), from a source to a receiver. They are used, for example, in medical instruments (fibrescopes) to examine internal body cavities, such as the stomach and bladder.

**Optic Chiasma.** The crossing and partial decussation of fibers of the optic nerves located on ventral surface of the brain.

**Optic Lobes.** The corpora bigemina, two rounded bodies forming the roof of the midbrain and concerned with vision; well developed in amphibians, reptiles, and birds; absent In mammals.

**Optic Nerve.** The second cranial nerve : a paired sensory nerve that runs from each eye to the brain. It is responsible for conveying visual stimuli received by the rods and cones in the retina to the brain for interpretation.

**Optic Tract.** A band of fibers which extends from the optic chiasma to the lateral geniculate body of the thalamus.

**Oral**

1. Of or pertaining to the mouth or region of the mouth.
2. Spoken, in contrast to written.
3. Taken into, or used within the mouth.

**Oral Arm.** One of four extensions of the manubrium which surround the mouth in scyphozoan medusae.

**Oral Cone.** The hypostome of a hydroid.

**Oral Disc.** In anthozoans the flattened, circular area surrounding the mouth.

**Oral Funnel.** Buccal funnel.

**Oral Groove.** In ciliates, a surface groove which leads to the cytostome.

**Oral Hood.** A hoodlike fold bearing cirri which surrounds the vestibule of a lancelet.

**Oral Spear.** A pointed structure or stylet in soil nematodes used in penetrating roots, or once within a root, in piercing cells.

**Oral Sucker.** In flukes, the sucker which surrounds the mouth.

**Oral Valves.** In fishes, two folds within the mouth opening which prevent the backflow of water during respiratory movements.

**Orange.** A spherical globose fruit, a berry of a small evergreen tree of the genus Citrus or the tree that produces it.

**Orangutan.** A large, arboreal, anthropoid ape (Pongo pygmaeus) of the swamps of Sumatra and Borneo.

**Orbicular.** Almost circular and flattened, as are the leaves of the fringed water lily (Nymphoides peltata).

**Orbiculate.** Circular or nearly circular in shape, said of leaves; disc-shaped.

**Orbit**

1. In crustaceans, the cavity which contains the eyestalk.
2. In insects, the region along the inner border of the eye, as in dipterans.

3. In vertebrates, the eye socket, a cavity, of the skull which contains the eye.

**Orbital.** Of, pertaining to, or located in on near an orbit.

**Orbital Glands.** Large mucous glands located in the orbit whose ducts open into the mouth cavity, as in members of the dog family.

**Orchid.** Any monocot plant of the family Orchidaceae, noted for the beauty of their flowers and high degree of specialization, especially with respect to pollination. Most are tropical plants; many are epiphytic.

**Orchidaceae.** A very large monocotyledonous family, the orchid family, containing about 18000 species in about 750 genera. Orchids are widely cultivated for their distinctive flowers, which may be recognized by the characteristic lower lip or labellum. The anthers and carpels lie opposite the labellum and are fused into a structure called the column. The column is very diverse in form, the various modifications being related to the different pollinating animals. The pollen grains are clumped together into a definite number of pollen masses, termed pollinia, on the column. Following pollination and fertilization, seeds are produced in vast numbers, but each contains only a rudimentary embryo. Seed maturation and germination is thus a lengthy process, which may take a number of years. In addition, orchids live in symbiotic association with various fungi and the appropriate fungus is needed before a seed can germinate. These factors have hindered the commercial multiplication of orchids though orchid growers have been quick to utilize tissue culture methods of multiplication. Orchid breeding is facilitated by the 'promiscuous' nature of orchids and the ease with which they form viable hybrids. This ability is demonstrated by the number of naturally occurring orchid hybrids, which exceeds those of all other plant families added together. About half the species of orchids (including most in the cultivated species) are epiphytic and thus need special compost mixtures.

**Order** (in taxonomy). A category used in the classification of organisms that consists of one or several similar or closely related families. Similar orders form a class. Order names typically end in -ales in botany, *e.g.*, Rosales (roses and orchard fruits), and in -a in zoology, *e.g.*, Carnivora (flesh eaters).

**Ordination**. A technique used in ecological work to relate the composition of different stands of vegetation to each other. It is used by those who consider that no two stands of natural vegetation are ever the same and thus they cannot be classified into distinct associations (compare classification). Certain properties of each stand, namely data on the species present, are plotted against one or more axes, each axis representing some environmental gradient. The end result should be an arrangement in which the different vegetation stands are ordered in a manner that best reflects their similarities and differences.

**Ordination Method**. Method for arranging individuals (or sometimes attributes) in order along one or more lines. The method is used, with many techniques, in the biological and earth sciences, and especially in biology. There is an extensive ecological literature that discusses ordination methods, their applicability to different situations, and the relative merits of ordination as opposed to classification schemes.

**Ordovician**. The second period of geological time in the Palaeozoic era, about 500—440 million years ago. There are no known terrestrial organisms in this period.

**Odrovician Period**. The second period of the Paleozoic era following the Cambrian and preceding the Silurian characterized the rise of the first vertebrates, the ostracoderms.

**Ordure.** Excrement, dung, feces.

**Organ.** Any distinct part of an organism that is specialized to perform one or a number of functions. Examples are ears, eyes, lungs, and kidneys (in animals) and leaves, roots, and flowers (in plants). A given organ will contain many different tissues.

**Organ Culture.** The culture of excised organs in a suitable aseptic medium. Roots, leaves, embryos, meristems, and many other plant structures have been successfully maintained in culture. By observing growth in the presence and absence of various nutrients, valuable information about the physiology of the organ can be obtained. For example, chemical factors affecting sex expression have been studied using cultures of isolated flowers, and root nodule formation has been investigated in cultures of legume roots.

**Organelle.** A membrane-enclosed structure in the cytoplasm organized to carry out a specific process essential to the life of the cell. Examples are the mitochondria, chloroplasts, and golgi apparatus.

**Organic**

1. Pertaining to, consisting of, or related to organs.
2. Pertaining to, originating in, or derived from living organisms.
3. *chem.* Pertaining to compounds which contain carbon.

**Organic Evolution.** The evolution of life and living things; the origin of species.

**Organism**

1. A Living individual.

2. An individual capable of carrying on metabolic activities and reproducing, as a plant, animal, or protist.

**Organismic.** Applied to groups of organisms, or communities, that are thought to have properties *e.g.*, homoeostasis or reproduction) similar to those of a single living organism, making them 'supraorganisms'. The term is most used to describe plant communities by those who consider that discrete climax vegetation entities, *e.g.*, beech—oak woodlands, may be identified. These units will necessarily show a high degree of internal interdependence of species, and on the maturity and death of a community another identical plant association will replace it. This organismic concept forms the theoretical basis for a classificatory approach to the description of vegetation communities and their analysis. Compare individualistic hypothesis.

**Organizer.** An area of an animal embryo that causes adjacent areas of the embryo to develop in a certain way. The primary organizer (blastopore lip or archenteron roof) causes the gastrula to develop as a complete organism.

**Organ of Bojanus**

1. A nephridium.
2. The excretory organ of a bivalve.

**Organ of Corti.** The end organ of hearing, an elongated spiral structure resting on the basilar membrane of the cochlea. It contains hair cells, receptors for auditory stimuli.

**Organogensis.** The developmental changes that occur during the formation of a particular organ.

**Organomercurial Fungicide.** An organic fungicide containing mercury. Most of this group are phenylmercury derivatives, *e.g.*, phenylmercuric acetate, and are used as seed dressings. Mercurycontaining fungicides are highly toxic to mammals and treated grain must be clearly labelled or even dyed to distinguish it from edible grain.

**Organogenesis.** The development of specific organs or structures from undifferentiated tissue.

**[1]Organoid.** Organlike.

**[2]Organoid.** An organelle.

**Organ-pipe Coral.** An alcyonarian coral of the genus Tubipora with long, slender polyps encased in brick-red skeletal tubes.

**Organ System.** System.

**Oriental Realm.** A major biogeographic realm comprising Asia south of the Himalayas. It includes India, Malay Peninsula, Sumatra, Borneo Java, Celebes, and the Philippine Islands.

**Orifice.** An opening or aperture; a mouth [or mouthlike opening.

**Origin**

1. The act of coming into existence.
2. That from which anything originates.
3. The relativity fixed end of attachment of a muscle.

**Origin of Life.** The process by which living organisms developed from inanimate matter, which is generally thought to have occurred on earth between 3500 and 4000 million years ago. It is supposed that the primordial atmosphere was like a chemical soup containing all the basic constituents of organic matter : ammonia, methane, hydrogen, and water vapour. These underwent a process of chemical evolution using energy from the sun and electric storms to combine into ever more complex molecules, such as amino acids, proteins, and vitamins. Eventually self-replicating nucleic acids, the basis of all life, could have developed. The very first organisms may have consisted of such molecules bounded by a simpte membrane.

**Ornithine.** A nonprotein amino acid, formula $OH_2(CH_2)_3$-$CH(NH_2)COOH$. It is an intermediate in the synthesis of arginine, and many alkaloids, *e.g.* the tropane alkaloids, are derived from ornithine. It also occurs in the cell walls of some bacteria.

**Ormer.** An abalone, especially Haliotis tuberculata, of the English channel.

**Ornate.** Elaborately marked or embellished, as the ornate scallop (Pecten ornatus) or ornate ticks, as Dermacentor and Amblyoma.

**Ornithine.** An amino acid, $C_5H_{12}O_2N_2$, present in the excreta of birds.

**Ornithine Cycle.** A cyclic series of reactions occurring in the liver resulting in the formation of urea; Krebs-Henseleit or urea cycle.

**Ornithischian.** Any rossil reptile of the Ornithischia, comprising birdlike, bipedal, herbivorous dinosaurs; the beaked and duck-billed dinosaurs.

**Ornithology.** The study of birds and bird life.

**Ornithophily.** Pollination by pollen carried by birds. It is an important form of pollination for many tropical species, the most common pollinators being hummingbirds (in South America) and sunbirds (in Africa). Many of the less specialized species of Fuchsia and Lopezia are bird pollinated. Bird-pollinated flowers are often red in colour. Pollination by insects (entomophily) is believed to be derived from ornithophily.

**Ornithosis.** A virus disease of birds, especially pigeons and domestic fowl, transmissible to man; resembles psittacosis.

**Oronasal Groove.** An external groove connecting the olfactory pit to the mouth, as in elasmobranchs.

**Orphan Virus.** A virus which has not been shown to cause a disease.

**Orthogenesis.** Evolutionary trends that remain fairly constant over long periods of time and so appear to lead directly from ancestor organisms to their descendants. This was once explained as the result of some internal directing force or 'need. within the organisms themselves. Such metaphysical interpretations have been displaced by the concepts of orthoselection and species selection.

**Orthognathous.** With jaws evenly aligned so that neither protrudes.

**Orthopedics.** The branch of medicine which deals with diseases of the bones and joints, especially the correction of skeletal deformities.

**Orthopnea.** A condition in which breathing is difficult unless subject is sitting in an upright position.

**Orthopteran.** Any insect of the order Orthoptera which includes the grasshoppers, locusts, katydids, crickets, cockroaches, mantids, and walking sticks. Front wings are straight and narrow and cover the hind wings which are folded like a fan; mouth parts biting; metamorphosis incomplete.

**Orthostichous.** In phyllotaxy, arranged in straight, vertical rows or ranks.

**Orthotropism.** A tropism in which the growth response is directly towards or away from the source of the stimulus. Thus the vertical growth of tree trunks may be described as negative orthogeotropism and the growth of the gills of agaric fungi positive orthogeotropism.

**Orthotropous** (atropous). Describing a form of ovule orientation in the ovary in which the ovule develops in an upright position from the placenta (illustration at ovule). This arrangement is rare but may be found in some members of the Polygonaceae. Compare anatropous, campylotropous.

**Oryx.** A large African antelope of the genus Oryx, with long, straight horns.

[1]**Os** pl. **Ora.** A mouth or opening.

[2]**Os** pl. **Ossa.** A bone.

**Oscillate.** To move back and forth; to swing like a pendulum.

**Oscillatoriales.** Hormogonales.

**Oscine.** Of or pertaining to passerine birds of the suborder Oscines which includes most of the common songbirds, characterized by possession of a syrinx.

**Os Cordis.** A heterotopic bone present in the heart of certain mammals, as the deer.

**Os Cornu** A mass on the frontal bone of a mammal from which a horn develops.

**Os Coxae.** The innominate or hipbone.

**Osculum** pl. **Oscula.** The excurrent opening of a sponge.

**Osmium Tetroxide.** A fixative (preservative) for proteins and phosphoglycerides that is used in the preparation of biological material for light microscopy and electron microscopy. It is fat soluble and is reduced to black osmium dioxide by unsaturated fats. Saturated fats in a specimen may be dissolved out in dehydration or embedding, the blackened unsaturated fats remaining. It is therefore used to stabilize and stain cell constituents. Often a preparation is prefixed with glutaraldehyde and post-fixed with osmium tetroxide to increase the extent of preservation.

**Osmeterium.** A repugnatorial gland in insects.

**Osmic Acid.** Osmium tetroxide, $OsO_4$, a crystalline substance used in microtechnique as an immobilizing and fixing agent.

**Osmoconformer.** An organism which is able to change its body fluid osmotically to adjust to the osmotic pressure of the medium in which it lives. Compare osmoregulator.

**Osmometer.** An apparatus designed to demonstrate osmosis and to measure osmotic pressure (water potential). One form of osmometer consists of a porous pot, rendered semipermeable by impregnation of its pores with copper ferrocyanide. The pot is filled with the solution under investigation and a piston placed on the solution. The pot is then immersed in a container of distilled water. Water passes by osmosis into the porous pot and lifts the piston until the force of the water entering the pot equals the hydrostatic pressure created by the weight of the piston.

**Osmophilic.** Adapted for living in a medium with a high osmotic pressure. Compare halophile.

**Osmoreceptor.** A receptor which is stimulated by changes in osmotic pressure.

**Osmoregulation.** The maintenance of proper water and electrolyte balance.

**Osmoregulator.** An organism which maintains a constant osmotic concentration in its body fluid regardless of the medium in which it lives.

**Osmoregulatory.** Pertaining to or involved in the regulation or control of osmotic pressure within an organism, accomplished by maintenance of proper water and electrolyte balance.

**Osmosis.** The passage of a solvent through a semipermeable membrane separating two solutions of different concentrations. A semipermeable membrane is one through which the molecules of a solvent can pass but the molecules of most solutes cannot. There is a thermodynamic tendency for solutions separated by such a membrane to become equal in concentration, the water (or other solvent) flowing from the weaker to the stronger solution. Osmosis will stop when the two solutions reach equal concentration, and can also be stopped by applying a pressure to the liquid on the stronger-solution side of the membrane. The pressure required to stop the flow from a pure solvent into a solution is a characteristic of the solution, and is called the osmotic pressure (symbol II). Osmotic pressure depends only on the concentration of particles in the solution, not on their nature. For a solution of *n* moles in volume V at thermodynamic temperature T, the osmotic pressure is given by IIV=RT, where R is the gas constant. Osmotic-pressure measurements are used in finding the relative molecular masses of compounds, particularly macromolecules. A device used to measure osmotic pressure is called an osmometer.

**Osmotic Potential** (solute potential). The component of water potential that takes into account the concentration of solutes in the cell. It is represented by the symbol $\psi_p$ and is always negative. Osmotic potential includes a component due to the matric potential of colloidal substances and organelles in the cytoplasm.

**Osmotic Pressure.** The pressure needed to prevent the passage of water or other pure solvent through a semi-permeable membrane separating the solvent from the solution. Osmotic pressure rises with an increase in concentration of the solution. Where two solutions of different substances or concentrations are separated by a semi-permeable membrane, the solvent will move to equalize osmotic pressure within the system.

**Os Palpebrae.** A heterotopic bony plate embedded in the eyelid of a crocodile.

**Os Penis.** A heterotopic bone of the penis.

**Osphradium.** A sensory receptor in gastropods and bivalves which functions as a chemoreceptor and for detection of sediment in water passing over the gills.

**Osprey.** A large fish hawk (Pandion haliaetus).

**Ossein.** A protein present in the organic matrix of bone.

**Osseous.** Bony; composed of, resembling, or of the nature of bone.

**Ossicle.** A small bone or bonelike structure, as *a.* one of the bones of the middle ear; ear ossicle; *b.* a small, calcareous plate in the skeleton of echinoderms; *c.* a toothlike structure in the gastric mill of a crustacean; *d.* a small bony plate embedded in the sclera of certain birds and reptiles.

**Ossification.** The process of bone formation. It is brought about by the action of special cells called osteoblasts, which deposit layers of bone in connective tissue. Some bones are formed directly in connective tissue (membrane bone); others are formed by the replacement of cartilage (cartilage bone).

**Ossify**

1. *anat.* To convert into bone or bonelike material.

2. *bot.* To develop a hard, bonelike structure, as the stony layer of a drupe.

**Osteichthyan.** Any vertebrate of the class Osteichthyes which includes the bony fishes, comprising the subclasses Choanichthyes (lung- and lobe-finned fishes) and Actinopterygii (ray-finned fishes).

**Osteichthyes.** The class of vertebrates comprising the bony fishes—marine and fresh-water fish with a bony skeleton. All have gills covered with a bony operculum, and a layer of thin overlapping bony scales covers the entire body surface. Bony fish have a swim bladder, which acts as a hydrostatic organ enabling the animal to remain suspended in the water at any depth. In some fish this bladder acts as a lung.

**Osteoblast.** A bone-forming cell.

**Osteoclast.** A large, multinuclear cell found where resorption of bone is taking place and thought to be the active agent in the process.

**Osteocranium.** The bony portion of the cranium. Compare chondrocranium.

**Osteocyte.** A mature bone cell lodged within a lacuna in the matrix of bone tissue.

**Osteoderm.** A minute bone in the dermis of certain reptiles.

**Osteogenesis.** Bone formation; ossification.

**Osteognnic.** Of or pertaining to bone formation.

**Osteoid.** The organic matrix of developing bone within which calcium salts are deposited.

**Osteology.** The study of bones, especially their formation and organization into the skeletal system.

**Osteomalacia.** Adult rickets; the softening of bones due to inadequate intake of calcium, phosphorus, or vitamin D.

**Osteone.** A haversian system.

**Ostiole.** A small pore found in the reproductive bodies of certain algae and fungi (*e.g.* the conceptacles of Fucus or the perithecia of certain ascomycete fungi) through which the spores are released.

**Ostium** pl. **Ostia**. An opening into a tube or cavity, as *a.* in sponges, an opening through which water enters a radial canal or spongocoel, *b.* in anthozoans, an opening in a septum; *c.* in arthropods, an opening in the heart through which blood enters; *d.* in bivalves, an opening through which water enters a water tube of a gill; *e.* in vertebrates, the opening to an oviduct or uterine tube.

**Ostracod.** A crustacean of the Ostracoda which includes mostly minute freshwater or marine forms with a bivalve carapace, as Cypris.

**Ostracoderm.** Any member of the Ostracoderma, an order of primitive, jawless, fishlike vertebrates with a heavy armor of dermal bone encasing head and anterior part of the trunk. All are fossil forms.

**Ostrich.** A large, flightless bird (Struthio camelus) inhabiting arid regions of Arabia, Syria, and North Africa; the largest of living birds.

**Otic.** Of or pertaining to the ear; auditory, auricular.

**Otic Vesicle.** An otocyst.

**Otoconia.** Ear dust or particles of calcium carbonate present in the otolithic membrane of the macula of the inner ear.

**Otocyst**

1. A statocyst.
2. *embryol.* The auditory or otic vesicle from which the membranous labyrinth of the inner ear develops.

**Otolith.** A calcareous body present in the statocyst of invertebrates or the saccule of vertebrates.

**Otolithic Membrane.** A gelatinous substance on the surface of a macula into which the hairs of hair cells project. It contains otoliths (otoconia), movement of which stimulates the hair cells.

**Otology.** The science which deals with the ear.

**Otoporpa.** In hydrozoan medusae, a tract containing nematocysts which extends upward from a lithostyle.

**Otter.** An aquatic, fur-bearing mammal of the family Mustelidae, as Lutra lutra, the Old World otter; L. canadensis, the North American or river otter, and Enhydra lutris, the sea otter.

**OTUs.** Operational Taxonomic Units.

**Outbreeding.** The production of offspring by the fusion of distantly related gametes. The consequences of outbreeding are opposite to those of inbreeding and mechanisms have been developed by the majority of plants to promote it. The main outbreeding mechanisms are incompatibility factors, heteromorphism (*e.g.* heterostyly), protogyny, protandry, and dioecism.

**Outcrossing.** Outbreeding.

**Outer Ear** (external ear). The part of the ear external to the tympanum (eardrum). It is present in mammals, birds, and some reptiles and consists of a tube (the external auditory meatus) that directs sound waves onto the tympanum. In mammals it may include an external pinna, which extends beyond the skull.

**Ouzel** also **Ousel.** The ring ouzel, a European bird (Turdus torquatus) related to the thrushes.

**Oval Window.** The fenestra ovalis, an opening in the vestibule of the inner ear which receives the footplate of the stapes.

**Ovarian.** Of or pertaining to the ovary.

**Ovariectomy.** Surgical removal of an ovary.

**Ovariotomy.** Surgical incision into an ovary : Ovariectomy.

**Ovary.** The swollen basal part of the carpel in angiosperms, which contains the ovules. The ovary is hollow and may contain one or many ovules in its locule, each attached by a funiculus. When the carpels are partially or totally united a compound ovary is formed, while may be either unilocular or multilocular depending on whether or not the fused carpel walls break down. Depending on its position in the flower an ovary may be described as inferior, when the other floral organs are inserted above it, or superior when the other floral organs are inserted below (epigyny, perigyny, hypogyny). The ovary wall is usually thick and serves to protect the developing ovules. After fertilization the ovary wall forms the pericarp of the fruit.

**Ovate.** Describing an organ, such as a leaf, that is egg shaped, with the broadest part nearest the point of attachment.

**Overdominance** (superdominance). In genetics, the phenomenon in which the character of the heterozygotes is expressed more markedly in the phenotype than in that of either, homozygote. Usually the heterozygote is fitter than the two homozygotes; this can give rise to monohybrid heterosis, the hybrid vigour obtained by crossing parents differing in a single specified pair of allelic genes.

**Over-representation.** In pollen analysis, the presence in considerable abundance of immediately local pollen which tends to obscure the general pattern of changes in the regional pollen-rain record, *e.g.* the predominance of pollen from bog plants at a peat bog site.

**Overspecialization.** An old theory which held that straight-line evolution or orthogenetic trends might proceed to the point at which the lineage was at an adaptive disadvantage. Over specialization was therefore considered as one of the causes of extinction. There is no reason to believe, however, that natural selection would permit evolution to proceed beyond maximum adaptation. More recently the term has been applied to highly specialized organisms which have proved incapable of responding to environmental change and so have become extinct.

**Overturn.** In limnology, the process occurring in lakes when, in the spring, surface water on warming becomes heavier and sinks to the bottom (spring overturn) or in the fall when surface water becomes relatively cooler and sinks to the bottom (fall overturn).

**Ovicell.** In ectoprocts, a modified zooecium which serves as a brood chamber or pouch.

**Oviducal.** Of or pertaining to an oviduct.

**Oviduct.** The tube that conveys an animal egg cell from the ovary to other parts of the reproductive system or to the outside. Eggs are passed along the oviduct by the action of muscles and cilia.

**Ovigerous.** Egg-bearing, as an ovigorous mantle in barnacles or ovigerous legs, in certain spiders.

**Oviparity.** Reproduction in which fertilized eggs are laid or spawned by the mother and hatch outside her body. It occurs in most animals except marsupial and placental mammals. Compare ovoviviparity; viviparity.

**Oviparous.** Applied to species that lay eggs; embryos develop outside the mother's body, each egg eventually hatching into a young animal. Little or no development occurs within the mother's body, unlike the viviparous condition. Examples of ovipary are found in birds and some reptiles, including all chelonians and crocodilians, and some (mainly tropical) snakes and lizards.

**Ovipositor.** Specialized egg-laying organ which in most insects is formed from outgrowths of the eighth and ninth abdominal segments. There are six outgrowths in all, known as valves, and these may be modified to form a variety of structures. In some insects the valves are short and in others they are drawn out to form along, stylet-like tube. Extreme forms of ovipositor occur in the sawflies, ichneumons, and wood wasps, where it may be longer than the entire body, and equipped apically with saw teeth to aid penetration of hard plant tissues. Worker bees and sterile female wasps have the ovipositor modified to form a stinging organ and poison sac.

**Ovisac.** A structure in which eggs are stored or, in some cases, developed, as *a.* the uterus in elasmobranches and amphibians; *b.* the egg sac in the fairy shrimp.

**Ovotestis.** An organ which produces both spermatozoa and ova, present in certain hermaphroditic animals, as snails.

**Ovoviviparity.** Reproduction in which fertilized eggs develop and hatch in the oviduct of the mother. It occurs in many invertebrates and in some fish and reptiles (*e.g.* the viper). Compare oviparity.

**Ovoviviparous.** Producing shelled eggs with considerable yolk which develop within the body of the female but the young do not receive nourishment from the mother through a placenta or similar structure, as in sharks.

**Ovulation.** The release of an egg cell from the ovary. The developing egg cell within its follicle migrates to the ovary surface; when mature, it is released from the follicle (which breaks open) into the body cavity, from where it passes into the oviduct.

**Ovule.** Structure in angiosperms and gymnosperms that, after fertilization, develops into a seed. In gymnosperms the ovules are unprotected, whereas in angiosperms they are protected by the megasporophyll (which forms the carpel). One or several ovules may be contained in the carpel and each is attached to the carpel wall by a stalk (funicle). When mature, the angiosperm ovule consists of a central mass of tissue, the nucellus, surrounded by one or two protective layers, the integuments, which eventually give rise to the seed coat. Within the nucellus is a large oval cell, the embryo sac, which has developed from the megaspore and contains the naked egg cell.

**Ovule, Culture.** The culture of excised ovules on suitable media in vitro. Ovules have been cultured with pollen grain of the same species in order to observe the processes of fertilization and embryo development. Culture with pollen of different species may enable certain crosses to be made that are normally impossible due to incompatibility factors in the sigma. Some ovules in culture give rise to callus tissue that subsequently forms numerou embryolike structures (embryoids). These can be separated and grown on to mature plants, so providing a means of plant propagation.

**Ovuliferous.** Bearing ovules.

**Ovuliferous Scale.** A scale that bears ovules and then seeds in the female strobilus or cone of the conifers. It is borne in the axils of the spirally arranged woody bracts that constitute the cone. The ovuliferous scale is a highly specialized megasporophyll and is homologous with a carpel.

**Ovum** (egg cell)

1. (in zoology). The mature reproductive cell (gamete) of female animals, which is produced by the ovary (oogenesis). It is spherical, has a nucleus, is covered with a vitelline membrane, and is not mobile.
2. (in botany). The oosphere of plants.

**Owl.** A nocturnal bird of prey of the order Strigiformes characterized by a large head, short neck, large eyes surrounded by facial discs, short, hooked bill, and long, sharp, curved talons. They feed on small animals, principally rodents and insects.

**Owlet.** A small owl; a young owl.

**Ox** pl. **Oxen.** A domestic bovine (Bos taurus), especially the castrated male, formerly used extensively as a draft animal.

**Oxalic Acid.** A dibasic acid, formula $(COOH)_2$, found in many plants *e.g.* rhubarb (Rheum raponiticum) and dumbcanes (Dieffenbachia). It helps remove excessive amounts of various cations, *e.g.* calcium, and potassium, by forming the respective oxalates.

**Oxaloacetic Acid.** A four-carbon dicarboxylic keto acid with the formula $HOOCCOCH_2COOH$. Oxaloacetate is a TCA cycle intermediate formed by oxidation of malic acid. It reacts with acetly CoA to form the six-carbon acid citrate. Oxaloacetate is also an intermediate in glucose synthesis, and in $C_4$ plants of the Hatch—Slack pathway. The carboxylation of pyruvate to form oxaloacetate is a major reaction for replacing TCA cycle intermediates that have been withdrawn to take part in synthetic reactions. The reverse of this reaction is an important route of glucose synthesis.

**Oxidase.** Any of the flavin-linked dehydrogenases in which the reduced coenzyme can be reoxidized by molecular oxygen, which forms hydrogen peroxide with water. An example is the enzyme L-amino acid oxidase, which catalyses the oxidative deamination of L-amino acids.

**Oxidation**

1. A reaction in which oxygen combines with another substance with the liberation of heat; combustion; burning.
2. The removal of hydrogen from a compound.
3. The loss of electrons with an increase in positive valence of an element. Compare reduction.

**Oxidation-Reduction** (redox). Originally, oxidation was simply regarded as a chemical reaction with oxygen. The reverse process—loss of oxygen—was called reduction. Reaction with hydrogen also came to be regarded as reduction. Later, a more general idea of oxidation and reduction was developed in which oxidation was loss of electrons and reduction was gain of electrons. This wider definition covered the original one and also applies to reactions that do not involve oxygen. However, it applies only to reactions in which electron transfer occurs—*i e.* to reactions involving ions. It can ce extended to reactions between covalent compounds by using the concept of oxidation number (or state). This is a measure of the electron control that an atom has in a compound compared to the atom in the pure element. An oxidation number consists of two parts :

1. its sign, which indicates whether the control has increased (negative) or decreased (positive);

2. its value, which gives the number of electrons over which control has changed.

The change of electron may be complete (in ionic compouds) or partial (in colvent compounds). Oxidation is a reaction involving an increase in oxidation number and reduction involves a decrease. Thus in

$$2H_2+O_2\rightarrow 2H_2O$$

the hydrogen in water is +1 and the oxygen—2. The hydrogen is oxidized and the oxygen is reduced. Compounds that tend to undergo reduction readily are oxidizing agents; those that undergo oxidation are reducing agents.

**Oxidation—reduction Reaction** (oxidoreduction, redox reaction). A process in which electrons are transferred from an electron donor or reducing agent to an electron aceptor or oxidizing agent. Oxidation—reductions are major energy supplying reactions in both autotrophic and heterotrophic organisms.

In aerobic organisms the final electron acceptor for oxidation—reduction reactions is oxygen. Anaerobic organisms however use an organic compound as a final electron acceptor, *e.g.* in yeasts acetaldehyde accepts electrons to form ethanol.

In all organisms there are intermediate oxidation—reduction enzymes and coenzymes between the fuel molecules and the final electron acceptor. The most important of these are the pyridine nucleotides (NAD, NADP).

**β-oxidation.** The principal route for the degradation of fatty acids to acetyl CoA. In β-oxidation, carbons are removed from the fatty acid chain two at a time; thus one molecule of acetyl CoA is formed on every turn of the spiral of β-oxidation (diagram). The acetyl CoA resulting from this process can be further oxidized in the TCA cycle to yield more energy or it can be converted to sugar via the glyoxylate cycle.

In germinating oil-rich seeds tee enzymes of β-oxidation are located in the glyoxysome along with the enzymes of the glyoxylate cycle.

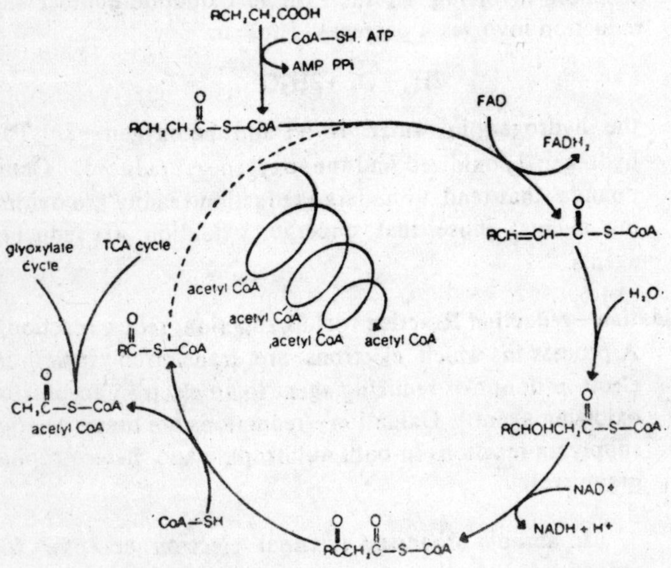


The β-oxidation spiral

**Oxidative Phosphorylation.** A reaction occurring during the final stages of aerobic respiration, in which ATP is formed from ADP and phosphate coupled to electron transport in the electron transport chain. The reaction occur in the mitochondria and takes place at three sites on the electron transport chain.

**Oxidize.** To bring about oxidation.

**Oxidoreductase.** Any enzyme that catalyses oxidation—reduction reactions. The two main groups are the pyridine-linked and the flavin-linked dehydrogenases. Electron-transfering proteins, notably the iron—sulphur proteins and the cytochromes, may also be classed as oxidoreductases.

**Oxpecker.** An African starling of the genus Buphagus which perches on the backs of large game animals and cattle and feeds on ectoparasites. And called tickbird.

**Oxygen.** Symbol O. A colourles odourless gaseous element. It is the most abundant element in the earth's crust (49.2% by weight) and is present in the atmosphere (28% by volume). Atmospheric oxygen is of vital importance for all organisms that carry out aerobic respiration.

**Oxygenation**

1. A combination with oxygen : Oxidation.
2. The loose combination of oxygen with hemoglobin to form oxyhemoglobin.

**Oxygen Debt.** The physiological state that exists in a normally aerobic animal when insufficient oxygen is available for metabolic requirements (*e.g.* during a period of strenuous physical activity). To meet the body's increased demand for energy, pyruvate is converted anaerobically (*i e.* in the absence of oxygen) to lactic acid, which requires oxygen for it breakdown and accumulates in the tissues. When oxygen is available again lactic acid is oxidized in the liver, thus repaying the debt.

**Oxygen-isotope Analysis.** Method for estimating past ocean temperatures. The ratio of the stable oxygen isotopes $^{18}O : ^{16}O$, in water is temperature dependent, $^{18}O$ increasing as temperature falls. Oxygen incorporated in the calcium-carbonate shells of marine organisms will reflect the prevailing $^{18}O : ^{16}O$ ratio. Acidification (to release oxygen) of these fossils under carefully controlled conditions can therefore be used, with appropriate celibration, to indicate the past temperature record.

**Oxygen Method.** Estimation of gross primary productivity by monitoring rates of production of oxygen, the by-product of photosynthesis. In field practice this principle is most often used for productivity measurement in aquatic ecosystems. Paired 'light and dark' bottles are filled with water from the required sample depth and suspended at this level for several hours. The dark bottle records oxygen uptake by respiration of phytoplankton and other micro-organisms during the measurement period. Changes in oxygen levels in the light bottle reflect production in photosynthesis as well as loss in respiration. Assuming that respiration rates in the paired bottles are similar, gross primary productivity may be estimated by adding oxygen loss in the dark bottle to the change recorded in the light bottle. The light bottle alone records net community productivity. Net primary productivity estimates are only possible in dense phytoplanktonic communities *e.g.* algal blooms in which the oxygen loss due to respiration of other micro-organisms is proportionately very small.

**Oxyhemoglobin.** Oxygenated hemoglobin ($Hb_4O_8$) a compound formed in red blood cells on their passage through the gills or lungs.

**Oxytocin.** A hormone, secreted by the posterior pituitary gland in mammals, that stimulates the ejection of milk in lactating females and the contraction of the uteres during parturition. Like vasoprissin, oxytocia is synthesized in the hypothalamus.

**Oyster.** A sessile, marine bivalve of the genus Ostrea, widely sought for and cultivated as a source of food. Adults have a rough, asymmetrical shell with a single adductor muscle; foot is lacking. Adults function alternately as males and females. Larva is a veliger; young are called spat. Common species is Ostrea virginica.

**Oyster Catcher.** A sandpiperlike bird (Haematopus palliatus) also called clam bird of oysterbird.

**Oyster Drill.** A carnivorous, boring gastropod (Urosalpinx cinerea), a serious pest in oyster beds. Also a related form, Eupleura caudata.

**Oyster Fungus.** Edible fruit body of Pleurotus ostreatus. The pileus is more of less shell-shaped, and variable in colour from bluish-grey to yellcw ish-brown. Whitish gills are strongly decurrent, anastomosing near the basee. The fungus is typically found in clusters on trunks, tree-stumps etc., and is common throughout the year.

**Oyster Feech.** A polyclad turbellarian worm (Stylochus) which feeds on oysters.

**Oystershell Scale.** A scale insect (Lepidosaphes ulmi), a serious pest to fruit and ornamental trees and shrubs.

**Oyt.** The least tern (Sterna antillarum)

**Ozone Layer** (ozonosphere). A layer of the earth's atmosphere in which most of the atmosphere's ozone is concentrated. It occurs 15-50 km above the earths surface and is virtually synonymous with the stratosphere. In this layer most of the sun's ultraviolet radiation is absorbed by the ozone molecules, causing a rise in the temperature of the stratosphere and preventing vertical mixing so that the stratosphere forms a stable layer. By absorbing most of the solar ultraviolet radiation the ozone layer protects living organisms on earth. The fact that the ozone layer is thinnest at the equator is believed to account for the high equatorial incidence of skin cancer as a result of exposure to unabsorbed solar ultraviolet radiation.

Encyclopaedic Dictionary of
# BIOLOGICAL SCIENCES

# ENCYCLOPAEDIC DICTIONARY OF BIOLOGICAL SCIENCES

**Vol. 3**

K. NARANG
R. RANI
M. PRAKASH

**ANMOL PUBLICATIONS PVT LTD**
**New Delhi-110002**

**ANMOL PUBLICATIONS PVT LTD**
4374/4B, Ansari Road
Daryaganj, New Delhi-110 002

*Encyclopaedic Dictionary of Biological Sciences*



First Edition, 1991
ISBN 81-7041-462-8 (Set)
ISBN 81-7041-465-2 (Vol.3)
**Reprint 1994**
**Reprint ... 1998**

**PRINTED IN INDIA**
Published by J.L. Kumar for Anmol Publications Pvt. Ltd. New Delhi and Printed at Mehra Offset Press.

# Preface

The *Encyclopaedic Dictionary of Biological Sciences* (set of six volumes) has been carefully compiled and edited to meet the long felt needs of increasingly large number of, those who have to deal with the different aspects of biological sciences in colleges, universities, and research institutes. These volumes provide a speedy means of reference to easily interpreted definitions of the terms selected from botany, zoology, environmental science, ecology, genetics, biochemistry, forestry, agriculture geomorphology, cell biology, plant pathology, anatomy, evolution and ecology.

This set of dictionary is more or less encyclopaedic in its contents and style of representation which is evident from the comprehensiveness of its coverage and contextual relevance of explanations with illustrations and chemical formulae wherever necessary.

The entries in this dictionary have been written in a clear and explanatory style to provide both straight forward definitions and invaluable background information. The presentation throughout has been aimed at sustaining the interest of readers while enriching their vocabulary and comprehension of technical terms and expressions.

Throughout the process of compilation and editing these volumes our sincere effort was to make the dictionary as a ready reference for undergraduate and post graduate biological, agricultural, environmental, medical, marine and biochemistry students and also for those appearing for competitive examinations, research scholars, teachers and authors.

The editors express their thanks to their friends and colleagues whose continuous inspiration have initiated them to bring out these volumes.

**The Editors**

# E

**Eagle.** A large bird of prey of the family Falconidae, as the golden eagle (Aquila chrysaetos) and bald eagle (Haliaeetus leucocephalus).

**Ear.** The organ which, in vertebrates, is concerned with the detection of sound and also with the sense of balance. 'Ears' also occur in other animals such as insects, but these are far less complicated structures and are concerned merely with the detection of sound. The human ear is typical of mammals and differs only in small details

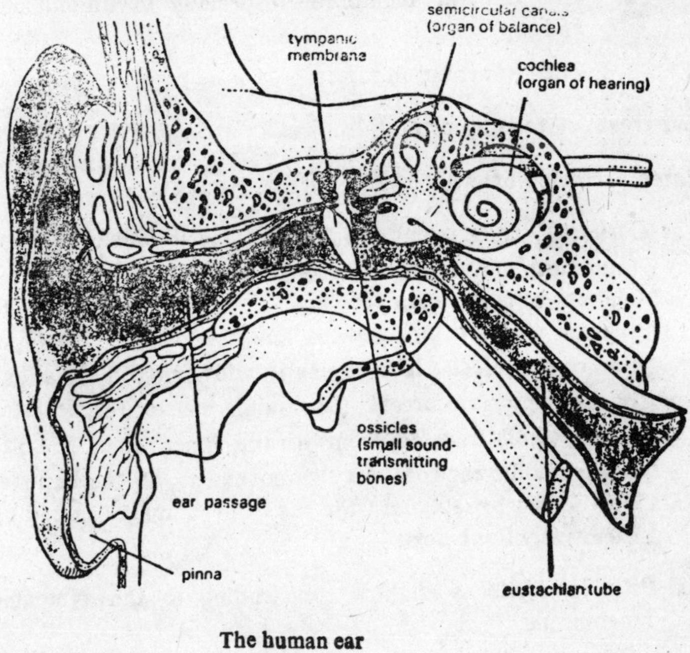


The human ear

from that of most other vertebrates. There are three main regions : the outer ear consisting of the ear lobe or pinna and the passage leading to the ear-drum (tympanic membrane); the middle ear which contains tiny bones transmitting sounds from the drum to the inner ear and which connects with the throat by means of the eustachian tube; and the inner ear which, encased in the bone of the skull, contains the actual sense organs of hearing and balance.

**Ear Bones.** The auditory or ear ossicles, the malleus, incus, and stapes (hammer, anvil, stirrup) which transmit vibrations from the tympanic membrane to the internal ear.

**Eardrum**

1. The tympanum or tympanic cavity; the middle ear.
2. The tympanic membrane, especially in amphibians and reptiles.
3. The tympanum in insects.

**Ear Dust.** Otoconia or otoliths.

**Eared.** Having external ears or earlike processes.

**Ear Ossicles.** Three small bones—the incus (anvil), malleus (hammer), and stapes (stirrup)—that lie in the mammalian middle ear, forming a bridge between the tympanum (eardrum) and the fenestra ovalis. The function of the ossicles is to transmit (and amplify) vibrations of the tympanum across the middle ear to the fenestra ovalis, which transfers them to the inner ear. Muscles of the middle ear constrict the movement of the ossicles. This serves to safeguard the ear from damage caused by excessively loud noise.

**Ear Pit.** In reptiles, a shallow pit leading to the tympanic membrane.

**Ear Stone.** A large otolith present in the ear of certain fishes.

**Earthworm.** A soil-inhabiting oligochaete, especially one of the genus Lumbricus; a night crawler.

**Earwax.** Cerumen.

**Earwig.** An insect of the order Dermaptera.

**Ebony.** A hard durable wood obtained from trees of the genus Diospryos grown principally in Asia and Africa.

**Ecblastesis.** The development of buds within a flower.

**Ecdysis** (moulting)

1. The periodic loss of the outer cuticle of arthropods. It starts with the reabsorption of some materials in the inner part of the old cuticle and the formation of a new soft cuticle. The remains of the old cuticle then split; the animal emerges and absorbs water or swallows air and increases in size while the new cuticle is still soft. This cuticle is then hardened with chitin and lime salts. In insects and crustaceans ecdysis is controlled by the hormone ecdysone.
2. The periodic sheeding of the outer layer of the epidermis of reptiles (except crocodiles) to allow growth to occur.

**Ecdysone.** A steroid hormone, produced by insects and crustaceans, that stimulates moulting (ecdysis) and metamorphosis. It acts on specific gene loci, stimulating the synthesis of proteins involved in the bodily changes.

**Ecesis.** The invasion of an area by a species which fails to establish itself there, and consequently dies out in a few generations.

**Echidna.** The spiny anteater, an insectivorous monotreme.

**Echinate.** Possessing prickles or spines.

**Echinoderm.** Member of a group of marine invertebrates with radially symmetrical bodies—*i.e.* the limbs and organs are arranged regularly around a central point. The group includes the sea urchins, starfishes, sea cucumbers and brittlestars. Echinoderms have no brains and no distinctive head, and the skin is embedded with chalky plates that give it a rough appearance. The animals have a unique system of water-filled canals running through their bodies, called a water vascular system. The canals end in small projections on the skin surface called tube-feet. By pumping water through the system the organisms create suction in the tube-feet; this helps them to adhere to rocks or to move about. Tube-feet are also used for respiration. Echinoderm larvae form part of marine plankton.

**Echinodermata.** A phylum of marine invertebrates that includes the sea urchins, starfish, brittlestars, and sea cucumbers. Echinoderms have an exoskeleton (test) of calcareous plates embedded in the skin. In many species (*e.g.* sea urchins) spines protrude from the test. A system of water-filled canals (the water vascular system) provides hydraulic power for thousands of tube feet : saclike protrusions of the body wall used for locomotion, feeding, and respiration. Echinoderms have a long history : fossils of primitive echinoderms are known from rocks 500 million years old.

**Echinoid.** An echinoderm of the class Echinoidea which includes the sea urchins, sand dollars, heart and cake urchins.

**Echolocation.** A method used by some animals (such as bats, dolphins, and certain birds) to detect objects in the dark. The animal emits a series of high-pitched sounds that echo-back from the object and are detected by the ear or some other sensory receptor. From the direction of the echo and from the time between emission and reception of the sounds the objects is located, often very accurately.

**Eclosion.** *entomol*

1. Hatching or escape of the young from the egg.
2. Emergence of the imago or adult from the pupa case.

**Ecocline.** A cline that has been shown to be due to a specific environmental factor. For example, a gradual increase in heavy-metal tolerance can be correlated with increasing metal concentration in the soil.

**Ecological Efficiency.** Used for describing the percentage of energy received by a tophic level in unit time that is passed on to the next higher trophic level(s) in unit time *i.e.*

$$\text{Ecological efficiency of a trophic level} = \frac{\text{Amount of energy passed on to next higher trophic level(s) by the trophic level in unit time}}{\text{Amount of energy received by the trophic level in unit time from preceding lower trophic level(s).}}$$

**Ecological Factor** Anything in the environment which may be affecting the growth, development and distribution of plants, and hence determines the characteristics of the plant community.

**Ecological Niche.** The status or role of an organism in its environment. An organism's niche is defined by the types of food it consumes, its predators, temperature tolerances, etc. Two species cannot coexist stably if they occupy identical niches.

**Ecological Pyramids.** Used for describing a graphic representation of some relationship which exists between trophic levels of an ecosystem. Magnitude of characteristic for each level has been represented by the length of a horizontal bar and such bars have been drawn one above the other, starting from producers at the base to top carnivores at the top. Resulting pyramidical diagram is ecological pyramid which shows the relationship between trophic levels with respect to particular characteristic. Generally, pyramids of numbers, biomass and energy transfer have been drawn in the study of ecosystem as a rough representation of numerical, biomass or energy relationship among trophic levels of the ecosystem.

**Ecological System.** Ecosystem.

**Ecology.** The study of animal and plant communities and the ways in which they react with each other and to any changes in the environment.

**Economic Botany.** The study of plants of importance to man, especially plants as sources of food, clothing, drugs, and products used in industry.

**Economic Zoology.** The study of animals of importance to man, especially animals as sources of food, clothing, and various commercial products.

**Ecophene.** Used for the range of phenotypes which are produced by one genotype within a particular habitat. One genotype may be considered to be taken as a mean of a class of closely related genotypes.

**Ecospecies.** A category of variant individuals capable of genetic recombination with other similar groups, but liable to reduce fitness or fertility from it.

**Ecosphere.** Biosphere.

**Ecosystem.** An ecological system, a natural unit of living and nonliving components which interact to form a stable system in which a cyclic interchange of materials takes place between living and nonliving units, as in a balanced aquarium or in a large lake or forest.

**Ecotone.** A boundary between two plant communities of major rank.

**Ecotype.** A distinct population of organisms within a species that has adapted genetically to its local habitat. For example, some organisms may be able to tolerate different conditions of temperature or light intensity from other members of the same species. This may result in changes in their morphology or physiology. However, they are able to reproduce with other ecotypes of the same species and produce fertile offspring. These ecotypes may be sufficiently distinct to be given subspecific names, in which case they may be termed ecospecies. Compare cline.

**Ectocarp.** Exocarp.

**Ectocommensal.** An organism which lives as a commensal on the surface of another organism, as certain ciliates on Hydra.

**Ectocrine.** An ectohormone.

**Ectoderm.** The outermost of the three primary germ layers. It gives rise to epidermis and its derivatives, all nervous tissue and sense organs, and the linings of the nasal cavity, mouth, and anal canal.

**Ectogenesis.** Variation occurring due to conditions outside the plant.

**Ectogenic**

1. Of pacteria, living on the outside of a body.
2. Describing the effect of pollen on the tissues of the female organs of a flowering plant.

**Ectohormone.** A chemical substance produced by an organism which has an effect on nearby organisms; an ectocrine.

**Ectolecithal.** A type of egg in which the yolk lies outside the ovum, as in triclad turbellarians.

**Ectoparasite.** A parasite which lives on the surface of an organism, as a mite, tick, louse, or flea.

**Ectophloic Siphonostele.** Siphonostele.

**Ectophyte.** An ectoparasitic plant.

**Ectopic.** Occupying an abnormal position.

**Ectoplasm.** The peripheral layer of protoplasm of a cell, usually more rigid and lacking granules.

**Ectoblast.** Term formerly applied to ectoderm.

**Ectoproct.** Any invertebrate belonging to the Ectoprocta, a phylum of sessile, bilaterally symmetrical, lophophorate metazoans which form arborescent and encrusting colonies. Formerly comprised a class of the phylum Bryozoa. Examples are Plumatella, Bugula.

**Ectosome.** The outer layer of a sponge enclosing the inner choanosome.

**Ectotrophic.** Securing nourishment from without.

**Ectotrophic Mycorrhiza** (ectophytic mycorrhiza). A form of mycorrhizal association in which there is a well developed mycelium forming a mantle on the outside of the root. Such associations are found on most trees and often a tree will not grow properly unless the appropriate fungus is present. It is thus a common practice when planting young trees to inoculate the soil with mycorrhizal fungi. These are frequently members of the Agaricales. Infected roots commonly show a characteristic coralloid form of growth in which the lateral roots fail to elongate and instead branch repeatedly forming a swollen mass. Initially some of the hyphae penetrate the cortex and form an intercellular meshwork termed the Hartig net. The outer mantle, which replaces the piliferous layer of the root, subsequently arises from this net. It has been demonstrated that mycorrhizal roots take up nutrients better than uninfected roots, while the fungi obtain carbohydrates and possibly B-group vitamins from the tree.

**Ectozoan.** An ectoparasitic animal.

**EDTA.** Ethylenediaminetetracetic acid,

$$(HOOCCH_2)_2N(CH_2)_2N(CH_2COOH)_2$$

A compound that acts as a chelating agent, reversibly binding with iron, magnesium, and other metal ions. It is used in certain culture media bound with iron, which it slowly releases into the medium.

**Edaphic.** Pertaining to or influenced by soil conditions.

**Edaphon.** The fauna and flora of the soil.

**Edaphic Factor.** A factor relating to the physical or chemical composition of the soil found in a particular area. For example, very alkaline soil may be an edaphic factor limiting the variety of plants growing in a region.

**Edema.** A term used for describing the accumulation of interstitial fluid in abnormally large amounts. It takes place due to the increased filtration pressure, decreased osmotic pressure, gradient across capillary, increased capillary permeability and inadequate lymph flow.

**Eel**

1. An elongated, snakelike fish of the order Apodes (Anguilliformes), as Anguilla rostrata of eastern North America. Adults inhabit freshwater streams but spawn in the Atlantic. Larvae are called leptocephali.
2. Any of a number of animals shaped like an eel, as the electric eel, lamprey eel, moray eel, vinegar eel.

**Effector.** An organ that acts in response to a signal. Muscles and glands are the main effectors. Receptors receiver stimuli from outside the body and send messages to the brain. The brain then sends the appropriate message to the effectors which take the necessary action.

**Effector Organ.** A structure which, when stimulated, responds, as a muscle or gland.

**Efferent.** Carrying (nerve impulses, blood, etc.) away from the centre of a body or organ towards peripheral regions. The term is usually applied to types of nerve fibres or blood vessels. Compare afferent.

**Efflorescence.** The period of flowering : Anthesis.

**Effuse**

1. *bot.* Diffuse, expanded, spread out.
2. *zool.* With edges of valves separated by a gap.

**Effusion.** The flow of a gas through a small aperture. The relative rates at which gases effuse, under the same conditions, is approximately inversely proportional to the square roots of their densities.

**Eft.** A newt, as the American newt (Diemictylus viridescens), especially its terrestrial stage in development.

**Egest.** To discharge or cast from the body. Compare ingest.

**Fgesta.** Matter discharged from the body : Excrement.

**Egg**

1. *zool.* *a.* An ovum; a female gamete or germ cell. *b.* A reproductive body produced by females of various animals (flat and round worms, reptiles, birds) from which, after a period of development or incubation, the young emerge or hatch.
2. *bot.* A female gamete, variously called oosphere, ovum, macrogamete, megagamete.

**Egg Apparatus.** *bot.* The egg cell and two synergid cells located in the micropylar end of the embryo sac (female gametophyte) of angiosperms.

**Egg Burster.** A sharp process on the dorsal surface of the head of a developing insect which aids in rupture of the eggshell.

**Egg Case.** An ootheca, a protective covering or capsule enclosing one or more eggs, as in insects (cockroach), some mollusks (cephalopods), and vertebrates (sharks, rays).

**Egg Membrane.** The layer of material that covers an animal egg cell. Primary membranes develop in the ovary and cover the egg surface in addition to the normal cell membrane. The primary membrane is called the vitelline membrane in insects, molluscs, birds, and amphibians, the chorion in tunicates and fish, and the zona pellucida in mammals. Insects have a second thicker membrane, also called the chorion. Secondary membranes are secreted by the oviducts and parts of the genital system while the egg is passing to the outside. They include the jelly coat of frogs' eggs and the albumen and shell of birds' eggs.

**Eggplant.** A large, branching herb (Solanum melongena) cultivated for its fruit, a large, ovoïd white or purple berry about the size of a coconut.

**Egg Pod.** A structure formed by several eggs glued together, as that formed by a grasshopper.

**Egg Tooth.** A calcareous structure on the tip of the upper mandible of a developing bird or reptile which serves to cut the egg membrane and shell, thus aiding in hatching.

**Ektexine.** Exine.

**Elaioplast.** A leucoplast in which oil is stored.

**Elasmobranch.** Of or pertaining to fishes of the class Chondrichthyes, or any member of this class which includes the sharks, skates, and rays, characterized by a cartilaginous skeleton.

**Elasmobranchii** (Chondrichthyes). A class of vertebrates comprising the fishes with cartilaginous skeletons. The majority belong to the order Selachi (skates, rays, and sharks). Most cartilaginous fishes are marine carnivores with powerful jaws. Unlike bony fishes, they have no swim bladder, and therefore avoid sinking only by constant swimming with the aid of an asymmetrical (heterocercal) tail. There is no operculum covering the gill slits, the first of which is modified as a spiracle. Fertilization is internal so the few eggs produced are consequently yolky, large, and well-protected. Some elasmobranchs show viviparous development of the young.

**Elastase.** An enzyme occurring in succus entericus (intestinal juice). It acts upon elastin and digests it.

**Elastic.** Capable of resuming its original length, size, or shape after being stretched or deformed.

**Elastic Cartilage.** Used for describing a cartilege in which yellow and elastic fibres are found in the matrix. It occurs in the pinna, epiglottis and trachial rings.

**Elastin.** Refers to a substance of the elastic fibres. It is a scleroprotein which is insoluable upon boiling but dissolves in proteolytic enzymes. Elastin fibres occur in the wall of large arteries and between vertebrae (intervertebral discs of mammals).

**Elater.** Any of the numerous elongate helically thickened cells intermixed with the spores in the capsule of most liverwort sporophytes. As the mature capsule dries out, tension builds up in the thickening of the elater. This tension is released when the capsule dehisces, dispersing the spores over a distance.

**Elder.** A deciduous shrub or small tree belonging to the honeysuckle family. It has clusters of white flowers and juicy black berries that are frequently used for making wine. The bark is thick and soft and the leaves have several leaflets.

**Electric Organ.** An organ occurring on the body or tail of certain fish, such as the electric ray (Torpedo) and electric eel (Electrophorus electricus). It gives an electric shock when touched and is used either to stun prey or predators or, in some species, to maintain a weak electric field in the surrounding water that is used in navigation. The organ is composed of modified muscle cells (electroplate cells), nervous stimulation of which greatly increases the potential difference across the cell. The electroplates are in series so a high overall voltage can be achieved.

**Electric Ray**. An elasmobranch fish (Torpedo) which possesses large electric organs located dorsally on each side of the head.

**Electrocardiogram** (ECG). A tracing or graph of the electrical activity of the heart. Recordings are made from electrodes fastened over the heart and usually on both arms and a leg. Changes in the normal pattern of an ECG may indicate heart irregularities or disease.

**Electroencephalogram** (EEG). A tracing or graph of the electrical activity of the brain. Electrodes taped to the scalp record electrical waves from different parts of the brain. The pattern of an EEG reflects an individual's level of consciousness and can be used to detect such disorders as epilepsy, tumours, or brain damage.

**Electron Density**. The contrast between parts of a specimen observed by transmission electron microscopy. Electron dense structures deflect most of the electron beam and appear dark whereas electron lucent features do not deflect many electrons and appear bright. Such differences are often accentuated by the use of electron stains that render parts of the specimen electron dense that would otherwise appear electron lucent.

**Electron Microscope**. A form of microscope that uses a beam of electrons instead of a beam of light (as in the optical microscope) to form a large image of a very small object, such as a cell organelle, a virus, or a DNA molecule. In optical microscopes the resolution is limited by the wavelength of the light. High-energy electrons, however, can be associated with a considerably shorter wavelength than light; for example, electrons accelerated to an energy of $10^5$ electronvolts have a wavelength of 0.04 nanometre, enabling a resolution of 0 2-0.5 nm to be achieved. The transmission electron microscope has an electron beam, sharply focused by electron lenses (coils producing a magnetic field or electrodas between which an electric field is created), passing through a very thin metallized specimen (less than 50 nanometres thick) onto a fluorescent screen, where a visual image is formed. This produced by certain cells (ameloblasts) of the oral enithelium and protects the underlying dentine of the tooth. Enamel may also be found in the placoid scales of certain fish, which demonstrates the common developmental origin of scales and teeth.

**lectron Stain.** Staining.

**lectron Transport Chain.** A series of membrane-linked oxidation-reduction reactions in which electrons are transferred from an initial electron donor through a series of intermediates to a final electron acceptor (usually oxygen). The electron transport systems of respiration and photosynthesis are the major chemical energy sources in aerobic organisms.

A number of other electron transport systems are known besides those of respiration and photosynthesis. Heterotrophic bacteria have a respiratory chain similar to that in eukaryotes and a microsomal electron transport system is responsible for desaturation of fatty acids.

**ctrophoresis.** A technique used to separate mixtures of solute molecules or colloidal particles in solution by placing them in an electric field. Molecules with a net positive charge (cations) move towards the cathode (negative electrode) and those with a net negative charge (anions) move towards the anode (positive electrode). The speed of movement of the molecules depends on their net charge, which in turn depends on the pH of the medium.

The size of the molecule and the strength of the voltage applied also affect the speed of movement. Often the solvent is a gel of, for example, starch, agar, or polyacrylamide. These prevent the passage of small molecules, which become caught within the molecules of the gel (gel filtration), so enabling clearer separation of the larger molecules. Electrophoresis is often used to separate the components of protein mixtures and may be used in conjunction with paper chromatography.

**Electroplaxes**. Electric plates or discs arranged in piles in the electric organ of fishes.

**Elementary Bodies**. Minute bodies within inclusion bodies present in cells infected with certain viruses.

**Elfin Forest** (Krummholz). The dwarfed and deformed trees that are found in the zone between the timber line and the tree line. They tend to grow along the ground and are thus better able to withstand the strong winds in such regions. The zone of elfin forest is termed the Kampfzone.

**Elephant**. A large, five-toed mammal of the order Proboscidea characterized by possession of an elongated, muscular proboscis or trunk. Common species are the Indian elephant (Elephas maximus) and African elephant (Loxodonta africana).

**Elephantiasis**. Pathological enlargement of parts of the body resulting from blockage of lymph vessels, as that caused by a nematode worm (Wuchereria bancrofti). Also called filariasis.

**Elm**. One of several species of lumber and shade trees of the genus Ulmus, especially the American elm (U. americanus).

**Elytra**. The thickened horny forewings of the Coleoptera (beetles), which cover and protect the membranous hind wings when the insect is at rest.

**Elytron pl. Elytra**

1. The thickened, hardened forewing of a beetle.
2. A platelike respiratory structure on the dorsal surface of a scaleworm.

**Emarginate.** Describing a leaf, petal, or sepal that is indented at its tip. The notched petals of many cranesbills (*e.g.*, Geranium versicolor and G. pyrenacium) are examples.

**Emasculate**

1. *zool.* To castrate.
2. *bot.* To remove anthers from a bud or flower.

**Emasculation.** The removal of the anthers of a flower to prevent either self-pollination or the pollination of surrounding plants.

**Embden-meyerhof-parnas Sequence.** The second phase in glycolysis during aerobic respiration in which a molecule of hexose diphosphate is broken into two molecules of triose phosphate and two energy-rich phosphates are released. ADP is converted to ATP and NAD is reduced, with the formation of pyruvic acid :—

$$C_6H_{12}O_6-(2P)+2NAD+4ADP\rightarrow 2CH_3CO.COOH+2NADH_2+4ATP_3$$

**Embedding.** A process in microscopical preparation in which delicate tissue is impregnated by, and embedded in a solid supporting medium, such as paraffin wax, to enable thin sections of the material to be cut with a microtome. Tougher embedding materials (*e.g.* epoxy resins) are used in preparations for the electron microscope.

**Embolism.** The blocking of a blood vessel by an embolus.

**Embolus**

1. *pathol.* A mass of material, as a thrombus, oil droplet, air bubble, or tissue debris which is transported

by the bloodstream to a point where it lodges, forming an obstruction.

2. *zool.* A penislike projection on the pedipalp of certain male spiders.

**Emboly.** The process of invagination, as the formation of a two-layered gastrula from a blastula.

**Embryo.** The young plant individual after fertilization or parthenogenesis when the proembryo has differentiated into embryo and suspensor. Embryo cells are typically thin walled with dense cytoplasm and maintain mitotic activity. Cells exhibit polarity from early on, and in higher plants a plumule, radicle, and cotyledons may be identified. In seed-bearing plants the embryo is protected by integuments, which later form the seed coat. Further embryo development in the seed is usually controlled until environmental conditions are appropriate. Compare zygote.

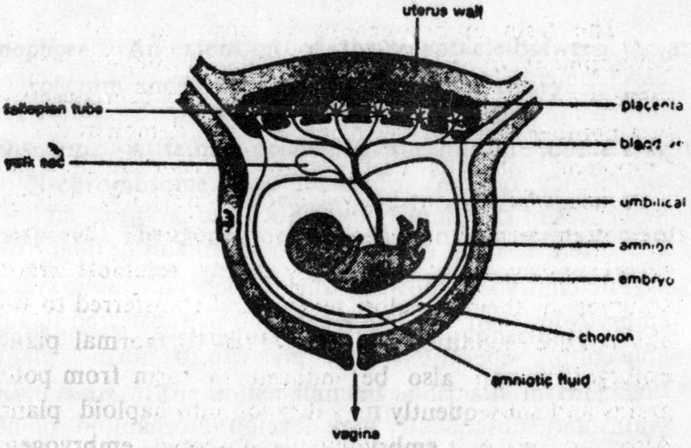


A developing human embryo

**Embryo Culture.** The growth of isolated plant embryos on suitable media in vitro. The technique is useful in plant breeding as it enables certain hybrids to be raised that would abort if left on the plant, either because of endosperm breakdown or endosperm incompatibility.

**Embryogenesis.** The development of an embryo; embryogeny. Compare blastogenesis.

**Embryogeny** (embryogenesis, embryony). The development of an embryo, normally from a fertilized egg cell. The first divisions of the zygote are at right angles to the long axis of the archegonium or embryo sac. In angiosperms and in some gymnosperms and pteridophytes these initial divisions give rise to a chain of cells, the suspensor. The embryo proper develops from a large cell at the tip of the suspensor at the end furthest from the micropyle. The pattern of embryo development differs markedly between groups of plants but normally globular, heart-shaped, and torpedo-shaped stages can be recognized. Embryogeny often lags behind the development of other parts of the seed so the embryo may grow at the expense of the previously formed endosperm. Certain cells of the embryo may be polyploid if DNA synthesis outstrips nuclear division.

The term embryogenesis is also applied to the development of embryos from diploid somatic cells in suspension cultures. This phenomenon has been described in a number of angiosperm species and demonstrates the totipotency of cells when removed from the inhibiting influences of the plant body. Such nonzygotic embryos are often termed embryoids to distinguish then from zygotic embryos. However they closely resemble zygotic embryos in their development and if transferred to suitable culture conditions may give rise to normal plants. Embryoids can also be induced to form from pollen grains and subsequently may develop into haploid plants. Also adventive embryony, endoscopic embryogeny, exoscopic embryogeny.

**Embryoid.** Embryogenesis.

**Embryology.** The study of the development of animals from the fertilized egg to the new adult organism. It is sometimes limited to the period between fertilization of the egg and hatching or birth.

**Embryophore.** The protective covering enclosing the embryo (onchosphere, coracidium) of certain tapeworms.

**Embryophyta** (Embryobionta). In certain classifications, one of two subkingdoms of plants (the other being the Thallophyta). It contains the bryophytes and vascular plants. These plants are grouped together because they all have an embryonic stage that is dependent on the parent plant for a greater or lesser period. This is generally not seen in the Thallophyta, though a situation approaching it is found in some red algae.

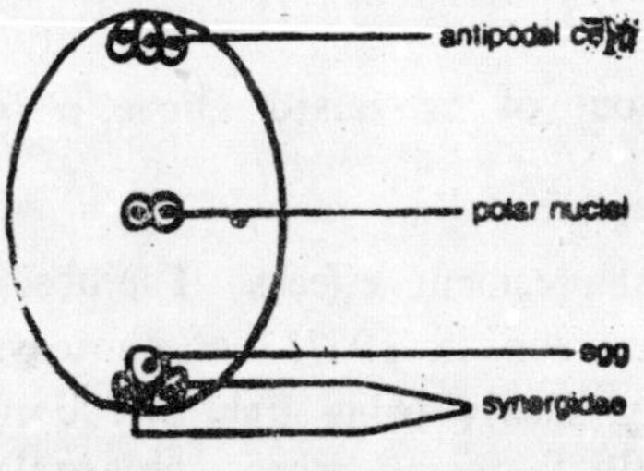


A typical embryo sac

**Embryo Sac.** A large cell that develops in the ovule of flowering plants. It is equivalent to the female gametophyte of lower plants, although it is very much reduced. Typically, it contains eight nuclei formed by division of the original female gamete. One, the oosphere (egg nucleus), is fertilized by a male nucleus and becomes the embryo. Two of the remaining nuclei fuse with a second male nucleus to form a triploid nucleus that gives rise to the endosperm.

**Embryotroph.** The nutrient material which nourishes a mammalian embryo during early pregnancy before establishment of the placenta : histotroph.

**Emeiocytosis.** Also known as cell vomiting. The cell membrane around a vacuole or secretion granule gets fused with cell membrane and the region of fusion breaks down thereby leaving contents of vacuole or secretion granule outside the cell membrane intact. It needs calcium and energy. It is also termed as exocytosis or reverse pinacytosis.

**Emergence**

1. *entomol.* The escape of an insect from a cell, cocoon, or puparium.
2. The coming into existence from a simpler group, as the emergence of land vertebrates.
3. *bot.* An outgrowth which contains some epidermal tissue, as the prickle of a rose.

**Emersed.** Rising out of or raised above a surface, as of water.

**Emerson Effect** (enhancement effect). The observation (made or Robert Emerson in 1957) that photosynthesis, which proceeds very slowly using light of 700 nm wavelength, can be greatly increased when chloroplasts are also illuminated with light of shorter wavelength (650 nm). This was a surprising observation as it was then thought that light absorbed by the chlorophylls and other pigments was all passed on to a small percentage of chlorophyll a molecules (the energy trap) absorbing at 700 nm. This and later work indicated a second energy trap absorbing at 680 nm.

**Emulsion.** A colloidal system consisting of minute droplets of a liquid suspended in another liquid, as oil in water.

**Enamel.** The material that forms a covering over the crown of a tooth (*i.e.* the part that projects above the gum). Enamel is smooth, white, and extremely hard, being rich in minerals containing calcium. It is an endodermis may also be seen in the stems of some plants.

**Enation**

1. An outgrowth, usually from a leaf. Enations may occur in response to virus infection, *e g.* cotten leaf curl virus.
2. A small lateral outgrowth of the stem that is produced by certain primitive vascular plants and may be an early stage in microphyll evolution.

**Encephalin** (enkephalin). A peptide neurotransmitter found principally in the brain. Two encephalins have so far been isolated. They bind to opiate receptors in the brain and their release is thought to control levels of pain and other sensations. Encephalins have also been found in spinal cord nerve cells and in gut epithelial cells. Compare endorphin.

**Encephalisation.** Means relatively greater role of cerebral cortex in various functions. An important phenomenon in species in which cerebral cortex has been highly developed.

**Encephalitis.** Refers to the inflamation of the brain which may be caused by virus, microbes or may be secondarily due to general infections such as that of measles, pneumonia etc.

**Endarch**. Designating the protoxylem or first-formed wood when it is centrally located next to the pith.

**Endartery**. One without branches or anastomoses.

**Endemic**. Describing a plant species that grows in a specific area and has a restricted distribution. Some species (broad endemics) are restricted to a particular large region. Other species (narrow endemics) are confined to a much smaller area, such as a few square kilometres, and tend to be very specialized. Examples of broad endemics are the sugar maple (Acer saccharum) in the eastern United States and the cacao tree (Theobroma cacao) in the Amazon basin. An example of a narrow endemic is Darcycarpus viellardii in the island of New Caledonia. Some endemic species (palaeoendemics) represent the relicts of once widespread species. For example, Lyonothamnus floribundus, which today is only found on the California Islands, grew throughout California in the Tertiary. Species found in two or more widely separated regions are termed discontinuous or disjunct, *e.g.* magnolias grow in southeast. Asia, eastern North America, and Central America, but nowhere in between. Compare cosmopolitan.

**Endexine.** Exine.

**Endocardium.** The innermost layer of the heart wall.

**Endocarp.** The innermost layer of the pericarp of an angiosperm fruit, internal to the mesocarp and exocarp and external to the seed(s). Sometimes the endocarp consists of a stony layer, as in the fruit of the peach (Prunus persica).

**Endochondral Ossification.** Bone formation in which a model of hyaline cartilage is formed and then replaced by bone except at joint surfaces as in development of a long bone, as the femur or humerus.

**Endocrine.** Secreting internally.

**Endocrine Gland** (ductless gland). Any gland in an animal that manufactures hormones and secretes them directly into the bloodstream to act at distant sites in the body (known as target organs or cells). Endocrine glands tend to control slow long-term activities in the body, such as growth and sexual development. In mammals they include the pituitary, adrenal, thyroid, and parathyroid glands, the ovary and testis, the placenta, and part of the pancreas (islets of Langerhans). The activity of endocrine glands is controlled by negative feedback, *i.e.* a rise in output of hormone inhibits a further increase in its production, either directly or indirectly via the target organ or cell.

**Endocrine System.** Collectively, the endocrine glands, which, in vertebrates, include the pituitary, thyroid, parathyroid, pancreas, adrenal ovary, and testis. Other structures which secrete hormones are the placenta, intestinal mucosa, and hypothalamu.

**Endocrinology.** The study of the structure and functions of the endocrine glands and of the hormones they produce.

**Endocyst.** The inner layer of the wall of a cyst.

**Endocytosis.** The entry of particles or fluid into cells by methods other than diffusion or active transport across the plasma membrane. In phagocytosis, exhibited by some unicellular holozoic algae, protrusions, of the outer regions of the cell, formed by flowing movements of the cytoplasm, surround food particles, enclosing them in a membrane-bound food vacuole. Lysosomes become associated with the food vacuoles, the intervening membranes break down, and hydrolytic enzymes are released to digest the particles.

Pinocytosis is a process by which submicroscopic particles (macromolecules or molecular aggregates) or droplets of extracellular fluid enter cells. The particles adhere to the plasma membrane (absorptive endocytosis) and an invagination forms. This becomes pinched off so taking the particles into the cytoplasm in a membrane-bound vesicle—a pinocytotic or endocytotic vesicle. Alternatively extracellular fluid enter a pitlike invagination that becomes pinched off and enters the cytoplasm (fluid endocytosis). Water is absorbed from the vesicles as they move through the cytoplasm. Eventually the membrane breaks down, releasing the contents into the cytoplasm.

**Endoderm** (entoderm). The internal layer of cells of the gastrula, which will develop into the alimentary canal (gut) and digestive glands of the adult.

**Endodermis.** A layer of cells at the boundary of the cortex and stele, usually regarded as the innermost layer of the cortex. It is generally clearly seen in all roots and in pteridophyte and certain dicotyledon stems. A Casparian strip is usually present. When the endodermis contains numerous starch grains, it is known as a starch sheath.

**Endoenzyme.** An intracellular or endocellular enzyme; one that acts within a cell.

**Endogamy.** The fusion of reproductive cells from closely related parents, *i e.* inbreeding. Compare exogamy.

**Endogenous.** Describing any process, substance, or organ that arises from within an organism. Examples are endogenous rhythms, the origin of lateral roots from the pericycle, and the capacity of certain tissue cultures to manufacture their own growth substances. Compare exogenous.

**Endogenous Insulin.** Insulin which is secreted inside the body when it enters the portal vein, the liver is normally exposed to concentrations of insulin that are 3-10 times greater than those in peripheral tissues. Liver is able to bind about half a dose of insulin injected into the portal vein but only 25% of a peripherally injected dose.

**Endolymph.** Aqueous liquid having high potassium concentration and present in scala media of cochlea of mammalian ear.

**Endogenous Rhythms.** Sequential physical or biochemical processes that occur in a plant or plant part in response to internal stimuli. An example is the apparently autonomic component of the nyctinastic movements of certain plants, the leaflets of which continue to follow a periodic folding and unfolding sequence even if kept in continuous darkness.

**Endolymph.** The fluid that fills the membranous labyrinth of the vertebrate inner ear.

**Endolymphatic Duct**

1. In elasmobranchs, the invagination canal.

2. A blind duct which grows out of the sacculus terminating in the endolymphatic sac.

**Endometrium.** The mucous membrane which lines the uterus.

**Endomitosis.** A sequence of changes in the nucleus resulting in division of the chromosomes, as in mitosis, but no separation of the chromatids into daughter nuclei. The resulting nucleus is therefore polyploid. The process can be induced in isolated tissues by treatment with colchicine, which prevents spindle formation so the centromeres of the daughter chromosomes are unable to move apart into separate nuclei. It may occur as an error in part of a plant, producing, for example, a tetraploid branch on a diploid plant. It occurs as a normal feature in some tissues of higher plants, *e.g.* the phloem cells of some leguminous plants are polyploid. This type of polyploidy, where some of the cells of a plant have more than the normal complement of chromosomes for the species, is known as endopolyploidy. If endomitosis occurs in cells in the germ line or during the second division of meiosis then unreduced gametes may result.

**Endomixis.** A process occurring in certain protozoans which involves nuclear disintegration, reorganization, and reconstruction.

**Endomycetales.** An order of the Hemiascomycetes containing about 200 species in some 50 genera. It includes the family Saccharomycetaceae, the yeasts, which contains the commercially important species Saccharomyces cerevisiae (brewer's yeast), used in bread and beer making, and S. ellipsoideus, used in wine making. The yeasts reproduce asexually by budding or by dividing into two equal cells as in Schizosaccharomyces (fission yeasts). Sexual reproduction is by ascus formation.

**Endomysium**. A delicate network of reticular fibers which envelopes individual muscle fibers within a fasciculus.

**Endoneurinm** A delicate covering of connective tissue which encloses individual nerve fibers.

**Endoparasite**. A parasite that lives inside its host's body.

**Endophoresis**. Phoresis in which one of the two organisms lives within a cavity of the other, as the fierasfier, a fish within the cloaca of a sea cucumber.

**Endophyte**. A plant which grows within the tissues of another plant.

**Endophytic Mycorrhiza**. Endotrophic mycorrhiza.

**Endoplasm**. The inner, more granular portion of the protoplasm of a cell.

**Endoplasmic Reticulum**. A cell organelle consisting of a complicated network of fine, branching, and anastomosing tubules or spaces (cisternae) or isolated vesicles present in the cytoplasm of most cells. It forms a structural framework for the cell and a circulation pathway between the plasma membrane and nuclear membrane. Its surface may bear ribosomes, the site of protein synthesis.

**Endopodite**. The inner ramus or division of a biramous appendage ; endopod.

**Endopolyploidy**. Describing a type of polyploidy where some of the cells of a plant are having more than normal complement of chromosomes for he species.

**Endoral**. Within the mouth or buccal cavity.

**End Organ.** The structure at the end of a peripheral nerve. Examples of end organs are the muscle end plate at the end of a motor neurone and the receptor at the end of a sensory neurone.

**Endorphin.** A peptide neurotransmitter found in the pituitary gland and hypothalamus that has pain-relieving properties similar to the encephalins.

**Endoscopic.** With the apical pole of the embryo directed towards the base of the archegonium, as in Selaginella.

**Endoscopic Embryogeny.** Embryogeny in which the embryo develops from the inner of the two cells that result from the first division of the zygote. The outer cell often forms the suspensor. Endoscopic embryogeny is seen in the Lycopsida, most of the Filicinae, and all the Gymmospermae and Angiospermae. Compare exoscopic embryogeny.

**Endoskeleton.** An internal skeleton, as the bony skeleton of vertebrates.

**Endosome**

1. A solid body present in the nucleus of certain protozoans.
2. Choanosome.

**Endorsperm.** The storage tissue in the seeds of most angiosperms, derived from the fusion of one male gamete with two female polar nuclei. The endosperm is a compact triploid tissue, lacking intercellular spaces and storing starch, hemicelluloses, proteins oils, and fats. Seeds containing an endosperm or perisperm at maturity are termed albuminous, whereas those lacking such tissue are termed exalbuminous.

**Endoplasmic Reticulum.** A complex interconnecting system of flattened membrane-surrounded channels and vesicles (cisternae) that spreads throughout the cytoplasm of eukaryotic cells. The membranes appear to be continuous with the plama membrane at the outer surface and with the tonoplast and nuclear membrane, and have the same general structure. Some cisternae have a granular appearance in electron micrographs due to ribosomes that are attached to the cytoplasm side of the enclosing membranes. They are thus called rough endoplasmic reticulum. Others are devoid of ribosomes and are called smooth endoplamic reticulum. Polypeptides can be identified in the channels of the rough endoplasmic reticulum. The function of the endoplasmic reticulum is the segregation of newly synthesized products and their further processing and intracellular transport.

**Endospore**

1. An extremely resistant resting spore formed by certain bacteria, especially those of the Bacillaceae, *e.g.* Bacillus and Clostridium. Only one endospore is formed in any given cell. Sporulating cells are termed sporanigia and the size, shape, and position of the endospore is characteristic of the species. Endospores are resistant to heat, desication, radiation, and chemicals, including organic solvents. They retain the capacity to germinate for a considerable number of years.

2. A naked cell, many of which are formed by division of the protoplast in certain, usually unicellular, blue-green algae. On release they form a cell wall and develop into new individuals.

**Endosporic Gametophyte.** A gametophyte that develops within a spore. For example, the female gametophyte of Selaginella is contained within the megaspore and at maturity only a portion, bearing the archegonia, is exposed through the spore wall. Such gametophytes are better able to withstand dry conditions and this pattern of development may be seen as a step in the evolution of the seed habit.

**Endosteum.** A fibrous membrane lining the marrow cavity of compact bone and covering trabeculae of cancellous bone.

**Endothelium.** A single layer of thin platelike cells that line the inner surfaces of blood and lymph vessels and the heart. Endothelium is derived from the mesoderm. Compare epithelium; mesothelium.

**Endothermous.** Warm-blooded : Homoiothermous.

**Endotoxin.** A toxin produced by a bacterial cell which is released only after death and disintegration of the cell.

**Endotrophic.** Nourished from within, said of mycorrhiza which obtain their nourishment from their host.

**Endotrophic Mycorrhiza** (endophytic mycorrhiza). A form of mycorrhizal association in which the fungus lives between and within the cells of the cortex and growth on the outside of the root is limited. Such associations are found on many herbaceous species, especially orchids and heathers, and on certain woody plants, such as rhododendrons. The fungi involved are usually species of Rhizoctonia on orchids or Phoma on heathers. The hyphae form tightly coiled masses, termed pelotons, within the cells of the outer cortex. Plants that commonly develop such associations cannot grow normally without the appropriate fungus.

**Endozoic.** Living within an animal; entozoic.

**End Plate.** The area of muscle cell membrane that lies immediately beneath a motor nerve ending. Release of a neurotransmitter at the end plate induces contraction of the muscle fibre.

**End-plate Potential.** A brief localized depolarization or potential change which takes place across the membrane in the motor end-plate region of a muscle fibre, at a neuromuscular junction. A neurotransmitter substance gets released from the presynaptic nerve endings on stimulation by an impulse and increases the permeability of the postsynaptic (muscle) membrane to ions, causing the EPP. The size of the EPP has been bound to depend on the amount of neurotransmitter released but normally it is sufficiently large to cross the threshold level for respose and set off an action potential, which gets propagated along the length of the muscle fibre.

**Endysis.** Development of a new coat of hair or feathers.

**Enhancement Effect.** Emerson effect.

**Enolase.** The enzyme which is catalysing the formation of phosphoenolpyruvic acid from 2-phosphoglyceric acid.

**Ensheathed.** Enclosed within a sheath, as certain larval nematodes.

**Enteric.** Of or pertaining to the intestine.

**Enterobiasis.** Infestation of the intestine by Enterobius vermicularis, a nematode worm commonly called the pinworm or seatworm; oxyuriasis.

**Enterocoel.** The cavity of a mesodermal somite which has arisen as an outpoketing of the archenteron.

**Enteron.** The alimentary canal or digestive tract.

**Enteronephric.** Emptying into the intestine, said of certain types of nephridia.

**Entire.** Describing a leaf, petal, or sepal margin that has a smoth undivided outline.

**Entire**

1. Complete; whole; without parts or divisions.
2. With a continuous edge or margin, said of leaves or bacterial colonies.

**Entomology.** The study of insects.

**Entomophagous.** Feeding upon insects; insectivorous.

**Entomophilous.** Pollinated by insects.

**Entomophily.** Pollination of a flower in which the pollen is carried on an insect. Entemophilous flowers are usually brightly coloured and scented and often secrete nectar. In some species (*e.g.*, primulas) there are structural differences between the flowers to ensure that cross-pollination occurs. Other examples of entomophilous flowers are orchids and antirrhinums. Compare anemophily; hydrophily.

**Entomophthorales.** Zygomycetes.

**Entomostracan.** Any of a large number of small, aquatic crustaceans formerly comprising the Entomostraca, a subclass which included the copepods, ostracods, and others.

**Entophyte.** A plant which lives within another plant; an endophyte.

**Entozoan.** An animal which lives as a parasite within another animal.

**[1]Enucleate.** Without a nucleus.

**[2]Enuleate.** To remove a nucleus.

**Enumeration Data.** Data in which the material under observation falls into discrete classes.

**Environment.** The conditions in which an organism lives. The external environment includes the nonliving physical and chemical factors such as light, nutrients, etc., together with the effects of other living organisms. Genetically similar plants growing in different environments may appear different (plasticity). Such intraspecific variation is termed environmental variation and is not inherited. An organism also has an internal environment, which is the result of its own metabolism.

**Enzyme.** A protein that acts as a catalyst in biochemical reactions. Each enzyme is specific to a particular reaction or group of similar reactions Many require the association of certain nonprotein cofactors in order to function. The molecule undergoing reaction (the substrate) binds to a specific active site on the enzyme molecule to form a short-lived intermediate : this greatly in creases (by a factor of up to $10^{20}$) the rate at which the reaction proceeds to from the product. Enzyme activity is influenced by substrate concentration and by temperature and pH, which must lie within a certain range. Other molecules may compete for the active site, causing inhibition of the enzyme or even irreversible destruction of its catalytic properties.

Enzyme production is governed by a cell's genes. Enzyme activity is further controlled by pH changes, alterations in the concentrations of essential cofactors, feedback inhibition by the products of the reaction and activation by another enzyme, either from a less active from or an inactive precursor (zymogen). Such changes may themselves be under the control of hormones or the nervous system.

The names of most enzymes end in –ase, which is added to the names of the substrates on which they act. Thus lactase is the enzyme that acts to break down lactose.

**Enzyme Technology**. The use of isolated purified enzymes as catalysts in industrial processes. The enzymes used are normally extracellular enzymes with no requirements for complex cofactors. Examples are proteases, amylases, cellulases, and lipases extracted from bacterial or yeast cultures. Cell-free enzymes have certain distinct advantages over the use of microorganisms, a major one being that only the desired enzymatic reaction will occur and substrate is not wasted in the formation of unwanted by-products or microbial biomass.

**Eocene**. The second geological epoch of the Tertiary period. It extended from the end of the Palaeocene epoch, about

54 million years ago, to the beginning of the Oligocene epoch, about 38 million years ago. The term was first proposed by Sir Charles Lyell (1797–1875) in 1833. In some classifications of geological time the Palaeocene is included as part of the Eocene. Mammals were dominant in the Eocene : rodents, artiodactlys, carnivores, perissodactyls (including early horses), and whales were among the groups to make their first appearance.

**Eocene Epoch.** The second epoch of the Tertiary period characterized by the rise of modern mammals.

**Eolith.** A crude stone instrument of the Dawn Stone Age.

**Eosin.** An acid stain that colours cytoplasm pink and cellulose red. It is often used with a counterstain, such as methylene blue or haematoxylin. Wright's stain, Leishman's stain, and Giemsa stains are all mixtures of eosin and methylene blue mixed with alcohol.

**Epaxial.** Above or dorsal to an axis.

**Ephedrales.** Gnetales.

**Ephedrine.** A white crystalline alkaloid whose effects are similar to epinephrine; obtained from Ephedra equisetina or produced synthetically.

**Ephemeral.** A plant with a short life cycle that may be completed many times in one growing season. Examples are groundsel (Senecio vulgaris) and shepherd's purse (Capsella bursa-pastoris). Some desert plants also have short life cycles that can be completed in a short period following rain. Compare annual, biennial, perennial.

**Ephippium.** In cladocerans, a modified portion of the carapace which forms a protective capsule for fertilized eggs.

**Epibasal Cell.** The outer of the two cells formed by the first division of the zygote. It gives rise to the embryo in plants showing exoscopic embryogeny and to the foot in those showing endoscopic embryogeny. Compare hypobasal cell.

**Epiboly.** Expansion and growth of one part over another, as occurs in the development of certain gastrulae.

**Epicalyx.** A ring of bracts below a flower that resembles a calyx. It is seen, for example, in the strawberry flower.

**Epicardium**

1. In vertebrates, the visceral pericardium forming the outer layer of the wall of the heart.
2. In tunicates, a tubular structure surrounding the stomach and intestine.

**Epicarp.** Exocarp.

**Epicone.** In a dinoflagellate, the portion of the body anterior to the annulus.

**Epicotyl.** The apical end of the axis of an embryo above the cotyledon(s), which gives rise to the stem and associated organs. Compare hypocotyl, plumule.

**Epidemiology.** The study of factors causing and influencing widespread outbreaks of disease.

**Epidemic.** Affecting large numbers of a population at the same time, said of certain diseases.

**Epidermis**

1. *bot.* The outermost layer of cells of the primary plant body; the superficial layer of cells of various parts, as the root, stem, leaf.
2. *zool.* The outermost layer of cells of various invertebrates.
3. *anat.* The surface layer of the skin of a vertebrate.

**Epididymis.** A long coiled tube in which spermatozoa are stored in vertebrates. In reptiles, birds, and mammals it is attached at one end to the testis and opens into the sperm duct (vas deferens) at the other.

**Epigamic.** Pertaining to factors other than those of a sexual nature which serve to attract the opposite sex, as colors and songs of birds.

**Epigeal.** Describing seed germination in which the seed leaves (cotyledons) emerge from the ground and function as true leaves. Examples of epigeal germination are seen in sycamore and sunflower. Compare hypogeal.

**Epigenesis.** The theory that an organism develops from a fertilized egg by a gradual series of interdependent physiological and physical changes, brought about by the genes, that result in an increase in the complexity of its separate parts. It refutes the earlier preformation theory, which stated that either the male or female gamete contained a miniature version of the adult and that only an increase in size followed thereafter.

**Epigenous.** Growing on a surface, as that of a leaf.

**Epigeous**

1. Lying close to or growing on the surface of the ground.
2. Appearing above the surface of the ground, with reference to the cotyledons of a seedling.

**Epiglottis.** A flap of cartilaginous tissue in the throat that closes the windpipe opening (glottis) when food is swallowed.

**Epignathous.** Condition in which the upper jaw or mandible is longer than the lower jaw.

**Epigynous.** Flowers in which the petals, etc., arise from above the enclosed carpels. The carpels are inferior (*e.g.*, apple).

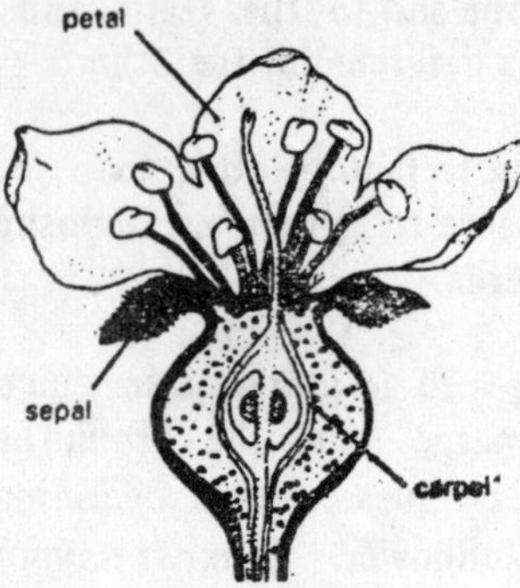


Epigynous flower

**Epigyny.** An arrangement of floral parts in which the staments, sepals, and petals are inserted above the ovary, giving an inferior ovary. Epigynous flowers are seen in many members of the Rosaceae, *e.g.*, quinces (Chaenomeles). The receptacle is urn shaped and completely encloses the ovary, the other floral parts arising from the top of the receptacle. A type of pseudocarp, the pome, commonly forms from such flowers. Compare hypogyny, perigyny.

**Epilimnion.** In a lake, the upper layer of warm, circulating water.

**Epimatium.** A specialized type of ovuliferous scale that bears and completely encloses a single inverted ovule. It is found in the monkey-puzzle tree (Araucaria araucana) and in certain of the Podocarpaceae.

**Epimerase.** An enzyme that catalyses the transfer of a hydroxyl group from one position to another within a molecule. Epimerases are a form of isomerase and are important biologically in the interconversion of sugars.

**Epimerite.** The hooked, anchoring structure on the protomerite of a gregarine.

**Epimorphic.** Designating a mode of development in which larval stages are suppressed and the individual hatches as a postlarva, as in certain crustaceans.

**Epinasty.** A nastic movement in which the resultant bending of the plant part is downwards, due to increased growth on the upper side of an organ. This occurs in the opening of many flowers when the bracts and perianth parts curl downwards to expose the sexual organs. Epinasty can also occur in leaves where the petiole bends so that the leaf points to the ground rather than upwards. Compare hyponasty.

**Epinephrine.** A hormone, one of two catecholamines secreted the adrenal medulla. It raises blood pressure and brings about other changes necessary for the quick mobilization and release of energy as required in emergency situations : Adrenalin.

**Epipelagic.** Pertaining to suspended organisms living in water between surface and a depth of 200 meters.

**Epipetalous.** Describing stamens that arise from the petals, as occur in many flowers with tubular corollas.

**Epipharynx.** A lobelike or pointed structure on the inner surface of the labrum or clypeus of and insect.

**Epiphragm.** A membrane which closes an opening, as *a. bot.* the platelike structure which closes the capsule in certain mosses; *b. zool.* a calcareous plate which closes the aperture of the shell in certain hibernating gastropods.

**Epiphysis.** The terminal section of a growing bone (especially a long limb bone). It is separated from the bone shaft (diaphysis) by cartilage. New bone is produced on the side of the cartilage facing the diaphysis, while new cartilage is produced on the other side of the cartilage disc. When the bone reaches adult length the epiphysis merges with the diaphysis.

**Epiphyte.** A plant growing on another but using it only for support and not drawing food from it (*e.g.*, mosses and orchids on trees).

**Epiphytotic.** A widespread outbreak of disease among plants.

**Epipleuron.** The turned-down, lateral margin of the elytron of a beetle.

**Epipodite.** A flat, leaflike structure attached to the coxa of certain appendages in various crustaceans which functions as a gill separator.

**Epipodium.** A lateral fold or ridge along the edge of the foot in certain gastropods.

**Episematic.** Pertaining to recognition marks or colors.

**Episepal.** Epicalyx.

**Episepalous.** Attached to or adnate to the sepals, with reference to floral parts.

**Episome.** A replicon in a bacterial cell, either attached to the bacterial chromosome or existing in the cytoplasm and replicating independently.

**Epistasis.** A form of gene interaction in which one gene affects the expression of a second gene. It usually arises because the two genes affect sequential steps in the same biochemical pathway. It is most easily detected as a modification of the Mendelian ratio in the $F_2$. The phenomenon was first reported in the inheritance of flower colour. For example, suppose there are two enzymes, A′ and B′, produced by the normal alleles of two unlinked genes, A and B, but not by their recessive alleles, *a* and *b*. The substrate of A′ is a white pigment and the product of B′ is a purple pigment. In addition the product of A′, a red pigment, is also the substrate of B′. Thus the sequence of reactions white pigment to red pigment to purple pigment can only take place if there is at least one normal allele at both gene loci. The genotype aa— — would give a white phenotype (no enzyme A′; gene B is immaterial), genotype A—*bb* would give a red phenotype (enzyme A′ but not B′), and genotype A—B— would give a purple phenotype (both A′ and B′). Instead of the $F_2$ forming a 9 : 3 : 3 : 1 ratio, a 9 : 3 : 4 ratio (=9 : 3 : [3+1]) would be obtained, since *aa*B—would be indistinguishable from *aabb*. In this case, gene A is the epistatic gene, and gene B the hypostatic gene. Other variants are 9 : 7, 13 : 3, and 12 : 3 : 1 ratios.

**Epistome.** A structure lying anterior to or overhanging the mouth in various invertebrates.

**Epithelium.** A sheet of cells that lines most cavities of the body and covers the exterior. The skin, the lining of the gut and other organs, such as the lungs and blood vessels, are examples. The cells of epithelia may serve very different purposes. Those lining the salivary glands and the glands in the intestine for example, produce digestive enzymes. The ones forming the outer covering of the skin are mainly protective, while the cells of the lung lining produce the wet mucus in which the oxygen dissolves before passing to the blood. Many epithelia are ciliated—*e.g.* windpipe—and the cilia help to waft out the foreign particles (dust).

*Simple.* Unicellular which is usually composed of flat cells. It is called squamous epithelium. It is present in Bowman's capsule.

*Cuboidal.* It is composed of cuboidal cells and formed in glands and ducts.

*Columnar.* It is composed of relatively tall cells which look like columns. It is found in gastrointestinal canal.

*Stratified.* It is composed of more than one layer. It is present usually in skin.

*Pseudostratified.* It is composed of more than one layer. Layers are not even because the cells are of various shapes. It is present in trachea.

*Ciliated.* It is composed of cells which are either cuboidal or columns but cells bear cilia. It is found in trachea and some ducts.

**Epizoon.** An animal which lives on the surface of another animal; Compare ectozoan.

**[1]Epizootic.** Attacking many animals at the same time, said of a disease.

**[2]Epizootic.** A disease which is prevalent among animals.

**Epoch.** In geologic time, a subdivision of a period.

**Eponym.** A person for whom or from whom the name of an animal or plant or a part of it takes its name, as Malpighi (Malpighian corpuscle).

**Equine.** Of, pertaining to, or resembling a horse.

**Equisetum.** Horsetail.

**Equitant.** Overlapping, said of leaves whose bases overlap the bases of the leaves above them, as in the iris.

**Era.** A major division of geologic time.

**Erect.** Upright; not reclining or leaning.

**Erectile.** Capable of being erected, as erectile tissue of the penis or clitoris.

**Erection.** The act of becoming erect; becoming swollen and turgid, with special reference to the penis or clitoris.

**Ergastic Matter.** Non-protoplasmic by-products of protoplasmic activity. They include crystals, starch grains, tanins and oil droplets. Many such substances are waste matter but many are storage products.

**Ergodic Hypothesis.** The succession of vegetation in different places at one time will show the same sequence that one place will show in successive time.

**Ergosterol.** A sterol present in yeast and other plants which, upon irradiation by ultraviolet rays, is converted into vitamin $D_2$ or calciferol.

**Ergot**

1. A fungus disease of grasses and cereal plants, especially, rye, caused by species of Claviceps, an ascomycete.
2. The dried sclerotia of Calviceps purpura which contains a number of alkaloids, some of medical importance. It induces powerful uterine contractions.

**Erepsin.** An obsolate name for a mixture of protein-degrading enzymes secreted by the small intestine.

**Ergastic Matter.** Nonprotoplasmic substances that are produced as by-products of protoplasmic activity. It includes crystals, starch grains, tannins, and oil droplets. Many ergastic substances are regarded as waste matter, some are storage products, while the functions of other materials are unknown.

**Ergocalciferol.** Vitamin D.

**Ergonomics.** The study of the engineering aspects of the relationship between workers and their working environment.

**Ergosterol.** A sterol occurring in fungi, bacteria, algae, and higher plants. It is converted into vitamin $D_2$ by the action of ultraviolet light.

**Ericaceae.** A large family of dicotyledonous usually shrubby plants, commonly called the heath or heather, family, numbering about 3000 species in some 100 genera. It is virtually cosmopolitan in distribution though members are poorly represented in Australia. Ericaceous plants have simple often evergreen leaves that lack stipules and may be reduced to needles, *g.e.* bell heather (Ericacinerea), or rolled, *g.e.* cowberry. The flowers are usually actinomorphic and bisexual and may be borne singly or in racemes. The petals, normally four or five, are usually fused at the base. Over half the described species are in the two genera Rhododendron (about 1200 species) and Erica (about 500 species). Both show unusual distributions, species of Erica being concentrated in South Africa (the Cape heaths number some 450 species) while Rhododendron species are concentrated in the Himalayan foothills and New Guinea. Over half the Rhododendron species are cultivated as ornamentals (the azaleas are included in this genus). Many heaths (Erica) and heathers (Calluna) are also grown as ornamentals. The berries of certain species, notably bilberry (Vaccinium myrtilus) and cranberry (Vaccinium oxycoccus), are valued as food in many areas.

**Erichthus.** The ciliated larva (pseudozoea) of certain stomatopod crustaceans.

**Error Variance.** The variance which is arising from agents unrecognized or uncontrolled in an experiment, with which the appareat effect of any recognized agent, controlled, or uncontrolled, is to be compared.

**Eruciform Larva.** A caterpillarlike larva with well-defined segmentation, prolegs, and stigmata along sides of body, as in Lepidoptera.

**Erysiphales.** An order of the Plectomycetes containing about 150 species (20 genera) of obligate parasites that cause powdery mildew diseases of plants. The diseases are so named because the superficial hyphae produce masses of powdery conidiospores.

**Erythroblast.** Any of the cells in the myeloid tissue of red bone marrow that develop into erythrocytes (red blood cells). Erythroblasts have a nucleus and are at first colourless, but fill with haemoglobin as they develop. In mammals the nucleus disappears.

**Erythroblastosis Foetalis** Refers to condition in foetus in which due to mother-father Rh factor incompatability, the infant's blood ($Rh^+$) may clot when it comes in contact with mother's blood ($Rh^-$). The father is having $Rh^+$—blood.

**Erythrocytes.** RBC's of blood. Haemoglobin having cells which are characteristic of all the vertebrates and chordates. They are able to transport oxygen in the body. They are rounded oval, biconcave or biconvex and mostly have a nucleus except in mammals. They are formed within lymph nodes and spleen in non-mammals and in the red bone marrow in mammals. Their life period is about 100 days in non-mammals like frog and 120 days in mammals. The number is 5 million/ml of blood of man. In women the number is more. Process of their formation is known as erythropoisis.

**Erythrophore.** A melanophore with red pigment.

**Erythropoiesis.** The formation of red blood cells.

**Erythropoisis.** Refers to the process of RBCs formation. It gets inhibited by a rise of RBCs in blood to supernormal value and stimulated by anaemia. This process is normally controlled by a circulating glycoprotein hormone which is called erythropoitin. Its steps are as follows :

Uncommited stem cell→Commited stem cell→Proerythroblasts→Early nomoblasts→Intermediate nomoblasts→Late nomoblasts→Reticulocytes→Erythrocytes.

**Erythrose.** A four-carbon aldose sugar (illustration at aldose). In the phosphorylated form, erythrose 4-phosphate, it is an intermediate in the Calvin cycles. In the shikimic acid pathway, the first reaction step is the joining of erythrose 4-phosphate with phosphoenolpyruvate to form a seven-carbon keto sugar acid.

**Escape**

1. *bot.* *a.* The breaking away from, as spores or seeds from a capsule. *b.* The ability of a susceptible plant to avoid becoming infected through some condition or factor other than natural, inherent resistance factors.
2. *physiol.* A release from control, as the escape of the heart from vagus control.

**Escargot.** A snail, especially one prepared for eating.

**Essential Amino Acid.** An amino acid that an organism is unable to synthesize in sufficient quantities. It must therefore be present in the diet. In man the essential amino acids are arginine, histidine, lysine, threonine, methionine, isoleucine, leucine, valine, phenylalanine, and tryptophan. These are required for protein synthesis and deficiency leads to retarded growth and other symptoms. Most of the amino acids required by man are also essential for all other multicellular animals and for most protozoans.

**Essential Element.** Any of a number of elements required by living organisms to ensure normal growth, development, and maintenance. Apart from the elements found in organic compounds (*i.e.* carbon, hydrogen, oxygen, and nitrogen), plants, animals, and microorganisms all require a range of elements in inorganic forms in varying amounts, depending on the type of orgainism. The major elements, present in tissues in relatively large amounts (greater than 0.005%), are calcium, phosphorus, potassium, sodium, chlorine, sulphur, and magnesium.

The trace elements occur at much lower concentrations and thus requirements are much less. The most important are iron, manganese, zinc, copper, iodine, cobalt, selenium, molybdenum, chromium, and silicon. Each element may fulfil one or more of a variety of metabolic roles. Sodium, potassium, and chloride ions are the chief electrolytic components of cells and body fluids and thus determine their electrical and osmotic status. Calcium, phosphorus, and magnesium are all present in bone. Calcium is also essential to nerve and muscle activity, while phosphorus is a key constituent of the chemical energy carriers (*e g.* ATP) and the nucleic acids. Sulphur is needed primarily for amino acid synthesis (in plants and microorganisms). The trace elements may serve as cofactors or as constituents of complex molecules, *e.g.* iron in haem and cobalt in vitamin $B_{12}$.

**Essential Fatty Acids.** Fatty acids that must normally be present in the diet of certain animals, including man. Essential fatty acids, which include linoleic and linolenic acids, all possess double bonds at the same two positions along their hydrocarbon chain and so can act as precursors of prostaglandins. Deficiency of essential fatty acids can cause dermatosis, weight loss, irregular oestrus, etc. An adult human requires 2—10 g linoletic acid or its equivalent per day.

**Essential Oil** (ethereal oil). Any of the volatile oils secreted by aromatic plants that give them their characteristic taste or odour. Most essential oils are terpenoids, while some are derivatives of benzene. Many xerophytic plants produce essential oils as a means of reducing their transpiration rates. In hot conditions the evaporating oils distribute to the density of the boundary layer at the leaf surface. The higher the density of the boundary layer, the greater resistance it offers to diffusion of water vapour. Some essential oils repel insects while others, *e.g.* those of Myoporum deserti, are toxic to grazing animals. Many allelopathic substances are essential oils.

**Esterase.** An enzyme which catalyzes the hydrolysis of an ester to an alcohol and an acid.

**Estipitate.** Lacking a stipe.

**Estipulate.** Lacking a stipule.

**Estival.** Of or pertaining to summer.

**Estivation**

1. *bot.* The arrangement of floral parts within a floral bud; also aestivation.
2. *zool.* A state of dormancy or inactivity induced by the heat of summer.

**Estrogen.** A substance, natural or synthetic, capable of inducing estrus and the development of female secondary sexual characteristic; a female sex hormone. In man the principal estrogens are estradiol, estrone, and estriol, steroid hormones secreted by the ovarian follicle, corpus luteum, placenta, adrenal cortex, and testis.

**Estrous Cycle.** The sequence of events from the beginning of one estrus to the beginning of the next. Stages include estrus, metestrus, diestrus, and proestrus.

**Estrus.** Among mammals other than primates, the period of sexual excitement and receptivity in the adult female during which mating usually occurs; the period of heat or rut; oestrus.

**Etaerio.** A cluster of fruits formed from the unfused carpels of a single flower. For example, the anemone has an etaerio of acheness, larkspur an etaerio of follicles, and blackberry an etaerio of drupes.

**Ethology.** The study of the biology of animal behaviour. Central to the ethologist's approach is the principle that animal behaviour (like physical characteristics) is subject to evolution through natural selection. Ethologists therefore seek to explain how the behaviour of an animal in its natural environment may contribute to the survival of the maximum number of its relatives and offspring. This involves recognizing the stimuli that are important in nature (sign stimulus) and how innate predispositions interact with learning in the development of behaviour (instinct). Studies of this sort were pioneered by Konrad Lorenz (1903— ) and Niko Tinbergen (1907— ).

**Ethylene** (ethene). A colourless gaseous hydrocarbon, $C_2H_4$, that occurs naturally in many plants and acts as a growth substance. Among its effects are the inhibition of longitudinal growth and the radial expansion of tissues, the promotion of fruit ripening and (in some species) flowering, and the breaking of seed dormancy in some species.

**Ethylene Chlorohydrin** (ethylene chlorhydrin). A chlorinated derivative of ethylene glycol formula $CH_2ClCH_2OH$, used to break bud dormancy.

**Etiolation** The condition, seen when plants are growing with an inadequate light supply, in which there is abnormal chlorophyll development. It causes the plant to look pale and there is excessive elongation of the internodes and poor development of the leaves. It is an adaptation to hasten the plant's location of a light source. When plants are growing from underground stems, etiolation is manifested by extreme elongation of the petioles. This phenomenon is exploited in the growth of certain vegetables, such as rhubarb and celery, which may be kept in darkness to either blanch (whiten) the leaf stalks or to force them on early.

**Etiology.** The study of the causal agents of a disease.

**Etioplast.** A partially differentiated plastid, 1.5—2.2 $\mu$m in diameter, found in the cells of plants that have been kept in darkness (etiolated plants). A three-dimensional lattice, the prolamellar body, occupies almost the whole of the central region. Etioplasts contain protochlorophyll, which is converted to chlorophyll on exposure to light. Compare proplastid.

**Eubacteria.** The true bacteria, *i.e.*, those typically having simple unbranched cells, rigid cell walls, and flagella for movement.

**Eubacteriales.** An order containing easily stained rod-shaped or spherical bacteria with, in the motile forms, numerous flagella (peritrichous). The rod-shaped organisms are assigned to the following families : Azotobacteraceae (which contains free-living nitrogen-fixing soil bacteria, *e.g.*, Azotobacter), Achromobacteraceae, Rhizobiaceae (which contains symbiotic nitrogen fixers, *e.g.*, Rhizobium, and some gallforming bacteria, *e.g.*, Agrobacterium), Enterobacteriaceae (which contains some plant parasites, *e.g.*, Erwinia), Brucellaceae, and Bacteroidaceae. All these families are gram-negative. Gram-positive rods are assigned to the families Brevibacteriaceae, Lactobacillaceae (lactic acid bacteria), Propionibacteriaceae, Corynebacteriaceae (containing Corynebacterium, which causes certain plant rots), and Bacillaceae. The spherical organisms are divided into the gram-negative Neisseriaceae and the grampositive Micrococcaceae.

**Eucamptodromous.** Camptodromous.

**Eucaryotic.** Possessing a true nucleus.

**Euchromatin.** A type of chromatin present in chromosomes which stains densely during metaphase but weakely during interphase. It is active genetically, containing the genes. Compare heterochromatin.

**Eugenics.** The study of methods of improving the quality of human populations by the application of genetic principles. Positive eugenics would seek to do this by selective breeding programmes. Negative eugenics aims to eliminate harmful genes (*e.g.*, those causing haemophilia and colour blindness) by counselling any prospective parents who are likely to be carriers.

**Euglena.** A group of aquatic single-celled organisms that are on the border line between plants and animals. Because most can photosynthesize, they are more commonly classed as plants, though they are mobile and can also feed like primitive animals. Euglena propel themselves through the water with a whip-like organ called a flagellum. They often from scum on the surface of lakes and ponds.

**Euglenophyta.** A division of very variable, predominantly unicellular, flagellate algae. It contains both pigmented (autotrophic or facultatively heterotrophic) and unpigmented (obligately heterotrophic) genera. When pigments are present they are similar to those found in the Chlorophyta. A cell wall is absent, enabling certain of the unpigmented forms to ingest food by phagocytosis. Such forms are probably better classified as Protozoa even though they most likely evolved from photosynthetic forms. Food is stored as paramylum and fat.

**Eukaryote** (eucaryote). An organism consisting of cells in which the genetic material is contained within a distinct nucleus. All organisms, except bacteria and blue-green algae, are eukaryotes.

**Eukaryotic** (eucaryotic). Describing cells that have a nucleus, or organisms made up of such cells (compare prokaryotic) The genetic material of eukaryotes consists of chromatin and is divided into a number of chromosomes, which are located in the nucleus. Eukaryotic cells usually divide either by mitosis or meiosis while division in prokaryotes is amitotic. In certain classifications all eukaryotic organisms are placed in the kingdom Eukaryota, to emphasize the difference between these and the prokaryotes, or Prokaryota.

**Eumycota** (Mycobionta). The division containing the true fungi, which differ from the Myxomycota in having a mycelial (or occasionally unicellular) thallus. It contains the subdivisions Mastigomycotina, Zygomycotina, Assomycotina, Basidiomycotina, and Deuteromycotina.

**Eunuch**. A castrated male person.

**Euphorbiaceae.** A large family of dicotyledonous plants, mainly tropical in distribution, containing over 5000 species in some 300 genera. It is commonly known as the spurge family. Most members have simple alternately arranged leaves and unisexual flowers. In the tribe Euphorbieae the small flowers are grouped into an inflorescence, which, due to the presence of various petal-like structures (*e.g.*, highly coloured bracts and grandular appendages), resembles a single flower. The 'flowers' of poinsettia (Euphorbia pulcherrima) are examples. The specialized inflorescence of Euphorbia species is termed a cyathium. The fruit is often a regma and in many genera the seeds are carunculate.

The family contains many commercially important species including Hevea brasiliensis, the main source of natural rubber, Manihot esculenta (cassava), and Ricinus communis (castor oil).

**Euplankton**. True plankton minus debris.

**Euploidy**. The condition in which the number of chromosomes in a nucleus is an exact multiple of the haploid number. This is the most common and stable condition. Compare aneuploidy.

**Eurotiales** (Plectascales, Aspergillales). An order of the Plectomycetes containing about 150 species (80 genera) of various moulds (*e.g.* Eurotium) that show a perfect stage. Their imperfect stages resemble those of certain members of the Hyphomycetales. Asci are produced by crozier formation.

**Eurybathic.** Having a wide depth range in ocean waters.

**Eurypterid.** A scorpionlike, aquatic arachnid of the extinct order Eurypterida, which included the largest known arthropods.

**Eurythermic.** Capable of withstanding wide extremes in temperature.

**Eurytopic.** Tolerating wide extremes in environmental conditions, hence having a wide range of distribution.

**Eusporangium.** A type of sporangium that is derived from several initials. There are several layers of cells in its wall and it usually produces a large number of spores. The eusporangium is typical of ferms in the Marattiales and Ophioglossales. Compare leptosporangium.

**Eustachian Tube.** A tube running from the middle ear to the throat of most tetrapods. It enables pressures on each side of the ear drum to remain equal.

**Eustele.** A type of dissected siphonostele, typical of dicotyledons, in which the vascular cylinder appears (in transverse section) as a ring of collateral or bicollateral vascular bundles separated by medullary rays. Compare atactostele.

**Eutheria** (Placentalia). A subclass of mammals in which the embryos are retained in a ulterus in the mother's body and nourished by a placenta. The young are thus fully protected during their embryonic development and kept at a constant temperature. Placental mammals evolved during the Cretaceous period (about 100 million years ago). Modern placentals are a highly diverse group that occupy all types of habitate in all parts of the world. They include the orders Artiodactyla, Carnivora, Cetacea, Chiroptera, Insectivora, Perissodactyla, Primates, Proboscidea, and Rodentia. Compare Metatheria; Prototheria.

**Eutrophic.** Rich in minerals and bases. The term is usually used of nutrient-rich lakes and ponds but it may be applied in other contexts, *e.g.* to fen peats that contain relatively high proportions of minerals and bases. Eutrophic lakes and ponds support a prolific growth of aquatic plants. When these plants die they accumulate as a thick layer on the lake bottom. The organisms decomposing this material diminish the dissolved oxygen in the water so fish are scarce or absent. Eutrophication may unwittingly be accelerated by man when, for example, sewage effluents enter a lake, or water rich in dissolved fertilizers seeps in from surrounding fields. In such instances the amount of oxygen used to decompose the plant remains may be so great that the fish die from oxygen deprivation. Compare oligotrophic.

**Eutrophic Lake.** One whose waters contain a minimal amount of dissolved oxygen, usually a shallow lake with abundant organic matter.

**Eutropic.** Twining in a clockwise direction.

**Ever-bearer, Ever-bloomer.** A plant producing leaves and flowers for a long period of the growing season, and often bearing flowers and fruits at the same time.

**Evergreen.** A plant that bears leaves throughout the year. Leaves are lost and replaced as part of a continual process. Most conifers are evergreen, as are a small number of broad-leaved trees, *e.g.* holly and holm oak.

**Evisceration**

1. Removal of thoracic or abdominal organs.
2. Protrusion of the viscera through an opening in body wall.
3. Removal of the contents of an organ, as the eye.
4. Reflex discharge of internal organs through the anal opening, as occurs in holothuroids.

**Evocation.** The ability of experimental stimuli (*e.g.* chemicals or tissue implants) to cause unspecialized embryonic tissue to develop into specialized tissue.

**Evolution.** The process whereby living things are believed to have arisen from less advanced forms by gradual change. A great deal of evidence supports the idea of evolution, especially the evidence provided by the fossil record. Darwin and Wallace put forward the theory of Natural, Selection to explain how these gradual changes could be passed on to succeeding generations.

**Evolve.** To undergo evolution; to become more specialized.

**Ewe.** The female of the sheep.

**Exalbuminous Seed.** A seed that lacks an endosperm at maturity. In such seeds the cotyledons absorb the food reserves from the endosperm and act as storage organs.

**Exarate.** With legs and wings free of secondary attachment to the body, with reference to insect pupae.

**Exarch.** Describing xylem maturation in which the older cells (protoxylem) are further from the centre of the axis than the younger cells. Development is thus centripetal. Compare endarch, mesarch.

**Exasperate.** Having stiff, hard, projecting points, as a leaf.

**Excrement.** Excreted waste material : Feces.

**Excrescence.** An outgrowth of the body. May be normal, as a hair or horn, or abnormal, as a wart.

**Excretion.** The removal from the body of waste products—unwanted and often poisonous substances produced by the vast number of biochemical reactions going on in the body. The simple act of breathing out carbon dioxide is a form of excretion, but the term is generally restricted to the removal of nitrogen-containing waste. These result from the breakdown of proteins in the body—proteins from surplus food perhaps, or from old and worn-out tissues that are continually being replaced. All but the simplest animals have special organs to get rid of this waste material. In the vertebrates this kind of excretion is performed by the Kidney and associated organs.

**Excretory Organ.** An organ or structure which functions in excretion, as a contractile vacuole, flame bulb, nephridium, Malpighian tubule, green, gland, or kidney.

**Exfoliation.** Shedding in flakes or thin layers, as *a. zool.* the shedding of the epidermis of the skin; *b. bot.* shedding of the bark of certain trees.

**Exine.** The outer part of the wall of a pollen grain external to the intine. Several alternative systems exist for recognizing different layers in the exine (diagram). In some morphological systems it is divided into an outer sexine and an inner nexine. Other systems based on chemical differences recognize an outer ektexine and an inner endexine. Various projections of the exine surface may confer a characteristic sculpturing to the pollen grain. This sculpturing, together with information on pollen size and shape and the positioning of the germinal apertures, can be so distinctive that individual genera and even species can be recognized.

The exine is composed of a carotenoid polymer called sporopollenin, which is highly resistant to decay. This has enabled palynologists to study fossil pollen and deduce the composition of earlier floras. Such studies have also thrown light on the evolution of plants.

**Exobiology.** The study of extraterrestrial life.

**Exocarp** (epicarp, ectocarp). The outermost layer of the pericarp of an angiosperm fruit, external to the mesocarp. It is usually only a thin layer, as in the plum, where it forms the outer skin.

**Exocrine.** Secreting externally.

**Exocrine Gland.** A gland that discharges its secretion into a body cavity (such as the gut) or onto the body surface. Examples are the sebaceous and sweat glands, the mammary glands, and part of the pancreas. Exocrine glands are formed in the embryo from the invagination of epithelial cells. Their secretions pass initially into a cavity (an alveolus acinus) and then out through a duct or duct network, along which the secretion may become modified by exchange with the blood across the duct epithelium.

**Exodermis.** A layer of cells, often lying immediately beneath the epidermis or velamen of the root, that is essentially a specialized hypodermis. Exodermal cells often resemble those of the endodermis and usually possess a suberized lamella on the inside of the primary cell wall.

**Exogamy.** The fusion of reproductive cells from distantly related or unrelated organisms, *i.e.* outbreeding. Compare endogamy.

**Exogenous.** Describing any process or substance arising from outside the organism, or organs arising in the peripheral layers of the body. Examples are the external supplies of nutrients and growth substances needed to maintain growth in cultures, and the origin of branches from the stem. Compare endogenous.

**Exon.** A polynucleotide sequence in a structural gene that codes for a protein, *i.e.* a section between two introns. This terminology is not applicable to bacteria, which do not have introns.

**Exophthalmos.** Abnormal protrusion of the eyeballs.

**Exoscopic.** With apex of the embryo directed toward the neck of the archegonium, as in bryophytes.

**Exoscopic Embryogeny.** Embryogeny in which, of the two cells resulting from the first division of the egg cell, the outer gives rise to the embryo and the inner to the foot. It is seen in the Bryophyta, Psilopsida, and Sphenopsida. Compare endoscopic embryogeny.

**Exoskeleton.** A rigid external covering for the body in certain animals, such as the hard chitinous cuticle of arthropods. An exoskeleton protects and supports the body and provides points of attachment for muscles. The cuticle of arthropods must be shed at intervals to allow growth to occur (ecdysis). Other examples of exoskeletons are the shells of molluscs and the bony plates of tortoises and armadillos. Compare endoskeleton.

**Exosmosis.** In osmosis, the passage of water outward.

**Exotic** (allien). Describing an organism that has originated from another region and is not native to the area in question. The term is used especially of tropical plants grown in greenhouses or indoors in temperate regions. An exotic plant that has become adapted to its new environment and can grow successfully without help from man is termed naturalized. An example in the UK is the monkey flower (Mimulus guttatus), which originated from North America. Many naturalized plants are garden escapes.

**Exotoxin.** A toxin produced by a microorganism which diffuses through the cell membrane into the surrounding medium.

**Expiration.** The expulsion of air from the lungs; breathing out; exhalation.

**Expire**

1. To breathe out or exhale.
2. To die.

**Explantation.** The removal of parts of living organisms (explants) for culture in a suitable artificial medium. This may be done to study the growth and development of tissues and organs and how they respond to different nutrient conditions. Explants are often only small segments of tissue, such as leaf discs or meristems. Their placement into or onto the culture medium is termed inoculation by analogy with microbiological techniques. The regenerative capacity of plant explants had led to their use as a means of plant propagation.

**Explosive Fruit.** One which bursts suddenly and violently, scattering seeds over a considerable area, as in the squirting cucumber.

**Exponential Growth.** A form of population growth in which the rate of growth is related to the number of individuals present. Increase is slow when numbers are low but rises sharply as numbers increase. If population number is plotted against time on a graph a characteristic-J-shaped curve results. In animal and plant populations, such factors as overcrowding lack of nutrients, and disease limit population increase beyond a certain point and the J-shaped exponential curve tails off giving an S-shaped (sigmoid) curve.

**Expressivity.** The extent or degree to which a character or trait manifests itself in individuals possessing its gene.

**Exstipulate.** Lacking stipules.

**Extant.** Now living or existing.

**Extension.** *anat.* Straightening of a limb or a part. In man, the backward or posterior movement of the head, trunk, or limbs.

**Extensor.** A muscle which extends or straightens a part.

**External.** Outside of, from the outside, pertaining to the exterior; toward the outside or away from the center.

**Exteroceptor.** A receptor which responds to stimuli from the outside, as the eye, ear, olfactory cells, and various cutaneous receptors.

**Extracellular.** Located or occurring outside the cell. Cuticularization is an example of an extracellular process.

**Extracorporcal.** Outside the body.

**Extrachromosomal Inheritance.** Cytoplasmic inheritancc.

**Extrafloral Nectary.** Used for nectary which is situated outside the flower or at any place other than inside of flower *e.g.*, gland spines of certain cacti where they attract seed dispersal agents such as ants.

**Extraembryonic Membranes.** The yolk sac, amnion, allantois, and chorion, auxillary structures concerned with protection, nutrition, respiration, and excretion in the embryo. Also called embryonic membranes.

**Extrastellar Cambium.** Used for the cambium which is formed outside the stele *i.e.*, not from intra and interfascicular cambia. It may be formed in parioyclic region or in the ground tissue.

**Extrorse.** Describing anthers that release their pollen to the outside of the flower so promoting cross pollination. Compare introrse.

**Extremity**

1. The terminal portion of a structure.
2. *anat.* A limb of the body and the bones to which it is attached. The upper extremity includes the pectoral girdle and upper limb; lower extremity includes pelvic girdle and lower limb.

**Exudation**

1. The passage of fluids, such as sweat, sap, or gums through minute openings from an organism; oozing out; bleeding.
2. The passage of certain constituents of the blood into tissue spaces, as occurs in inflammation.

**Exuviation**. The act of shedding a surface covering; ecdysis; molting.

**Eye.** The organ of sight. There are many different designs, but the eye is basically a lens which focuses light rays from the surroundings onto sensitive cells. When the light rays stimulate the cells, they send signals to the brain, which then 'translates' the signals back into a picture of the surroundings. The simplest eyes may not be able to do more than detect light and dark areas, but human eyes, like those of all the vertebrates, are very complicated and usually very efficient.

The vertebrate eye is essentially a fluid-filled ball with a very tough wall, called the sclera, and a lens

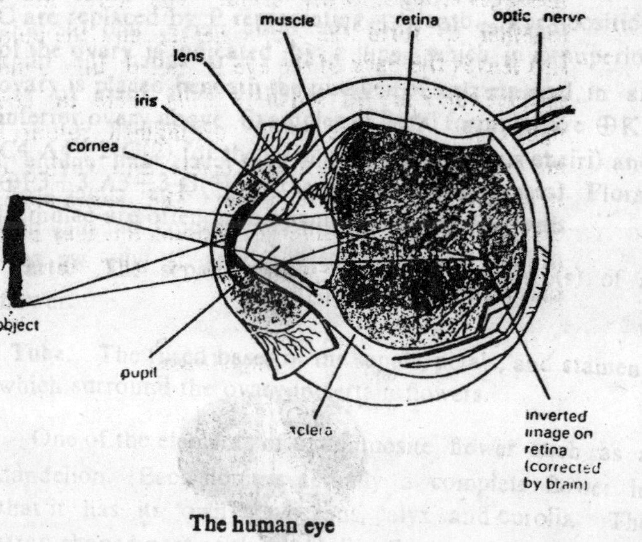


**The human eye**

suspended near the front. The light-sensitive cells from a layer known as the retina at the back of the eye-ball. The front of the sclera is tranparent and known as the cornea, and between this and the lens there is a muscular ring known as the iris. This is the coloured part of the eye. Light rays pass through the cornea and then through the pupil in the middle of the iris. Then they pass through the lens, where they are bent and focused onto the retina. The lens is relatively soft and its shape can be altered so that it can focus light rays from near and far. Muscles around the inside of the sclera produce these changes in the lens without any conscious control. The muscles of the iris also work automatically, enlarging the pupil in dim light and closing it in bright light so that the right amount of light gets through to affect the retina. The pupil is generally circular, but in some animals, such as cats, it is slit-like in daylight.

The cells of the retina are of two main types, known as rods and cones. Each cell is connected to a nerve fibre, and when light rays strike the cells the fibres carry messages straight to the brain. The fibres are bundled together to form the optic nerve, and the point where this leaves the back of the eye is called the blind spot—because there are no sensitive cells there to receive the light rays. The rods cannot distinguish colour, but they are sensitive to very low light levels and enable a person to see when it is quite dark. The cones are able to distinguish between different colours, but they need plenty of light to work properly. This is why we see only in black and white at night.

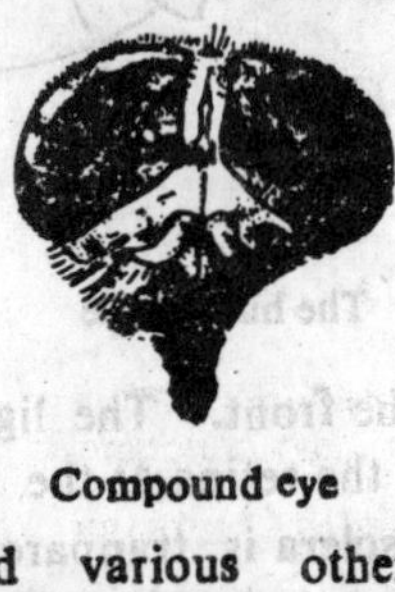


Compound eye

Insects and various other arthropods possess compound eyes, built to a completely different design. Each eye has numerous minute lenses called facets, and each lens sends its own image to the brain via its own nerve fibre. The insect thus sees a picture made up of lots of tiny dots—one for each facet receiving light rays. Dragonflies, which chase other insects through the air, need good eyesight and their eyes have up to 30,000 facets, producing a very detailed picture. Many ants, on the other hand, which spend much of their life below ground, have very few facets and some have no eyes at all.

**Eyeball.** The eye proper; the globe of the eye as distinguished from the accessory structures.

**Eyebright.** A small annual herb of Eurasia and North America found on grasslands as a rule. It has leaves with cut edges, and small white and yellow flowers. Eyebright is a semi-parasite, taking water from the roots of neighbouring plants. There are several species.

**Eye Gnat.** A frit fly or eye fly, a small dipterous insect of the families Chloropidae and Oscinideal of importance in the transmission of eye diseases.

**Eyespot** (stigma). A pigmented structure in motile unicellular algae and in flagellated reproductive bodies of some multicellular algae. It consists of one or more concentrically arranged curved plates composed of orange-red carotenoid granulea. The eyespot is situated close to the bases of the flagells. It functions as a light absorbing shield, which, depending on the position of the organism relative to the light source, prevents light from reaching photoreceptive areas at the bases of the flagella. This enables the organism to detect the direction of light and respond by movements of the flagella.

**Eye Tooth.** A canine tooth in the upper jaw.

[illegible]

[illegible] It is [illegible] through the [illegible] Dinoflagellates, [illegible] through the [illegible] good [illegible] up to [illegible] [illegible]

Eyeball. The eye proper, the globe of the eye, [illegible] from the accessory structures.

Eyebright. A small [illegible] herb of Euphrasia [illegible] with [illegible] [illegible] of [illegible] plants. [illegible]

Eye-gnat. A [illegible] of the family Chloropidae and Drosophilidae [illegible] important in the transmission of [illegible].

Eyespot (Stigma). A pigmented structure in motile [illegible] gae and in flagellated reproductive bodies of some [illegible] It consists of one or more segments [illegible] plates composed of [illegible] granules. The eyespot is situated [illegible] in the base of the [illegible] functions as a light [illegible] depending on the position of the [illegible] of the light source [illegible] base of the flagellum [illegible] transmission of light [illegible].

Eye Tooth. A canine tooth in the upper jaw.

# F

**F.** Notation, introduced by the geneticist Sewall Wright, for the inbreeding coefficient.

**$F_1$.** The offspring of a cross in which homozygous parents differ in one or more traits; the first filial generation.

**F. Generation.** The first generation of offspring (first Filial generation) from a cross between two individuals homozygous for contrasting alleles. In this case the $F_1$ must necessarily be heterozygous for the gene under investigation and the phenotypes are consequently similar. The $F_1$ generation thus shows far less variation than subsequent generations ($F_2$ generation) in which segregation becomes apparent. The term $F_1$ is also commonly, though incorrectly, used to mean the offspring produced from unspecified parents.

**$F_2$ (second filial generation).** The second generation of offspring in breeding experiments, obtained by crosses between individuals of the $F_1$ generation.

**$F_1$ Hybrid.** A crop variety that has been produced by crossing two selected parental pure lines. $F_1$ hybrids are favoured because they can combine the qualities of the parental lines and because they usually show hybird vigour. However they do not breed true and seed must consequently be produced each year. In such seed production selfing within the parental lines, which would give nonhybrid seed, must be prevented. This may be achieved by emasculation and hand pollination but this is only commercially feasible for particularly valuable crosp. Selfing can be prevented by ensuring that the parental lines both contain (different) reliable incompatibility alleles, *i.e.* S alleles high in the dominance series. This method is employed in producing $F_1$ hybird varieties of certain brassica vegetables. Alternatively one parental line may be male sterile; however use of male sterility halves the yield of hybird seed since seed set is only possible on one parent line. $F_1$ hybrid varieties of maize may be produced this way.

**Fabaceae.** Leguminosae.

**Face.** The anterior part of the head; the region bearing the mouth, nasal openings and the orbits.

**Facet**

1. *anat.* A small, smooth flat surface, as that on a bone forming an articulating surface.
2. *zool.* The surface of an ommatidium.

**Facilitated Diffusion**. The transport of molecules across the outer membrane of a living cell by a process that involves a specific carrier located within the cell membrane but does not require expenditure of energy by the cell. The carrier is believed to combine with a molecule on one side of the membrane, move through the membrane, and release the molecule on the other side. Compare active transport.

**Factor**

1. A circumstance, fact, condition, or influence which tends to produce, alter, or modify a result; a constituent.
2. *genetics.* A gene or hereditary determiner.

**Factorial Experiment**. An experiment in which the material is divided into a number of groups, such that each combination of treatments can be tried separately on at least one group and there are enough groups for every combination to be applied.

**Facultative.** Not limited to a specific condition; having the ability to live under varying conditions; optional.

**FAD** (flavin adenine dinucleotide). A coenzyme important in various biochemical reactions. It comprises a phosphorylated vitamin $B_2$(riboflavin) molecule linked to the nucleotide adenine monophosphate (AMP). FAD is usually tightly bound to the enzyme forming a flavoprotein. It functions as a hydrogen acceptor in dehydrogenation reactions, being reduced to $FADH_2$. This in turn is oxidized to FAD by the electron transport chain, thereby generating ATP (two molecules of ATP per molecule of $FADH_2$).

**Faeces.** Waste material that is eliminated from the alimentary canal through the anus. Faeces consist of the indigestible residue of food that remains after the processes of digestion and absorption of nutrients and water have taken place, together with bacteria and dead cells shed from the gut lining.

**Fagaceae.** A family of hardwood trees containing about 1000 species but only eight genera. However these include Quercus (oaks), Fagus (beeches), Castanea (chestnuts), and Nothofagus (southern beeches), which together make up a large proportion of the broadleaved forests of the world. It is probable that, in terms of biomass, this is the most abundant family of flowering plants. Representatives are not, however, found in the equatorial rain forests of Africa and South America.

The flowers are unisexual and usually borne in catkins or spikes. The fruit is a nut, which is partly or completely enclosed within a cupule. Certain species of chestnut, especially sweet chestnut (C. sativa), are grown for their fruits. However timber, obviously, is the most economically important product of this family and, on a far smaller scale, certain species of oak yield cork (Q. suber) and tannins. Many species are grown as ornamentals.

**Fairy Shrimp.** One of a number of branchiopod crustaceans occurring in temporary ponds in the early spring, as Branchinecta, Eubranchipus.

**Falcate.** Sickle-shaped. The term is usually used of leaves.

**Falciform.** Falcate.

**Falcon.** One of a number of birds of prey of the family Falconidae, especially the peregrine falcon or duck hawk (Falco peregrinus) used in the sport of hawking or falconry.

**Fall.** Any of the three large drooping outer petals of an Iris flower. In some species (*e.g.* I. germanica) they are bearded.

**Fallopian Tube.** In female mammals, the duct connecting the uterus and the peritoneal cavity. The muscular contraction and ciliary action of the tube moves eggs from the ovary to the uterus, and sperms from the uterus to the upper part of the tube, where fertilization occurs.

**Fallow Deer.** A European deer (Dama dama), a common park deer of Great Britain and western Europe.

**False Fruit.** Pseudocarp.

**Family**

1. A group of closely related persons, consisting of parents and their children.
2. A group of persons related by common ancestry, as the Smith family.
3. *biol.* A taxonomic group which comprises the principal division of an order and in turn is divided

into genera. In zoology, the family name ends in-idae; in botany, the family name usually ends in -aceae.

**Famulus.** A microsensory seta on the legs of mites.

**Fan.** The tail feathers of a bird; a flabellum.

**Fang.** A long, sharp, pointed tooth or toothlike structure, as *a.* the canine tooth of a carnivore; *b.* the long, hollow, curved tooth of a venomous reptile; *c.* a chelicera of a spider.

**Fanworm.** One of a number of sedentary polychaete worms which possess a crown of pinnate processes (radioles), as Sabella, feather duster.

**Far-red Light.** Electromagnetic radiation of approximately 740 nm. wavelength. It has been shown that far-red light inhibits many physiological processes in plants, *e.g.*, the germination of lettuce seeds It also counteracts the effect of red light. For example, if an etiolated plant is exposed to short periods of red light this results in more normal growth. However if the periods of red light are followed by periods of far-red light the plant remains etiolated. It is believed that far-red light is absorbed by a pigment, phytochrome, which mediates such responses.

**Farsighte Dness.** Hypermetropia.

**Fascia.** A sheet of fibrous connective tissue occurring beneath the skin and also enveloping glands, vessels, nerves, and forming tendon sheaths.

**Fasciate.** Bound or compressed into a bundle.

**Fasciation.** An abnormal form of growth in which a shoot becomes enlarged and flattened, giving the appearance of several shoots fused together. It is often seen in dandelions (Taraxacum). It may be caused by mechanical injury, by fungi or mite attack, or by infection with a bacterium of the genus Phytomonas, especially P. fasciens.

In some plants, *e.g.*, cock's comb (Celosia argentea cristata), it is due to a mutation.

**Fascicle.** A group, cluster, or compact bundle, as a fascicle of nerve fibers, muscle fibers, leaves, or roots; a fasciculus.

**Fascicular Cambium** (intrafascicular cambium). The part of the vascular cambium that originates within the vascular bundles (fascicles) between the xylem and phloem. Compare interfascicular cambium.

**Fasciculate.** Fascicled.

**Fast Green.** A green dye used in optical microscopy that stains cellulose, cytoplasm, collagen, and mucus green. It is frequently used to stain plant tissues, with safranin as a counterstain. Unlike light green, a similar dye, it does not fade easily.

**Fastigiate.** Describing a tree in which the branches grow almost vertically, such as the Lombardy poplar (Populus nigra italica).

**Fat**

1. A fatty, greasy substance present in adipose tissue and in certain seeds as those of cotton, soy beans, and corn.

2. A lipid, one of a class of substances containing carbon, hydrogen, any oxygen, which is soluble in alcohol or ether but not in water and which, upon saponification of alkaline hydrolysis yields glycerol and soap. True fats are esters of glycerol and fatty acids.

**Fat Body.** A structure containing stored fat which is utilized during periods of metamorphosis, hibernation, or dormancy. Present in amphibians, reptiles, and insects.

**Father.** The male parent of a child.

**Fatigue**

1. Weariness, exhaustion.
2. Inability of reduced capacity of muscle cells to perform work or nerve cells to respond to stimulation.
3. The sensation or feeling of weariness or exhaustion.

**Fatty Acid.** An organic compound consisting of a hydrocarbon chain and a terminal carboxyl group (carboxylic acids). Chain length ranges from one hydrogen atom (formic acid, HCOOH) to nearly 30 carbon atoms. Acetic, propionic, and butyric acids are important in metabolism. Long-chain fatty acids (more than 8—10 carbon atoms) most commonly occur as constituents of certain lipids, natably glycerides, phospho-lipids, sterols, and waxes, in which they are esterified with alcohols. These long-chain fatty acids generally have an even number of carbon atoms; unbranched chains predominate over branched chains. They may saturated (*e.g* , palmitic acid and stearic acid) or unsaturated, with one double bond (*e.g.*, oleic acid) or two or more double bonds, in which case they are called polyunsaturated fatty acids (*e.g.*, linoleic acid and linolenic acid).

The physical properties of fatty acids are determined by chain length, degree of unsaturation, and chain branching. Short-chain acids are pungent liquids, soluble in water. As chain length increases, melting points are raised and water-solubility decreases. Unsaturation and chain branching tend to lower melting points.

**Fatty Acid Metabolism.** The breakdown or synthesis of fatty acids. In plants fatty acids can be broken down to yield carbon dioxide, water, and energy but in many lipid-metabolizing tissues, especially germinating oil-rich seeds, fatty acids are metabolized to sugars. The major route for fatty acid breakdown is the β-oxidation cycle, which degrades fatty acids to acetyl CoA. The acetyl CoA can then either undergo further oxidation or can be converted into sugar via the glyoxylate cycle.

Fatty acid synthesis is a membrane-associated process The enzymes responsible for fatty acid synthesis aggregate in synthetase complexes, which are found associated with the various membranebound organelles of the cell. Three different types of synthetase complex have been identified, each with a different specificity.

**Fauces.** The passageway from mouth or buccal cavity to the pharynx.

**Fauna.** The animal life of a locality or region or that existing during a specific geological period or time.

**Faveolate.** Having cavities or cells like those of a honeycomb; favose : Alveolate.

**Fawn.** A young deer.

**Feather.** A growth from the skin of birds made up of the horny substance keratin. Feathers form the plumage and probably evolved from reptile scales. They are very important both in flight and in keeping a bird warm. Contour feathers cover a bird's body except for the feet and legs. They consist of a central shaft with a series of branches or barbs growing on each side. The barbs are linked together by a series of hooks called barbules to form a smooth, almost continuous surfase. Down feathers are the soft fluffy feathers that cover young birds. They also lie beneath the contour feathers of some adult birds, insulating them from the cold.

**Feather Duster.** A fanworm.

**Fecundity.** The capacity or power of producing abundant fruit or numerous offspring.

**Feedback.** The use of part of the output of a sysem to control its performance. In positive feedback, the output is used to enhance the input; in negative feedback, the output is used to reduce the input. Many biological processes rely on negative feedback. As the population of a species expands, so its food supply per individual is diminished; the result is that the population then begins to fall. Many biochemical processes are controlled by feedback inhibition.

**Feedback Inhibition**. A type of inhibition in which the end product of a multienzyme sequence inhibits the activity of an enzyme at or near the beginning of the pathway. An example is the inhibition by isoleucine of the enzyme threonine dehydratase, the first enzyme in the biosynthetic pathway from threonine to isoleucine. The opposite of feedback inhibition, feedforward stimulation, occurs when the first substrate of a reaction sequence stimulates subsequent reactions in the sequence.

Variations of simple feedback inhibition are found in branching pathways.

**Feedback Loop** (feedback mechanism). Control device in a system. Homoeostatic systems have numerous negative-feedback mechanisms which tend to counterbalance positive changes and so maintain stability. For example, denitrifying bacteria counteract the effects of nitrogen-fixing bacteria. Positive feedback reinforces change and in natural systems may result in radical environmental alteration. For example, an exceptionally cool summer in high mid-latitudes of the northern hemisphere may impede the melting of snow, leading to unusually high albedo, which reduces absorption of solar energy, leading to further cooling, etc.

**Feedback Mechanism**. A controlling mechanism in a cell or organism by which functional activity is regulated through factors which are returned or fed back to the controlling center with resultant depression or stimulation.

**Feedback Regulation**. Process by which the product of a metabolic pathway influences its own production by controlling the amount and or activity of one or more enzymes involved in the pathway. Normally this influence is inhibitory.

**Feeler.** A tactile organ; as an antenna, tentacle, or vibrissa.

**Fehling's Solution.** A mixture of two solutions used to detect the presence of reducing sugars and aldehydes in solution. Fehling's A, which is a copper (II) sulphate solution, is added to the test solution followed by an equal amount of Fehling's B (a mixture of sodium potassium tartrate and sodium hydroxide solutions). On boiling, a brick red precipitate of copper (I) oxide indicates a positive result.

**Feline**

1. Of or pertaining to the cat family, Felidae, a group of carnivores which includes the lion, tiger, leopard, puma, jaguar, wildcat, lynx, cheetah, and the domestic cat. Most belong to the genus Felis.

2. Any member of the family Felidae.

**Female.** Describing either the reproductive parts or a whole organism that bears the megaspore-producing apparatus. After fertilization the female may nurture the developing embryo. Compare male.

**Femoral.** Of or pertaining to the femur or thigh.

**Femur**

1. In tetrapods, the upper bone of the hind limb.
2. In Insecta, the third segment in the leg, which articulates with the trochanter proximally, and with the tibia distally. The femur is the largest and most robust segment of the leg in most adult insects. Movement with respect to the trochanter is usually limited.

**Fen.** A flat region of land that has developed from open stretches of base-rich water that have gradually silted up and passed through the hydrosere or halosere stage of vegetation. There is a build up of basic peat but the persistence of wet marshy conditions means that large trees cannot grow, resulting in a subclimax community. If the level of peat is raised sufficiently then certain woody plants that can tolerate wet conditions, such as alders (Alnus) willows (Salix), and guelder rose (Viburnum opulus), may become established. These fen woodlands are known as carr. Drained fenland, as for example that of the eastern English counties of Lincolnshire, Cambridgeshire, and Norfolk, is agriculturally very productive.

**Fenestra**

1. A small opening.
2. *entomol.* A transparent spot or clear area in the wing of an insect.

**Fenestra.** Either of the two delicate membranes between the middle ear and the inner ear. The lower membrane is the fenestra ovalis (fenestra vestibuli, or oval window). The stapes (the third ear ossicle) transmits to the fenestra ovails the vibrations it has received (via the other two ear ossicles) from the tympanum (eardrum). Vibrations in the fenestra ovalis are transmitted to the cochlea in the inner ear. The lower membrane, the fenestra rotunda (fenestra cochleae, or round window), vibrates in response to changes in pressure in the fluid (perilymph) surrounding the cochlea.

**Fer-de-lance.** Bothrops atrox, a large, venomous snake of tropical America.

**Ferment** An enzyme.

**Fermentation.** The anaerobic breakdown of glucose and other organic fuels to obtain energy. Fermentations are throught to be the oldest energy-yielding catabolic pathways.

Various types of fementation are known, which differ in their substrate and their final product or products. The best known fermentation is glycolysis, in which glucose is broken down to pyruvic acid. Alcoholic fermentation in yeast yields ethanol and carbon dioxide as end products. Other fermentations in microorganisms and bacteria lead to such end products as butyric acid and acetone.

**Fermenter.** An apparatus that is designed to contain, control, and monitor a biological process and collect the product of that process. For example, alcoholic fermentation, in which alcohol is produced by yeast cells, can be carried out on an industrial scale in a suitably designed fermenter. Industrial fermenters are used in brewing, effluent disposal, yeast production for bakeries, and in the production of important organic substances such as antibiotics, amino acids, single-cell protein, etc.

**Fern.** A group of green flowerless plants that reproduce by spores. Ferns have roots and a system of vessels for carrying water and food. The plants can therefore grow far larger than the mosses and liverworts. Fern leaves are usually called fronds. They may be quite large and are often divided into many small leaflets. Spores are produced on the underside of the frond in a series of spore capsules. Once scattered, a spore develops into a small heartshaped plate called a prothallus. This is the sexual stage of the plant. The union of a male and female sexcell results in the growth of a new spore-bearing plant. Bracken is a typical fern.

**Ferredoxin.** One of the components of the electron transport chain in chloroplasts. Ferredoxins are nonhaem iron-sulphur proteins, *i.e.* they utilize an iron-containing reaction centre but the structure is not that of a haem, as in cytochromes, but iron and acid-labile sulphur are present instead. In chloroplasts ferredoxin mediates the transfer of electrons between photosystem I and the ultimate electron acceptor, NADP. It accepts an electron, via a ferredoxin reducing substance, from the excited P700 chlorophyll a molecule, and transfers it, through a reaction catalysed by ferredoxin-NADP reductase, to NADP. Bacteria and animals also contain iron-sulphur proteins, some free in solution and some membrane bound.

**Ferret.** A domesticated version of the polecat which has been used for centuries to catch rabbits. The muzzled ferret is sent into a rabbit hole to chase the rabbits out into nets. The blackfooted ferret is a rare North American animal. It it about 30 cm long and, like the ordinary ferret, related to the weasel. It feeds on prairie dogs.

**Fertile**

1. Rich, productive, fruitful.
2. Capable of growing, with reference to seeds or eggs.
3. *bot.* Capable of producing fruit.
4. *zool.* Fertilized and capable of developing, said of eggs.

**Fertility**

1. Condition of a soil relative to the amount and availability to plants of elements necessary for plant growth. Soil fertility is affected by physical elements, *e.g.* supply of moisture and oxygen, as well as by the supply of chemical plant nutrients.
2. (fecundity, fruitfulness). The number of eggs that develop in a mated female over a specified period. It is usually calculated at the stage when this number

is readily observable (*i.e.* in oviparous animals when eggs are laid, in viviparous animals when young are born, or in seed plants when seeds are borne), although strictly speaking it applies from the time that fertilization occurs. Sometimes the term 'fertility' is applied only to the production of fertilized eggs (ova), while 'fecundity' is used for the production of fruit (in angiosperms) or offspring (in animals), so excluding those embryos which fail to develop.

**Fertilization.** Union of two gametes to produce a zygote, which occurs during sexual reproduction. Fertilization involves the fusion of two haploid nuclei (containing genetic material from two distinct individuals (cross-fertilization) or from one individual (self-fertilization). The resulting zygote then develops into a new individual. Some aquatic animals, *e.g.* echinoderms, achieve fertilization externally, gametes uniting outside the body of the parents. Most other animals, particularly terrestrial species, have internal fertilization, with the union of gametes inside the female.

**Fertilization Membrane.** A membrane at the surface of a fertilized ovum which prevents other sperm from entering.

**Fertilizer.** Any substance that is applied to land to raise soil fertility and increase plant growth. Fertilizers include natural products such as farmyard manure, guano, and bonemeal, as well as proprietary chemicals. Organic fertilizers tend to have longer lasting effects than inorganic fertilizers but are generally more expensive and slower acting. However they have the advantage of improving soil structure. The three main constituents of fertilizers are usually nitrates, phosphates, and potash (potassium oxide). The relative amounts of these in a compound fertilizer are expressed by the N : P : K ratio.

**Fertilizin**. A substance present on the surface of certain ova which causes sperm to adhere. Separate from the egg, it agglutinates sperm.

**Fetal Membranes**. Extraembryonic membranes.

**Fetus** (foetus). The embryo of a mammal, especially a human, when development has reached a stage at which the main features of the adult form are recognizable. In humans the embryo from eight weeks to birth is called a fetus.

**Feulgen Reaction.** A test for determining the presence of DNA based on the formation of a purple colored substance following treatment with Schiff's reagent (decolorized fuchsin) after acid hydrolysis.

**Feulgen's Test.** A test used to detect DNA in nuclei, especially during cell division. A section of tissue is first placed in dilute hydrochloric acid for ten minutes at 60°C to hydrolyse DNA, removing the purine bases and exposing the aldehyde groups of deoxyribose. When the tissue is soaked in Schiff's reagent the location of the DNA is shown by the development of a magenta colour.

**F Factor.** Plasmid.

**Fibre**

1. Type of plant cell in which the wall has been thickened to perform a structural role. Typically, fibres are elongated cells and have fewer cavities in the thickenings than do other types of thickened cells—however, neither feature is diagnostic. Such cells can be found in the cortex, phloem, and xylem. Commercially, the term refers to a strand of fibre cells, or to the epidermal cells of cotton or kapok seed pods. Flax and hemp fibres come from the phloem. Sisal is extracted from highly lignified leaf fibres of Agave. The name 'fibre' is also given to a fine or narrow root.

2. Collagen.

**Fibre-tracheid.** A xylary fibre that resembles a tracheid in its possession of bordered pits, although these are usually less conspicuous than those of tracheids. Fibre-tracheids appear to exhibit characters intermediate between those of fibres and tracheids and are believed to represent evidence for a phylogenetic relationship between the two.

**Fibril**

1. A minute, threadlike structure within the cytoplasm of a cell, as a myofibril or neurofibril.
2. A minute component of a fiber.

**Fibrillation.** A local, quivering movement of muscle fibers.

**Fibrin.** Insoluble protein found in blood clots, which it helps to form. It is formed at the site of a wound from a soluble precursor, fibrinogen, by the action of the enzyme thrombin.

**Fibrinogen.** The protein dissolved in the blood plasma that, when suitably activated, is converted to insoluble fibrin fibres.

**Fibrinolysis.** The breakdown of the protein fibrin by the enzyme plasmin (or fibrinolysin), which occurs when blood clots are removed from the circulation.

**Fibroblast.** A cell present in connective tissue which functions is the formation of fibers and the a morphous ground substance.

**Fibrous.** Containing or consisting principally of fibers or fibrous structures.

**Fibrous Layer.** Endothecium.

**Fibrous Root System.** The type of root system that develops when the radicle or primary root does not persist as the main root but is either replaced by adventitious (seminal) roots, as occurs in grasses, or becomes highly branched. Fibrous root systems are typical of monocotyledons.

**Fibula**. The smaller of the two bones of the hind or lower limb extending from knee to ankle. It lies lateral to the tibia.

**Field Capacity**. The amount of water held in the soil by capillary action after excess or gravitational water has run off or percolated down to the water table. At field capacity the water potential of the soil is high. The percentage of water held at field capacity varies with soil texture, clay having a high field capacity and sand a low field capacity.

**Field-emission Microscope**. A type of electron microscope in which a high negative voltage is applied to a metal tip placed in an evacuated vessel some distance from a glass screen with a fluorescent coating. The tip produces electrons by field emission, *i.e.* the emission of electrons from an unheated sharp metal part as a result of a high electric field. The emitted electrons form an enlarged pattern on the flourescent screen, related to the individual exposed planes of atoms. As the resolution of the instrument is limited by the vibrations of the metal atoms, it is helpful to cool the tip in liquid helium. Although the individual atoms forming the point are not displayed, individual adsorbed atoms of other substances can be, and their activity is observable.

**Field-ionization Microscope** (field-ion microscope). A type o electron microscope that is similar in principle to the field-emission microscope, except that a high positive voltage is applied to the metal tip, which is surrounded by low-pressure gas (usually helium) rather than a vacuum. The image is formed in this case by field ionization : ionization at the surface of an unheated solid as a result of a strong electric field creating positive ions by electron transfer from surrounding atoms or molecules. The image is formed by ions striking the fluorescent screen. Individual atoms on the surface of the tip can be resolved and, in certain cases, adsorbed atoms may be detected.

**Field Mushroom.** Common name for the fruit body of the fungus Agaricus campestris, which resembles the cultivated mushroom. It is edible and highly esteemed, and is common in fields, meadows, lawns, etc. in summer and autumn.

**Fig.** A tree or shrub of the genus Ficus or the fruit it produces. Types include common figs, caprifigs, Smyrna figs, and San Pedro figs.

**Filament.** One of the strands of protein, variously grouped according to diameter (in the range 4,15 nm), found in many types of cell. Their functional significance is incompletely understood, but since they are largely composed of the contractile proteins actin and/or myosin it is presumed that the motility of the cell or its contents forms part of their role.

**Filamentous Iron Bacteria.** Chlamy-dobacteriales.

**Filamentous Sulphur Bacteria.** Beg-giatoales.

**Filaria.** A slender, threadlike nematode worm of the super-family Filaroidea. Most are parasites of vertebrates; larvae or microfilariae are usually transmitted by blood-sucking arthropods.

**File.** The notched portion of a stridulating organ in insects.

**Filial.** Of or pertaining to offspring.

**Filicales** (Polypodiales). The largest order of the Filicinae containing about 9000 species. Its members differ from those of the Marattiales and Ophioglossales in the development of the sporangium, which originates from one initial cell, while in the other orders it develops from a group of initials. Although secondary vascular tissue is not clearly developed in any of the Filicinae some members of the Filicales, the tree ferns, attain heights of 10 m. In these species bands of schlerenchyma strengthen the stem. The lamina of the fern frond usually shows differentiation into palisade and spongy mesophyll but in the filmy ferns the leaf is only one cell thick.

The larger homosporous families of the Filicales include (according to one of many classifications): the Osmundaceae (royals ferns) with some 20 species in 3 genera; the Gleicheniaceae (staghorn ferns) with some 150 species in 5 genera; the Polypodiaceae with about 1050 species in some 55 genera; the Schizaeaceae, including the climbing ferns, with about 160 species in 6 genera; the Adiantaceae, including the maidenhair ferns, with about 850 species in some 20 genera; the Cyatheaceae, including the brackens, filmy ferns, and tree ferns, with about 1500 species; and the Aspleniaceae, including the spleenworts and lady ferns, with about 1900 species in some 75 genera. The heterosporous families all contain aquatic ferns and are often classified into separate orders, the Marsileales, comprising the Marsileaceae (about 70 species in 3 genera), and the Salviniales, comprising the Salviniaceae (10 species in the genus Salvinia) and the Azollaceae (5 species in the genus Azolla).

**Filicinae.** A class of mainly terrestrial vascular plants—the ferns—belonging to the Pteropsida. Ferns are perennial plants bearing large conspicuous leaves (fronds) usually arising from either a rhizome or a short erect stem. Bracken is a common example. Only the tree ferns have stems that reach as appreciable height. There is a characteristic uncurling of the young leaves as they expand into the adult form. Spores are borne on the underside of specialized leaves (sporophylls).

**Filiform.** Filamentous; threadlike; long and slender.

**Filipendulous.** Hanging by a thread.

**Filly.** A young mare or female horse.

**Filoplume.** A minute, hairlike feather.

**Filopodium.** A filamentous pseudopodium consisting entirely of ectoplasm.

**Filose.** Terminating in a threadlike structure.

**Filter.** *bacteriol.* A special type of filter, as one of diatomaceous earth, porcelain, or asbestos through which bacteria cannot pass.

**Filterable.** Capable of passing through the pores of a bacterial filter, with reference to viruses.

**Filter Feeding.** Obtaining food by passing water through a filtering mechanism, as the fine processes on the appendages of certain crustaceans.

**Fimbria.** A fringe or fringelike border.

**Fimbriate.** Having a margin that is fringed, usually with hairs.

**Fimbrillate.** Bearing a fringe of minute processes.

**Fin.** Appendage of fish and fish-like aquatic animals used for locomotion, steering, and balancing of the body. The skinfold forming the fin membrane is supported by cartilaginous, horny, or bony fin rays, which can be soft and flexible (soft rays) or hard and inflexible (fin spines). The median unpaired fins of fish include the dorsal fin on the back, the caudal fin or tail-fin, and the anal fin behind the vent or anus. Usually there are also two pairs of lateral fins : the pectoral fins and the pelvic (also called ventral or abdominal) fins.

**Finback.** The finner whale (Balaenoptera physalus), also called the rorqual or razorback.

**Finch.** A small seed-eating songbird found in many parts of the world. There are many different species which together form the largest of all bird families, Fringillidae. Among the finches are the Bullfinch, Canary, Chaffinch, Crossbill, Goldfinch, Greenfinch and Grosbeak.

**Fine Structure.** Ultrastructure.

**Fin Rays.** Slender supporting structures of dermal origin in the fins of fishes. Types include ceratotrichia, actinotrichia, lepidotrichia, and camptotrichia.

**Fins.** The locomotory organs of aquatic vertebrates. In fish there are typically one or more dorsal and ventral fins (sometimes continuous), whose function is balance; a caudal fin around the tail, which is the main propulsive organ; and two paired fins : the pectoral fins attached to the pectoral (shoulder) girdle and the pelvic fins attached to the pelvic (hip) girdle, which are used in steering. These paired fins are homologous with the limbs of tetrapods. Fins are strengthened by a number of flexible fin rays, which may be cartilaginous, bony and jointed, horny, or fibrous and jointed.

**Finger.** A digit of the forelimb other than the thumb.

**Fingerling.** A young fish from time of disappearance of the yolk sac to the end of the first year of growth.

**Fir.** A coniferous tree of the genus Abies, especially the balsam fir (Abies balsamea). Term is also applied to certain other coniferous trees, as the Douglas fir (Pseudotsuga taxifolia).

**Fire Algae.** Algae of the phylum Pyrrophyta which includes the cryptomonads and dinoflagellates.

**Fire Ant.** Solenopsis geminata and S. saevissima, the imported fire ant of the southern states, noted for the severity of their stings.

**Fireblight.** A serious disease of pears and other trees of the family Rosaceae caused by the bacterium Erwinia amylovora. The disease attacks blossoms and leaves in the spring and, as the disease progresses, individual branches or whoie trees look as if they have been scorched by fire. The host forms cankers in response to infection. The bacteria overwinter in the cankers and are spread by insects and rainsplash to infect flowers in the spring. Hawthorn (Crataegus), an alternate host, can also be a source of inoculum.

**Firefly.** A lightning bug, as Photinus pyralis, one of several species of soft-bodied beetles of the family Lampyridae capable of emitting cold light from their abdominal segments.

**Fish.** An aquatic vertebrate, well adapted to a life in water with, typically, a streamlined body and a series of fins. The two sets of paired fins correspond to the limbs of land animals. Fishes take in oxygen from the water by means of gills. A few species of fish have a form of lung and can breathe air : they are known as lungfishes. Most fishes have scales on the skin and all are cold-blooded—that is, their body temperature is the same as that of their environment. Many species possess a sense apparatus called the Lateral Line that is sensitive to pressure and helps the fish detect nearby objects. Some also possess a Swim-Bladder to heep them bouyant. There are four basic groups of fishes : the bony fishes, which include about 95 per cent of all species; the cartilaginous fishes, such as sharks and rays, which have cartilage (gristle) instead of bone; the chimaeras, which are toothless cartilaginous fishes; and the primitive sucking fishes, *i.e.*, the hagfishes and lampreys, which have no jaws—and are also cartilaginous. The gills of bony fishes are protected by a plate called an operculum. Those of the cartilaginous fishes have no such covering and open directly into the water. Bony fishes and jawless fishes have representatives in both fresh and sea water, but the other two groups are found exclusively in the sea. Some fishes, notably the eels and salmon, spend part of their lives at sea and part in fresh water, often migrating many thousands of kilometres to spawn.

**Fish Culture.** Cultivation of marine and freshwater fish in ponds or enclosures. In some cases (*e.g.* trout, carp, and some aquarium species), fish are hatched from eggs, then grown from the larval stage until they attain marketable size. In other cases, juvenile fish are caught and reared until they reach commercial size (*e.g.* milkfish, eel, and yellowtail).

**Fisher.** A carnivorous, fur-bearing mammal (Martes pennanti) of the family Mustelidae. Also called pekan.

**Fishery.** The planning and execution of techniques designed to catch fish. Recreational fishery (sport fishing) in recent years almost equals the economic and ecological impact of commercial fishery. Continuing research is required, therefore, to monitor *e.g.*, possible over-fishing, pollution of water, or influence of the environment. In commercial fisheries additional factors, *e.g.* cost of operating boats and fishing gear, national and international competition, and legal aspects, must be taken into account.

**Fish Hawk.** An osprey.

**Fission.** A method of asexual reproduction in which the nucleus and then the cytoplasm splits into equal parts to form new individuals genetically identical to the parent. It is seen in many microorganisms, such as bacteria and the fission yeasts (Schizosaccharomyces). The new cells may often sporulate in adverse conditions. The parent usually divides into two equal parts (binary fission). Compare budding, fragmentation.

**Fission Fungi.** Schizomycetes.

**Fission-track Dating.** A method of estimating the age of glass and other mineral objects by observing the tracks made in them by the fission fragments of the uranium nuclei that they contain. By irradiating the objects with neutrons to induce fission and comparing the density and number of the tracks before and after irradiation it is possible to estimate the time that has elapsed since the object solidified.

**Fission Yeasts.** Endomycetales.

**Fissure.** A deep groove or cleft.

**Fistula.** An abnormal tube or opening forming a communication between *a.* two hollow organs; *b.* a hollow organ or cavity and the outside.

**Fistular.** Cylindrical; elongated and hollow.

**Fitness** (Darwinian fitness). Natural selection has been described as the 'survival of the fittest'. The environment, and the competition or struggle for survival within it, determines which individuals are fittest to survive and propagate their genes in the next generation.

**Fixation**

1. In microscopy, the process of treatingc ells and tissues so that their structure is maintained and altered as little as possible by subsequent procedures.
2. *chem.* Converting from a gaseous to a usable solid form, as nitrogen fixation.

**Fixative.** Fixation.

**Fixator.** A muscle which stabilizes a part, thus preventing desired movement.

**Flabellate.** Shaped like a fan; bearing a fanlike process or projection.

**Flabcid.** Limp, flabby; lacking rigidity.

**Flagellate.** Member of a group of tiny, single-celled animals that move around by means of a whip-like organ called a flagellum. The most familiar flagellate is euglena, which forms green scum on the surface of stagnant ponds.

**Flagellum.** A relatively long (up to 150 $\mu$m) fine whiplike structure present on the surface of certain cells, particularly motile reproductive cells (*e.g.* spermatozoa), bacteria, and certain protozoans. Flagella occur singly or in small groups. Beating of flagella produces movement of the cell, but some flagella (*e.g.* in Hydra) beat to cause movement of the surrounding fluid. Compare cilium.

**Flame Bulb.** A ciliated structure consisting of a part of a cell, a flame cell, or a group of cells found at the terminations of excretory tubules in a number of invertebrate groups.

**Flame Cell.** A cell containing a tuft of cilia found at the ends of excretory tubules in certain invertebrates, especially flat worms.

**Flatworm.** The general name for members of the invertebrate phylum Platyhelminthes. Most have flattened, ribbon-like bodies. Free-living forms are found under stones in damp spots, in fresh water and in the sea. Others, such as the Fluke and the Tapeworm, live as parasites in the bodies of other animals.

**Flavanones.** A group of flavonoid compounds the members of which lack a double bond between carbons two and three of the $C_3$ group in the centre of the flavonoid nucleus. An example is naringenin, which is responsible for the bitterness of lemons.

**Flavin.** One of a group of yellow, water-soluble pigments isolated from various plant and animal sources, an important constituent of certain yellow enzymes, as flavoprotein.

**Flavin Adenine Dinucleotide.** FAD.

**Flavin Mononucleotide.** FMN.

**Flavones.** A group of flavonoid pigments the members of which contain an unaltered flavonoid nucleus. It includes flavone, found in certain Primula species, and the more widespread apigenin and luteolin. Isoflavones are isomers of flavones in which the B group of the flavonoid nucleus is attached to the third rather than second carbon of the central $C_3$ group. Isoflavones are particularly common in the Leguminosae. Some isoflavones have oestrogen-like properties, which has led to sterility in sheep grazing on certain legume fodder crops, notably subterranean clover (Trifolium subterraneum).

**Flavonoid.** One of a group of naturally occurring phenolic compounds many of which are plant pigments. They include the anthocyanins, flavonols, and flavones. Patterns of flavonoid distribution have been used in taxonomic studies of plant species.

**Flavonols.** A group of flavonoid compounds, the members of which have a hydroxyl group on the third carbon of the $C_3$ group in the centre of the flavonoid nucleus. They are formed by the addition of a hydroxyl ion to a flavanone. Common flavonols include quercitin and kaempferol.

**Flavoprotein.** A yellow enzyme, one of a group of dehydrogenases each consisting of a protein carrier and a prosthetic group, a flavin.

**Flax.** A family of slender plants with clusters of blue or white open flowers, mostly five-petalled; commonly found on grasslands.

**Flea.** A wingless, bloodsucking insect of the order Siphonaptera, as Pulex irritans, the human flea.

**Fledgling.** A young bird which has just acquired feathers necessary for flight.

**Flesh.** The soft parts of an animal, especially muscle tissue.

**Flesh Fly.** Any of a number of dipterous insects of the family Sarcophagidae which deposit their eggs or larvae in carrion or in wounds or body openings. Important genera are Sarcophaga and Wohlfahrtia.

**Fleshy**

1. *bot.* Succulent, pulpy, with reference to fruits, plump, tender, with reference to leaves.
2. *zool.* Of, pertaining to, or of the nature of flesh; plump; fat.

**Flexion**

1. The bending of a part in which the angle of the joint is reduced.
2. In man, the forward movement of the head, vertebral column, arm, or thigh.

**Flexor.** A muscle which bends or flexes a part.

**Flies.** Diptera.

**Flight.** The act of flying or passing through the air with the aid of wings or winglike structures.

**Flimmer.** A mastigoneme.

**Flimmer Flagellum** (tinsel flagellum, pantonematic flagellum). A threadlike projection arising from motile algal and fungal cells that has longitudinal rows of fine hairs (mastigonemata) along its outer membrane. Internally the fibrillar structure is typical of a flagellum.

**Flipper.** A broad, flat limb adapted for swimming, as that of a seal or whale.

**Flittermouse.** An insectivorous bat.

**Float.** A gas-filled structure which supports an organism in water, as the pneumatophore of coelenterates or the air bladder of seaweeds.

**Flocculation.** The coalescence of finely divided or colloidal particles into larger masses which form a precipitate.

**Flocculus**

1. A small, detached mass of wool or hair.
2. A small body forming part of the cerebellum.

**Flora** (floral, floristic). All the plant species that make up the vegetation of a given area. The term is also applied to assemblages of fossil plants from a particular geological time, or from a geographical region in a former geological time. Examples of all three types of usage, respectively, are : British flora, Carboniferous flora, and Gondwana flora. Compare fauna.

**Floral.** Of, pertaining to, or consisting of flowers.

**Floral Diagram.** A stylized representation of the structure of a flower in which the whorls of floral parts are shown as a series of concentric circles. All floral segments arising at the same level are placed, in their correct relative positions, in the same circle. When appropriate, fusion of parts is also indicated. The ovary is represented in cross section in the centre of the whorls. The bottom of the diagram represents the anterior side of the flower, *i.e.* the side furthest from the axis of the inflorescence. Any bracts subtending the flower are inserted at the base of the diagram, while the inflorescence axis is shown as a circle at the top (posterior) side of the diagram. Floral diagrams are usually presented in conjunction with a longitudinal section through the centre of the flower.

**Floral Formula.** A method of recording floral structure by a series of symbols, letters and numbers. The formula begins either with the sign ⊕, representing actinomorphy, or with ·|· or ↑, representing zygomorphy. This is followed by a series of letters in the order K (for calyx). C (for corolla), A (for androecium and G (for gynoecium). The number of parts (sepals, petals, stamens, and carpels respectively) in each whorl is given by a number following the appropriate letter. If this number exceeds 12 the symbol ∞ (infinity) is used. If the parts are fused then the number is bracketed. If the parts are in distinct whorls or groups this is indicated by splitting the number appropriately. Thus in the garden pea (Pisum sativum) there are ten stamens, nine of which are fused and the tenth separate. This is represented A(9)+1. If two whorls are united then the representative symbols are joined by a single bracket. Thus in the primrose (Primula vulgaris) the stamens are inserted on the corolla tube. This is represented.

C(5)A5

If the sepals and petals are indistinguishable then K and C are replaced by P representing perianth. The position of the ovary is indicated by a line, which in a superior ovary is placed beneath the number of carpels and in an inferior ovary above. Examples of floral formulae are ⊕K4 C4 A4+2 G(2) for the wallflower (Cheiranthus cheiri) and ⊕P3+3 A3+3 G(3) for the tulip (Tulipa species). Floral formulae are often accompanied by floral diagrams.

**Floral Parts.** The sepals, petals, stamens, and pistil(s) of a flower.

**Floral Tube.** The fused bases of the sepals, petals, and stamens which surround the ovary in certain flowers.

**Floret.** One of the elements of a composite flower such as a dandelion. Each floret is actually a complete flower in that it has its own sex-organs, calyx and corolla. The strap-shaped part of the dandelion floret and of the outer florets of daisies is called the ligule.

**Floriculture.** The growth and cultivation of flowers for ornamental purposes.

**Florid.** Bright red in color; ruddy.

**Florideae** (Florideophycidae). Rhodophyta.

**Floridean Starch.** The assimilation product of algae in the Rhodophyta. It has a structure similar to amylopectin.

**Florigen.** A flower-forming substance or hormone produced where flowers are forming which, when transported to other parts of the plant, is capable of inducing flower formation.

**Floristics.** The branch of botany concerned with identifying and listing all the plant species present in a particular area. The check list so produced gives the floristic composition of the region. Once this has been established further work may be undertaken to describe the abundance and distribution of the various species and to consider the affinities of the regional flora.

**Flotoblast.** A floating statoblast in an ectroproct.

**Flower.** That part of the flowering plant that is concerned with reproduction. A flower is made up of several parts, all of which can be seen in a flower such as the buttercup. The stalk of each flower is called the pedicel and is swollen at the tip, forming the receptacle. The floral organs develop in more or less concentric circles on the receptacle. The first-formed organs are the sepals, of which there are five in the buttercup. They are green and leaf-like and together form the calyx whose chief function is the protection of the developing flower. Above the sepals are the five yellow petals, each with a small nectary at the base. The group of petals is called the corolla and, with the calyx, forms the perianth.

The petals and nectaries attract pollinating insects to the flowers and also help to protect the essential organs within. These essential organs are the stamens and carpels. The stamens are the male, pollen-producing organs and form the androecium. Each stamen consists of a filament and anthers. The carpels, the female organs, each contain an ovule and form the gynaecium in the centre of the flower. The stigma is the tip of the carpel through which the pollen tube from the pollen grain grains access to the ovule. The buttercup has many stamens and carpels but this is not so in all flowers. Below the flower there may be one or two tiny leaves called bracteoles.

The buttercup has all four types of floral organ—sepals, petals, stamens and carpels—arranged in a regular manner and is a so-called 'perfect flower'. There are, however, many variations of this pattern. Not all plants have bisexual flowers—the hazel for example has separate male and female flowers with only stamens or carpels. The flowers of peas and many orchids are highly irregular and have oddly-shaped petals. Petals (and sepals) often join and form a tube (*e.g.* primrose, bluebell) or may even be absent—grass flowers have neither petals nor sepals. These are just a few of many variations.

**Flower Bud.** A bud which develops into a flower; an unopened flower. Also called a fruit bud, if the flower develops into a fruit.

**Flowering.** The act or state of producing flowers; blossoming.

**Fluctuation.** A variation.

**Flowering Glume.** Lemma.

**Flowering Plants.** Anglospermae.

**Fluke.** A group of parasitic flatworms found in a wide range of animals, including humans. Flukes either attach themselves to the outside of their host's body or else live inside the host, sometimes within the blood vessels. There are almost 6000 different species of fluke. One of the commonest is the liver fluke which causes liver rot in sheep. The larval stage of the liver fluke is spent inside a water snail. When the larva emerges it forms a cyst on grass which may subsequently be eaten by a sheep. The fluke then escapes from the cyst and makes its way to the sheep's liver. Eggs pass out with the sheep's droppings and the cycle starts again.

**Fluid-mosaic Model.** Plasma membrane.

**Flukes.** Trematoda.

**Fluorescence Microscopy.** A type of microscopy that uses ultraviolet light as the source of illumination and involves the treatment of the specimen (prior to viewing) with a fluorescent dye (fluorochroming). The short wavelengths of ultraviolet light passing through the specimen cause the dye to fluoresce, *i.e.* emit long wavelengths of visible light. A fluorescent image is thus produced against a dark background. The technique is used widely. In bacteriology, fluorescent antibody reactions involve the addition of a fluorescent dye to either the antibody or antigen to locate the site of antibody-antigen reactions.

**Fluorescent-antibody Technique.** Method for detecting the location of a specific antigen in a cell by staining a section of the tissue with antibody (specific to that antigen) that is combined with a fluorochrome (a substance that fluoresces in ultraviolet light). The antigen is located wherever fluorescence is observed.

**Fluoridation.** The process of adding very small amounts of fluorine salts (*e.g.* sodium fluoride, NaF) to drinking water to prevent tooth decay. The fluoride becomes incorporated into the substance of the growing teeth and reduces the incidence of caries.

**Flushing.** The process by which soluble substances in the lower layers of the soil are washed upwards and deposited on or near the soil surface. It occurs, for example, in water-meadows, fenland, and where there are springs. Compare leaching.

**Fly** pl. **Flies**

1. A two-winged insect of the order Diptera, especially those of the family Muscidae.

2. Any of a number of insects of various orders, as a mayfly, butterfly, dragonfly sawfly.

**Flying Fish.** One of several fishes of the family Exocoetidae with greatly enlarged pectoral fins which enable them to glide through the air after leaping from the water, as Cypselurus cyanopterus.

**Flying Flox.** A fruit-eating bat, especially one of the genera Pteropus and Epomophorus.

**Flying Lemur.** The colugo or cobego, a herbivorous mammal of southeast Asia comprising a single species, Cynocephalus variegatus of the order Dermoptera.

**Flyway.** A definite migratory route followed by birds in flying to and from their breeding grounds.

**[1]Foal.** A colt or the young of any of the horse family, Equidae.

**[2]Foal.** To give birth to a colt.

**FMN** (flavin mononucleotide). A riboflavin-derived coenzyme, similar to FAD, that acts as a prosthetic group to several dehydrogenases. NADH dehydrogenase, the enzyme that catalyses transfer of electrons from NADH to coenzyme Q in the respiratory chain, is an FMN-containing enzyme.

**Foetus** Fetus.

**Folacin.** Folic acid.

**Foliage.** Collectively, the leaves of a plant.

**Foliar.** Of or pertaining to leaves.

**Foliate**

1. Furnished with or possessing leaves.

2. Resembling a leaf or possessing leaflike parts.

**Folic Acid.** A member of the B group of vitamins first isolated from spinach leaves. In its activated form tetrahydrofolic acid it acts as a coenzyme in reactions involving the transfer of hydroxymethyl, formyl, and methyl groups. Such transfers are important in the synthesis of the purines and the pyrimidine thymine.

**Foliferous.** Bearing leaves or leaflike structures.

**Foliose.** Describing organisms that bear leaflike structures, used especially of leafy lichens (*e.g.* Peltigera) and sometimes of leafy liverworts (*e.g.* Diplophyllum).

**Follicle**

1. *anat.* A small, closed, or nearly closed cavity, as that found in the ovary or thyroid gland.
2. *bot.* A simple, dry, dehiscent fruit consisting of one carpel and splitting along one suture, as that of the milkweed or columbine.

**Follicle-stimulating Hormone.** FSH, a gonadotrophic hormone secreted by the anterior lobe of the pituitary which promotes growth and maturation of ovarian follicles. In the male, it stimulates the seminiferous tubules.

**Follicle-stimulating Hormone** (FSH). A hormone, secreted by the anterior pituitary gland in mammals, that stimulates, in female mammals, ripening of specialized structures in the ovary (Graafian follicles) that produce ova and, in males, the formation of sperm in the testis. It is a major constituent of fertility drugs, used to treat failure of ovulation and decreased sperm production.

**Food.** A nutritive substance which serves as a source of energy or is utilized in growth and repair of tissues or in the regulation of bodily processes. The term is generally restricted to energy sources, namely carbohydrates, fats, proteins.

**Food Accessory.** A nutrient substance which is utilized by the body but does not provide energy, as water, mineral salts, vitamins.

**Food Chain.** A series of organisms, each successive group of which feeds on the group immediately previous in the chain, and is in turn eaten by the succeeding group. Green plants (producers) are normally the first step in a food chain, herbivores (primary consumers) the second step, with carnivores (secondary consumers) making up the remaining two or three stages. The different stages are termed trophic levels and organisms that are removed from the beginning of the chain by the same number of steps are said to occupy the same trophic level. The chain is effectively a series of energy transfers, with considerable amounts of energy being lost at each transfer (bioenergetics). A food chain consequently rarely has more than four or five stages since there is not enough energy in the system to maintain more. A consequence of this is that, for a given consumer level, considerably more individuals can be maintained if an earlier consumer stage is omitted. For example, a given amount of grain will support many more people if it is eaten as grain, rather than being first converted to meat by feeding to livestock.

Food chains rarely exist in isolation but are interconnected to form a food web. Thus any of the links in one food chain may, through the activity of decomposers, saprophytes, or parasites, lead into a number of different food chains. In addition, most plants and herbivores have a number of different predators.

**Food Web.** A complex pattern of several interlocking food chains in a complex community or between several communities.

**Foot.** The basal portion of an embryo, sporophyte, or spore-producing body, which is embedded in the parental tissue. It serves as an anchor and to absorb nutrients.

**Food-and-mouth Disease** (hoof-and-mouth disease, aphthous fever). Extremely contagious disease which affects many types of animal and which is of great economic importance. The form of the disease varies with animal species. In cattle it involves fever and the development of blister-like vesicles in the mouth and nose, and on the udder and hoofs. Sheep, goats, and pigs may show lameness. It is caused by a virus in the Picornaviridae. Disease control is effected by vaccination or by the slaughter of infected animals.

**Foot Rot.** A plant disease in which there is rotting of the root system and the bottom part of the stem. Foot rot of tomato is caused by Phytophthora cryptogea and P. parasitica. Stem tissues around soil level appear brown or blackish and the root system is found to be rotten.

**Foramen** pl. **Foramina**. An opening or perforation, as that in a bone.

**Foramen Magnum**. An opening in the occipital bone through which the spinal cord passes to the cranial cavity.

**Forceps**. A pincerlike structure formed of cerci at the posterior end of an earwig.

**Forearm.** The portion of the upper extremity between elbow and wrist.

**Forebrain** (prosencephalon). One of the three sections of the brain of a vertebrate embryo. The forebrain develops to form the cerebrum, hypothalamus, and thalamus in the adult. Compare hindbrain, midbrain.

**Foregut**

1. *invert.* The portion of the digestive tract lying anterior to the midgut; the stomodeum.
2. *embryol.* The anterior portion of the enteron from which the alimentary canal from mouth to midportion of the intestine develops.

**Forelimb**. The anterior limb of a tetrapod.

**Forest**. Any major community (biome) in which the dominant plants are trees. There are three main types of forest; cold forests, temperate forests, and tropical forests. The cold forests include the northern coniferous forest (boreal forest or taiga), where there are relatively few types of tree, mainly fir, pine, and spruce with some deciduous birches and larches. The latter are found mainly on the borders of the tundra where it is too cold and exposed for the conifers to grow. However conifers are well adapted to survive long cold winters and can take advantage of the short growing season as they retain their leaves. Boreal forest is found in North America and northern Eurasia. The mountain coniferous forest and pine forest of the south-east United States are also boreal forests.

Temperate forests have abundant and fairly evenly distributed rainfall with moderate temperatures, but there is a marked seasonal change. The vegetation consists of broad-leaved deciduous trees, an adaptation to the lack of available water during winter (physiological drought). There are usually several different species of trees and the term mixed deciduous forest is often used. Warm temperate and cool temperate rain forests also exist, *e.g.* in south China and New Zealand respectively. Broad-leaved evergreen forest is characteristic of a Mediterranean-type climate with hot dry summers and mild wet winters.

Tropical forests include tropical rain forest, monsoon forest, and thorn forest. Rain forests have regular heavy rain, constantly high temperatures, and therefore prolific plant growth, Rain forest regions, such as the Amazon basin and the Malay-Indonesian region, contain thousands of different species. Essentially similar forests, known as riverine forests, occur along river banks in drier regions. Monsoon forests have a period of drought, which may last for several months. They do not have such a great variety of species as tropical rain forest and have a more open canopy and very dense undergrowth. Many of the trees shed their leaves in the dry season. They are found in India, Burma, and Indo-China. Thorn forest is a transitional type of vegetation with some similarities to savanna and semidesert vegetation. It grades into tropical forests and is found in Central and South America, Australia, and Africa.

Generally trees need more light and moisture than other plant forms, although some trees are adapted to survive long periods of drought and cold.

**Form** (forma). The lowest rank normally used by practising taxonomists for sporadic distinct variants that sometimes occur in populations. These may be relatively minor genetic variants (*i.e.* based on one or a few linked characters) but their effects can be conspicuous. The most obviously recognizable forms are those in which flower colour is modified (*e.g.* albino individuals occurring in a population of purple-flowered plants). The category form may relate directly to species but it is more commonly used to distinguish variants of subspecies and varieties.

**Forestry**

1. Practice of growing and managing forest trees for commercial timber production. This includes the management of specially planted forests, of native or exotic species, as well as the commercial use of existing forest, and the genetic improvement of timber trees for selected purposes.
2. Scientific study of tree growth and timber-production systems.

**Forget-me-not.** Several species of low-growing plant belonging to the borage family. They are hairy plants with small, usually blue flowers. The wood forget-me-not bears it vivid blue flowers on long stalks. The water forget-me-not sometimes has pink or white flowers, and is found in very wet places.

**Form**

1. A category used in the classification of organisms into which different types of a variety may be placed.

2. Any distinct variant within a species. Seasonal variants, *e.g.* the tawny brown (summer) and blue-white (winter) forms of the blue hare, may be called forms, as may the different types that constitute a polymorphism.

**Formalin.** An aqueous solution of formaldehyde containing not less than 37% by weight. It is an antiseptic, disinfectant, deodorant, and preservative.

**Formalin-acetic-alcohol** (FAA). A fixative containing 17 parts of 70% alcohol to 2 parts 40% formaldehyde to 1 part glacial acetic acid.

**Form Genus**

1. Any genus in which imperfect states of fungi are placed. Similarly a form species is a species of imperfect fungus. When the connection between an imperfect state and a perfect state is established then the name of the perfect state takes precedence, although both names are still valid.

2. A group of fossil species whose affinities are unknown.

**Form Group.** A taxonomic group, as a form family or form genus, so designated to indicate that its members do not necessarily form a natural group, as the Fungi Imperfecti.

**Fornicate**

1. Arched.

2. Bearing arched, scalelike appendages.

**Fossa** A depression; a pit or concavity, especially one on the surface of a bone.

**Fossil.** The remains of a once-living organism, generally those that lived prior to the last glacial period, *i.e.* fossils are older than 10 000 years. They include skeletons, tracks, impressions, trails, borings, and casts. Fossils are usually found in hard rock, but not always : for example, woolly mammoths living 20 000 years ago were recovered from the frozen tundra of Siberia.

**Fossiliferous.** Containing fossils.

**Fossil Hominid.** Hominid.

**Founder Effect.** A new population (*e.g.* on an oceanic island) may be derived from a single individual or a limited number of immigrants. This is the founder effect. The founder or founders will represent a very small sample of the genetic pool to which it or they formerly belonged. Natural selection operating on this more restricted genetic variety soon yields gene combinations quite different from those found in the ancestral population.

**Fovea** (fovea centralis). A shallow depression in the retina of the eye, opposite the lens, that is present in some vertebrates. This area contains a large concentration of cones with only a thin layer of overlying nerves. It is therefore specialized for the perception of colour and sharp intense images. The clarity is enhanced when light is focused on the foveae of both retinas simultaneously.

**Fowl**

1. Any bird, especially a large edible bird.
2. Collective term for birds of one type or an area, as waterfowl, wildfowl.
3. The domestic cock or hen of the species Gallus domestica, especially when used for used.

**Fox.** A carnivorous, fur-bearing mammal of the family Canidae noted for its speed, cunning, and resourcefulness, as

Vulpes fulva, the common red fox and its color mutations, the black and silver foxes.

**Fragmentation.** A method of asexual reproduction, occurring in some invertebrate animals, in which parts of the organism break off and subsequently differentiate and develop into new individuals. It occurs especially in certain coelenterates and annelids. In some, regeneration may occur before separation, producing chains of individuals budding from the parent.

**Fraternal Twins** (dizygotic twins). Two individuals that result from a single pregnancy, each having developed from a separate fertilized egg. The two egg cells contain different combinations of alleles and so do the two sperm that fertilize them. The twins therefore have no more genetic similarity than brothers or sisters from single births. Compare identical twins.

**Free-central Placentation.** A form of placentation in which the placentae develop on a central dome or column of tissue. It is seen in unilocular compound ovaries, such as those of the Primulaceae and Caryophyllaceae.

**Free-living.** Capable of living independently, not parasitic, not sessile.

**Freemartin** The sterile, masculinized female member of a pair of unlike twins in cattle.

**Free Space.** The part of the protoplasm where there is relatively free exchange of inorganic ions between the protoplasm and extracellular fluids. This occurs because the outer membrane of the protoplasm is permeable to most inorganic ions. The membrane surrounding the cell vacuole is not so permeable and though ions may enter by active transport they cannot pass out again; certain salts thus tend to accumulate in the vacuole. The composition of the free space and the vacuole may therefore be quite different.

**Freeze Drying.** A technique for the removal of water from a specimen by sublimation of ice under vacuum. It is used as a method of drying in cases where the action of heat would cause damage, *e.g.*, the concentration of labile solutes such as enzymes and the drying of fragile specimens for electron microscopy and storage (*e.g.* herbarium specimens). It is also used when the presence of liquid water would cause distortion of tissue by surface tension. Rapid freezing prevents the formation of ice crystals that would otherwise cause disruption.

**Freeze Etching.** Freeze fracturing.

**Freeze Fracturing.** A technique used in electron microscopy in which the specimen is frozen quickly at very low temperatures and then fractured along lines of weakness. The new surface so formed is coated with a thin layer of carbon or platinum, which is then floated off to form a replica of the surface. Freeze etching is a modification of the technique in which the water vapour is allowed to evaporate from the fracture surface before the replica is made. This takes longer but allows higher resolution of the specimen.

**Frenulum**

1. *anat.* A thin, membranous fold of skin or mucous membrane which attaches a structure and checks its movement, as that of the tongue, prepuce, or clitoris, a frenum.
2. *zool.* A structure on the hind wing of a moth or butterfly which locks it to the front wing.

**Frog.** The frogs and toads are amphibians making up the order Salientia. They use their long, webbed hindlegs for both jumping and swimming. The smooth-skinned species tend to be called frogs and the rough-skinned species toads, though this is not a scientific division. Some frogs and toads live permanently in the water. Others live permanently on land. But the vast majority lead lives like that of the common frog, where the adults spend most of their time on the land and return to the water only for a short time during the breeding season. The frogs pair up in the water and the male fertilizes the eggs as soon as the female has laid them. The jelly-coated egg mass is known as frogspawn. The eggs develop into limbless larvae called tadpoles which breathe through feathery external gills and swim through the water with the aid of their long tails. During development the gills are replaced by internal gills, rather like those of fishes, and finally by air-breathing lungs. Meanwhile the hindlegs and then the forelegs form and the tail begins to disappear. Eventually the tadpole becomes a miniature frog and leaves the water.

**Frond**. A large leaf or leaflike structure. The term is most frequently used of the dissected leaves of ferns, cycads, and palms. More rarely it is applied to the thalli of foliose lichens and certain macroscopic algae.

**Frontal Bone**. A bone forming the anterior dorsal portion of the cranium.

**Frost Resistance**. The ability, possessed by many temperate and arctic plants, to withstand subzero temperatures. The resistance is technically frost tolerance as the plant cannot avoid the cold conditions and resultant freezing of water in the intercellular spaces. This causes a lowering of the water potential in the intercellular spaces so water moves out of the protoplast to regions of ice crystallization. Frost damage is thus often a result of severe cellular dehydration. However this dehydration increases the solute concentration of the cell and thus makes ice formation within the cell less likely. Dormant organs and seeds tend to show more frost resistance than actively growing tissue. The mechanism of frost resistance is uncertain but membrane elasticity and reduction in cell size appear to play a part.

**Fructification.** Any seed- or spore-bearing structure, especially one that is easily visible as, for example, the aerial fruiting bodies of many higher fungi.

**Fructose** (fruit sugar; laevulose). A simple sugar, $C_6H_{12}O_6$, stereoisomeric with glucose. (Although natural fructose is the D- form, it is in fact laevorotatory.) Fructose occurs in green plants, fruits, and honey and tastes sweeter than sucrose (cane sugar), of which it is a constituent. Derivatives of fructose are important in the energy metabolism of living organisms. Some polysaccharide derivatives (fructans) are carbohydrate energy stores in certain plants.

**Fructose 1, 6-bisphosphate.** A phosphorylated derivative of fructose, situated at the main control point of glycolysis. In glycolysis fructose 1, 6-bisphosphate is formed from fructose 6-phosphate by the allosteric enzyme phosphofructokinase, which is inhibited by ATP and citrate, and stimulated by ADP and AMP. This reaction is the rate-limiting step of glycolysis. The reverse reaction, which is a step in glucose synthesis, also involves an allosteric enzyme, fructose bisphosphatase. Fructose 1, 6-bisphosphate is also an intermediate in the pentose phosphate pathway.

**Fruit.** A feature of flowering plants which is formed from the carpel (s) and which helps to protect and distribute the seeds. Fruits which are derived from the carpel (s) alone are called true fruits : those that contain parts of other organs as well are false fruits. True fruits include the Drupe (*e g.* plum), the Berry (*e.g.* tomato), Dehiscent fruits (*e.g.* pea pod) and Indehiscent fruits (*e.g.* acorn). False fruits include the Pome (*e.g.* apple).

**Fruit Drop.** The premature abscission of fruit before it is fully ripe. It is a normal process and in many fruits certain peak periods of fruit drop can be identified. For example, apple fruits are lost immediately following pollination (post-blossom drop), when the embryos are developing rapidly (June drop), and during ripening (preharvest drop). Like leaf fall, fruit drop is associated with low auxin levels and auxin sprays have been used to prevent excessive fruit drop.

**Fruit Fly**

1. A pomace fly, any of a number of species of flies which frequent ripe and decaying fruits and vegetables. Most belong to the genus Drosophila, family Drosophilidae.
2. A trypetid, a small to medium sized fly of the family Trypetidae, some of which are serious pests, as Ceratitis capitata, the Mediterranean fruit fly.

**Fruiting Body.** The spore-producing structure of certain fungi, made up of many tightly-packed threads or hyphae. Mushrooms and toadstools are both examples of fruiting bodies.

**Fruit Sugar.** Fructose.

**Frustule.** The intricately sculptured siliceous cell wall of a diatom. It is made up of two halves, one of which fits within the edges of the other in the same way that the bottom of a Petri dish fits within its lid. The patternings of the frustule are important in the classification of the diatoms.

**Fruticose.** Describing organisms that are erect and branching, especially the erect or pendent branching lichens (*e.g.* Usnea).

**FSH.** Follicle-stimulating hormone.

**Fuc-, Fuco-.** A prefix denoting seaweeds. For example, fucin and fucoidin are colloids found onlp in the walls of brown algae (Phaeophyta). Fucoxanthin is a carotenoid pigment found in the Bacillariophyta, Phaeophyta, and Chrysophyta. Fucosterol is the main type of sterol found in seaweeds.

**Fucales** (wracks). The only order of the Cyclosporae, a subclass of the Phaeophyta. It consists solely of marine forms with the commoner species (*e.g.* Fucus, Pelvetia, Ascophyllum) making up a large proportion of the vegetation of the coastal littoral zone. The thallus is differentiated into holdfast and lamina and often contains air bladders. Reproduction is oogamous with the gametangia developing in specialized invaginations, the conceptacles. There is no alternation of generotions, the life cycle being diplontic.

**Fucoxanthin.** Fucoxanthol, $C_{40}H_{60}O_6$, a brown pigment present in brown algae.

**Fugacious.** Falling off soon or fading away; temporary; not permanent, as the petals of a flower.

**Fumaric Acid.** A carboxylic acid, HCOOHC : CHCOOH, that is an intermediate in the Krebs cycle, being formed by the dehydrogenation of succinic acid.

**Fumigant.** A volatile chemical used to kill pathogens in the soil or in glass-houses. Fumigants are usually applied to the soil by injection. Chemicals used as fumigants include methyl bromide, chloropicrin, formaldehyde, metham, ethylene, dibromide, and carbon disulphide.

**Fumitory**

1. A plant or plant product which is smoked for pleasure, physiological effects, or for use in religious ceremonies, as tobacco, opium, cannabis.
2. Any plant of the fumitory family, Fumariaceae, as Fumaria, the earth-smoke.

**Funaria** (order Funariales). Genus of mosses in which the leaves are often crowded towards the tops of short stems. The leaves are tongue-shaped to ovate. The capsule is pyriform. It is a cosmopolitan genus of about 250 species. F. hygrometrica is commonly taken as a 'typical moss' in elementary bryology studies. The shoots are yellowish-green to green and often occur in extensive green carpets. The capsules are often numerous and are initially green and pear-shaped, becoming yellowish to orange-brown when ripe; they are borne on long, usually curved setae. The species is found on bare soil (in fields, on heaths and moors, in woodland, etc.), particularly on sites of previous fires.

**Fundus.** The bottom or base of an organ; the part farthest from the aperture.

**Fungi.** A group of simple plant lacking chlorophyll. Some authorities do not regard fungi as plants and include them with other organisms of uncertain affinities in the kingdrom Protista. Fungi are classified in the toxonomic division Mycota or Fungi. They can either exist as single cells or make up a multicellular body called a mycelium, which consists of filaments known as hyphae. Most fungal cells are multinucleate and have cell walls composed chiefly of chitin. Fungi exist primarily in damp situations on land and, because of the absence of chlorophyll, are either parasites or saprophytes on other organisms. The Mycota can be subdivided into four main classes, the Phycomycetes, Ascomycetes, Basidiomycetes, and Fungi Imperfecti. The principal criteria used in classification are the nature of the spores produced and the presence or absence of cross walls within the hyphae.

**Fungicide.** A chemical that kills fungi. Fungicides are used to prevent or control fungal diseases. They are applied to seeds as a dust or slurry and to standing crops usually as a spray. For control of postharvest diseases fruits may be dipped or sprayed, or packed in fungi-cide-impregnated materials. Fungicides can also be applied to the soil for control of damping-off and root diseases.

Fungicides, like other pesticides, usually have three names—the chemical name of the active ingredient, the approved common name, and the trade name. For example, methyl N-[1-(butylcarbamoyl)-2-benzimidazole] carbamate is the chemical name of benomyl, which has the trade name Benlate.

Fungicides fall into two major categories: the inorganic fungicides including copper fungicides and sulphur dust; and the organic fungicides, a group comprising the more modern fungicides, including systemic fungicides. Also quinone fungicide, organomercurial fungicide, dithiocarbamate fungicide, dinitro compounds, fumigant, seed dressing.

**Fungiform**. Shaped like a mushroom.

**Fungi Imperfecti** (imperfect fungi). A class of fungi in which sexual reproduction is absent. Otherwise they are generally similar to Ascomycetes and are consequently thought to be Ascomycetes that have lost the ability to produce ascospores. Examples of imperfect fungi are the Penicillium moulds.

**Fungus.** Member of a large group of flowerless plants that contains the mushrooms, toadstools, puffballs, moulds and yeasts among many others. They have no leaves and there is never any of the green colour (chlorophyll) found in most other plants. The bulk of the body consists of a mass of fine threads, called hyphae, which spread through or over the food material, *e.g.* dead plant matter, and absorb nutrients from it. The toadstools that we actually see are the reproductive parts of the fungi—the fruiting bodies, usually produced only at certain times of the year. They consist of densely packed and entwined hyphae. They do not produce seeds like the flowering plants, but scatter millions tiny spores which are usually carried away by the wind. The simplest fungi, such as pin moulds, carry their spores in little capsules on the hyphae and produce no special fruiting bodies. Many toadstools have spore-bearing gills on the underside of the cap. The colour of the gills and the way in which they are attached to the stalk is important in identifying many species.

**Fungus Garden.** A mass of fungi cultivated within the nests of termites or fungus ants for use as food.

**Funicle.** The stalk that attaches an ovule to the placenta in the ovary of a flowering plant. It contains a strand of conducting tissue leading from the placenta into the chalaza.

**Funiculus** (funicle). The stalk attaching the ovule, and later the seed, to the placenta or ovary wall in angiosperms. It serves as an anchor and provides a vascular supply to the ovule and seed.

**Funnel**

1. *bot.* A space beneath the outer coat of a macrospore in aquatic plants of the waterclover family.
2. *zool.* The excurrent siphon of a squid or octopus : Hyponome.

**Funnelform**

1. Shaped like a funnel.
2. Designating flowers in which the tube gradually widens into an expanded corolla.

**Funori.** A phycocolloid obtained from red algae, used as a sizing, thickening, and adhesive agent.

**Fur.** The soft, fine, hairy coat of a mammal.

**Furanose.** A sugar having a five-membered ring containing four carbon atoms and one oxygen atom.

**Furanose Ring.** A ring containing four carbon atoms and an oxygen atom. Such rings are formed by ketose sugars with five or more carbon atoms. When such sugars are in solution the ketone group on the second carbon of the sugar reacts with the hydroxyl group on, the fifth carbon atom. Fructose existing in this form is termed fructofuranose. Aldose sugars can also form furanose rings. However aldoses also form pyranose rings, which are far more stable and so predominate in solutions of aldose sugars.

**6-Furfurylaminopurine.** Kinetin.

**Furrowed.** Bearing longitudinal grooves or channels : Sulcate.

**Fur Seal.** One of several species of eared seals, especially Callorhinus ursinus, the Alaska fur seal noted for its summer migrations to the Pribil of Islands; also called sea bear.

**Fusarium Disease.** Any of a number of rots, blights, and wilts caused by parasitic phycomycete fungi of the genus Fusarium.

**Fusiform.** Elongated and tapering at each end, as does a fusiform initial.

**Fusiform Initials**. More or less elongate initials in the vascular cambium that give rise to the components of the axial (longitudinal) system of the secondary xylem and secondary phloem (*e.g.* vessel elements, tracheids, and sieve tube elements). They also give rise to the ray initials.

# G

**$G_1$ Phase, $G_2$ Phase.** Cell cycle.

**Gadwall.** A surface-feeding duck (Anas strepera).

**Gaggle.** A flock of geese.

**Gaian Hypothesis.** Hypothesis, formulated by Jaines E. Lovelock and Lynn Margulis, that the presence of living organisms on a planet leads to major modifications of the physical and chemical conditions pertaining on the planet, and that subsequent to the establishment of life the climate and major biogeochemical cycles are mediated by living organisms themselves.

**Galactan.** A polysaccharide in which the major monosaccharide subunit is galactose, though other sugars, notably arabinose, are often also present. Galactans are structural polysaccharides, often found among the pectic substances of cell walls.

**Galactose.** A simple sugar, $C_6H_{12}O_6$, stereoisomeric with glucose, that occurs naturally as one of the products of the enzymic digestion of milk sugar (lactose) and as a constituent of gum arabic.

**Galacturonic Acid.** Uronic acids.

**Galea**

1. *bot.* A helmet-shaped structure forming a part of the calyx or corolla in certain flowers.
2. *zool.* A lobelike structure on the maxilla of certain insects, as the grasshopper.

**Gall.** An abnormal localized swelling or outgrowth produced by a plant as a result of attack by a parasite. Galls are caused by bacteria, fungi, nematodes, insects, or mites or by a combination of these agents. Crown gall is a common gall produced as a result of bacterial infection. The root knots produced by nematodes of the genus Meloidogyne are another example. Galls caused by insects are very diverse and include the oak apple caused by the gall wasp Neuroterus lenticularis and the pincushion galls on roses caused by the gall wasp Rhodites rosae.

**Gall Bladder.** A small pouch attached to the bile duct, present in most vertebrates. Bile, produced in the liver, is stored in the gall bladder and released when food (especially fatty substances) enters the duodenum.

**Gallfly.** A gall-producing dipterous insect (Eurosta) of the family Trypetidae, the cause of stem galls on goldenrod.

**Gall Gnat.** A gall midge, a small dipterous insect of the family Cecidomyiidae, the larvae of which live in plants, forming galls.

**Gallinaceous**

1. Of or resembling domestic fowl.
2. Of or pertaining to the order Galliformes, which includes most upland game birds, as the grouse, prairie chicken, quail, Hungarian partridge, pheasant, and wild turkey.

**Gall Insect.** Any of a number of insects which cause galls to develop on plants.

**Gallinule.** A henlike bird of the family Rallidae, as Gallinula chloropus, the Florida gallinule.

**Gall Midge.** A gall gnat.

**Gall Mite.** An elongated, four-legged mite of the family Eriophyidae which causes galls to form on various plants.

**Gallstone.** A concretion or calculus found in the gallbladder or bile ducts.

**Gall Wasp.** One of a number of small hymenopterous insects of the family Cynipidae which cause galls to form on plants.

**Gam.** A group of whales or porpoises swimming together.

**Game.** Various animals, principally birds and mammals which are hunted for sport and for their value as food.

**Game Birds.** Birds considered worthy of pursuit and capture by sportsmen, principal ones of which are upland game birds and waterfowl.

**Gamecock.** A male game fowl.

**Game Cropping.** Culling or husbanding of game animals for meat and other products, all of them usually for human consumption. Game cropping is often advocated as an ecologically sound method of forming the African savannah and similar environments : it is argued that the wide variety of game animals, with their different food preferences, utilize the primary production more efficiently than cattle, and are generally better adapted to the environment. This gives added reason for conservation of the wild ungulate population. Other social, economic, and political difficulties mean that game cropping is practised less widely than may seem desirable.

**Game Fishes.** Fishes sought the anglers because of their cunning or wariness or difficulty in landing when caught.

**Game Fowl.** One of a breed of poultry bred for its fighting qualities.

**Game Mammals.** Mammals which are hunted for sport. Small game includes the cottontail, jackrabbit, and squirrel; big game includes deer, elk, moose, antelope, caribou, bighorn sheep, mountain goat, bear, and peccary. The term is also applied to animals as the lion, tiger, rhinoceros, and elephant.

**Gametangiophore.** An upright structure that bears the female gametes (archegoniophore) or male gametes (antheridiophore) in certain liverworts. Gametangiophores are extensions of the thallus and are most elaborate in the genus Marchantia.

**Gametangium.** A plant sex organ that produces gametes. The term is usually restricted to the sex organs of algae and fungi.

**Gamete.** Specialized haploid cell (sometimes called a sex cell) whose nucleus and often cytoplasm fuses with that of another gamete—from the opposite sex or mating type—in the process of fertilization, thus forming a diploid zygote. In some animals, *e.g.* mammals, the gametes are differentiated: the male is a motile sperm with reduced cytoplasm, and the female is immobile with a large amount of cytoplasm called the egg or ovum, which develops when stimulated. Usually there are many small male gametes, but only a few or one female gamete.

**Gametocyte.** A cell which develops into a gamete.

**Gametogenesis**

1. The formation of gametes. Gametes are usually formed mitotically by the gametophyte generation though in some groups (diplontic) gametogenesis corresponds with meiosis. Gametes may form in any cell of the gametophyte, as occurs in the green alga Ulva, or they may be confined to specialized organs, such as antheridia and archegonia. Compare sporogenesis.

2. The growth and development of the gametophyte generation.

**Gametophore.** A structure upon which gametangia are borne.

**Gametophyte.** Haploid phase of the life cycle of plants, during which gametes are produced by mitosis. It arises from a haploid spore produced by meiosis from a diploid sporophyte. In lower plants (such as mosses), the gametophyte is the dominant and conspicuous generation.

**Gamic.** Sexual

**Gamma-ray Spectrometry.** Analytical method used is some branches of chemistry and physics for the measurement of the intensities and energies of gamma radiation. Scintillation or semiconductor radiation detectors, coupled to various types of electronic circuitry, enable a spectrum to be accumulated. This may be used to identify the gamma-emitting radioisotopes, and their energy intensities can be used to determine the corresponding element concentrations.

**Gamogenesis.** Sexual Reproduction.

**Gamone.** Any substance released by a gamete that serves to attract another gamete. For example, in certain ferns malic acid is believed to be released from the archegonia and to attract the male gametes.

**Gamopetalous** (sympetalous). Having petals that are fused along their margins to the base, forming a corolla tube. Most plants possessing such flowers are grouped together in the Sympetalae.

**Gamosepalous.** Synsepalous; a condition in which sepals of a flower are united.

**Gander.** An adult male goose.

**Ganglion** (plural ganglia). A swelling in a Nerve which contains the actual cell bodies and nuclei of the nerve cells or neurons. The rest of the nerve contains bundles of fibres which actually carry the neurons' signals from one part of the body to another. Each fibre is, of course, connected to a cell body in one of the numerous ganglia. The brains of some simple animals, such as earthworms, are little more than large ganglia.

**Gangrene**

1. Condition in which tissues die due to a restriction in the blood supply. Dry types do not usually allow bacterial infection, but moist types do : gas gangrene results from the infection of a deep wound by various species of Clostridium, especially C. perfringens (formerly C. welchii).
2. Rot of stored potato tubers, caused by fungi of the genus Phoma.

**Gannet.** A large, fish-eating seabird of the family Sulidae, as Morus bassana, the northern gannet.

**Ganoid Fishes.** The garpikes, sturgeons, and their allies, primitive fishes with ganoid scales.

**Ganoid Scale.** A type of fish scale consisting of layers of ganion deposited on a layer of lamellate bone.

**Gap.** A break in the continuity of the vascular cylinder of a stem, as leaf gap or bud gap.

**¹Gape.** To open the mouth widely.

**²Gape.** A wide opening as that between *a.* the opened jaws of a vertebrate; *b.* the two valves of a bivalve mollusk; *c.* the scutes of a barnacle.

**Gap Junction.** Communicating junction between cells, which provides a rapid passage for ions and small molecules such that they need not cross the bilipid layer of the opposed membranes. At the junction these membranes are only 2—3 nm apart, and within the intervening space there are arrays of closely packed cylinders, approximately 7 nm in diameter, each of which is pierced by a central channel. These junctions are a particular feature of cells in direct electrical coupling with one another, *e.g.* nerve and heart muscle cells, and perhaps embryonic cells.

**Gapeworm.** Syngamus trachea, a parasitic nematode worm which infects the respiratory passages of fowl, causing gapes

**Gar.** The garpike, one of several species of primitive, ray-finned fishes of the genus Lepisosteus inhabiting central United States.

**Garigue** (garrigue). A type of scrub woodland characteristic of limestone areas with low rainfall and thin poor dry soils. The low-growing vegetation consists of aromatic, often spiny, species, such as sage (Salvia officinalis), thymes (Thymus), and lavender (Lavandula vera). Many bulbous plants grow between the shrubs and there are numerous species that are also present in maquis. This type of vegetation is widespread in Mediterranean countries.

**Garlic.** A pungent bulbous plant related to the Onion. It was originally wild in Central Asia. Unlike the onion, each garlic 'bulb' is actually a cluster of small wedge-like bulbs called cloves. Garlic is used as a flavouring. The plant has a tall stalk with whitish flowers.

**Garlic Mustard.** A hairless flowering plant related to the cabbage. The slender stem bears long-stalked leaves which smell of garlic. The small white flowers are arranged in a cluster at the tip. The plant is found on waste ground and in hedges.

**Garter Snake.** A harmless, viviparous snake (Thamnophis sertalis).

**Gas.** A fluid which exists in the form of a vapor.

**Gaseous.** In the form of or of the nature of a gas or gases; pertaining to gases.

**Gaseous Exchange.** The diffusion of gases into and out of the cells of an organism. For exchange to occvr, the gases usually have to pass through a liquid boundary layer. The rate of diffusion of gases dissolved in water is much slower than diffusion through air, an important consideration in calculations of gaseous exchange. During photosynthesis carbon dioxide is taken in and oxygen given off; the reverse occurs in respiration. The passage of water vapour is usually in one direction only—out of the plant.

**Gas Gland.** A gland which secretes a gas, as that of a siphonophore or the red gland of fishes.

**Gaster.** The portion of the abdomen lying posterior to the petiole, as in various hymenopterans, for example, ants.

**Gasteromycetes.** A class of the Basidiomycotina containing the most advanced basidiomycetes. These have a well developed basidiocarp and basidiospores that are not discharged forcibly. It contains about 700 species in some 150 genera and includes the orders Hymenogastrales (false truffles), Lycoperdales, Nidulariales, and Phallales.

**Gastralia.** Ventral, riblike, dermal bones present in the alligator and other long-bodied reptiles.

**Gastric.** Of, pertaining to, or originating in the stomach.

**Gastric Juice.** An acidic mixture of inorganic salts, hydrochloric acid, and digestive enzymes (*e.g.* pepsin) produced by glands in the stomach lining.

**Gastric Filaments.** Nematocyst-bearing threads borne on the septa of the gastrovascular cavity of scyphozoans.

**Gastric Glands.** Tubular glands of the stomach which secrete gastric juice, a digestive fluid containing hydrochloric acid (0.4%), pepsin, and a lipase.

**Gastric Mill** (proventriculus). A type of gizzard occurring in many crustaceans. It is situated in the anterior region of the stomach and consists of a set of bones (ossicles) and muscles that grind food particles. The food particies are then filtered by bristles in the posterior section of the stomach.

**Gastric Pouch.** One of four pouches extending from the central stomach of a scyphozoan jellyfish.

**Gastric Shield.** In various mollusks, a platelike structure in the dorsal wall of the stomach with which the tip of the crystalline style comes in contact.

**Gastrin.** A hormone, produced in the stomach, that controls the release of gastric juice. The secretion of gastrin is stimulated by the presence of food in the stomach. It is one of the hormones that integrates and controls digestive processes.

**Gastrocoel.** The cavity of the gastrula : Archenteron.

**Gastrodermis.** The layer of epithelium which lines the gastrovascular cavity of a coelenterate.

**Gastrolith.** A calcareous body in the lateral wall of the stomach of a crayfish.

**Gastropod.** Any mollusk of the class Gastropoda which includes the snails, slugs, limpets, periwinkles, and whelks.

**Gastropoda.** A class of molluscs that includes the snails, whelks, limpets, land and sea slugs, and conches. Molluscs have a well-developed head with tentacles, a large flattened foot, and a coiled twisted shell. They occupy marine, freshwater, and terrestrial habitats; in the terrestrial and some freshwater gastropods the mantle cavity acts as a lung instead of enclosing gills.

**Gastrotrich.** Any member of the Gastrotricha, a phylum or class of pseudocoelomate animals, mostly minute, bottom-dwelling, marine and freshwater animals, as Chaetognathus.

**Gastrovascular.** Pertaining to both digestion and circulation.

**Gastrozooid.** A nutritive polyp of a colonial coelenterate : Trophozooid.

**Gastrula.** The stage in embryonic development which follows the blastula. In its simplest form, it is cup-shaped with a wall of two layers, ectoderm and endoderm, enclosing a cavity, the gastrocoel or archenteron with a single opening, the blastopore.

**Gastrulation.** Complicated process of cell movements that carry those cells whose descendants will form the future internal organs from their largely superficial position in the blastula to approximately their final positions inside the animal embryo. This process usually occurs at the end of the cleavage period. In many embryos, gastrulation occurs in the two main groups of cells : the endoderm (future guit, etc.) and mesoderm (future muscle, blood, etc.). The ectoderm (future external layer and also future nervous system, which later becomes internal) is also rearranged at this time to its approximate final position.

**Gas Vacuole.** A structure made up of numerous gas-filled vesicles, many of which may be found in the cells of certain aquatic bacteria and blue-green algae. The density of the cell depends on how much gas is contained within the vesicles. The position of the organism in a column of water can thus be regulated by these structures. The vesicles are unusual in being bound by a protein rather than phosphoglyceride membrane.

**Gazelle.** One of a number of small, graceful, swift-running antelopes inhabiting Asia and Africa, especially those of the genus Gazella.

**Gel.** A lyophilic colloid that has coagulated to a rigid or jelly-like solid. In a gel, the disperse medium has formed a loosely-held network of linked molecules through the dispersion medium. Examples of gels are silica gel and gelatin.

**Gelatin(e).** A colourless or pale yellow water-soluble protein obtained by boiling collagen with water and evaporating the solution. It swells when water is added and dissolves in hot water to form a solution that sets to a gel on cooling. It is used in photographic emulsions and adhesives, and in jellies and other foodstuffs.

**Gelatinous Fungi.** Tremellales.

**Gelding.** A castrated animal, especiall a horse.

**Ge l Filtration.** A type of column chromatography in which a mixture of liquids is passed down a column containing a gel. Small molecules in the mixture can enter pores in the gel and move slowly down the column; large molecules, which cannot enter the pores, move more quickly. Thus, mixtures of molecules can be separated on the basis of their size. The technique is used particularly for separating proteins but it can also be applied to cell nuclei, viruses, etc.

**Gemma**

1. A specialized multicellular unit of vegetative reproduction found in certain mosses and liverworts, and in Psilotum. It may take various forms, from being disc- or platelike to being filamentous or heart shaped. When separated from the parent it develops into a new individual identical to the parent. Gemma cups may be formed where several gemmae are produced on a protective receptacle, as seen in the moss

Tetraphis pellucida. Clusters of gemmae may also be seen at leaf tips or in the leaf axils, on specialized stalks or pseudopodia, and on rhizoids. Reproduction by gemmation occurs more frequently than spore formation and in some species it is the only form of reproduction seed.

2. Chlamydospore.

**Gemmation.** A type of vegetative propagation in which small clumps of undifferentiated cells (gemmae) develop on the surface of a plant. These are shed and dispersed to other areas, where they grow to produce new individuals. Gemmation is found only in certain lower plants, such as mosses and liverworts.

**Gemmule**

1. An asexual, internal reproductive body produced by certain sponges.
2. One of the numerous, spinelike processes on the dendrite of a neuron.

**Gemsbuck.** A large, African antelope of the genus Oryx; gemsbok.

**Gena.** The check or side of the face.

**Gene.** The unit of inheritance. Defined no more precisely than this, the term 'gene' corresponds with Mendel's 'factors' responsible for the manifestation of a particular characteristic.

A particular gene may be further defined as being located at a specific point on one of the chromosomes and capable of existing in alternative forms or alleles. Thus there would be a gene for 'seed colour' in peas, with alternative alleles of 'green' and 'yellow'. In a diploid cell, alleles of a gene are paired, one on each of a pair of homologous chromosomes. If contrasting alleles are present in the same organism, *e g.* one for

genes that have been superseded by improved cultivars. Normally seed material is dried down to about 4% moisture and stored at around 0°C preferably in hermetically sealed containers. For many seeds such conditions will maintain viability for 10—20 years and longer. The seeds, of some species, including many tropical plants, cannot be dried without killing them and yet have a limited life-span in the hydrated state. Such material must be maintained in the growing condition. The problems space and maintenance that this entails may in some instances be overcome by tissue-culture methods. All material must periodically be sown to check viability and multiply seedstock. Pollen may also be stored in gene banks though generally the longevity of pollen is less than that of seeds.

**Genealogy.** An account or diagram of the descent of an individual, family, or race from its progenitors or ancestors; pedigree : Lineage.

**Gene Centre** (centre of diversity). An area that shows considerable genetic diversity of certain crop plants and their relatives. Some gene centres, the primary centres, are believed to correspond to the region where a particular crop originated. For example, numerous forms of wheat exist in the Middle East and, since many of the wild relatives of wheat are also found in this area, it is believed the crop was first domesticated there. Other centres, the secondary centres, do not eontain wild relatives and are believed simply to be areas where the crops have been cultivated for a considerable period. Ethiopia is an example of a secondary centre.

Gene centres are typically found in mountainous regions. This may be because human communities are more isolated and climatic conditions more variable in such areas—both conditions that would lead to more rapid divergence of crop populations. The recognition of gene centres is important in conservation and plant breeding work as such areas are important reservoirs of 'green' and one for 'yellow', then the phenotype of the organism will depend upon the dominance relationship between the alleles.

However, in addition to determining characteristics, inherited 'information also mutates and recombines. A gene defined as a unit of function (cistron) may be a piece of DNA several hundred number sides long, whereas a gene defined a unit of mutation (muton may be a single nucleotide. The unit of recombination (recon) lies between these two extremes. In modern usage the term gene is most commonly applied to functional units of DNA. Thus structural genes determine protein structure and regulator, promoter, and operator genes control the regulation of protein production. Genes are extremely stable and so spontaneous mutation occurs very rarely. However it is the ultimate source of all genetic variation, *i.e.* the reason why the 'seed colour' gene exists in different forms, such as green and yellow. Once mutation has created alternative alleles, a further source of genetic variation is by genetic recombination, *i.e.* the rearrangement of whole chromosomes or parts of chromosomes during meiosis.

Though the majority of DNA, and hence the genes, is confined to the chromosomes, some DNA is present in such organelles as mitochondria and chloroplates. The pattern of inheritance shown by cytoplasmic genes differs from that of chromosomal (Mendelian) genes and they are referred to as plasmagenes in order to distinguish them from the latter.

**Gene Bank.** An institution where plant material, in danger either of becoming extinct in the wild or of being lost from cultivation, is stored in a viable condition. In many such centres the emphasis is on maintaining collections of plants of demonstrated or potential use to man, *e.g.* crop varieties containing useful gymnosperms it gives rise to the body cell and stalk cell whereas in angiosperms it gives rise directly to the two male gametes or generative nuclei.

**Gene Pool.** All the genes and their different alleles that are present in a population of a plant or animal species.

**General Adaptation.** Adaptation that fits an organism for life in some broad environmental zone, as opposed to 'special adaptations' which are specializations for a particular way of life. Thus the wing of a bird is a general adaptation, while the particular kind of bill is a special adaptation. Major groups of organisms are differentiated very largely on the basis of general adaptations.

**General-adaptation Syndrome** (GAS). A range of abnormal physiological systems reflecting pathological social stress, and serving to regulate population growth, where no external resource limitation exists. Essentially it is a behavioural regulation of population growth. Mechanisms include the supression of the oestrous cycle, inadequate lactation, enlarged adrenal glands, increased aggression, etc. It has been demonstrated experimentally with overcrowded laboratory rats.

**Generalized.** Of a general nature; not speclfic; not highly differentiated.

**Generate.** To originate, produce, propagate, beget, or bring forth.

[1]**Generation.** The act or process of producing offspring.

[2]**Generation.** All the individuals comprising a stage in natural descent, as the $F_1$ generation or gametophyte generation.

**Generation Time.** The interval between the beginnings of consecutive cell divisions. It may be as short as 20 minutes in bacteria.

**Generative.** Having the power to bring forth or produce.

**Generative Cell.** The cell in a pollen grain which gives rise to two male gametes.

**Generative Organ.** Reproductive Organ.

**Generative Nuclei.** In angiosperms, the two male gametes that are formed by division of the generative cell. They migrate down the pollen tube behind the vegetative nucleus. When the pollen tube enters the embryo sac the tip of the tube breaks down to release the generative nuclei. On entering the nucellus and embryo sac they participate in the fertilization process. One fuses with the egg nucleus to form the zygote and the other usually fuses with the polar nuclei or definitive nucleus to form the primary endosperm nucleus.

**Generative Nucleus.** One of the two male gametes in the pollen tube of angiosperms.

**Generic.** Pertaining to or having the rank of a genus.

**Generic Cycles, Theory of.** Theory which envisages a life cycle for a species or genus that resembles that of an individual. The first stage is characterized by vigorous spread; the second by maximum phyletic activity giving rise to new forms; the third marks a phase of decline in area due to completion within the offspring species; and the fourth and final stage sees the extinction of the species. Although in many ways a useful analogy, there is no evidence that species become senile and die out spontaneously.

**Genesis.** The beginning or coming into existence; the origin of anything.

**Genet.** A small Old World carnivore of the genus Gennetta, related to the civet and mongoose.

**Gene Therapy.** The application of genetic engineering techniques to alter or replace defective genes. The techniques are still at the experimental stage but the eventual aim is to prevent such genetic diseases as sickle cell anaemia and thalassaemia.

**Genetic.** Of or pertaining to genetics or heredity.

**Genetic Code.** The sequence of nucleotides along the DNA of an organism within which is incorporated the information necessary for protein synthesis. By controlling the type and amount of protein manufactured the genetic code controls the growth, development, and characteristics of an organism. The observation that DNA could specify the incorporation of twenty different types of amino acids into protein but itself consisted of only four bases implied that more than one base must code for a single amino acid. The shortest sequence of any four bases that could specify all the types of amino acids found in protein is three, since $4^3=64$ possible combinations. (Pairs of any four bases could only code for $4^2=16$ amino acids, which is not enough). Thus arose the base triplet or triplet code hypothesis. It was further proposed that the triplets were sequential, not overlapping. This would account for the almost infinite variation in the sequence of amino acids in a protein. If there was a tendency for some amino acids to follow others in a polypeptide, then this might indicate an overlapping code, *i.e.* one where the last one or two bases of one triplet acted as the first one or two in the next triplet. However, this is not the case.

The theory that the genetic code consists of base triplets received considerable support from frame-shift experiments. These demonstrated that mutations resulting from the addition or loss of three base pairs close together produced protein resembling that of normal individuals. However, mutations resulting from the addition or loss of one, two, or four pairs produced significantly different protein. When three bases were added or lost only a short segment of protein was affected, whereas if other numbers were added or lost, the code for the whole protein was thrown out of sequence.

**Genetic Code.** The set of correspondences between base (nucleotide pair) triplets in DNA and amino acids in protein. These base triplets carry the genetic information for protein synthesis. For example, the triplet CAA (cytosine, adenine, adenine) codes for valine.

**Genetic Drift.** The random fluctuations of gene frequencies in a population such that the genes amongst offspring are not a perfectly representative sampling of the parental genes. Although drift occurs in all populations its effects are most marked in very small isolated populations, in which it gives rise to the random fixation of alternative alleles so that the variation originally present within single (ancestral) populations comes to appear as variation between reproductively isolated populations.

**Genetic Engineering.** Manipulation of DNA using restriction enzymes which can split the DNA molecule and then rejoin it to form a hybrid molecule—a new combination of non-homologous DNA (so-called recombinant DNA). The technique allows the by-passing of all the biological restraints to genetic exchange and mixing, and may even permit the combination of genes from widely differing species. Genetic engineering developed in the early 1970s, and has become one of the most fertile areas of genetics.

**Genetic Equalibrium.** Equilibrium in which the frequencies of two alleles at a given locus are maintained at the same values generation after generation. A tendency for the population to equilibrate its genetic composition and resist sudden change is called genetic homoeostasis.

**Genetic Erosion.** The loss of genetic variation and the consequent narrowing of the genetic base of cultivated plants through the introduction of new improved varieties of crops that can be grown over wide areas. The continued existence of locally adapted primitive varieties is threatened by their large-scale replacement with adaptable high-yielding varieties. The situation is particularly serious in gene centres, where valuable genes for such characters as disease resistance may be lost.

**Genetic Load.** The average number of lethal mutations per individual in a population. Such mutations result in the premature death of the organisms carrying them. Three main kinds of genetic load may be recognized :

(*a*) input load, in which inferior alleles arein troduced into the gene pool of a population either by mutation or immigration;

(*b*) balanced load, which is created by selection favouring allelic or genetic combinations that, by segregation and recombination, form inferior genoty pesevery generation;

(*c*) substitutional load, which is generated by selection favouring the replacement of an existing gene by a new allele. Originally called the 'cost of natural selection' by the geneticist J.B.S. Haldane, substitutional load is the genetic load associated with transient polymorphism. The term 'genetic load' was originally coined by H.J. Muller in 1950 to convey the burden that deleterious mutations provide, but it is probably better recognized as a measure of the amount of natural selection associated with a certain amount of genetic variability, which provides the raw material for continued adaptation and evolution.

**Genetic Map.** The linear arrangement of mutable sites on a chromosome, deduced from genetic recombination experiments. The percentage of recombinants is used as a quantitative index of the distance between two gene pairs, and this distance, together with those between other gene pairs, provide a map of their arrangement on the chromosome. One 'genetic map unit' is defined as the distance between gene pairs for which one product of meiosis out of one hundred is recombinant (*i.e.* it equals a recombination frequency of 1%).

**Genetic Polymorphism.** Occurrence in a population of two or more genotypes in frequencies that cannot be accounted for by recurrent mutation. Such occurrences are generally long-term. Genetic polymorphisms may be balanced (such that allele frequencies are in equilibrium with one another at a given locus), or transient (such that a mutation is spreading through the population in a constant direction). In the former case, the different alleles may be maintained by different environmental conditions (in space or time), one being favoured under one set of circumstances and another under another set; or a heterozygous genotype may be in some way superior to the genotypes that are homozygous at that locus—this is termed a 'heterozygous advantage'.

**Genetic Resources.** The diversity and availability of alleles in both natural and artificially maintained stocks of organisms. For a number of years concern has been expressed about the need to maintain a diverse range of genotypes in domesticated plants and animals and their close relatives in the wild. A broad genetic base increases the capacity for variation and successful adaptation, such as resistance to pathogens or hostile environments. Both national and international programmes exist to maintain genetic resources of agriculturally important organisms. This had led to the establishment of a number of gene banks or seed banks where potentially valuable seeds are evaluated, multiplied, and stored under ideal conditions.

**Genetics.** The branch of biology concerned with the study of heredity and variation. Classical genetics is based on the work of Gregor Mendel (Mendelism). During the 20th century genetics has expanded to overlap with the fields of ecology and animal behaviour (behavioural genetics; population genetics), and important advances in biochemistry and microbiology have led to clarification of the chemical nature of genes and the ways in which they can replicate and be transmitted.

**Genetic Spiral** (developmental spiral). A hypothetical spiral formed by drawing a line through and joining the centres of successive leaf primordia at a shoot apex. The form of the spiral depends on the angle of divergence and the distance between successive primordia. The first is often 137.5° and the second depends on the rate of vertical growth of the apex. It is often found that this distance increases geometrically. Compare parastichy.

**Genic.** Of or pertaining to genes.

**Geniculate.** Bent sharply, as at the knee.

**Genital.** Of or pertaining to the sex organs or the organs of reproduction.

**Genitalia.** The reproductive organs, male or female, especially the external reproductive structures.

**Genome.** All the genes contained in a single set of chromosomes *i.e.* in a haploid nucleus. Each parent, through its reproductive cells, contributes its genome to its offspring.

**Genotype.** The genetic composition of an organism, *i.e.* the combination of alleles it possesses. Compare phenotype.

**Genotype**

1. *genetics a.* A group of individuals with identical genes. *b.* The genetic constitution of an individual usually represented by a formula such as AABB or AaBb, in contrast to the appearance of an individual. Compare phenotype.
2. *taxonomy.* The type species of a genus.

**Gentian.** A group of hairless flowering plants, common to colder regions and mountains, with blue, purple or yellow bell-shaped flowers. The spring gentian forms low tufts on the ground and produces blue star-shaped flowers. The great yellow gentian has large clusters of starry yellow blooms. All the gentians favour damp, boggy places.

**Genus.** A category used in the classification of organisms that consists of a number of similar or closely related species. The common name of an organism (especially a plant) is sometimes similar or identical to that of the genus, *e.g.* Lilium (lily), Antirrhinum. Similar genera are grouped into families.

**Geocarpy.** The development of a fruit beneath the ground which originated from a flower above the ground, as the peanut.

**Geochronology.** Varve dating.

**Geoduck.** A large, edible clam (Panope generosa) of the Pacific coast; gweduc.

**Geographical Distribution.** The distribution of organisms over the surface af the earth.

**Geographical Floral Element.** Group of plant species that has marked geographical affinities. The flora ofa given territory includes different geographical elements. For example, the Mediterranean element in the British flora comprises 38 species, concentrated in the extreme south and south-west of England. The majority are flowering annuals or biennials, categories of plants well represented in the sunny Mediterranean. When the full ranges of the 38 species is examined, they are all found to occur in the Mediterranean basin, with northerly extensions to Britain.

**Geographical Isolation.** Isolation of species resulting from geographic factors acting as barriers, as oceans or high mountains acting as a barrier to distribution of terrestrial forms.

**Geographic Range.** The area of the earth's surface occupied by a species, outside of which it does not normally occur.

**Geological Distribution.** The distribution of animals and plants in time as determined by presence of their fossil remains in sedimentary rocks.

**Geological Time Scale.** A time scale that covers the earth's history from its origin, estimated to be about 4600 million years ago, to the present. The chronology is divided into a hierarchy of time intervals : eras, periods, epochs, ages, and chrons.

**Geologic Timetable.** A table listing the geological eras and their subdivisions with the principal forms of life occurring in each.

**Geometer.** A moth of the family Geometridae whose larvae (inchworms or measuring worms) move by looping movements, as the spring cankerworm.

**Geonasty.** Curving towards the earth.

**Geophilous**

1. *bot.* Fruiting underground.
2. *zool.* Living in or on the ground; terrestrial.

**Geophyte.** A plant with its perennating buds situated below ground on a rhizome, tuber, bulb, or corm.

**Geotaxis.** Orientation of a motile organism with respect to gravity.

**Geotropism.** Directional movement of a plant in response to the stimulus of gravity. Primary tap roots show positive geotropism; vertical primary shoots show negative geotropism; horizontal stems and leaves are diageotropic; and branches and secondary roots at oblique angles are plagiogeotropic.

**Geranium.** A family of flowering plants, often with aromatic leaves, whose fruit ends in a pointed beak. Most species are for this reason named cranesbills or storksbills.

**Gerenuk.** Litocranius walleri, a long-necked gazelle of East Africa.

**Germ**

1. A small bit of protoplasm capable of developing into a new organism, as a spore, egg, or seed.
2. The embryo of a seed, as wheat germ.
3. Any microorganism, especially a pathogenic bacterium.
4. Any minute disease-causing agent, as a virus, rickettsis, spirochaete.

**German Measles** (rubella). Acute, infectious disease of humans which is normally mild, involving a skin rash and enlargement of the lymph nodes. However, if contracted during the first 3-4 months of pregnancy, permanent damage to the foetus may occur. The disease is caused by a virus of the Togaviridae.

**Germ Ball.** A mass of germinal cells in a developmental stage of a fluke.

**Germ Band.** A thickened area on the ventral surface of an insect egg from which the embryo develops.

**Germ Cell.** Any cell in the series of cells (the germ line) that eventually produces gametes. In mammals the germinal epithelium of the ovaries and testes contain the germ cells.

**Germ-free.** Gnotobiotic.

**Germicide.** An agent which kills microorganisms.

**Germinal.** Of or pertaining to reproductive cells.

**Germinal Disc.** A blastodisc.

**Germinal Epithelium.** An epithelium which gives rise to sex cells, as *a.* that covering the surface of an indifferent gonad in an embryo, *b.* that lining a seminiferous tubule or covering the surface of the ovary in mammals.

**Germinal Selection**

1. Selection of germ cells (sex cells from which gametes are derived) that possess recognized superior qualities, for use in the production of a subsequent generation. This method is used by humans for their domesticated animals, and it is proposed by those supporting eugenics that the method should also be applied to humans. In the latter case, germ cells would be stored, frozen, in germ banks, and would be available for couples who wished to use them rather than their own germ cells to generate a family.
2. Selection during gametogenesis against induced mutations that retard the spread of mutant cells.

**Germination.** The beginning of growth of a seed or spore, usually following a period of dormancy, and generally in response to the return of favourable external conditions, most notably warmth, moisture, and oxygen. The internal biochemical status of the seed or spore must also be appropriate. In seeds, germination may be epigeal, with cotyledons emerging above the ground, or hypogeal, with the cotyledons staying below ground.

**Germination.** The early growth of a seed that results in a new plant. The process requires moisture and warmth before it can proceed. First the seed swells up with water until the seed-coat bursts open. Then a root, or radicle, emerges and begins to grow downwards into the soil. Finally the young shoot or plumule begins to grow upwards towards the light.

**Germ Layer.** One of the three primary layers of an embryo from which the definitive tissues and organs develop.

**Germ Plasm.** The reproductive tissues of the body as distinguished from the soma (nonreproductive tissues).

**Germ Pore.** A thin-walled area on a spore or pollen-grain wall through which the germ tube may emerge on germination. In the pollen grain the germ pore is an area where the exine is either thinner or absent. Pollen grains may be identified to some extent by the shape and number of the germ pores.

**Germ Tube.** The filament that emerges on germination of a spore. The structure that emerges from a pollen grain is termed a pollen tube.

**Gerontology.** The study of old age and various phenomena associated with aging.

**Gestation.** The period in animals bearing live young (especially mammals) from the fertilization of the egg to birth of the young (parturition). In man gestation is known as pregnancy and takes about nine months (40 weeks).

**Gestation Period.** The period from fertilization to birth in mammals. It varies from about three weeks in house mice, to about 40 weeks in human beings and nearly 2 years in elephants.

**Giant**

1. Of unusual size, power, or strength.
2. A person of extraordinary stature or size.

**Giant Chromosomes.** Extremely large chromosomes present in the salivary glands of Drosophila, characterized by distinct banding.

**Giant Fibre.** A nerve fibre with a very large diameter, found in many types of invertebrate (*e.g.* earthworms and squids). Its function is to allow extremely rapid transmission of nervous impulses and hence rapid escape movements in emergencies.

**Giant Fibers.** Extremely large axons of neurons found in various invertebrates (annelids, crustaceans, mollusks) and some vertebrates (fishes, amphibians).

**Giantism.** Gigantism.

**Gibberellic Acid** ($GA_3$). The first of the gibberellins to be isolated and characterized. It was obtained from the fungus Gibberella fujikuroi, which causes a disease of rice seedlings characterized by excessive elongation of shoots and leaves. The basic structure of gibberellic acid and most other compounds with gibberellin-like activity is the gibbane carbon skeleton (diagram). Gibberellic acid is a terpenoid and is synthesized from mevalonic acid. Other gibberellins are synthesized by the same pathway and there is probably much interconversion in the plant between the different gibberellins. Gibberellic acid is the gibberellin most widely used in experiments.

**Gibberellin**. Any of a group of plant growth substances chemically related to gibberellic acid. Gibberellins promote shoot elongation in certain plants, often overcoming genetic dwarfism. They are also involved in the release of buds from dormancy and in promoting seed germination.

**Gibbon.** One of several species of small long-armed, anthropoid apes of the genera Hylobates and Symphalangus of southeast Asia, noted for their powerful voices.

**Gibbosity**. An asymmetrical swelling or protuberance usually near the base of an organ.

**Gibbous.** Swollen or bulging on one side. The calyx of the narrow-leaved vetch (Vicia angustifolia) is an example of a gibbous structure.

**Gid.** A disease principally of sheep caused by development within the brain of the larva (coenurus) of a tapeworm (Multiceps Multiceps).

**Giga-.** Symbol G. A prefix used in the metric system to denote one thousand million times. For example, $10^9$ joules=1 gigajoule (GJ).

**Gigantism.** Abnormal size or tallness resulting from over-production of the growth hormone of the anterior pituitary.

**Gill.** The organ which allows fishes and many other aquatic animals to breathe underwater by absorbing oxygen dissolved in the water. The gills of fishes consist of small finger-like organs connected to the throat and opening to the ouside of the body through gill slits. The gills of crabs and lobsters are feathery outgrowths from the body.

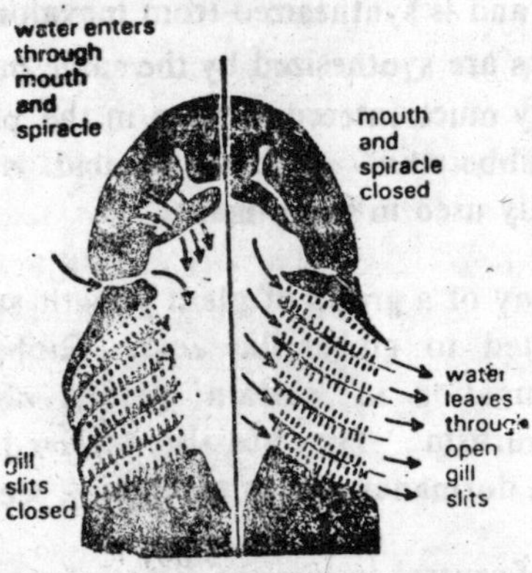


Gills of a Shark

**Gill Arch.** A branchial arch.

**Gill Bar.** A cartilaginous support for the tissue between the gill slits in lower chordates, such as Amphioxus.

**Gill Bypass.** A blood vessel in the larvae of caudate amphibians through which blood passes directly from the ventral aorta to dorsal aorta without passing through the gills.

**Gill Fungi.** Mushrooms or toadstools of the family Agaricaceae whose fruiting body bears leaflike plates or gills upon which basidiospores develop.

**Gill Pouch.** Part of the respiratory system of lampreys and hagfish, which have a row of gill pouches on each side of the head. A gill pouch consists of a muscular wall with many respiratory lamellae lodged on its inner side. In lampreys the gill pouches each have a separate opening to the exterior.

**Gill Raker.** Gills of most bony fish carry not only numerous filaments, but also, on the inner side of the gill arch, a row of gill rakers : fairly stiff tooth-like processes, which strain the water flowing past them. In some fish (*e.g.* mullet and herring) the gill rakers are long and closely set, thereby acting as a sieve capable of retaining food particles.

**Gill Rays.** Branchial rays, slender, cartilaginous, supporting structures in the interbranchial septum of a gill.

**Gill Slit.** An opening leading from the pharynx to the exterior in aquatic vertebrates and Amphioxus. In Amphioxus they function in filter feeding. In fish they contain the gills and are usually in the form of a series of long slits. They are absent in adult tetrapod vertebrates (except for some amphibians) but their presence in some form in the embryos of all vertebrates is a characteristic of the phylum Chordata.

**Gilt.** A young female swine.

**Ginger.** A spice and condiment obtained from the rhizomes of the ginger plant (Zingiber officinale) an erect perennial herb which is also used medicinally.

**Gingiva** (gum). The part of the epithelial tissue lining the mouth that covers the jaw bones. It is continuous with the sockets surrounding the roots of the teeth.

**Gingival.** Of or pertaining to the gums of the oral cavity.

**Ginkgo.** A deciduous tree also called the maidenhair tree, and the only living representative of a group of trees that flourished millions of years ago. Native to China, it is commonly grown in Europe as an ornamental tree. The leaves are heart-shaped, and male and female flowers are borne on separate trees. The fruit is small and fleshy, and smells unpleasant.

**Ginkgoales.** An order of gymnosperms containing only one living species, the maidenhair tree (Ginkgo biloba), which is known only in cultivation. It is a tall deciduous tree and bears fan-shaped leaves, usually with a distinct notch opposite the petiole. The leaf venation is exceptional among extant gymnosperms in being dichotomously branching. The Ginkgoales were more abundant in the Mesozoic and are possibly an offshoot of the Cordaitales.

**Giraffe.** A large ruminant (Giraffa camelopardalis) with an extremely long neck, mobile, hairy lips and an extensible tongue, a native of Africa. Also called camelopard.

**Girdle**

1. An encircling or confining structure.
2. *bot.* The region where the two valves of a diatom overlap.
3. *zool.* *a.* The mantle of a chiton, especially the peripheral portion. *b.* The annulus of a dinoflagellate. *c.* A supporting structure in vertebrates, as the pectoral or pelvic girdle.

**Girdler.** An insect which cuts a groove about a twig causing it to fall to the ground, as the beetle, Oncideres cingulata.

**[1]Girdling.** Making a cut encircling a part of a plant.

**[2]Girdling.** The arrangement of leaf traces in cycads.

**Girdling.** Cutting transversely across the vascular tissue in a stem so that downward transport of substances is unable to occur within the plant. The term is used when a tree is cut right around its circumference to a depth that penetrates through the bark and into the wood : the tree is thus killed.

**Gizzard.** A muscular compartment of the alimentary canal of many animals that is specialized for breaking up food. In birds the gizzard lies between the proventriculus and the duodenum and contains small stones and grit, which assist in breaking up the food when the gizzard contracts.

**Glabella.** A smooth region of the frontal bone between the superciliary arches.

**Glabrate.** Approaching a glabrous condition, especially at maturity.

**Glabrous.** Describing a surface that is devoid of hairs or other projections.

**Gladiate.** Shaped like a sword : Ensiform.

**Gladiolus**

1. *anat.* The middle portion of the sternum.
2. *bot.* A plant (Gladiolus) of the iris family, or its corm or flower.

**Gland.** A group of cells or a single cell in animals or plants that is specialized to secrete a specific substance. In animals there are two types of glands, both of which synthesize their secretions. Endocrine glands discharge their products directly into the blood vessels; exocrine glands secrete through a duct or network of duct into a body cavity or onto the body surface. Secretory cells are characterized by having droplets (vesicles) containing their products.

In plants glands are specialized to secrete certain substances produced by the plant. The recretions may be retained within a single cell, secreted into a special cavity or duct, or secreted to the outside. Examples are the water glands (hydathodes) of certain leaves, nectaries (nectar), and the digestive glands of certain insectivorous plants.

**Glandular.** Of or pertaining to glands; bearing glands or gland cells.

**Glandule.** A retinactulum of orchids.

**Glans**

1. *anat.* A conical structure at the tip of the penis or clitoris.
2. *bot.* A nut enclosed within a cup-shaped involucre, as the acorn.

**Glass Snake.** A limbless lizard (Ophisaurus ventralis) with an extremely long, fragile tail.

**Glaucescent.** Slightly glaucous.

**Glaucous**

1. Yellowish-green.
2. *a.* Having a surface with a waxy bloom. *b.* Possessing a whitish coating which rubs off, as that of a plum or cabbage leaf.

**Gleba.** The mass of spore-producing tissue that forms in the fruiting bodies of such fungi as truffles, —puff balls, earthstars, and stinkhorns. It is enclosed by the peridium.

**Glenoid.** Having the shape of a shallow depression.

**Glenoid Cavity.** The socket-shaped cavity in the scapula (shoulder blade) that holds the head of the humerus in a ball-and-socket joint.

**Gley** (glei). A waterlogged (hydromorphic) intrazonal soil lacking in oxygen. In such conditions there is little decomposition of organic matter by bacteria, resulting in the accumulation of mor or raw humus. Beneath it is a gley horizon of blue-grey clay including ferrous compounds. Localized areas of oxidized rust-coloured ferric compounds may occur giving the soil a mottled appearance. Gleyzation may be seen in bog, meadow, and tundra soils.

**Gliadin.** A storage protein found in the caryopses of wheat.

**Glial Cell.** Type of cell that occurs in vast numbers in the central nervous system, surrounding and separating neurones and their processes. Apparently, the role of glial cells is to act as mediators of normal neuronal metabolism and/or as insulators between neurones to prevent unwanted interactions.

**Gliding Bacteria.** Beggiatoales.

**Globigerina Ooze.** Vast marine deposits consisting principally of the calcareous skeletons of foraminiferans, especially those of the genus Globigerina.

**[a]Globoid.** Globe-shaped or globular.

**[1]Globoid.** A minute globular structure as that in the aleurone grains of certain seeds, as in the castor bean.

**Globular.** Shaped like a globe; spherical.

**Globulin.** Any of a group of animal and plant proteins which are insoluble in water, soluble in salt solutions and coagulable by heat, as serum globulin of the blood and edestin from hemp seed.

**Glochid.** A short barbed hair, many of which arise in tufts from the areoles of some cacti. It is a type of glochidium. The presence of glochids is one character used to separate. the subfamily Opuntioideae, whose members possess glochids, from the other two subfamilies of the Cactaceae, Pereskioideae and Cactoideae, in which glochids are absent

**Glochidium.** The larva of freshwater clams of the family Unionidel which on leaving the gill of the mother, attaches to the gills or skin of fishes where it lives as a temporary parasite for 3 to 12 weeks.

**Gloger's Rule.** Individuals of many species of insects, birds, and mammals are darkly pigmented in humid climates and lightly coloured in dry ones. This may well be a camouflage adaptation—moist habitats are usually well vegetated and tend to lack pale colours. There are many exceptions to this so-called rule.

**Glomerate**

1. Grouped into a compact cluster.

2. Rolled into a ball-like structure.

**Glomerule.** A small, compact cluster, especially an inflorescence of this type.

**Glomerulus.** A small convoluted mass, as *a.* the capillary mass within a renal capsule ; *b.* the coiled proximal portion of the process of a spinal ganglion cell.

**Glomus pl. Glomera.** A small globular mass or body.

**Glossal.** Pertaining to the tongue.

**Glottis**

1. In most vertebrates, the opening of the larynx between the vocal cords.

2. In man, the sound-producing apparatus of the larynx, comprising the vocal folds (cords) and the opening between them, the rima glottidis.

**Glowworm.** Any of a number of larvae or wingless beetles of the family Lampyridae, which are capable of producing cold light.

**Glucagon.** A hyperglycemic-glycogenolytic factor (HGF) present in pancreatic extracts which causes a rise in blood sugar.

**Glucan.** Any polysaccharide made up exclusively of glucose subunits. Examples of glucans are starch and cellulose.

**Glucocorticoid.** One of a group of 11-oxygenated corticoids secreted by the adrenal cortex which markedly influence carbohydrate metabolism. Also called GC.

**Gluconeogenesis.** The formation of glucose from various precursors, such as pyruvate, certain amino acids (glucogenic amino acids), and intermediates of the TCA cycle. Most of the stages in the pathway are reversals of the reactions involved in glycolysis, with two exceptions. Phosphoenolpyruvate cannot be formed from pyruvate by reversal of the pyruvate kinase reaction of glycolysis. An alternative sequence of reactions involving the formation of oxaloacetate and malate and the input of a molecule each of ATP and GTP is performed to bypass this step. Similarly fructose 1,6-bisphosphate cannot be converted to fructose 6-phosphate by reversal of the glycolytic reaction catalysed by phosphofructokinase. The reaction is instead catalysed by the enzyme fructose bisphosphatase.

In plants glucose is formed predominantly by photosynthesis. Amino acids may be converted to glucose by the TCA and glyoxylate cycles though, unlike animals, no distinction is made between glucogenic and nonglucogenic amino acids, all being suitable for gluconeogenesis by this pathway. Plants can also bring about the net synthesis of glucose from fatty acids via the succinate produced by the glyoxylate cycle. This process is utilized by germinating fatty seeds.

**Glucose** (dextrose, grape sugar). An aldohexose sugar (illustration at aldose). In solution it forms a six-membered pyranose ring. Glucose is the major fuel source of nearly all organisms and the basic substrate from which starch, cellulose, sucrose, and other carbohydrates are synthesized.

**Glucose 1-phosphate.** A phosphorylated derivative of glucose, formed by isomerization from glucose, 6-phosphate. Glucose 1-phosphate is an intermediate in the synthesis of UDP-glucose, from which starch and cellulose are formed. It is also the predominant breakdown product of starch and cellulose.

**Glucose 6-phosphate.** A phosphorylated derivative of glucose. It can be formed by the action of hexokinase on glucose or by isomerization from glucose 1-phosphate. Glucose 6-phosphate is an important activated form of glucose. In glycolysis and in the pentose phosphate pathway the first step is activation of glucose to glucose 6-phosphate. It is also an intermediate in sucrose formation.

**Glucoside.** A compound such as digitonin or indican which upon hydrolysis yields a sugar, usually d-glucose, and another product. Also called glycoside.

**Glucuronic Acid.** Uronic acids.

**Glumaceous.** Bearing glumes; composed of or resembling glumes.

**Glume**

1. One of a pair of bracts subtending each spikelet in the inflorescence of grasses. Compare palea, lemma.
2. The bract subtending a flower in the inflorescence of reeds and sedges.

**Glomerulus.** A tangled mass of blood capillaries enclosed by the cup-shaped end (Bowman's capsule) of a kidney tubule (nephron). Waste products and water pass from these capillaries into the Bowman's capsule and down the nephron.

**Glottis** The opening from the pharynx to the trachea (windpipe). In mammals it also serves as the space for the vocal cords.

**Glucagon.** A hormone, secreted by the islets of Langerhans in the pancreas, that increases the concentration of glucose in the blood by stimulating the metabolic breakdown of glycogen. It thus antagonizes the effects of insulin.

**Glucocorticoid.** Corticosteroid.

**Gluconeogenesis.** Glycolysis.

**Gluconic Acid.** An optically active hydroxy-carboxylic acid, $CH_2(OH)(CHOH)_4COOH$. It is the carboxylic acid corresponding to the aldose sugar glucose, and can be made by the action of certain moulds.

**Glucose** (dextrose, grape sugar). A white crystalline sugar, $C_6H_{12}O_6$, occurring widely in nature. Like other monosaccharides, glucose is optically active : most naturally occurring glucose is dextrorotatory. Glucose and its derivatives are crucially important in the energy metabolism of living organisms. It is a major energy source, being transported around the body in blood, lymph, and cerebrospinal fluid to the cells, where energy is released in the process of glycolysis. Glucose is present in the sap of plants, in fruits, and in honey and is also a constituent of many polysaccharides, most notably starch and cellulose. These yield glucose when broken down, for example by enzymes during digestion.

**Glutamic Acid**. An acidic amino acid with the formula $HOOC(CH_2)_2CH(NH_2)COOH$ (illustration at amino acid). Glutamic acid plays a central role in the cell's nitrogen metabolism. Along with glutamine it is the primary product of nitrogen assimilation, being formed from α-ketoglutaric acid by reductive addition of ammonia. Some amino acids are formed directly from glutamate (*e.g.*

proline, ornithine), while others receive their amino group from glutamate in a transamination reaction. Glutamate is also a precursor in the synthesis of purines, pyrimidines, and porphyrins.

In amino acid catabolism, glutamate is formed in transamination reactions with other amino acids. The carbon skeleton of these amino acids can then be further broken down, while the glutamate can undergo oxidative phosphorylation to reform α-ketoglutarate.

**Glutamine.** A polar uncharged amino acid with the formula $NH_2CO(CH_1)_2CH(NH_2)COOH$ (illustration at amino acid). Glutamine is formed by the ATP-assisted addition of ammonia to glutamic acid. Breakdown is by a reversal of this reaction but without concomitant formation of ATP. Like asparagine, glutamine is important in the neutralization and storage of free ammonia. It is also an amino group donor, particularly in purine and pyrimidine synthesis.

**Glutathione.** A peptide comprising the amino acids glutamic acid, cysteine, and glycine. It occurs widely in plants, animals, and microorganisms, serving chiefly as an antioxidant. Reduced glutathione reacts with potentially harmful oxidizing agents and is itself oxidized. This is important in ensuring the proper functioning of proteins, haemoglobin, membrane lipids, etc. Glutathione is also involved in amino acid transport across cell membranes.

**Glutelin.** Any of a group of plant proteins that are soluble in dilute acids and alkalis but insoluble in neutral salt solutions and in water and alcohol. Glutenin from wheat and oryzenin from rice are examples. Glutenin is the binding agent in flour pastes and dough. Compare prolamine.

**Gluten.** A mixture of two proteins, gliadin and glutenin, occurring in the endosperm of wheat grain. Their amino acid composition varies but glutamic acid (33%) and proline (12%) predominate. The composition of wheatglutens determines the 'strength' of the flour and whether or not it is suitable for biscuit or bread making, Sensitivity of the lining of the intestine to gluten occurs in coeliac disease, a condition that must be treated by a gluten-free diet.

**Glutenin.** Glutelin.

**Glutinous**

1. Like glue, viscid, sticky.
2. *bot.* Covered with a sticky exudate.

**Glyceraldehyde.** The simplest of the monosaccharides containing an aldehyde group. It has the formula CHOCH(OH) $CH_2OH$ (illustration at aldose). In its phosphorylated form, glyceraldehyde 3-phosphate (formula CHOCH(OH) $CH_2OPO_3^{2-}$), it is important in many metabolic pathways. In glycolysis glyceraldehyde 3-phosphate is formed, together with dihydroxyacetone phosphate, by the cleavage of fructose 1,6-bisphosphate. Glyceraldehyde 3-phosphate is also one of the compounds formed in the Calvin cycle.

**Glyceride** (acylglycerol). A fatty-acid ester of glycerol. Esterification can occur at one, two, or all three hydroxyl groups of the glycerol molecule producing mono-, di-, and triglycerides respectively. Triglycerides are the major constituent of fats and oils found in living organisms. Alternatively, one of the hydroxyl groups may be esterified with a phosphate group forming a phosphoglyceride (phospholipid) or to a sugar forming a glycolipid.

**Glycerine.** Glycerol.

**Glycerol** (glycerine). A trihydroxy alcohol with the formula $CH_2OHCHOHCH_2OH$. Glycerol is a basic component of nearly all complex lipids. Triacylglycerols are esters of glycerol and fatty acids, while phosphoglycerides and glycolipids are esters of glycerol derivatives and fatty acids. Phosphorylated derivates of glycerol are intermediates in glycolysis and other areas of metabolism. Glycerol is often used as a mounting medium in microscopy.

**Glycerophosphatide.** Phosphoglyceride.

**Glycine.** The simplest amino acid. It has the formula $NH_2CH_2COOH$ (illustration at amino acid). There are several pathways of glycine biosynthesis. It can be made directly from ammonia, carbon dioxide, and a methyl group donated by the methylating agent $N^5,N^{10}$ methylenetetrahydrofolic acid (mTHFA). In another reaction involving mTHFA, glycine can be formed from serine. A third pathway, from phosphoglyceric acid, involves transamination of glyoxylate. Glycine can be broken down either by reversal of the first or second synthetic pathway, or by deamination to glyoxylate and hence into the TCA cycle via malic acid.

Glycine is one of the basic components of porphyrins, along with succinic acid. It is also necessary in purine synthesis.

**Glycogen.** A storage polysaccharide, similar in structure to starch, important in animals but not found in plants. It is however present in certain bacteria, blue-green algae, and fungi. It is a branched glucan, like amylopectin, but the branching is more frequent, occurring every 8-12 glucose residues. The enzyme that catalyses glycogen synthesis in bacteria is similar to starch synthetase in that it requires ADP-glucose as a substrate. Breakdown of glycogen, like starch breakdown, is catalysed by amylase.

**Glycogenesis.** The formation of glycogen.

**Glycogenolysis.** The conversion of glycogen to glucose.

**Glycolate Cycle.** Complex metabolic pathway, parts of which occur in the chloroplasts, mitochondria, and peroxisomes of plant cells. Its principal function is thought to be the formation of the amino acids serine and glycine from nonphosphorylated intermediates of the carbon-reduction cycle of photosynthesis.

**Glycolic Acid.** The substrate that is oxidized during photorespiration in $C_3$ plants. It is formed by the oxidation of ribulose bisphosphate to phosphoglyceric acid and phosphoglycolic acid. Hydrolysis of the phosphoglycolic acid yields free glycolic acid. During photorespiration the enzyme glycolate oxidase catalyses the oxidation, by molecular oxygen, of glycolic acid to glyoxylic acid. This reaction, which also produces hydrogen peroxide, takes place in the peroxisomes. The glyoxylic acid then appears to be transformed into glycine. In the cytoplasm two molecules of glycine react together to form serine and carbon dioxide. It is this carbon dioxide that is released in photorespiration.

**Glycolipid** (glycosyldiacylglycerol). Any of a group of acylglycerols containing a carbohydrate group, commonly a mono-, di- or trisaccharide or an amino sugar. Glycolipids are the major lipid constituents of chloroplasts. No triacylglycerols are found in chloroplasts and phosphoglycerides are present only in small quantities. The commonest glycolipids are monogalactosyl- and digalactosyldiacylglycerols. They are synthesized from diacylglycerols and UDP derivatives of galactose.

Under aerobic conditions, however, it is important principally not as an energy-supplying pathway but as a preparation of glucose for entry into the TCA cycle.

The enzymes of glycolysis are located in the cytosol, the most important being phosphofructokinase, which is the major regulatory enzyme in glycolysis. It is inhibited by ATP and citrate and stimulated by ADP and AMP.

**Glycolysis** (Embden-Meyerhof pathway). The series of biochemical reactions in which glucose is broken down to pyruvate with the release of usable energy in the form of

ATP. One molecule of glucose undergoes two phosphorylation reactions and is then split to form two triose-phosphate molecules. Each of these is converted to pyruvate. The net energy yield is two ATP molecules per glucose molecule. In aerobic respiration pyruvate then enters the Krebs cycle. Alternatively, when oxygen is in short supply or absent, the pyruvate is converted to various products by anaerobic respiration. Other simple sugars, *e.g.* fructose and galactose, and glycerol (from fats) enter the glycolysis pathway at intermediate stages. Many of the glycolytic reactions are reversible and are used to reform glucose from pyruvate in the process of gluconeogenesis.

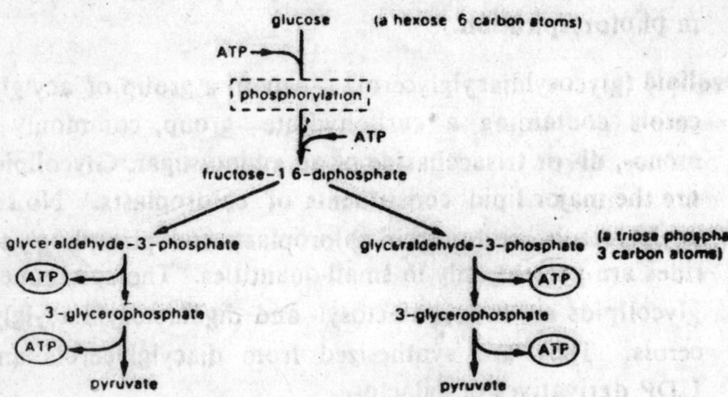


The principal stages of glycolysis

**Glyconeogenesis.** The formation of glycogen from noncarbohydrate sources, as fats and proteins.

**Glycoprotein.** A macromolecule consisting of a protein backbone along which short oligosaccharide branches are attached at intervals. The most important plant glycoprotein is extensin, a structural component of cell walls. The protein backbone of extensin is unusual in that it contains a large number of hydroxyproline residues (about 30% of the total amino acid residues). The hydroxyproline serves to provide attachment points for the carbohydrate chains

—in extensin these side chains are tetrasaccharides of arabinose.

**Glycoside.** A compound formed by the reaction of a pyranose sugar with a nonsugar molecule (an aliphatic or aromatic hydrocarbon) termed the aglycone. The aglycons replaces the hydrogen in the hydroxyl group of carbon atom one of the sugar ring. Glucose is the sugar component of many glycosides such compounds being called glucosides. Some rare sugars are only found in glycosides, *e.g.* digitalose, which has only been detected in certain Digitalis glycosides. Major classes of glycosides include the anthoxanthin glycosides, important as plant pigments, the steroid glycosides (saponin, cardiac glycoside), and the cyanogenic glycosides, which release hydrogen cyanide on hydrolysis. An example of the last group is the glucoside amygdalin, which is obtained from certain members of the Rosaceae, *e.g.* almond (Prunus amygdalus) and peach (Prunus persica). Cyanogenic glycosides may act to deter grazing animals.

**Glyoxylate** Cycle (glyoxalate cycle). A cyclic series of reactions involving TCA cycle intermediates in which one molecule of succinate is formed from two molecules of acetyl CoA.

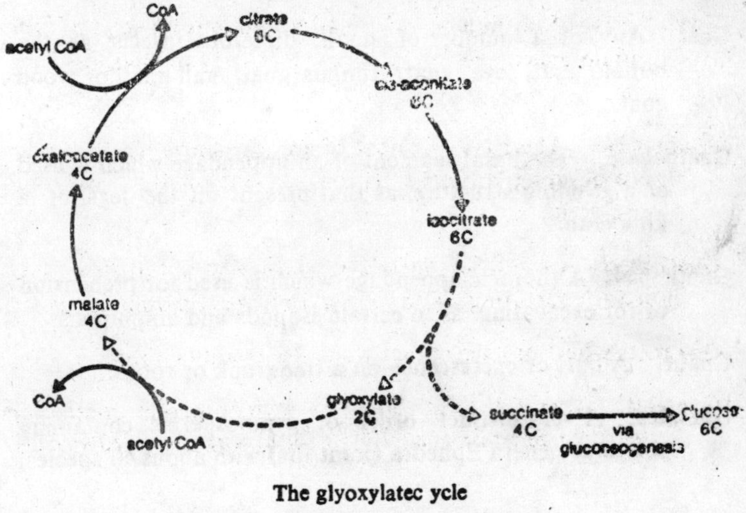


The glyoxylatec ycle

The reactions that differ from those of the TCA cycle are indicated by broken arrows in the diagram. These reactions are catalysed by isocitrate lyase and malate synthase respectively. The glyoxylate cycle avoids the carbon dioxide forming steps of the TCA cycle and thus allows net synthesis of carbohydrates from fatty acids via succinate (gluconeogenesis). The enzymes of the glyoxylate cycle are active in germinating oil-bearing seeds and in other set-metabolizing plant tissues. The cycle also takes place in microorganisms but not in higher animals.

**Glyoxysome.** A microbody that contains the five enzymes of the glyoxylate cycle. Acetyl residues that are derived from the fatty acids of stored fats are converted to carbohydrates via succinic acid released in the glyoxylate cycle. Glyoxysomes are therefore found in those cells of higher plants where fats are utilized in this way, *e.g.* in the endosperm or cotyledons of fat-storing seeds. They also contain an enzyme that catalyses the decomposition of hydrogen peroxide to water and oxygen.

**Gnathostomata.** A subphylum consisting of all vertebrates that possess jaws. It includes the fishes, amphibians, reptiles, birds, and mammals. Compare Agnatha.

**Gnat.** Any of a number of small, dipterous insects, as the buffalo gnat, eye gnat, fungus gnat, gall gnat, or wood gnat.

**Gnathobase.** The basal segment of an appendage which is used as a grinding structure, as that present on the legs of a king crab.

**Gnathopod.** A thoracic appendage which is used for prehension or for excavating, as in certain isopods and amphipods.

**Gnaur.** A burl or excrescence on a tree trunk or root.

**Gnetales.** A very distinct order of gymnosperms containing the three genera Ephedra (joint firs) with about 40 species,

Gnetum with about 30 species, and Welwitschia, containing the one species W. mirabilis. Certain species of Ephedra are important as sources of the alkaloid drug ephedrine. Each genus shows eertain advanced characteristics reminiscent of angiosperms. For example, their tracheids are arranged in columns and have highly perforated end walls similar to angiosperm vessels, while in Gnetum the sieve cells are closely associated with parenchvmatous cells, reminiscent of companion cells. The leaves of Gnetum have a broad oval lamina with reticulate venation, very similar to certain angiosperm leaves. The Gnetales also have compound male and female strobili with superficially sepal- or petal-like structures, while the female gametophytes of Gnetum and Welwitschia lack archegonia. In some species of Ephedra there is a form of double fertilization, whereby one sperm nucleus fuses with the egg cell and the other with the ventral canal cell. However only the zygote undergoes further development. These angiospermlike characteristics led some to consider the Gnetales as ancestral to the angiosperms but it is now generally considered that the group simply represents a specialized offshoot of the gymnosperms. The three genera of the Gnetales are considered so different from each other that in certain classifications they are raised to the status of orders (Ephedrales, Welwitschiales, and Gnetales) within the subdivision Gneticase (Pinophyta).

**Gnotobiotic.** Designating frome-free conditions, especially those in which experimental animals are inoculated with known strains of microorganisms.

**Gnu.** The wildebest, an ungainly appearing antelope of Africa, as the white-tailed gnu (Connochaetes gnu) and brindled gnu (Gorgon taurinus).

**Goat.** Any of a number of hollow-horned ruminants of the genus Capra, family Bovidae. True goats include the wild goat (Capra hircus), ibex (C. ibex), angora goat (C. angorensis), and milch goat (C. hircus).

**Goatsucker.** An insect-eating bird of the family Caprimulgidae, as the nighthawk, whippoorwill, and oil bird.

**Goblet Cell.** An epithelial cell which secretes mucinogen, the precursor of mucin.

**Goiter.** Enlargement of the thyroid gland, commonly the result of iodine deficiency.

**Golden-brown Algae.** Chrysophyta.

**Golgi Apparatus.** A cytoplasmic organelle especially well-developed in neurons and secretory cells, thought to play a role in the process of secretion; Golgi complex, internal reticular apparatus.

**Gonad.** Any of the usually paired organs in animals that produce reproductive cells (gameters). The most important gonads are the male testics, which produces spermatozoa, and the female ovary, which produces ova (egg cells). The gonads also produce hormones that control secondary sexual characteristics.

**Gonadotrophic.** Gonad-stimulating. Also gonadotropic.

**Gonadotrophic Hormone.** A gonadotrophin, one of several hormones secreted by the anterior lobe of the pituitary or the placenta which act on or stimulate the gonads.

**Gonadotrophin** (gonadotrophic hormone). Any of several hormones, secreted by the mammalian anterior pituitary gland, that stimulate reproductive activity of the testes or ovaries (the gonads). Gonadotrophins include follicle-stimulating hormone, luteinizing hormone, and a hormone produced by the placenta (chorionic gonadotrophin) that suppresses the menstrual cycle and whose presence in urine in large amounts is an indication of pregnancy.

**Gonangium**. In colonial coelenterates, a reproductive polyp consisting of a blastostyle bearing gonophores (medusa buds) enclosed within a gonotheca.

**Gonidium**

1. A minute reproductive body in certain bacteria.
2. An asexual reproductive cell, as in Volvox.

**Gonococcus**. Neisseria gonorrhoeae, the causative organism of gonorrhea.

**Gonocoel**. A cavity of the coelom within which a gonad lies.

**Gonoduct**. A duct which conveys gametes from a gonad.

**Gonophore**. *zool.* An asexual bud in hydrogen coelenterates which gives rise to a medusa, a sessile medusoid, or in some cases sex cells directly.

**Gonopod**. A modified appendage which functions as a copulatory structure, as in certain millipedes and insects.

**Gonopodium**. The modified portion of an anal fin which functions as a copulatory organ, as in certain teleost fishes.

**Gonopore**

1. The external opening of a reproductive duct.
2. In hydrozoans, the external opening of a gonotheca.

**Gonorrhea**. A contagious venereal disease characterized by inflammation of the mucous membrane of the urinogenital tract, caused by a bacterium (Neisseria gonorrhoeae).

**Gonosome**. Collectively, the reproductive structures of a hydrozoan coelenterate.

**Gonotheca**. The vaselike covering of a blastostyle in coelenterates.

**Gonotyl**. A retractile, genital sucker in certain heterophyid flukes.

**Gonozooid.** In colonial coelenterates and tunicates, a reproductive zooid.

**Goose.** A large semi-aquatic bird belonging to the family Anatidae which also includes the ducks and swans. Example include the Barnacle Goose, the Canada Goose, the Greylag Goose, and the Hawallan Goose.

**Gooseberry.** A small spiny shrub related to the currant. It produces green flowers and a green, usually hairy fruit which is edible.

**Goosefoot.** A group of flowering plants with inconspicuous, green, petalless flowers arranged in spikes. They are weeds of cultivated land and are often found near the sea. The Fat-Hen is the most common species.

**Gorge.** The throat of a flower.

**Gorilla.** The largest of the man-like apes, the male reaches almost 2 metres in height and weighs around 200 kg. The hair varies in colour from brownish black to jet black. Gorillas normally walk on all fours, in a semi-upright posture because their arms are longer than their legs. There are several races of gorilla found in different parts of central Africa. They are peaceable creatures, living in troops and feeding largely on fruit, especially bananas.

**Goshawk.** A large, long-tailed hawk (Accipiter gentilis) of the family Accipitridae.

**Gourd**

1. Any plant of the genus Cucurbita, a tendril-bearing vine of the gourd family, Cucurbitaceae, including the cucumber, melon, squash, and pumpkin.
2. The hard-shelled fruit of certain species of the gourd family especially those of the genera Coccinea (ivy gourd), Lagenaria (calabash gourd), and Trichosanthes (snake gourd).

**Graafian Follicle.** Fluid-filled spherical vesicle in the ovary of a mammal, containing an oocyte attached to its wall, and responsible for oestrogen production in the ovary. A cavity first appears amongst follicle cells surrounding the oocyte, around the end of the period of cytoplasmic growth of the oocyte. In mammals with an oestrous cycle, it enlarges during the early part of the cycles, so that follicle cells separate into two layers, one around the oocyte and the other an external layer, until the follicle bursts on to the surface of the ovary, discharging the oocyte (ovulation). Most follicles, however, will not ovulate but will simply degenerate; the rest form the corpus luteum in most mammals. Follicle growth is under the influence of the pituitary gland.

**Grackle**

1. One of a number of blackbirds of the family Icteridae, especially Quiscalus quiscula, the purple grackle.
2. One of a number of Old World starlings.

**Gradient**

1. A gradual ascent or descent or a curve which represents such.
2. *biol.* A system of relationships within an organism which involves changes of increasing and decreasing magnitude with reference to metabolism, growth, pressure, velocity, or other physiological activities.

**Graft**

1. (noun). Small piece of plant or animal tissue implanted into an intact organism.
2. (verb). Transfer a part of an organism from its normal position to another position on the same organism (autograft), or to a different organism of the same species (homograft), or an organism of a

different species (heterograft). The source of the part that is grafted is called thedon or (in animals) of the scion (in plants), and the organism to which it is united is called the host or recipient (in animals) or stock (in plants). A graft hybrid is an organism made up of two genetically distinct tissues due to fusion of host and donour (or scion and stock) after grafting. In cultivation, a stem from one plant (the scion) is fused with a rooted portion of another (the stock) to form a single plant. Most fruit trees are produced by grafting, the type of fruit being determined by the scion, but the size of the tree by the stock.

**Graft Hybrid.** A type of plant chimaera that may be produced when a part of one plant (the scion) is grafted onto another plant of a different genetic constitution (the stock). Shoots growing from the point of union of the graft contain tissues from both the stock and the scion.

**Grafting.** A horticultural method of plant propagation in which a segment (the scion) of the plant to be propagated is inserted onto another plant (the stock) in such a way that their vascular tissues combine, so allowing growth of the grafted segment. The technique, which is mainly used on woody species, relies on the natural regenerative capacities of plants following wounding. In addition to the cambia of scion and stock growing together to form a continuous column, prolific development of callus around the graft area ensures a firm union. Grafting is only successful between closely related species. Thus apples are usually grafted on to different varieties of apple rootstock. Pears however are usually grafted onto quince rootstocks.

**Grain**

1. A simple, single, dehiscent fruit produced by cereal grasses : Caryopsis.

2. Any single, small, hard seed.
3. Collectively, the seeds or fruits of cereal grasses, as wheat, oats, maize, rice, millet, or the plants which produce them.
4. A single hard particle, as a grain of salt.
5. A unit of weight of the troy, avoirdupois, and apothecaries' system. Abbreviated gr.

**Gramineae** (Poaceae). A monocotyledonous family containing the grasses, which number about 9000 species in about 620 genera. Grasses generally have long narrow parallel-veined leaves inserted distichously on a round hollow stem. The inconspicuous flowers are usually borne in a terminal panicle, spike, or raceme consisting of a number of spikelets. Each flower is surrounded by two bracts. The fruit is a caryopsis. Grasses are the dominant vegetation in savannas, prairies, and steppes (grasslands). Economically they are the most important family of plants as they contain all the cereals, which are man's staple diet. Wheats (Triticum), maize (Zea mays), rice (Oryza sativa), barely (Hordeum vulgare), oats (Avena sativa), rye (Secale cereale), sugar cane (Saccharum officinarum), and sorghums (Sorghum) are all grasses. They are also widely planted for pasture and fodder.

**Gram-negative Bacteria**. Gram stain.

**Gram-positive Bacteria**. Gram stain.

**Gram-reaction**. Reaction obtained when bacteria are subjected, in the laboratory, to a certain staining procedure called the Gram stain or Gram's stain (after the Danish scientist Christain Gram). The bacteria are killed, and stained for example with crystal violet; the stained cells are then treated with acetone or ethanol, for instance. Bacteria fall into two categories; those that are readily decolorized under these conditions, and those that retain the stain. Cells of the former type are said to be Gram-negative; those of the latter type are said to by Gram-positive.

The difference in reaction reflects a fundamental difference in the structure of the cell wall in the two types of bacteria.

**Gram's Method.** A procedure by which bacteria are divided into two large groups, gram-negative and gram-positive bacteria.

**Gram's Stain.** A staining method used to differentiate bacteria. The bacterial sample is smeared on a microscope slide, stained with a violet dye, treated with acetone-alcohol (a decolourizer), and finally counterstained with a red dye. Gram-positive bacteria retain the first dye, appearing blue-black under the microscope. In Gram-negative bacteria, the acetone-alcohol washes out the violet dye and the counterstain is taken up, the cells appearing red. It is named after the Danish bacteriologist H. C. J. Gram (1853-1938), who first described the technique (since modified) in 1884.

**Grana.** Distinct stacks of lamellae seen within chloroplasts. They contain the pigments, electron transfer compounds, and enzymes essential to the light-dependent reactions of photosynthesis.

**Granular.** Consisting of, containing, or of the nature of granules.

**Granule.** A minute grain or particle.

**Granulocyte.** A polymorphonuclear leukocyte containing granules in its cytoplasm, as a neutrophil, basophil, or eosinophil.

**Granum** (*pl.* grana). A stack of platelike bodies (thylakoids), many of which are found in plant chloroplasts. Grana bear the light-receptive pigment chlorophyll and contain the enzymes responsible for the light reactions of photosynthesis.

**Grape.** A woody vine of the nortn temperate zone, bearing bunches of juicy berries. The leaves are large, lobed and with toothed edges. Cultivated on a very large scale, the vines do best in dry, warm regions. Grapes are used for wine, to dry as raisins, sultanas and currants, or just to eat.

**Grape Ferm.** One of a number of ferns of the genus Botrychium, whose sporophylls resemble a cluster of grapes.

**Grapefruit.** The pomelo, a large thin-skinned citrus fruit or the tree (Citrus maxima or C. parodisa) which produces it.

**Grape Sugar.** D-glucose or dextrose.

**Graptolites.** A group of extinct marine colonial animals that were common in the Palaeozoic era. Graptolites are generally regarded as being related to the Coelenterata. They had chitinous outer skeletons in the form of simple or branched stems, the individual polyps occupying minute cups (thecae) along these stems. Fossils of these skeletons are found in Palaeozoic rocks of all continents; they are particularly abundant in Ordovician and Silurian rock strata, for which they are used as index fossils. At the end of the Silurian many graptolites became extinct but a few groups continued into the early Carboniferous.

**Grass.** The grasses are members of one of the largest plant families—the Gramineae. They grow almost everywhere. They have jointed stems, and long selender leaves which grow from the base. The tiny dull flowers are surrounded by papery scales (chaff) to form spikelets. Grasses include Cereals.

**Grass Flower.** A spikelet.

**Grasshopper.** A herbivorous, leaping, orthopteran insect of the families Acrididae (short-horned grasshoppers or locusts), Tettigoniidae and Gryllacrididae (long-horned grasshoppers).

**Grassland.** A major regional community (biome) in which grasses are the dominant vegetation. Usually the rainfall is insufficient for trees to grow (about 250—500 mm annually in temperate regions and 750—1500 mm in the tropics). Grasslands are common in continental interiors where the rain falls mainly in spring and summer. Most grasses are perennials but some are annuals or biennials. There are the low-growing closely packed turf-forming grasses of temperate regions and the tufted or tussock grasses, which grow in separate clumps and occur widely in temperate, tropical, and tundra regions.

Temperate grasslands do contain other herbaceous plants though trees are found only along rivers and streams. They include the North American prairies, the steppes of southwest Russia, the grasslands of Manchuria and Mongolia, and the South American pampas.

Tropical grasslands, known as savanna, have tall coarse tufted grasses and there are often scattered trees. In Africa baobab (Adansonia digitata) Acacia and Euphorbia species are and common. The climate alternates between cool dry winters and hot summers with heavy rains, Savanna is found in large areas of South America, East and South Africa, South-east Asia, and northern Australia.

**Gravid.** Pregnant; bearing eggs or young.

**Gray** Symbol Gy. The derived SI unit of absorbed dose of ionizing radiation (radiation units). It is named after the British radiobialogist L. H. Gray (1905—65).

**Grayling.** A freshwater game fish (Thymallus signifer) of northern United States and Canada.

**Gray Matter.** The gray substance of the spinal cord and brain consisting principle of the cell bodies of neurons and neuroglia cells.

**Grebe.** One of several species of aquatic, ducklike birds of the family Podicipedidae.

**Green**

1. Of a color characteristic of growing herbage, as grass.
2. Immature, not ripe, said of fruits.

**Green Algae.** A group of simple flowerless plants growing in fresh or salt water. Most freshwater species are microscopic, but can colour a whole pond green. A number of green algae grow on damp tree-trunks, fences, etc. The larger plants are seaweeds, found on shores throughout the world.

**Green Gland.** An excretory organ located in the base of the antenna of the crayfish and other crustaceans.

**Greenhouse Effect**

1. The effect within a greenhouse in which solar radiation mainly in the visible range of the spectrum passes through the glass roof and walls and is absorbed by the floor, earth, and contents, which re-emit the energy as infrared radiation. Because the infrared radiation cannot escape through the glass, the temperature inside the greenhouse rises.
2. A similar effected in which the earth's atmosphere behaves like the greenhouse and the surface of the earth absorbs most of the solar radiation, re-emitting it as infrared radiation. This is absorbed by carbon dioxide, water, and ozone in the atmosphere as well as by clouds and reradiated back to earth. At night this absorption prevents the temperature falling rapidly after a hot day, especially in regions with a high atmospheric water content.

**Green Manner.** A fast-growing inexpensive crop that is sown towards the end of the growing season with the intention of ploughing or digging it in a short while later when it is still green. This increases the amount of organic matter in the soil. Legumes, such as clovers (Trifolium) and lupins (Lupinus), also increase the nitrogen content of the soil and are often used.

**Green Pigments.** The chlorophylls.

**Green Sulphur Bacteria.** Photosynthetic bacteria.

**Grey Matter.** Part of the tissue that makes up the central nervous system of vertebrates. It is brown-grey in colour, consisting largely of nerve cell bodies, synapses, and dendrites. The grey matter is the site of coordination between nerves of the central nervous system. Compare white matter.

**Gregarious**

1. *zool.* Living together in groups, as flocks or herds.
2. *bot.* Growing in clusters.

**Grit Cell.** A stone cell in a fleshy fruit.

**Groooming.** Behaviour concerned with the care of the body surface, performed by an animal upon itself (autogrooming), or by one animal upon another of the same species (allogrooming). In some animals (*e.g.* rodents) the spreading of saliva on the fur during grooming may serve a role in thermoregulation. Autogrooming may serve to change the state of arousal of an animal; allogrooming strengthens social bonds and helps to provide all members of a group with a scent characteristic of the group, by means of which group members may identify one another.

**Ground Elder.** A low-growing weed related to the carrot. It produces clusters of tiny white flowers and forms patches on wasteground.

**Ground Hopper.** A group of small insects similar to grasshoppers and also known as grouse locusts. Unlike grasshoppers they do not sing.

**Ground Meristem.** The central part of the apical meristem, the derivatives of which give rise to the ground tissue (ground parenchyma) and associated tissues. Compare procambium, protoderm.

**Ground Pine.** Common name for Lycopodium, a club moss

**Ground Tissues.** All the plant tissues formed by the apical meristems except the epidermis and vascular tissue. The principal ground tissues are the cortex, pith, and primary medullary rays, and they consist chiefly or parenchyma.

Collenchyma is a form of ground tissue less frequently observed. It consists of cells with limited amounts of additional cellulose thickening in the walls and is most commonly found in the stemendex

**Group Selection.** Theory that holds that some kinds of behaviour (*e.g.* in certain species the decline in reproductive rates of a population that has passed the optimal density) are due to group selection, which works to the advantage of populations rather than individuals. There is general scepticism about this theory.

**Group Translocation.** Mechanism widely utilized for the transportation of sugars across bacterial membranes and perhaps those of some higher cells. A donor compound is used to activate sugar molecules through the provision of a high-energy phosphate group. The activated sugar can thus more readily traverse the membrane. A number of membrane proteins have been implicated in the transfer process.

**Growth**

1. Increase in mass; increase in size of an organism or one of its parts. Hypertrophy, hyperplasia.
2. The processes involved in coming to maturity.
3. Increase in numbers, as growth in population.

**Growth Correlation.** The relationship that exists between the different growth rates of various parts of a plant body. Growth rates depend on the balance of growth substances in the region and the competition between parts for nutrients.

**Growth Factor.** Any substance that affects the growth rate of a plant or plant part. The term covers food reserves and minerals as well as the various growth substances and growth inhibitors found within plant systems.

**Growth Hormone** (somatotropin). Proteinaceous hormone secreted by the anterior lobe of the pituitary (the adenohypophysis), which promotes growth of the body and has a siimulatory effect on many aspects of metabolism.

**Growth Inhibitor.** Any substance that retards the growth of a plant or plant part. Almost any substance will inhibit growth if present at high enough concentrations but two common hormonal inhibitors are abscisic acid and ethylene, which both have effect at very low concentrations, similar to the effective concentrations of auxins, gibberellins, and cytokinins. Other inhibitors, which must be present in much higher concentrations to take effect, include certain of the phenolics, quinones, terpenes, fatty acids, and amino acids.

**Growth Regulator.** Synthetic compound that, when applied to a plant, promotes, inhibits, or otherwise modifies the growth of that plant.

**Growth Retardant.** One of a group of synthetic compounds that reduce stem elongation in plants by inhibiting the activity of the subapical meristem. An important agricultural use is in the prevention of lodging in cereals. In horticulture retardants are used to give more compact plants. Some of these compounds inhibit gibberellin synthesis.

**Growth Ring** (annual ring). Any of the rings that can be seen in a cross-section of a woody stem (*e.g.* a tree trunk). It represents the xylem formed in one year as a result of fluctuating activity of the vascular cambium. In temperate climates pale soft spring wood, characterized by large xylem vessels, is formed in spring and early summer. Growth slows down in late summer and a darker autumn wood with smaller xylem vessels is formed. The age of a tree can be determined by counting the rings. Under certain circumstances two or more growth rings may form in one year, giving rise to false annual rings.

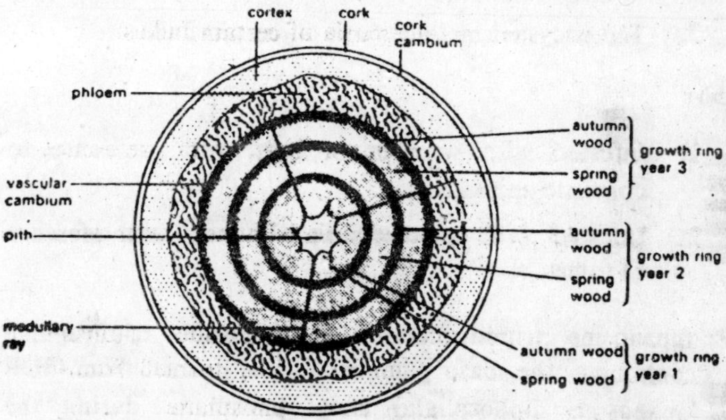


**Transverse section through a three-year-old woody stem to show the growth rings**

**Growth Substance** (hormone, phytohormone). Any substance that has a marked and specific effect on plant growth and that produces this effect when present in very low concentrations. Growth substances may stimulate plant growth by promoting cell division (cytokinin) or cell elongation (gibberellin) while others, such as abscisic acid and ethylene, inhibit certain developmental processes. The term includes substances produced within the plant and also artificial, often structurally related, chemicals that have similar effects. Endogenous growth substances are often produced in a particular region, for example auxin is synthesized in shoot apices. They are then transported from these regions and take their effect at sites far removed from the point of production. Normal growth is only achieved when there is a correct balance of the various growth substances. Abnormal growth and even death may result from unusually high or low concentrations of a growth substance. This reaction is exploited in the use of certain weedkillers that contain synthetic auxins.

**Grub**

1. The thick-bodied larva of various insects, especially beetles.
2. The encysted metacercaria of certain flukes.

**Grubby**

1. Infested with warbles or bots, with reference to domestic animals.
2. Infested with metacercaria of flukes, with reference to fishes.

**GIP** (guanosine triphosphate). A nucleoside triphosphate containing the base guanine. It is formed from GDP (guanosine diphosphate) and phosphate during the deacylation of succinyl CoA to succinate in the TCA cycle. GTP plays a role in the activation of fatty acids, in gluconeogenesis, and in the initiation and elongation of polypeptide chains during protein synthesis.

**Guanidine.** A crystalline basic compound related to urea $HN:C(NH_2)_2$.

**Guanine.** A nitrogenous base, more correctly described as 2-amino-6-oxypurine, derived from amino acids and sugars and found in all living organisms. Guanine combines with pentose sugar phosphates to form one of the nucleotides making up RNA and DNA. In addition hydrolysis of the nucleoside guanosine triphosphate (GTP) releases energy to drive some energetically unfavourable reactions.

**Guanosine Triphosphate.** GTP.

**Guard Cells.** The pair of specialized crescent-shaped epidermal cells immediately surrounding the stomatal pore and forming the stoma. The opening and closing of the stoma is controlled by changes in turgidity of the guard cells, facilitated by the pronounced thickening of the cell walls adjacent to the stomatal pore. Compare subsidiary cell.

**Guava.** A small tropical or sub-tropical American tree, producing egg-sized red or yellow fruit. The leaves are dark green and oval with downy backs, and the flowers are white. It is related to myrtle. The guava is widely cultivated in the tropics.

**Guest.** An organism which lives within the nest or den of another, as those inhabiting the nests of termites, ants, or bees.

**Gular.** Of or pertaining to the upper part of the throat.

**Gular Pouch**

1. An inflatable extension of the larynx in chameleons.
2. An expansible pouch attached to the mandible in fish-eating birds as the pelican.

**Gull.** A group or medium to large seabirds with black, grey and white plumages. They are familiar birds of the seashore, making raucous cries as they squable for scraps of food.

Gulls eat animal food when they can get it, but are not good at catching fish. They are scavengers and are commonly found near human habitation. Some travel inland to visit ploughed fields or gardens in search of worms and insects.

Gulls nest in colonies on cliffs or on the ground. At least 14 species are found around European coasts.

The common gull is similar in appearance to the Herring Gull but has yellow legs and no red spot on the underside of its bill. Despite its name it is not the commonest gull; the herring and the Black-Headed Gull are far more numerous.

**Gullet.** An invagination at the anterior end of the cell of egulenoid algae. It has an expanded basal region or reservoir, a narrow passage rising to the surface, the cytopharynx, and an opening to the exterior, the cytosome. In the reservoir, in a region where there is no pellicle, particles from the surrounding medium can be taken into the cytoplasm by endocytosis.

**Gulper.** An eelike, deep-sea fish of the order Lyomeri.

**Gum**

1. Any of a variety of substances obtained from plants. Typically they are insoluble in organic solvents but form gelatinous or sticky solutions with water. Gum resins are mixtures of gums and natural resins. Gums are produced by the young xylem vessels of some plants (mainly trees) in response to wounding or pruning. The exudate hardens when it reaches the plant surface and thus provides a temporary protective seal while the cells below divide to form a permanent require. Excessive gum formation is a symptom of some plant diseases.
2. Gingiva.

**Gum Arabic.** A polysaccharide, found in the cell walls of certain plants, made up of D-galactose and D-glucuronic acid and arabinose and rhammose. It is obtained commercially from Acacia and is used in glues and pastes and as a mounting medium in microscopy.

**Gummosis.** A symptom of certain plant diseases in which there is an abundant formation of gum. Gummosis often occurs on trees but may occur on herbaceous plants, *e.g.* infection of young cucumber fruits with the cucumber scab fungus (Cladosporium cucumerinum) results in secretion of gum at the edge of the lesions.

**Gustatory.** Of or pertaining to the sense of taste.

**Gut**

1. The alimentary canal, especially the intestine.
2. The embryonic digestive tube or cavity.

**Guttation.** Extrusion of water and sometimes salts from the aerial parts of plants. This may happen in plants that are less than about 10 m high, where hydrostatic pressure is insufficient to prevent the flow of water into the xylem when the rate of transpiration is low.

**Gymnoblastic.** Lacking a hydrotheca or gonotheca, with reference to buds in colonial coelenterates.

**Gymnocarpous.** Having a naked or uncovered fruiting body, as lichens with exposed apothecia or fungi with exposed hymenia.

**Gymnorhinal.** With nostrils not covered by feathers.

**Gymnospermae.** A subdivision of the Spermatophyta or a class of the Pteropsida containing the conifers (Coniferales) and related species, such as cycads (Cycadales) and ginkgos, as well as the extinct seed ferns (Pteridospermales). Gymnosperms have an extensive fossil record going back to the late Devonian. The gametes are carried in male and female cones, fertilization usually being achieved by wind-borne pollen. The ovules and the seeds into which they develop are borne unprotected (rather than enclosed in a carpel, as are those of the Angiospermae). (The term gymnosperm means naked seed). Internal tissue and cell structure of these species is not as advanced as in the angiosperms.

**Gymnospore**

1. *bot.* A naked spore, that is, one not produced within a sporangium.
2. *zool.* A spore formed by gregarines in the hindgut of crustaceans.

**Gynaecium** (Gynoecium). The female sex organs (carpels) of a flower. Compare androecium.

**Gynander.** A gynandromorph.

**Gynandromorph.** A sex mosaic, an individual in which sex characteristics are intermixed, as in certain insects.

**Gynandrous.** Having stamens and pistils united, as in the orchid.

**Gynocandrous.** Having staminate and pistillate flowers on the same spike, the pistillate being located at the apex, as in sedges.

**Gynecogenic.** Inducing the development of female characteristics; estrogenic.

**Gynecology.** The branch of medicine which deals with diseases of women, especially those involving the reproductive organs.

**Gynecomastia.** Excessive development of the breast in males.

**Gynecophoric Canal.** A groove on the ventral side or a male blood fluke which encloses the female during copulation.

**Gynobase.** The expanded or enlarged basal portion of the receptacle bearing the gynoecium.

**Gynodioecious.** With some flowers perfect, others pistillate, but on different plants.

**Gynoecium** (gynaecium). The female component of the angiosperm flower, which may be made up of one or more carpels. The gynoecium usually occupies the most central part of the floral axis, although in more advanced forms it may not be symmetrically placed. If the gynoecium contains only one carpel it is termed monocarpellary, unicarpellous, or stylodious. If there are two or more separate carpels it is apocarpous and if the carpels are fused syncarpous. The gynoecium is represented by the letter G in the floral formula. Compare androecium.

**Gynoecy.** A condition in which only females are known to exist in a species.

**Gynogametophyte.** The mega or macrogametophyte.

**Gynogenesis.** Pseudogamy.

**Gynomonoecious.** Describing plants that bear female and hermaphrodite flowers on the same individual. For example, many members of the Compositae have female ray florets and hermaphrodite disc florets. Compare gynodioecious, andromonoecious.

**Gynophore.** An extension of the receptacle between the androecium and gynoecium that bears the ovary.

**Gynosperm.** A female-producing sperm; one containing the X-chromosome.

**Gynospore.** The megaspore of seed plants or certain plants of the Isoetales.

**Gynostegium.** A structure covering the gynoecium.

**Gynostemium.** The united stamens and pistil in orchids.

**¹Gyrate.** Moving in a circular or spiral fashion.

**²Gyrate**

1. *zool*. Of or pertaining to a gyrus.
2. *bot*. Winding or coiled; curved so as to form a circle. Circinate.

**Gyration**

1. A turning, whirling or rotating movement.

2. One of the whorls of a spiral shell of a gastropod.

**Gyroscopic Organs.** Balancing organs, as the halteres of dipterans.

**Gyrus.** A convolution or fold, as those on the cerebral hemispheres of the brain.

# H

**Habit**

1. *bot.* A characteristic form or mode of growth.
2. *zool.* *a.* A body build or constitution. *b.* A fixed, repetitive behaviour pattern.

**Habitat**. The place in which an organism lives, which is characterized by its physical features or by the dominant plant types. Freshwater habitats, for example, include streams, ponds, rivers, and lakes.

**Habituation**. The process of becoming accustomed to a new environment. The term is applied specifically to the ability of certain long-established callus cultures to synthesize auxin and hence become independent of exogenous supplies. Such habituated cultures are also called anergized cultures.

**Hackle**. A long, slender feather on the neck of gallinaceous birds.

**Haem** (heme). An iron-containing molecule that binds with proteins as a cofactor or prosthetic group to form the haemoproteins. These are haemoglobin, myoglobin, and the cytochromes. Essentially haem comprises a porphyrin with its four nitrogen atoms holding the iron(II) atom as a chelate. This iron can reversibly bind oxygen (as in haemoglobin and myoglobin) or (as in the cytochromes) conduct electrons by conversion between the iron(II) and iron(III) series.

**Haematochrome.** A red pigment that accumulates in certain terrestrial green algae, *e.g.*, Trentepohlia, under drought conditions.

**Haematoxylin.** A blue dye obtained from the leguminous tree logwood (Haematoxylon campechianum) that stains nuclei and cellulose cell walls blue. Haematoxylin itself is not a stain until it has been oxidized to haematin. It also usually requires a mordant, such as iron alum or an aluminium salt. Different haematoxylin solutions can be prepared, *e.g.* Delafield's haematoxylin, which can be used as a counterstain with safranin.

**Haemocyanin** (hemocyanin). Any of a group of copper-containing respiratory proteins found in solution in the blood of certain arthropods and molluscs. Haemocyanins contain two copper atoms that reversibly bind oxygen, changing between the colourless deoxygenated form (CuI) and the blue oxygenated form (CuII). In some species, haemocyanin molecules form giant polymers with molecular weights of several million.

**Haemoglobin** (hemoglobin). Conjugated protein that binds molecular oxygen in a loose, easily reversible manner and is used as a respiratory pigment in numerous groups of animals, particularly the vertebrates. Each haemoglobin molecule is a tetramer of four peptide chains, each bound to haem group. In lower animals the haemoglobin occurs freely in the blood plasma, but in the vertebrates it is confined on the surface of specialized blood cells, the erythrocytes.

**Haemolysis.** The breakdown of red blood cells. It may be due to the action of disease-causing microorganisms, poisons, antibodies in mismatched blood transfusions, or certain allergic reactions. It produces anaemia.

**Haemophilus.** Genus of bacteria not assigned to a taxonomic family. The cells are small, ovoid to rod-shaped or occasionally filamentous, Gram-negative, and non-motile.

There are many species. They are strictly parasitic in animals, including humans, and sometimes cause disease.

**Haemosporidian.** A sporozoan of the order Haemosporidia which includes a number of parasitic protozoans inhabiting the blood of reptiles, birds, and mammals. Includes the causative agents of malaria and Texas fever.

**Hair**

1. *bot.* A slender outgrowth of the epidermis, serving glandular, protective, or absorptive functions.
2. *zool.* *a.* A horny, threadlike outgrowth of the epidermis in man and other mammals. *b.* Collectively the entire hairy coat of an animal or a part of it, as the hair of the head.

**Hair Ball.** A mass of hair and other undigested material which forms in the stomach of cattle, cats, and other mammals who lick themselves.

**Hair Cell.** A neuroepithelial cell whose free end bears fine hairlike processes, as those in a macula, crista, or organ of Corti.

**Hair Follicle.** A narrow tubular depression in mammalian skin containing the root of a hair. It is lined with epidermal cells and extends down through the epidermis and dermis to its base in the subcutaneous tissue. The ducts of sebaceous glands empty into hair follicles.

**Hairworm.** Any of a number of minute, slender nematodes, *a.* of the family Trichostrongylidae, parasitic in the intestines of various mammals, *b.* of the genus Capillaria, parasitic in rats and other mammals.

**Hallux**

1. The 'great the'. On the pentadactyl hind limb, the digit on the tibial side, which is often shorter than the other digits.

2. The first digit of the foot of a bird, forming the hind toe in many species. In some (*e.g.* Coliidae) it is reversible, in others (*e g.* Apodidae) it points forward, but in some species it is reduced or absent.

**Halobacteriaceae.** Family of bacteria which can grow only in the presence of high concentrations of salt (sodium chloride). Cells are spherical or rod-shaped, with cell walls atypical of the bacteria. They are chemo-organotrophic. There are two genera, found in most saline environments : the sea, salt lakes, salted foods, etc.

**Halobacterium** (family Halobacteriaceae). Genus of bacteria which require the presence of salt for survival and growth; in the absence of salt the cells disintegrate. Some strains can carry out a unique type of energy-yielding process, obtaining energy directly from sunlight in a non-photosynthetic process which involves a specialized region of the cell membrane called the 'purple membrane'.

**Halo Spot.** Disease of barley, caused by the fungus Selenophoma donacis (Septoria oxyspora). Lesions on upper leaves have pale centres with dark margins. The disease is important only in a few regions of Britain, including the wetter western regions of England, Wales, and Ireland.

**Halobiont.** An organism which lives in an environment in which salt concentration is high.

**Halophile.** An organism which cannot live in a salt-free environment.

**Halophyte.** A plant that can tolerate a high concentration of salt in the soil. Such conditions occur in salt marshes and mudflats. Examples of halophytes are thrift (Armeria), sea lavender (Limonium), and rice grass (Spartina).

**Halosere.** A pioneer plant community that develops in a low-lying region of land originally beneath the sea and subsequently silted up with mud, silt, and shingle. The plants must be adapted to survive inundation by the tide twice a day. A major pioneer plant is glasswort (Salicornia europaea), which gradually gives way tos alt-marshg rasses (Puccinellia) or sea aster (Aster tripolium). When the salinity decreases other species, such as thrift (Armeria maritima) and seablites (Suaeda), grow. The region becomes stabilized to form mudflats and salt marshes.

**[1]Hamate**

1. Shaped like a hook.
2. Bearing a hooklike process.

**[2]Hamate.** One of the carpal bones in man.

**Hammer.** The malleus, an ear bone.

**Hammerhead**

1. A shark of the genus Sphyrna with lateral processes extending from the sides of the head.
2. A heronlike African bird of the genus Scopus, family Scopidae.

**Hamstring.** One of the tendons on the posterior side of the knee.

**Hamulate.** Pertaining to or involving hooks or hooklike structures.

**Hamulus** pl. **Hamuli.** A hook or hooklike process.

**Hand**

1. In man, the terminal portion of the forearm consisting of the wrist, metacarpus, and digits, the manus.
2. In tetrapods, the corresponding portion of the forelimb.
3. The terminal portion of any appendage when modified and functioning as a prehensile organ.

**Haplodont.** Pertaining to or possessing molar teeth with simple crowns.

**Haploid.** Describing a nucleus, cell, or organism with a single set of unpaired chromosomes. The haploid number is designated as *n*. Reproductive cells, formed as a result of meiosis, are haploid. Fusion of two such cells (fertilization) restores the normal (diploid) number.

**Haploid Number.** The number of chromosomes in a gamete, designated *n*. It is in contrast with the number of chromosomes in *e.g.* sometic cells, which is usually some multiple of this number, usually 2*n* (diploid), but sometimes 3*n* (triploid), 4*n* (tetraploid), or many-*n* (polyploid). A haploid cell thus has only one chromosome set, and a haploid organism contains only haploid cells.

**Haplontic.** Designating a type of life cycle in which adults are haploid, meiosis occurring in the zygote following fertilization, as in blue-green algae.

**Haplostele.** A protostele in which the central core of xylem is circular when seen in transverse section. This is believed to be the most primitive type of protostele and was present in the earliest vascular plants, *e.g*, Rhynia.

**Hapteron** (*pl.* haptera)

1. holdfast.
2. The outer wall of the spore in species of Equisetum (horsetails). It differentiates into an elongated X-shaped structure, the arms of which are tightly coiled around the spore. Following release of the spores from the sporangium the haptera dry out and uncoil, this movement assisting in the dispersal of the spores. They are thus similar in function to elaters.

**Haptonasty.** A nongrowth nastic movement in which a plant part moves in response to a tactile stimulus. An example is the rapid and progressive collapse of Mimosa pudica (sensitive plant) leaflets, often throughout the whole plant, after those of one particular branch are touched.

**Haptonema.** A threadlike structure that arises between the two flagella in algae belonging to the Haptophyta. It is not involved in cell movement, but may be used for temporary anchorage. The length varies and in some cases it is coiled when the cell is motile. Internally it consists of three concentric membranes surrounding a ring of fibres and a central space.

**Haptophyta.** A division comprising mainly unicellular biflagellate algae most of which have a haptonema between the two flagella. It contains a single class, the Haptophyceae with many genera that used to be included in the Chrysophyta. The new division was recognized on the basis of evidence from electron-microscope studies, which revealed certain characteristic features, such as the presence of scales covering the cells. Certain marine forms, the coccolithophorids, have small intricate plates (coccoliths) of calcium carbonate completely covering the cell. Cretaceous chalks contain the remains of vast numbers of such algae.

**Haptor.** An organ of attachment in a monogenetic fluke.

**Haptotropism** (thigmotropism). A tropism in response to an external contact stimulus. The movements are most clearly exhibited by the tendrils of certain species. In passion flowers (Passiflora), the tendril is coiled spirally with the lower side facing outwards. The tendril later straightens and the sensitive tip undergoes circumnutation. If it touches a solid body, it bends towards the stimulated side, a process occupyine perhaps several minutes. The bending results in fresh parts of the tendril making contact with the stimulus and so the process is continuous, the tendril gradually encircling the support.

**Hardening.** Increasing the ability of plants to withstand freezing by gradually subjecting them to lower temperatures.

**Harderian Gland.** A sebaceous gland in amphibians, reptiles, and birds which secretes an oily fluid which lubricates the nictitating membrane.

**Hard Seeds.** Seeds impervious to water, as alfalfa, sweet clover.

**Hardwood**

1. Any dense, heavy, close-grained wood.
2. *Forestry.* Wood produced by broad-leafed, deciduous trees.

**Hardy-Weniberg Law.** Law that states that in an infinitely large, interbreeding population in which mating is random and in which there is no selection, migration, or mutation, gene and genotype frequencies will remain constant from generation to generation. In practice these conditions are rarely strictly present, but unlers any departure is a marked one, there is no statistically significant movement away from equilibrium. Consider a single pair of alleles, A and *a*, present in a diploid population with frequencies of $p$ and $q$ respectively. Three genotypes are possible, AA, A*a* and *aa*, and these will be present with frequencies of $p^2$, $2pq$, and $q^2$ respectively.

**Hare.** Any of a number of small to medium-sized, rodentlike mammals of the order Lagomorpha, family Leporidae, especially those of the genus Lepas. Term is commonly applied to the larger members of this family in contrast to the smaller members, called rabbits.

**Harem.** A group of female animals which mate with and are looked after by a single male.

[1]**Harrier.** A hawk of the genus Circus, especially C. cyaneus, the marsh hawk.

[2]**Harrier.** A hunting dog resembling the fox hound.

**Hart.** The male of the red deer, especially after the fourth year.

**Hartig Net.** Ectotrophic mycorrhiza.

**Harvestment.** An arachnid with long, slender legs of the order Phalangida, commonly called daddy longlegs.

**Hastate.** Shaped like an arrowhead but with basal lobes turned outward, said of leaves.

**[1]Hatch.** To bring forth young from an egg or eggs.

**[2]Hatch.** That which is hatched.

**Hatching** (of fish eggs). Process during which the developing fish wriggles free from the enveloping egg membrane; after this it is called 'larva' or 'fry'. Experiments on fertilized fish eggs have shown that water temperature is an important factor in the determination of the hatching period, *i.e.* the period between fertilization and hatching. The hatching period for eggs from Salmo gairdneri (rainbow trout) is about 14 days at 6 °C, but six days when the temperature is increased to 13 °C.

**Hatch-slack Pathway.** An alternative form of carbon dioxide ($CO_2$) fixation found in $C_4$ plants (diagram). In such plants the first product of $CO_2$ fixation is not the three-carbon phosphoglyceric acid (Calvin cycle) but the four-carbon oxaloacetate. This is formed by the carboxylation of phosphoenolpyruvate (PEP) by the enzyme PEP carboxylase. The oxalo-acetate is then either reduced to malate or transminated to form aspartate. These reactions occur in the cells of the mesophyll. The malate or aspartate is then transported to bundle-sheath cells situated around the leaf veins (Kranz structure) and decarboxylated to form $CO_2$ and pyruvate. The $CO_2$ so released reacts with ribulose 1,5-bisphosphate to form two molecules of phosphoglyceric acid. The normal Calvin sequence of reactions then commences. The pyruvate is returned to the mesophyll cells where it is converted to PEP with the concomitant formation of a molecule of AMP from ATP. This step, which uses up two high-energy phosphate bonds, is the reason why, overall, $C_4$ plants require 30 molecules of ATP for each molecule of glucose synthesized whereas, $C_3$ plants only require 18.

PEP carboxylase has a far higher affinity for $CO_2$ than RUBP carboxylase and $C_4$ plants are consequently more efficient at fixing $CO_2$ than $C_3$ plants. This accounts for their lower compensation points.

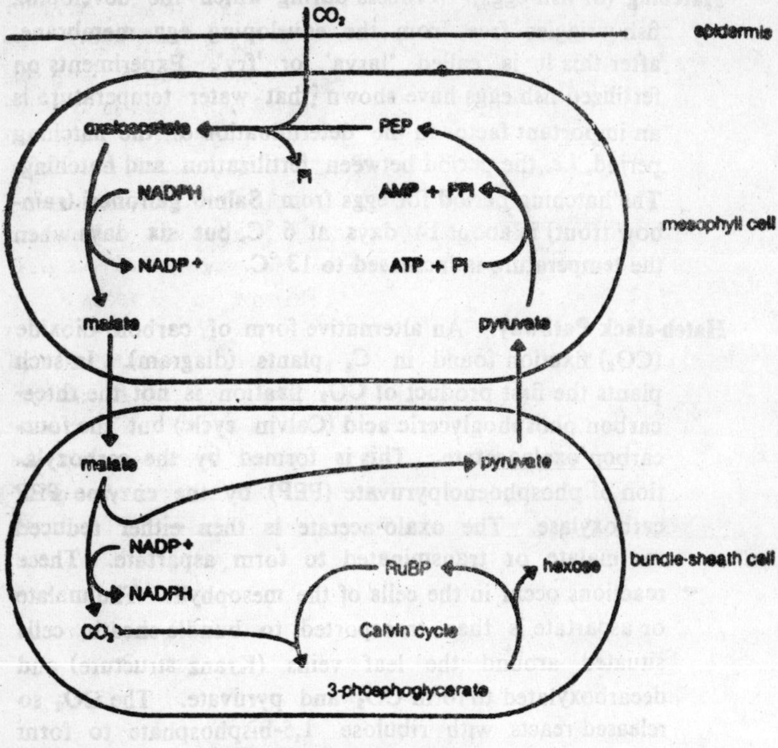


The Hatch-slack pathway

**Harvest Method.** Productivity measuring technique, most commonly used for estimates of primary productivity, especially in situations in which predation is low, *e.g.* among annual crops, on certain heathlands, in colonizing grasslands, and sometimes in pond ecosystems. Sample areas are harvested at intervals throughout the growing season, and the material is dried to estimate dry weight or calorific value. The method may also be used for woodlands, although usually only one final felling and dry-weight estimation is feasible. In such situations it is generally more reliable and ecologically more desirable to use indirect, nondestructive estimates, *e.g.* by monitoring carbondioxide profiles. Compare aerodynamic method.

**Heavy-metal Tolerance.** Biochemical and physiological adaptation to heavy metals shown by plant species or genotypes : such plants may therefore be found growing successfully on soils contaminated by metals, where other species or genotypes would fail. Many common grasses, *e.g.* Agrostis tenuis and Festuca ovina, have developed heavymetal-tolerant strains naturally on soils derived from geological strata rich in heavy metals. Seeds from these genotypes are used commercially in revegetating metal-contaminated spoil.

**Haunch.** The loin and hips taken together.

**Haustellum.** A tubular structure in insects adapted for sucking blood or plant juices.

**Haustoria** sing. **Haustorium.** Rootlike structures of parasitic plants which penetrate the cells of the host plant.

**Haustorium.** A specialized structure of certain parasitic plants that penetrates the cells of the host plant to absorb nutrients. In parasitic fungi haustoria are formed from enlarged hyphae and in parasitic flowering plants, such as the dodder (Cuscuta), they are outgrowths of the stem.

**Haversian Canals.** Narrow tubes within compact bone containing blood vessels and nerves. They generally run parallel to the bone surface. Each canal surrounded by a series of rings of bone (lamellae) is known as a Haversian system. Haversian systems are joined to each other by bone material.

**[1]Haw.** The hawthorn or red haw (Crataegus) of the rose family, or the fruit it produces.

**[2]Haw.** The nictitating membrane of various mammals, especially the horse.

**Hawk.** Any of a number of diurnal birds of prey of the order Falconiformes, comprising the true hawks (accipiters), buzzard hawks (buteos), marsh hawks (harriers), fish hawks (ospreys), and falcons.

**Hawk Moth.** Any of a number of stout-bodied moths of the family Sphingidae which hover over flowers sucking nectar through a long proboscis, as the tobacco hornworm moth (Protoparce sexta).

**Hazelnut.** The nut or fruit of the hazel, a shrub or small tree of the genus Corylus; a filbert.

**Head**

1. In vertebrates, the most anterior or uppermost portion of the body, containing the brain, sense organs, and openings to the digestive and respiratory tracts.
2. In invertebrates, the corresponding portion of the body.
3. The rounded end of a structure, especially when set off by a constricted region, as the head of a boner.
4. *bot.* *a.* A compact mass of foliage leaves, as a head of cabbage. *b.* A compact mass of flowers or flower buds, as in cauliflower. *c.* A dense cluster of sessile flowers on a short axis, as the sunflower or clover flower.
5. A capitulum.

**Head Kidney.** The pronephros when it persists in an adult, as in the hagfish.

**Head Louse.** A sucking louse (Pediculus humanus capitis).

**Hearing.** Audition; the act of perceiving sound; the power of interpreting sensory impulses from auditory receptors.

**Health Physics.** The branch of medical physics concerned with the protection of medical, scientific, and industrial workers from the hazards of ionizing radiation and other dangers associated with atomic physics. Establishing the maximum permissible dose of radiation, the disposal of radioactive waste, and the shielding of dangerous equipment are the principal activities in this field.

**Heart.** A hollow muscular organ that, by means of regular contractions, pumps blood through the circulatory system. Mammals have a four-chambered heart consisting of two atria and two ventricles; the right and left sides are completely separate from each other so there is no mixing of oxygenated and deoxygenated blood. Oxygenated blood from the pulmonary veins enters the heart through

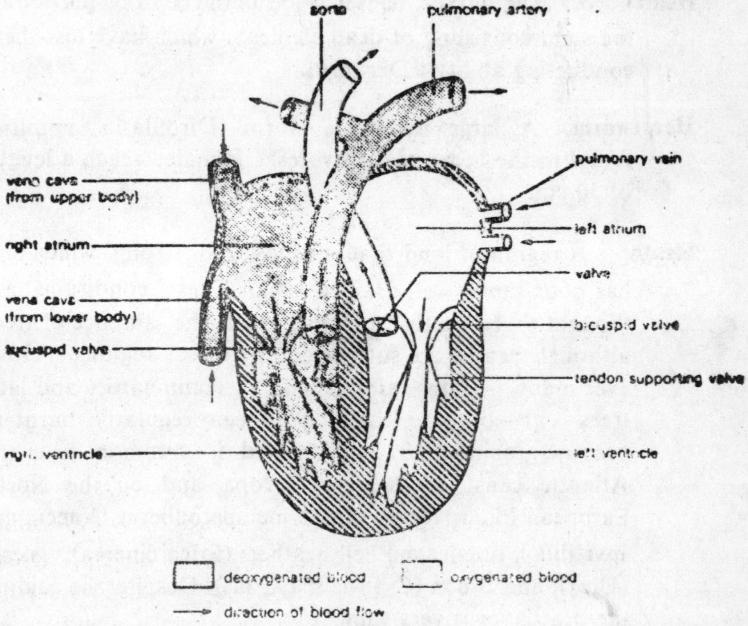


Structure of the mammalian heart

the left atrium, passes to the left ventricle, and leaves the heart through the aorta. Deoxygenated blood from the venae cavae enters the right atrium and is pumped through the right ventricle to the pulmonary artery, which conveys it to the lungs for oxygenation. The mitral and bicuspid valves ensure that there is no backflow of blood. The contractions of the heart are initiated and controlled by the pacemaker; in an average adult human the heart contracts about 70 times per minute.

The hearts of other vetebrates are similar except in the number of atria and ventricles (there may be one or two) and in the degree of separation of oxygenated and deoxygenated blood. Invertebrates, however, show great variation in the form and functioning of the heart.

**Heart Urchin.** An irregular echinoderm of the class Echinoidea, as Echinocardium.

**Heartwood.** The darker, denser wood in the central portion of the stem consisting of dead elements which have lost their conducting ability : Duramen.

**Heartworm.** A large nematode worm (Dirofilaria immitis) found in the heart of carnivores. Females reach a length of 30 cm.

**Heath.** A region of land that is exposed to strong winds and has poor sandy well drained soil. These conditions are thought to be partly responsible for the absence of trees although heaths are surrounded by forest regions. However many heaths are subclimax communities and lack trees only because they have been regularly burnt to provide grazing land. Heathland is common near the Atlantic coast of Western Europe and on the North European Plain. Heath plants include bilberry (Vaccinium myrtillus), fine-leaved bell heather (Erica cinerea), gorses (Ulex), and broon (Cytisus scoparius). Despite the acidity, the peat layer is very thin.

Subclimav communities on calcareous bils as seen, for example, on the downs in southeast England, are sometimes called heaths but should correctly be called chalk grassland. These have a very different flora including such species as salad burnet (Sanguisorba minor), upright brome (Zerna erecta), and meadow oat grass (Helictotrichon pratense). If shrubs and tres can grow, as in ungrazed areas, these include yew (Taxus baccata), juniper (Juniperus communits), and hawthorn (Crataegus monogyna).

**Hecto-** Symbol h. A prefix used in the metric system to denote 100 times. For example, 100 coulombs=I hectocoulomb (hC).

**Hectocotylus.** A modified arm of a squid or octopus which functions is the transfer of spermatophores to the female. The detached arm was originally thought to be a parasitic worm and described under the name Hectocotylus.

**Hedonic Glands.** Glands in amphibians and reptiles which secrete odoriferous substances which function as sexual attractants and excitants.

**Heel**

1. *anat.* The hind part of the foot in man or the corresponding part in other animals.
2. *bot.* The base of a tuber, cutting, or some other part of a plant which has been removed for propa gation.

**Heel Bone.** The calcaneus.

**Heliad.** A heliophyte.

**Helical.** In the form of a helix; spiral.

**Helotiales** (class Discomycetes). Order of fungi, in which the asci are more or less club-shaped; the ascospores are varied in shape. There are several families. They are saprotrophic or parasitic, and found in a variety of habitats.

**Helical Thickening.** Spiral thickening.

**Heliophyte.** A sun-loving plant.

**Heliotropic.** Responding to sunlight as a stimulus.

**Heliotropism.** Another word for phototropism, though implying movement in response to sunlight rather than artificial light.

**Heliozoan.** A protozoan of the order Heliozoida with numerous, stiff, slender pseudopodia radiating from a central mass, as the sun animalcule.

**Helix**

1. A spiral structure.
2. The outer rim of the auricle of the ear.

**Helminth.** A worm or wormlike animal.

**Helminthology.** The study of worms, especially parasitic worms.

**Helophyte.** A marsh plant with its perennating buds situated in the mud at the bottom of a lake or pond. Examples are bulrushes (Typha) and water plantains (Alisma).

**Hemal**

1. Of or pertaining to blood or the cardiovascular system.
2. Of or pertaining to the portion of the body lying ventral to the spinal axis, that is, the region containing the heart and major blood vessels.

**Hemal Arch.** An arch on the ventral side of the caudal vertebrae of fishes formed by chevron bones. Its tip forms a hemal spine.

**Hemal Canal.** A canal formed by successive hemal arches containing caudal blood vessels.

**Hemal System.** An ill-defined circulatory system of echinoderms.

**Hematin.** Heme.

**Hematochrome.** A carotenoid astaxanthin present in red granules of euglenoids.

**Hematophagous.** Feeding on blood, as a bloodsucking insect.

**Hematopoiesis.** Hemopoiesis.

**Hematoxylin.** A dye obtained from logwood which is widely used as a biological stain.

**Heme.** An iron porphyrin compound which with a protein, globin, comprises hemoglobin.

**Hemeranthous.** Day-flowering.

**Hemerythrin.** An iron-containing respiratory pigment found in annelids, sipunculids, and other invertebrates; hemoerythrin.

**Hemiascomycetes.** A class of the Ascomycotina containing ascomycetes that do not develop ascocarps. It contains about 330 species in some 60 genera. Such fungi are unicellular or produce a poorly developed mycelium. The Hemiascomycetes contains the orders Endomycetales, Taphrinales, and Protomycetales. In some classifications these fungi are considered a subclass, Hemiascomycetidae of the class Ascomycetes.

**Hemibasidiomycetes.** Teliomycetes.

**Hemibranch**

1. A half-gill.

2. A series of gill filaments or lamellae on one side of an interbranchial septum.

**Hemicarp**. A half-carpel.

**Hemicellulose**. Heterogeneous of group of compounds that in plant-cell walls form part of the matrix within which cellulose fibres are embedded. The two principal structural types are polymers of D-xylose and of glucose and mannose, known respectively as xylans and glucomannans.

**Hemichordata** (acorn worms). Phylum first encountered in the Middle Cambrian Burgess Shale, British Columbia, Canada. The acorn worms are related to the chordates, for although they lack a notochord, the gill slits are very similar to those of primitive vertebrates.

**Hemiptera** (true bugs; phylum Arthropoda, class Insecta). Order of insects in whose life cycle there is no true pupal stage, and which never, have an eleventh abdominal segment or cerci. The mouthparts are modified into a rostrum or, in non-feeding stages of some species, are completely lacking. There are typically two pairs of wings, of which the anterior pair are usuallly wholly or partly toughened to protect the membranaceous posterior pair over which they are folded at rest. There are two suborders, Homoptera and Heteroptera.

**Hemicryptophyte**. A plant with perennating buds situated at or just below the soil surface. Hemicryptophytes are usually herbaceous perennials and are commonly found in cold moist climates. Rosette plants are hemicryptophytes.

**Hemimetabolous**. Undergoing incomplete metamorphosis, with reference to insects.

**Hemipenis** pl. **Hemipenes**. One of two grooved copulatory structures present in the males of snakes and lizards.

**Hemipode.** A quaillike bird of the families Turnicidae and Pedionomidae.

**Hemipteran.** An insect of the order Hemiptera which includes the true bugs, characterized by sucking mouth parts and incomplete metamorphosis, as the squash bug, chinch bug.

**Hemixis.** A process involving fragmentation and reorganization of the macronucleus, as occurs in certain ciliates.

**Hemizygoid.** Haploid.

**Hemizygous.** The situation in which the normal diploid nucleus contains only one copy of a particular gene (or chromosome). Thus the unpaired section of the X chromosome in the heterogametic sex (XY) is described as hemizygous.

**Hemlock**

1. A poisonous herb (Conium maculata) of the family Umbelliferae, or the drink made from its fruit.
2. An evergreen, coniferous tree of the genus Tsuga.

**Hemocyanin.** A respiratory pigment containing copper instead of iron, present in [the blood of various mollusks and arthropods.

**Hemocoel.** A body cavity through which blood circulates, as in arthropods.

**Hemocyte**

1. An ameboid, hemoglobin-containing coelomocyte of echinoderms.
2. Any blood cell.

**Hemocytozoon.** A protozoan which lives as a parasite within red blood cells.

**Hemoglobin.** An iron-containing, respiratory pigment present in red blood cells of vertebrates and in the plasma of certain invertebrates. Abbreviated Hb.

**Hemolymph.** The circulatory fluid of animals with an open circulatory system.

**Hemolysin.** A substance which causes hemolysis.

**Hemolysis.** The liberation of hemoglobin from red blood cells resulting from their destruction or by its diffusion through an altered cell membrane.

**Hemophilia.** An hereditary, sex-linked disease occurring principally in males in which clotting time is excessively long and prolonged bleeding results.

**Hemopoiesis.** The formation of blood cells.

**Hemorrhage.** The escape of blood from a blood vessel of cavity.

**Hemostat.** An agent or instrument which stops the flow of blood.

**Hen** The female of most birds, especially gallinaceous birds.

**Hen-feathered.** Having plumage like that of a hen, said of castrated males.

**Hep.** Hip.

**Heparin.** A mucopolysaccharide with anticoagulant properties, occurring in vertebrate tissues, especially the lungs and blood vessels.

**[1]Hepatic.** Of or pertaining to the liver.

**[2]Hepatic.** A liverwort.

**Hepaticae.** A class of plants within the Bryophyta comprising the liverworts, which occur in moist situations (including fresh water) and as epiphytes on other plants. The plant body may be a thallus, growing closely pressed to the ground (thallose liverworts, *e.g.* Pellia,) or it may be many leaflike lobes (leafy liverworts). It gives rise to leafless stalks bearing capsules. Spores formed in the capsules are released and grow to produce new plants.

**Hepatic Portal System.** The vein (hepatic portal vein) or veins that transport blood containing the absorbed products of digestion from the intestine directly to the liver.

**Hepatic Portal Vein.** A large vein which drains the digestive organs and spleen and terminates in the liver.

**Hepatitis.** Inflammation of the liver, caused by infection with a virus, the nature of the disease depending on the virus concerned. With hepatitis A virus, the disease develops fairly rapidly and is not usually severe; with hepatitis B virus, the disease takes longer to develop and can become chronic. It may also be caused by non-A and non-B viruses.

**Hepatopancreas.** A digestive organ which functions as a liver and pancreas, present in certain crustaceans and xiphosurans.

**Herb**

1. A flowering plant in which persistent woody tissue does not develop.
2. A plant used for medicinal purposes or for its scent or flavor.

**Herbaceous.** Describing a plant that contains little permanent woody tissue. The aerial parts of the plant die back after the growing season. In annuals the whole plant dies; in biennials and herbaceous perennials the plant has organs (*e.g.* bulbs or corms) that are modified to survive beneath the soil in unfavourable conditions.

**Herbaceous Perennial.** Perennial.

**Herbage**

1. Growing plants on which domestic animals feed.
2. Ground vegetation (herbs), especially grass, when these are considered as an agricultural crop.
3. Payment made to the owner of an area of land in return for permission to graze livestock on that land.

**Herbarium** (hortus siccus). A collection of dried pressed plants, mounted on sheets of thin card, accompanied by data labels and stored in pest-proof wooden or metal cabinets. Smaller organs, including pollen grains, are perfectly preserved in this way, and many other features of the plant (*e.g.* anatomy, morphology, and chemistry) may be retained virtually unaltered. Details of floral structure can be observed by boiling or soaking in a wetting agent. The data labels, besides giving the plant's name, usually also include the data and place of collection and the collector's name. Notes on habitat, local names, and local uses of the plant (for food, medicine, etc.) may be invaluable in later searches for new sources of drugs, etc.

Specimens are normally arranged according to a particular taxonomic system (*e.g.* that of Bentham and Hooker in many UK herbaria) but occasionally material is filed in alphabetical order of family, genus, and species. Often specimens are further segregated into geographical regions within their family or generic groups. Herbaria may be small local collections, containing, for example, a country flora, or large international assemblages as at the Royal Botanic Gardens, Kew, where approximately five million specimens are housed. The larger herbaria are centres for taxonomic research and usually provide a plant identification service to other institutions and to the public.

**Herbicide** (weedkiller). Any chemical that, when applied to a plant, will either destroy it or seriously inhibit its growth.

Herbicides exist in many forms but may be subdivided into two basic categories : the contact and the systemic herbicides.

**Herbivore.** An animal that eats vegetation, especially any of the plant-eating mammals, such as ungulates (cows, horses, etc.). Herbivores are characterized by having teeth adapted for grinding plants and alimentary canals specialized for digesting cellulose.

**Herbivorous.** Feeding or subsisting principally or entirely on plants or plant products : Phytophagous.

**Herb.** A group of large animals which associate together, as cattle, sheep.

**Hereditary.** Capable of being transmitted genetically from parents to offspring.

**Heredity**

1. The capacity of an individual to develop traits present in parents or ancestors.
2. All the characteristics, morphological or physiological, which are dependent upon genetic factors received from parents.

**Heritability.** Measure of the degree to which a phenotype is genetically influenced and can be modified by selection. It is represented by the symbol $h^2$ : this equals $V_a/V_p$ where $V_a$ is the variance due to genes with additive effects (known as the additive genetic variance) and $V_p$ is the phenotypic variance. The variance V may also be written as $s^2$. Parent-offspring correlations, as used in studies of the heritability of human IQ, are estimates of familiality and not of heritability : they cannot account for environmental correlations between relatives. This definition of heritability is a narrow one; heritability in the broad sense (represented by $H^2$) is the fraction of total phenotypic variance that remains after exclusion of the variance due to environmental effects.

**Heritage.** That which is inherited.

**Hermaphrodite** (bisexual)

1. An animal, such as the earthworm, that has both male and female reproductive organs.
2. A plant whose flowers contain both stamens and carpels. This is the usual arrangement in most plants. Compare monoecious, dioecious.

**Hermatypic.** Possessing symbiotic, unicellular algae within their tissues, said of certain corals.

**Hernia.** The abnormal protrusion of an organ or a part of it, through the wall of the cavity in which it normally lies, as inguinal hernia.

**Herpes Simplex Virus.** Virus within the herpes-viruses which includes two types : one type can cause various localized conditions such as cold sores, inflammation of the gums and mouth, etc., while the second type appears to be associated with the formation of cervical tumours.

**Herpesviruses** (Herpesviridae). Group (family) of enveloped, DNA-containing viruses in which the virions are quite complex in structure. Herpesviruses can infect a wide range of animals, and often cause latent infections, no symptoms being apparent for many years. The group includes the causal agents of many localized and generalized diseases, *e.g.* cold sores, chickenpox, and some types of tumour.

**Herpetology.** The study of amphibians and reptiles.

**Hesperidium.** A type of berry that has a leathery epicarp, such as a citrus fruit. Fluid-filled trichomes fill the locule of each carpel to form the characteristic segments.

**Hessian Fly.** A small dipterous insect (Phytophaga destructor), a serious pest of wheat and other cereals.

**Heterandrous.** Having two sets of stamens, with reference to flowers with stamens of unequal size and length.

**Heterauxesis.** Allometry.

**Heterobasidiomycetidae.** Basidiomycotina.

**Heteroblastic Development.** A progressive change in the form and size of successive organs. In many grasses, for example, successive leaf blades are progressively longer and only after a maximum length is achieved will the plant begin to flower. In many plants with compound leaves it may be seen that the younger leaves are simpler than the later leaves. For example, in hemp (Cannabis sativa) successive leaves have a greater number of lobes and the margins become more serrated (diagram). This trend to greater complexity is often reversed after flowering.

**Heterocarpous.** Producing more than one kind of fruit.

**Heterochromatin.** Chromosome material that accepts stains in the interphase nucleus (unlike euchromatin). Such regions, particularly those containing the centromeric and nucleous organizers, may adhere to form a chromocentre. Some chromosomes are composed primarily of heterochromatin, these are termed heterochromosomes. In many species, the Y-chromosome is a heterochromosome.

**Heterochromous.** Of unlike colors.

**Heterochthnoous.** Foreign, not native or indigenous.

**Heterocoelous.** With ends of the vertebrae saddle-shaped, as in the cervical vertebrae of birds.

**Heterocyst.** Any of the large cells that occur at intervals in the filaments of certain species of blue-green algae. They do not contain chlorophyll but do possess large amounts of DNA. Narrow pores at one or both poles are also a distinguishing feature. It has been suggested that heterocysts are involved in nitrogen fixation. Some also consider they may be vestigial reproductive cells.

**Heterodactyl.** *ornith.* With toes I and IV directed backwards, as in trogons.

**Heterodont.** Describing animals that possess teeth of more than one type (*i.e.* incisors, canine teeth, premolars, and molars), each with a particular function. Most mammals are heterodont. Compare homodont.

**Heteroecious.** Describing a rust fungus in which the various spore forms are developed on two different and usually unrelated hosts. An example is Puccinia graminis, which causes black stem-rust of grasses and cereals and also infects barberry (Berberis). The urediospores, teliospores, and basidiospores develop on the grass host and the pycnospores and aeciospores develop on barberry. Compare autoecious.

**Heterogamete.** Either of a pair of gametes which differ in size and structure, as an ovum and spermatozoon.

**Heterogametic Sex.** The sex that has sex chromosomes that differ in morphology (*e.g.* XY), and that therefore produces two different kinds of gametes with respect to the sex chromosomes. The term may also refer to the possession of an unpaired sex chromosome (a single X-chromosome). In mammals and most other animals, the male is the heterogametic sex, usually with equal numbers of different gametes X and Y, although some men, for example, have XXY or even XXXY. In birds, reptiles, some fish and amphibians, and Lepidoptera, the female is the heterogametic sex.

**Heterogamous**

1. Producing unlike gametes.
2. Producing unlike flowers.

**Heterogeneous RNA.** Messenger RNA.

**Heterogenesis.** Alternation of Generations.

**Heterogonous.** Having two or more types of flowers.

**Heterogony.** Alternation of a parthenogenetic and a zygogenetic generation, as in rotifers and aphids.

**Heterograft.** A graft or transplant from one species to another, a xenograft.

**Heterogynism.** Having taxonomic characters more pronounced in the female than in the male.

**Heterogynous.** Having two or more kinds of females, as the fertile queens and infertile workers of honeybees.

**Heterokaryosis.** The occurrence of normally two nuclei of different genotypes in a fungal cell or mycelium. Heterokaryons tend to grow better than their constituent homokaryons. If one type of nucleus possesses a mutation such that it cannot synthesize a particular compound, then this deficiency is overcome by the other type of nucleus, a phenomenon termed complementation. Heterokaryosis also allows recombination in imperfect and homothallic fungi.

**Heterokaryotic.** Designating a hypha or mycelium which contains two or more genetically different nuclei, as may result from fusion of two hyphae.

**Heterokont.** Describing an organism having two different types of flagella, as have the motile stages of algae in the Xanthophyta, hence the former name of the taxon, Heterokontae. Compare isokont.

**Heterokontae.** Xanthophyta,

**Heterolactic Fermentation.** Mixed lactic fermentation.

**Heteromerous.** Describing lichens in which the algal cells are restricted to a layer situated between an upper plectenchymatous cortex and a iower loosely woven medulla of fungul tissue. It is the more usual tissue arrangement. Compare homoiomerous.

**Heteromorphic.** Literally, differing in form, and applied to : (*a*) phases/stages of organisms in which there is alternation of generations, particularly in algae where generations are vegetatively dissimilar; and (*b*) a chromosome pair that have some homology but that differ in size or shape, *e.g.* the X and Y sex chromosomes.

**Heteromorphosis**

1. The development of an organ or structure in an unusual position.
2. In regeneration, the development of a part that is different from the part injured or lost.

**Heterophyllous.** Having more than one type of foliage leaf borne on the same plant.

**Heterophylly.** The possession of two or more leaf types, often differing widely in morphology and function. For example certain species of Lycopodium and Selaginella have two rows of expanded lateral leaves and one or two rows of smaller adaxial or abaxial leaves. Many aquatic and semiaquatic plants have dissected submerged leaves and entire floating or aerial leaves (illustration). The submerged leaves are adapted to reduce resistance to water flow while the floating leaves have a broad lamina to maintain buoyancy. Compare heteroblastic development.

**Heterophyte.** A plant which secures its food directly or indirectly from another organism or its products; a saprophyte or parasite.

**Heteroplastic.** Pertaining to grafts in which the donor is of a different species than the host.

**Heteroploidy.** A condition in which the chromosome number is not a multiple of the haploid number, brought about by a loss or gain in number of chromosomes.

**Heterosis** (hybrid vigour). The exhibition by a hybrid of more vigorous growth, greater yield, or increased disease resistance than either parent. The effect is thought to be due to an accumulation of dominant alleles, each having additive effects, and masking the effects of deleterious recessive alleles. Thus, if a characteristic is affected by two genes X and Y, and the parents are XXyy and xxYY, the hybrid would be XxYy. Selfing or crossing between identical $F_1$ hybrids would produce an extremely variable $F_2$ generation with only half the heterozygosity of the $F_1$. Thus to maintain optimum heterosis and uniformity the seed of some crop plants (*e.g.* Brussels sprouts) is produced each year by crossing two different parental pure lines. Such crops are termed $F_1$ hybrids.

**Heterosporous.** Producing more than one kind of spore.

**Heterospory.** Production of spores of two different types on the same plant. Microspores are small and numerous; from these the male gametophytes develop. Megaspores, within which the female gametophytes develop, are larger and fewer. Compare homospory.

**Heteroptera** (plant bugs, water bugs; class Insecta, order Hemiptera). Suborder of bugs in which the head capsule is continuous ventrally behind the mouthparts. Stink glands are almost always present. Aradidae; assassin bug; Belostomatidae; Cimex lectularius; Cimicidae; Coreidae; Corixidae; Gerridae; kissing bug; Lygacidae; Miridae; Nepidae; Notonectidae; Oeciacus hirundinis; Pentatomidae; Pyrrhocoridae; Reduviidae; Saldidae; and Tingidae.

**Heterostyly.** Polymorphism amongst angiosperm flowers that ensures cross-fertilization through pollination by visiting insects. Flowers have anthers and styles of different lengths; usually the anthers of one morph are at the same level as the stigmas of another. A well-known example is the pin-eyed (long style) and thrum-eyed (short style) forms of Primula vulgaris (primrose).

**Heterothallic.** A condition in certain fungi and algae in which *a.* male and female gametes are not produced on the same filament or plant; *b.* morphologically similar sexual strains exist but conjugation occurs only between two inherently different sexual strains, usually designated plus (+) and minus (—), as in the Mucorales.

**Heterotrichous.** Describing a filament made up of both erect and prostrate parts, as found in green algae of the order Chaetophorales and in brown algae of the Ectocarpales.

**Heterotroph.** An organism which is incapable of manufacturing its own food; one which depends upon other organisms as sources of food, as all animals, saprophytes, and parasites.

**Heterotrophic.** Designating a type of nutrition in which an organism requires preformed carbohydrates or other organic compounds as sources of energy.

**Heterotrophism.** A type of nutrition in which energy is derived from the intake and digestion of organic substances, normally plant or animal tissues. The breakdown products of digestion are used to synthesize the organic materials required by the organism. All animals obtain their food this way; *i.e.* they are heterotrophs. Compare autotrophism.

**Heteroxenous.** Heteroecious.

**Heterozooid.** One of a number of specialized zooids in ectoprocts.

**Heterozygosity.** Presence of allales (different forms of a given gene) at a particular gene locus. Heterozygosity provides a measure of the genetic variation, either in a population (the frequency of individuals heterozygous at a particular locus), or in an individual (the proportion of gene loci that are heterozygous).

**Heterozygote.** Diploid or polyploid individual that has alleles (different forms of a given gene) at least one locus. Its phenotype is often identical to that of an individual that has one of these alleles in the homozygous state. (For example, the phenotype of $A_1A_2$ may be identical to that of $A_1A_1$, but different from that of $A_2A_2$.) If so, that allele ($A_1$) is said to be dominant over the other ($A_2$), which is said to be recessive. When there exist only two alleles of a gene and when one of these is dominant over the other, one may use a lower-case letter for the recessive allele, *e.g.* one may write A*a* rather than $A_1A_2$. However, alleles are not always dominant one over another; and often there are more than two alleles at a given locus, especially in polyploids. Because it has two or more different alleles at a given locus, a heterozygote does not breed true.

**Heterozygous.** Describing an organism that has two different alleles controlling a particular feature. The aspect of the feature displayed by the organism will be that determined by the dominant allele. Heterozygous organisms do not breed true. Compare hamozygous.

**Hexacanthe-** A six-hooked embryo of a tapeworm. Onchos phere.

**Hexapod**

1. A six-tooted animal, as an insect.
2. Any member of the class Insecta (**Hexapoda**).

**Hexose.** Any sugar with six carbon atoms. Most of the common monosaccharides are hexoses, *e.g.* glucose, fructose, galactose, and mannose.

**Hexose-monophosphate Shunt** (pentose phosphate shunt). Metabolic pathway, alternative to that of glycolysis, of carbohydrate interconversion : hexose-6-phosphate is converted into pentose phosphate and carbon dioxide.

The principal functions of the pathway are the production of deoxyribose and ribose sugars for nuclei-acid synthesis; the generation of reducing power in the form of NADPH for fatty-acid and/or steroid synthesis; and the interconversion of carbohydrates. Parts of the pathway are involved in the Calvin cycle in photosynthesis.

**Hibernal.** In ther winter. The term is used with reference to the six-part division of the year used by ecologists, especially in relation to studies of terrestrial and fresh-water communities. Compare aestival; autumnal; prevernal; serotinal; and vernal.

**Hibernate.** To pass the winter in a dormant or lethargic state.

**Hibernating Gland.** A mass of brown fat present in the neck and shoulder region of certain rodents.

**Hibernation.** A sleeplike state in which some animals pass the winter months as a way of surving food scarcity and cold weather. Various physiological changes occur, such as lowering of the body temperature and showing of the pulse rate and other vital processes, and the animal lives on its reserve of body fat. Animals that hibernate include bats, hedgehogs, and many fish, amphibians, and reptiles.

**Hierarchical and Non-hierarchical Classification Methods.** The grouping of individuals by a series of subdivisions or agglomerations to form a characteristic 'family tree' or dendrogram of groups. Alternatively classification may be non-hierarchical, *i.e.* proceeding not by an organized series of progressive joinings or subdivisions, but instead achieving groupings by a series of stimultaneous trial-and error clusterings (successive approximation) until an optimum and stable pattern is found. A possible scheme, for example, is to select at random a number of starter individuals, equal to the number of groups required, and to which other individuals are added or from which they are removed according to their characteristics and the classificatory philosophy used (that of seeking to minimize internal group heterogenity, or of seeking to maximize differences between groups). The chief advantage of hierarchical over the non-hierarchical methods is the clarity with which the routes to the final groupings may be followed, facilitating explanation of those groups. However, since most hierarchical classifications either dichotomize or pair at each division or join, natural clustering patterns may be distorted or poorly represented. Hierarchical classifications are also more likely to be unduly affected by irrelevant background information.

**Hierarchy**

1. Form of organization in which certain elements of a system regulate the activity of other elements.
2. Form of social organization in which individuals, or groups of individuals, possess different degrees of status, affecting feeding, mating behaviour, etc.

**High-energy Phosphate Bond.** A phosphate linkage with a negative standard free energy of hydrolysis, *i.e.* one that hydrolyses spontaneously, releasing energy. The last two phosphate bonds of ATP are examples.

Phosphate-bond energy is the major method of transfer of chemical energy from one enzymic reaction to another. For example, the high-energy phosphate bond of phosphoenolpyruvate can be broken to supply energy for the formation of ATP from ADP and phosphate. The ATP bond energy may then be used to drive an energy-requiring reaction, such as the formation of glutamine from glutamic acid.

**Hill Reaction.** The light-induced transport of electrons from water to nonhysiological electron acceptors, *e.g.* potassium ferricyanide, with the concomitant evolution of oxygen.

The result is the reduction of the electron acceptor (Hill reagent) against the chemical gradient. Four moles of potassium ferricyanide are reduced for every mole of oxygen evolved. The reaction is named after Robin Hill, who discovered it in isolated chloroplasts in 1937.

**Hilus.** An indented region of an organ, as the kidney or spleen, where blood vessels and nerves enter and make their exit; a hilum.

**Hilum.** A scar on the seed coat of a plant marking the point at which the seed was attached to the fruit wall by the funicle. It is a feature that distinguishes seeds from fruits.

**[1]Hind**

1. The adult female of the red deer.
2. A marine fish related to the groupers, as the red hind (Epinephelus guttatus), a food fish of the West Indies.

**[2]Hind.** Of or pertaining to the posterior portion or the region that is behind.

**Hindbrain** (rhombencephalon). One of the three sections of the brain of a vertebrate embryo. It develops to from the cerebellum, pons, and medulla oblongata, which control and coordinate fundamental physiological processes (including respiration and circulation of blood). Compare forebrain; midbrain.

**Hindgut**

1. The posterior part of the alimentary canal of vertebrates, comprising the posterior section of the colon.
2. The posterior section of the alimentary canal of arthropods.

**Hinge Joint.** A ginglymus, a joint which works like a hinge permitting movement in one plane only, as the elbow joint.

**Hind Limbs**. The posterior pair of appendages of a tetrapod.

**Hinge**. The articulation or joint between the two valves of a clam or brachiopod.

**Hinny**. A hybrid resulting from mating a stallion to a female ass.

[1]**Hip**. *bot*. The fruit of a rose consisting of the fleshy floral tube surrounding the matured ovaries.

[2]**Hip**. The upper portion of the thigh at its junction with the body; the lateral portion of the body at the region of the hip joint.

**Hipbone**. The os coxae or innominate bone consisting of three fused bones, the pubis, ischium, and illum, forming the lateral half of the pelvic girdle. In some mammals, it includes the cotyloid or acetabular bone.

**Hip Joint**. The articulation between the head of the femur and the hip bone, a ball and socket joint.

**Hippocampus**. A part of the verebrate brain consisting of two ridges, one over each of the two lateral ventricles. It is highly developed in advanced mammals (primates and whales) and its function appears to be related to the expression of responses that generate emotion (such as fear and anger).

**Hippopotamus**. The river horse, a large, herbiorous mammal (Hippopotamus amphibius) inhabiting rivers and lakes of Africa.

**Hirsute**. Hairy, shaggy; covered with hair, bristles, or hairlike structures.

**Hirudin**. An anticoagulant present in the secretion of the buccal glands of a leech.

**Hirudinea**. A class of freshwater and terrestrial annelid worms that comprises the leeches. They have suckers at both anterior and posterior ends but no bristles. Some are blood-sucking parasites of vetebrates and invertebrates but the majority are predators.

**Hispid**. Covered with rough or stiff hairs as, for example, the leaves of the bristly hawk's-beard (Crepts setosa).

**Histocompatibility Antigen**, Antigen; HL-A system.

**Histogen.** Meristem tissue in plants from which definitive plant tissues develop.

**Histogenesis.** The development of tissues from undifferentiated cells.

**Histogen Theory.** A concept of the organization and development of the apical meristem, in which the meristematic region is differentiated into three main zones, the dermatogen, periblem, and plerome. The dermatogen is supposed to give rise to the epidermis, the periblem to the cortex, and the plerome to all the primary tissues internal to the cortex. This theory has largely been replaced by the tunica-corpus theory.

**Histogram.** A type of graph with vertical rectangular columns, the height of each column indicating the number of times that each class of result occurs in a particular sample or experiment. For example, the height of individual organisms in a given sample of a population can be plotted in this way.

**Histology.** The microscopic study of the tissues of living organisms. The study of cells, a specialized branch of histology, is known as cytology.

**Histolysis.** The disintegration or dissolution of tissues.

**Histone.** Any of a group of water-soluble proteins found in association with the DNA of plant and animal chromosomes. They contain a large proportion of the basic (positively charged) amino acids lysine, arginine, and histidine. They are believed to be involved in the condensation and coiling of chromosome during cell division and have also been implicated in nonspecific suppression of gene activity. Histones do not occur in vertebrate sperm cells.

**HL-A System (histocompability Lymphocyte-A System).** A group of antigens in man, present on the surface of cell membranes, that is important in determining the acceptance or rejection by the body of a tissue or organ transplant graft. These antigens are one group of the so-called histocompatibility (or transplantation) antigens. Successful transplantation requires a minimum number of HL-A differences between the donor's and recipient's tissues.

**HnRNA.** Messenger RNA.

**Hoary.**

1. White or gray with age.
2. *bot*. Cancescent; white or grayish-white from a white pubescence.

**Hoatzin.** A pheasantlike bird (Opisthocomus hoazin) of the Amazon valley, the young of which have claws on the first and second digits of the wings.

**Hog.** A pig, sow, or boar.

**Hognose Snake.** A moderate-sized, nonpoisonous snake with an upturned snout of the genus Heterodon which feigns death when disturbed. Also called puff adder or spreading viper.

**Holandric Gene.** One in the nonhomologous portion of the Y-chromosome.

**Holdfast** (hapteron). A structure found at the base of many algae in flowing or tidal water that serves to attach the plant to a support. It is often dissected into many finger-like processes or rhizoids.

**Holistic** (holological). Relating to the whole. In ecology, the term refers to the 'black box' approach to ecosystem studies, which attempts to understand ecosystems by studying the inputs to and outputs from them rather than examining the component parts of the system. Compare merological approach.

**Holly.** A tree or shrub of the family Aquifoliaceae with persistent red berries and thick, spiny-toothed leaves widely used for Christmas decorations, as the American holly (Ilex opaca).

**Holoblastic.** Designating a type of cleavage which is total, resulting in blastomeres of approximately equal size, as occurs in isolecithal ova.

**Holobranch.** A complete gill consisting of two hemibranchs and the interbranchial septum.

**Holocarpic.** Condition in which the entire thallus is converted into one or more reproductive cells.

**Holocene** (Recent). The most recent geological epoch of the Quaternary period, comprising roughly the past 10000 years since the end of the Pleistocene up to the present. It follows the final glacial of the Pleistocene and thus is sometimes known as the Postglacial epoch. Some geologists consider the Holocene to be an interglacial phase of the Pleistocene that will be followed by another glacial.

**Holocrine.** Designating a type of gland in which the secretory product consists of the substance of dead and disintegrating cells, as a sebaceous gland.

**Holoenzyme.** A complex comprising an enzyme molecule and its cofactor. Only in this state is an enzyme catalytically active Compare apoenzyme.

**Hologynic.** Entirely female, with reference to a mode of inheritance in which a trait is transmitted through successive generations through females only.

**Holometabolous.** Designating insects which undergo complete metamorphosis.

**Holonephridium.** A type of nephridium, as that characteristic of most oligochaete worms.

**Holophytic.** Having a mode of nutrition like that of a green plant : Autotrophic.

**Holophytic.** Having the two compound eyes united or in contact as in certain flies.

**Holopneustic.** Pertaining to the type of respiratory system in insects in which all spiracles are function.

**Holosericeous.** Covered with fine, silky hairs.

**Holothurian.** An echinoderm of the class Holothuroidea which includes the sea cucumbers.

**Holotrich.** A protozoan of the class Holotricha with cilia of uniform length over entire body, as Paramecium.

**Holotype.** The sole specimen or other element either used by or designated by an author as the nomenclatural type of a species when he first published the description. Whenever a new taxon is described it is now imperative both to designate a holotype and state where it is deposited. Duplicates are known as isotypes.

**Holozoic.** Describing organisms that feed like animals, *i.e.* that are heterotrophic.

**Homeogenetic Induction.** The influence of a differentiated cell on an adjacent undifferented cell such that it brings about similar differentiation in the adjacent cell. The process is seen when vascular tissues are cut. The severed ends of the vascular bundles induce differetiation in adjacent pith cells and thus re-establish a connection.

**Homeostasis.** The regulation by an organism of the chemical composition of its blood and body fluids and other aspects of its internal environment so that physiological processes can proceed at optimum rates. Examples of homeostatic regulation are the maintenance of the acid—base balance and body temperature.

**Homeothermic.** Having a constant body temperature : Warm-blooded; Homoiothermous.

**Homing.** Home-returning.

**Homing Pigeon.** A pigeon trained to return home, formerly used in the transmission of messages over long distances.

**Hominid.** A member of the primate family Hominidae which includes the genus Homo to which modern man belongs

**Homo.** The genus of the order Primates which includes all races of modern man of the species Homo sapiens and recently extinct species.

**Homo** (order Primates, suborder Anthropoidea, superfamily Hominoidea, family Hominidae). The genus to which humans belong. Homo habilis ('handy man'), dating from about 1.9 million years ago, was until recently regarded as the oldest member of the genus, but new hominid fossils from E. African sites are thought by some authorities to be of even older representatives, dating from over 3 million years ago; and members of the genus Australopitheus are often included in Homo.

**Homoalletic.** Applied to allelic mutants of a gene that have different mutations at the same site; as opposed to hetero-alletic mutants, which have mutations at different sites with the one gene. Recombination between heteroallels can yield a functional cistron; recombination between homoallels cannot.

**Homobasidiomycetidae.** Basidiomycotina.

**Homocercal Tail.** A tail with two symmetrical or nearly symmetrical parts, as characterizes most present day teteost fishes.

**Homodont.** Describing animals whose teeth are all of the same type. Most vertebrates except mammals are homodont. Compare heterodont.

**Homoeology.** Similarity between chromosomes derived from different but related species. Depending on the degree of homoeology, pairing between homoeologous chromosomes may be seen at meiosis in segmental allopolyploids. Such polyploids display meiotic behaviour intermediate between autopolyploids and amphidiploids.

**Homo Erectus.** The predecessor of humans. H. erectus lived in Africa and Asia about 2—0.5 million years ago. It stood about 1.5 m tall and had a cranial capacity about 25% less than that of H. sapiens. Apart from the skull, however, the skeleton of H. erecuts was very similar to that of H. sapiens. The standardized tools made be some H. erectus are categorized as Acheulean.

**Homogametic Sex.** The sex that is determined by possession of two similar sex chromosomes (*i.e.* XX). In humans and many other mammals this is the female sex. All the reproductive cells (gametes) produced by the homogametic sex have the same kind of sex chromosome (*i.e.* an X chromosome). Compare heterogametic sex.

**Homogamy.** The condition in a flower in which the male and female reproductive organs mature at the same time, thereby allowing self-fertilization. Compare dichogamy.

**Homogeneous**

1. Composed of parts or consisting of individuals of the same kind.

2. Of uniform composition.

**Homogenous.** Consisting of homologous parts.

**Homograft.** A graft between individuals of the same species.

**Homo Habilis.** Hominid ('handy man') who lived in Africa about 1.75 million years ago (late Pliocene to early Pleistocene), and who may have given rise to H. erectus, although known fossils are too late for this. What are c aimed to be earlier fossils of the genus Homo, over 3 million years old, are now known from E. Africa. The cranial capacity, averaging 650 $cm^3$ was intermediate between H. erectus and the earlier 'australopithecines'.

**Homoiomerous.** Describing lichens in which the algal and fungal cells are evenly distributed, as in Collema. Compara heteromerous.

**Homoiothermous.** Having a more or less constant body temperature; warm-blooded, as birds and mammals: Homeothermic. Compare poikilothermous.

**Homoiothermy** (warm-bloodedness). The maintenance by an animal of its internal body temperature at a relatively constant value by using metabolic processes to counteract fluctuations in the temperature of the environment. Homoiothermy occurs in birds and mammals. The heat produced by their tissue metabolism and the heat lost to the environment are balanced by various means to keep body temperature constant: 36—38°C in mammals and 38—40°C in birds. The hypothalamus in the brain monitors blood temperature and controls thermoregulation by both nervous and hormonal means. This produces both shortterm responses, such as shivering or sweating, and long-term adjustments to metabolism according to seasonal changes in climate (acclimatization). Warm-blooded animals generally possess insulating feathers or fur. Their relatively high internal temperature permits fast action of muscles and nerves and enables them to lead highly active lives even in cold climates. However, in certain animals, homoiothermy is abandoned during periods of hibernation. Compare poikilothermy.

**Homolecithal.** Isolecithal.

**Homologous.** Term applied to organs or chromosomes. An organ of an animal is said to be homologous with that of another when both are thought to have the same evolutionary origin, although their functions may differ widely. Homology is generally deduced from similarity of structure and or position of the organ relative to other organs, seen particularly during embryonic development; an example is the ear ossicles of a mammal, which are homologous with certain bones involved in the articulation of the articulation of the jaw in fish. Homologous chromosomes are those which contain identical linear sequences of genes, and which pair during meiosis. Each homologue is therefore a duplicate of one of the chromosomes contributed by one of the perents; and each pair of homologous chromosomes is normally identical in shape and size. Compare heterologous.

**Homologous Chromosomes.** Chromosomes having the same structural features. In diploid nuclei, pairs of homologous chromosomes can be identified at the start of meiosis. One member of each pair comes from the female parent and the other from the male. Homologous chromosomes have the same pattern of genes along the chromosome but the nature of the genes may differ.

**Homomorphic**

1. Corresponding in external form or appearance but not in fundamental structure.
2. Having perfect flowers of one type only.

**Homonomous.** Having uniform or similar segments, as in the earthworm.

**Homonym.** A name of identical in spelling to another, yet based on a different type. The International Code of Botanical Nomenclature rules that all homonyms except the earliest are illegitimate. For example, Viburnum fragrans Bunge, described in 1831, is a later homonym of Viburnum fragrans Loisel., which was described in 1824. Since this was the first published name for the taxon, it must be adopted.

**Homoplastic.** Denoting similarity resulting from convergent evolution. Compare patristic.

**Homopteran.** A sucking insect of the order Homoptera, which contains the cicadas leafhoppers, aphids, and scale insects.

**Homo Sapiens Neanderthalensis.** 'Neanderthal man' is generally regarded as a subspecies of modern humans. The subspecies inhabited the periglacial regions of N. Europe between about 100 000 and 35 000 years ago. Although shorter and sturdier than modern men, the cranial capacity was about the same. Even so, the classic Neanderthal skull possessed a heavy brow-ridge above high, circular eye sockets; the forehead was flattened, and the chin weak or absent altogether. The back of the braincase was also swollen into a so-called 'occipital bun'. Neanderthal man was responsible for the stone tools and other artefacts that constitute the Mousterian culture.

**Homo Sapiens Sapiens.** Cro-Magnon, or fully modern man of European type. The subspecies appeared in western Europe about 35 000 years ago, and either displaced or absorbed the Neanderthals, who inhabited the tundra environments which were prevalent then. It is not known where H. sapiens sapiens developed after the subspecies diverged from H. sapiens neanderthalensis during the last interglacial, but other modern human types are known from S. Africa at about 60 000 years ago, and from Australia at the same time as the Cro-magnons peoples were responsible for cave art and flint blades of the Upper Palaeolithic culture.

**Homosporous.** Having spores of one kind only; isosporous.

**Homospory.** The production of only one type of spore by a species. The term is commonly used of certain nonseed-bearing vascular plants, such as the distinguish them from other vascular plants that produce megaspores and microspores (heterospory). Compare monoplanetic.

**Homostyly.** A condition in which flowers have styles of equal length.

**Homothallic.** Describing species in which the thalli are morphologically and physiologically identical and fusion can occur between gametes produced on the same thallus, as in some lower algae and fungi. Compare heterothallic.

**Homothetogenic.** Designating a type of fission in ciliate protozoans in which the fission plane cuts across the longitudinal rows of cilia or basal granules.

**Homotropous.** Curved in one direction with reference to the embryo in an ahatropous seed.

**Hamozygous.** A condition in which two members of a pair or a series of pairs of genes are alike, as AA or aa, consequently all eggs or sperm produced by such an organism are generally alike with respect to these particular genes.

**Homozygote.** Individual having the same genes at one or more loci. The phenotype of the genes for a particular locus will always be expressed since the two genes at the homologous loci are identical an individual will breed true at those homologous loci that are homozygous.

**Honey.** A thick, viscid substance prepared from nectar in the honey sac of various bees, especially the honeybee. It is stored in cells in the hive and used for food.

**Honey Ant.** A genus of ants (Myrmecocystus) of arid regions which has a special caste known as repletes which store honey brought to them by workers.

**Honeybee.** One of a number of honey-producing hymenopterous insects of the genus Apis, especially A. mellifera, a social insect living in colonies.

**Honey Buzzard.** A soaring hawk (Pernis apivorus).

**Honeycomb**

1. A structure built of wax in the nest or hive of bees consisting of compartments in which pollen and honey are stored and the young develop.
2. The reticulum or second portion of the stomach of a ruminant.

**Honeydew**

1. A substance passed from the anus of aphids which is relished by ants and other insects.
2. A sticky exudate which appears on plants infected with ergot, wheat rust, or other fungi.

**Honey Eater.** A nectar-feeding, oscine bird of the family Meliphagidae, as Zanthomiza phrygia, the regent honey eater of Australia.

**Honey Guides** (nectar guides). Lines or dots on the petals that direct a pollinating insect to the nectaries. An example is the orange spot on the lower lip of the flower of the common toadflax (Linaria vulgaris).

**Honeypot.** A replete.

**Hood**

1. *zool.* *a.* A flexible covering for the head and neck or a structure resembling such, as that present in arrowworms, lancelets, and other invertebrates. *b.* The expanded neck of a cobra. *c.* The crest of a bird.
2. *bot.* A hoodlike petal or sepal.

**Hooded**

1. Possessing a hood or hoodlike structure : Cuculate.
2. *ornith.* Having head plumage different from body plumage.

**Hood** pl. **Hooves** or **Hoofs**

1. A curved, horny structure which covers the end of the digit in various ungulates.
2. The entire foot of the horse and related species.

**Hooklet.** A small hook, especially the barbicel of a feather.

**Hoofed Mammals.** Odd-toed mammals of the order Perissodactyla (horse, zebra, tapir, rhinoceros) and even-toed mammals of the order Artiodactyla title, sheep, goats, deer) ungulates.

**Hookworm.** A small, parasitic nematode worm inhabiting the intestine of man and other mammals. Human species are Ancylostoma duodenale and Necator americanus.

**Hoolock.** A gibbon (Hylobates hoolock).

**Hop.** A twining, perennial vine (Humulus lupulus) of the hemp family.

**Hopper.** Any of a number of leaping insects, especially those of the order Homoptera (leafhoppers, planthoppers, tre-hoppers) and Orthoptera (grasshoppers).

**Hops.** The ripe, dried, pistillate catkins of the hop plant used in the brewing of malt liquors.

**Hordein.** A storage protein found in the grains of barley.

**Horizon.** Soil profile.

**Hormocyst.** A resting stage formed by certain filamentous blue-green algae from side branches of the filament.

**Hormogonales.** An order of the Cyanophyta containing the filamentous blue-green algae. The filaments may be composed of roughly equal-sized cells, as in Nostoc, or cell size may diminish from base to apex, as in Gloeotrichia. Heterocysts and hormogonia are often present.

**Hormogonium.** A short filament of more or less spherical cells that may be formed on germination of an akinete in certain filamentous blue-green algae. Although it does not possess flagella it is able to move, possibly by the streaming of mucilage along the surface. When it comes to rest on a suitable surface it gives rise to filaments.

**Hormone**

1. A substance that is manufactured and secreted in very small quantities into the bloodstream by an endocrine gland or a specialized nerve cell (neurohormone) and regulates the growth or functioning of a specific tissue or organ in a distant part of the body. For example, the hormone insulin controls the rate and manner in which glucose is used by the body. Other hormones include the sex hormones, corticosteroids, adrenaline, thyroxine, and growth hormone.
2. A plant growth substance,

**Horn**

1. *zool. a.* A stiff, pointed process borne on the head of various vertebrates, used principally for offense

and defense. Types include the hollow horns of ungulates, the pronghorn of the antelope, the antlers of deer, and the keratin-fiber horn of the rhinoceros. *b.* Any projection on the head which resembles a horn. *c.* The tough substance composed of keratin which covers, or forms the horns of animals, hooves, claws, or nails.

2. *bot.* An appendage resembling the horn of an animal.

**Hornbill.** A nonpasserine, tropical bird of the family Bucerotidae characterized by possession of an enormous bill.

**Horned.** Having a horn, horns or hornlike processes.

**Horned Toad** Phrynosoma cornutum, an insectivorous, inguanid lizard of western arid regions.

**Hornet.** A social, hymenopterous insect of the family Vespidae which constructs a large, exposed, paper-covered nest, as Vespula maculata, the common bald-faced hornet, which stings viciously.

**Horn Fly.** A dipterous insect (Siphona irritans), a serious pest to cattle.

**Horntail.** A large, hymenopterous insect of the family Siricidae, as Tremex colomba, the pigeon tremex. Its larvae are woodboring, infesting shade trees.

**Hornworm.** The larva of various sphinx months which bears a spinelike process on the eighth abdominal segment.

**Hornwort.** Any bryophyte of the class Anthocertotae, so named from their long, hornlike capsule.

**Horotolic.** Chronistics.

**Horse**

1. A large, solid-hoofed, herbivorous mammal (Equus caballus) of the family Equidae, domesticated since ancient times.

2. A male horse or stallion.
3. A castrated male or gelding as distinguished from a stallion or mare.

**Horsefly.** A large, bloodsucking, dipterous insect of the genus Tabanus, family Tabanidae, a serious pest to horses. Also called gadfly.

**Horsehair Worm.** A long selender worm of the phylum (class) Nematomorpha, as Gordius. Adults are free-living; larvae are parasitic in arthropods. Also called hairworm or hair snake.

**Horsetail.** A primitive vascular plant (Equisetum) of the order Equisetales related to the ferns; a scouring rush.

**Hortus Siccus.** Herbarium.

**Hose-in-hose.** Describing a flower that has an extra set of petals within the normal corolla. Such flowers are seen in some azalea varieties, for example the evergreens 'Kirin' and 'Rosebud'.

**Hospitator.** A plant which houses ants.

**Host**

1. An organism upon or in which another organism lives and for which it provides lodgment or nourishment or both.
2. The recipient of a graft in tissue or organ transplantation.
3. In conjoined twins, the larger of the two.

**Housefly.** A dipterous insect (Musca domestica) of the family Muscidae, a common household pest and carrier of diseas organisms.

**Hover Fly.** A syrphid or flower fly, one of a number of dipterous insects of the family Syrphidae which hover about flowers feeding upon pollen.

**Human.** Of, pertaining to, or related to man (Homo sapiens).

**Humeral**

1. Of or pertaining to the humerus or region of the shoulder.
2. *entomol.* Pertaining to the anterior basal portion of the wing or the lateral angle of the pronotum.

**Humerus.** The long bone of the upper arm of tetrapod vertebrates. It articulates with the scapula (shoulder blade) at the glenoid cavity and with the ulna and radius (via a condyle) at the elbow.

**Humification.** Development of humuns from dead organic material, by the action of saprotrophic organisms which use this dead material as their food source. Humification is essentially an oxidation process in which complex organic molecules are broken down into simpler organic acids which may subsequently be mineralized into simple, inorganic forms suitable for uptake by plants. Humification is therefore a vital stage in the cycling of nutrients.

**Humifuse.** Spread over the ground.

**Hummingbird.** One of a number of small, nonpasserine birds of the family Trochilidae, noted for their small size, rapid flight, long, needlelike bill, extensible tongue, and brilliant iridescent plumage, as Archilochus colubris, the ruby-throated humming bird.

**Hummingbird Moth.** A hawkmoth.

**Hummock and Hollow Cycle.** A cyclic change in the vegetation that takes place on a developing raised bog. A pool of water on the peat is invaded by Sphagmum mosses and a low hummock is built up. Other plants, such as Calluna vulgaris (ling) and Erica tetralix (crossleaved heath), then establish themselves. When the ling dies the hummock is easily eroded and reduced to a water-filled hollow surrounded by other hummocks in various stages. The cycle can then be repeated. Similar cycles occur in grassland, and in the tundra where frost hummocks of peat are formed by frost action and subsequently eroded.

**Humor.** Any fluid or semifluid substance of the body.

**Humoral.** Of or pertaining to a humor.

**Humoral Agent.** A substance transmitted by the blood or lymph, as a hormone.

**Humus.** The dark-coloured amorphous colloidal material that constitutes the organic component of soil. It is formed by the decomposition of plant and animal remains and excrement and has a composition. Being a colloid, it can hold water and therefore improves the water-retaining properties of soil; it also enhances soil fertility and workability. Acidic humus (mor) is found in regions of coniferous forest, where the decay is brought about mainly by fungi. Alkaline humus (mull) is typically found in grassland and deciduous forest : it supports an abundance of microorganisms and small animals (*e.g.* earthworms).

**Husk**

1. The dry, outer covering of various seeds and fruits.
2. The bracts enclosing the ear of Indian corn or maize.

**Hutia.** A rodent (Geocapromys) of the West Indies, related to the porcupine.

**Hyaline.** Glassy; transparent or translucent, like glass.

**Hyaline Cartilage.** A type of cartilage with a clear, homogeneous matrix, found in the septum of the nose, the trachea, and covering the articular surfaces of bones.

**Hyalin Cell.** One of the numerous, large, empty cells in sphagnum moss which are responsible for its water-absorbing properties.

**Hyaloplasm.** The clear, ground substance of the protoplasm of a cell in which organelles and inclusions are suspended.

**Hybird**

1. Individual plant or animal resulting from a cross between parents of differing genotypes. Strictly, most individuals in an outbreeding population are hybrids, but the term is more usually reserved for cases in which the parents are individuals whose genomes are sufficiently distinct for them to be recognized as different species or subspecies. A good example is the mule, produced by cross-breeding an ars and a horse (each of which can breed true as a species). Hybrids may be fertile or sterile depending on qualitative and/or quantitative differences in the genomes of the two parents. Hybrids like the mule, whose parents are of different species, are frequently sterile.
2. By analogy with (1), any heterozygote. Each heterozygote represents dissimilar alleles at a given locus, and this difference results from a cross between parental gametes possessing differing alleles at that locus.
3. (graft hybrid).

**Hybridization.** Natural or artificial processes that lead to the formation of a hybrid. The hybridization of normally self-pollinating species involves the removal of the anthers (emasculation) and the artificial transfer of pollen from another plant. A paintbrush is often used to place the foreign pollen on the stigma. Often hybridization techniques must overcome incompatibility systems. The development of new horticultural and agricultural cultivars involves hybridization techniques.

**Hybrid Sterility.** The reduced ability of some hybrids to produce viable gametes. This is caused by the absence of homologous pairs of chromosomes so that bivalents cannot form during meiosis. The resulting gametes are thus aneuploid. Hybrid sterility may be overcome by poloidy. Sterility does not necessarily correlate with poor growth or inviability. Indeed many hybrids show increased vigour.

**Hybrid Swarm.** Continuous series of hybrids that are morphologically distinct from one another, resulting from the hybridization of two species followed by the crossing and backcrossing of subsequent generations. The hybrids are very variable owing to segregation of alleles at each locus.

**Hybrid Vigour** (heterosis). The increased vigour displayed by the offspring from a cross between genetically different parents. Hybrids from crosses between different crop varieties ($F_1$ hybrids) are often stronger and produce better yields than the original varieties. Mules, the offspring of mares crossed with donkeys, have greater strength and resistance to disease and a longer lifespan than either parent.

**Hydatid Worm.** Echinococcus granulosus, a minute tapeworm of four segments which infests dogs and cats and other carnivores, its larva developing in man and various domestic and wild animals, forming hydatid cysts.

**Hydathode.** A pore found in the epidermis of the leaves of certain plants. Like stomata, hydathodes are surrounded by two crescent-shaped cells but these, unlike guard cells, do not regulate the size of the aperture. Hydathodes are used by the plant to secrete water under conditions in which transpiration is inhibited, for example, when the atmosphere is very humid. This process of water loss is called guttation.

**Hydra.** Any of a number of sessile, freshwater hydrozoans of the genera Hydra and Chlorohydra.

**Hydranth**

1. A hydralike feeding polyp of a colonial coelenterate.
2. Toe elongated, vase-shaped oral end of a hydrozoan polyp bearing the terminal mouth and surrounded by tentacles.

**Hydrarch Succession.** Pond succession or the successive changes which occur in plant and animal commuhities in the conversion of a pond or lake to a dry land community.

**Hydratuba.** A small polyp which develops from the planula in the life cycle of a scyphozoan jellyfish.

**Hydrobiology.** The study of aquatic organisms.

**Hydrocarpic.** Pollinated above, but developing below the surface of water, with reference to flowers of aquatic plants.

**Hydrocortisone.** Cortisol.

**Hydroecium.** A sheathlike extension of the bell in certain siphonophores.

**Hydrofuge Hair-pile.** In aquatic insects, an accumulation of dense, fine hairs which trap air to be utilized in respiration following submergence.

**Hydroid.** An elongated nonlignified water-conducting cell in the stems and leaves of certain bryophytes, such as Polytrichum, analogous to a tracheary element in vascular plants. Compare leptoid.

**Hydrolase.** Any enzyme that catalyses hydrolysis reactions. Examples are the phosphatases, glycosidases, and peptidases, which catalyse the hydrolysis of phosphate esters, glycosidic linkages, and peptide bonds respectively.

**Hydrolytic.** Of, pertaining to, or inducing hydrolysis.

**Hydrophilic.** Having a strong affinity for water, capable of combining with, attracting, or holding water.

**Hydrophilous**

1. Preferring moist places or water as a habitat.
2. Pollinated by the agency of water, said of flowers.

**Hydrophily.** A rare form of pollination in which pollen is carried to a flower by water. It occurs by one of two methods. In Canadian pondweed (Elodea canadensis) the male flowers break off and float downstream until they contact the female flowers. In Zostera, a marine species, the filamentous pollen grains are themselves carried in the water. Compare anemophily, entomophily.

**Hydrophyte.** Plant that is adapted morphologically and/or physiologically to grow in water or very wet environments. Adaptations include the development of finely-divided submerged leaves, large floating leaves, the presence of aerenchyma, and the reduction of root systems. The perennating bud lies at the bottom of fairly open water. With the leaves submerged or floating, only the inflorescence protrudes above the water surface (*e.g.* Nuphar lutea, yellow water-lily). Compare helophyte.

**Hydroponics.** Plant growth in a liquid culture solution rather than in soil. This approach is used commonly in experimental studies of mineral nutrient deficiencies or excesses, and their effects. Hydroponics also has commercial applications, though to date it has not been used extensively in this way.

**Hydrorhiza.** The anastomosing, rootlike structure by which a colonial hydrozoan is attached to the substratum.

**Hydrosere.** A pioneer plant community that develops in water when the depth is decreased by silting. The species present depend on the chemical nature of the ground water, typical species being various water lilies and pondweeds.

As the water becomes more shallow, reeds develop. The organic matter builds up to form peat and then the hydrosere gives way to swamp. Eventually mesophytes, such as coarse grasses, develop followed by shrubs and trees.

**Hydrosphere**. The aqueous envelope of the earth comprising all water (oceans, lakes, streams, subterranean water, and vapor of the atmosphere).

**Hydrostatic Organ**. An organ or structure which functions in the maintenance of equilibrium between the body of an aquatic organism and the surrounding water, as the swim bladder of a fish.

**Hydrotaxis**. A movement of an animal in response to moisture as a stimulus.

**Hydrotheca**. A transparent, vase-shaped structure enclosing a nutrient polyp of a colonial coelenterate.

**Hydrotropism**. The growth of a plant part in response to water. Roots, for example, grow towards water in the soil.

**5-Hydroxytryptamine**. Serotonin.

**Hydroxyproline**. A polar imino acid (diagram) formed by the hydroxylation of proline. The enzyme that catalyses this reaction only acts on proline residues that have been incorporated into a polypeptide chain. Hydroxyproline is rare in most proteins but common in cell-wall proteins. Degradation of hydroxyproline does not follow that of proline, instead it is broken down to alanine and glycine.

**Hydrozoan**. Any coelenterate of the class Hydrozoa which includes solitary polyps as Hydra, colonial forms as Obelia and the Portugese man-of-war, and a few medusae as Gonionemus.

**Hyena**. A large, nocturnal, carrion-feeding carnivore of the family Hyaenidae as Hyaena hyaena, the striped hyena of Africa and southern Asia.

**Hygroscopic.** Readily absorbing or taking up moisture from the air.

**Hygroscopic.** Describing a substance that can take up water from the atmosphere.

**Hygroecopic Movements.** Movements resulting from imhibition of loss of water, as that exhibited by the elaters of the spores of Equisetum.

**Hylacoious.** Dwelling in trees.

**Hylophyte.** A plant which grows in forests or wooded areas.

**Hymen.** A membrane which partially blocks the orifice to the vagina.

**Hymenium.** In the higher fungi, a fertile layer consisting of asci or basidia. In the ascomycetes the hymenium lines the ascocarp while in basidiomycetes it lines the basidiocarp. The hymenium may be exposed at maturity, as in the Discomycetes and the Hymenomycetes, or enclosed, as in the Plectomycetes, Pyrenomycetes, and Gasteromycetes.

**Hymenomycetes.** A class of the Basidiomycotina containing those basidiomycetes with a well developed basidiocapr and basidiospores that are forcibly discharged. It contains over 5000 species in some 675 genera. It is divided into two subclasses : the Phragmobasidiomycetidae (or Heterobasidiomycetidae), which have septate basidia, and the Holobasidiomycetidae (or Homobasidiomycetidae), with aseptate basidia. The former includes the order Tremellales and the latter includes the orders Aphyllophorales and Agaricales.

**Hymenophore.** The fruiting body of hymenomycete fungi.

**Hymenoptera.** An order of insects that includes the ants, bees, wasps, ichneumon flies, and sawflies. Hymenopterans generallp have a narrow waist between thorax and abdomen. The smaller hindwings are interlocked with the larger forewings by a row of tiny hooks on the leading edges of the hindwings. Some species are wingless. The mouth-parts are typically adapted for biting, although some advanced forms (*e.g.* bees) possess a tubelike proboscis for sucking liquid food, such as nectar. The long slender ovipositor can serve for sawing, piercing, or stinging. Metamorphosis occurs via a pupal stage to the adult from. Parthenogenesis is common in the group.

Ants and some bees and wasps live in colonies, often comprising numerous individuals divided into castes and organized into a coordinated and complex society. The colony of the honeybee (Apis mellifera), for example, consists of workers (sterile females), drones (fertile males), and usually a single fertile female—the queen. The sole concern of the queen is egg laying. She determines the gender of the egg by either withholding or releasing stored sperm. Unfertilized eggs become males; fertilized eggs become females. The workers fulfil a variety of tasks, including nursing the developing larvae, building the wax cells (combs) of the hive, guarding the colony, and foraging for nectar and pollen. The single function of the larger drones is to mate with the young queen on her nuptial flight.

**Hymenopteran.** Any insect of the order Hymenoptera which includes the wasps, ants, and bees, characterized by possession of two pairs of membranous wings, complete metamorphosis, and chewing mouth parts sometimes modified for lapping. The order also includes ichneumon flies, braconids, gall wasps, sawflies, and horntails.

[1]**Hyoid.** Pertaining to the second visceral arch or structures derived from it.

[2]**Hyoid.** The hyoid bone, a U-shaped bone in higher vertebrates to which the larynx is attached.

**Hypanthium.** The flat or cup-shaped receptacle found in perigynous flowers. It is joined to the ovary is inferior.

**Hypaxial**

1. Located below an axis.

2. Located ventral to the vertebral column.

3. Derived from the ventrolateral portions of myotomes, said of trunk muscles.

**Hyperbranchial.** Above the gills : Epibranchial.

**Hypermastia.** Possessing more than the normal number of mammary glands, polymastia.

**Hypermetamorphosis.** In insects, a form of metamorphosis in which there are two or more distinctly different larval forms, as in blister beetles.

**Hypermetropia** (hyperopia). Long-sightedness. A vision defect in which the lens of the eye is unable to accommodate sufficiently to throw the image of near objects onto the retina. It is caused usually by shortness of the eyeball rather than any fault in the lens system. The subject requires spectacles with converging lenses to bring the image from behind the retina back on to its surface.

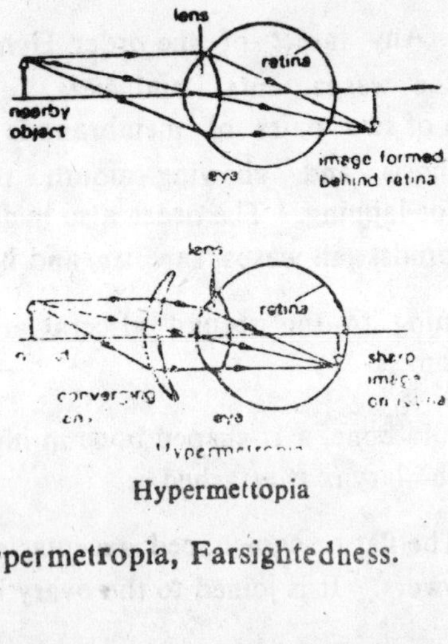


Hypermettopia

**Hyperopia.** Hypermetropia, Farsightedness.

**Hyperparasite.** Parasitic insect that lives in or on a host that is itself parasitic on another species of insect. If the parasite kills the host as a consequence of its own development it is more commonly called a 'parasitoid'.

**Hyperparasitism.** Condition in which a parasite is the host of a parasite, which in turn may be parasitized.

**Hyperphagia.** Excessive intake of food, associated with bulimia (excessive appetite).

**Hyperplasia.** Increase in size of a structure resulting from multiplication of cells.

**Hyperplasia.** Increase in the size of a tissue or organ due to an increase in the number of its component cells. Compare hypertrophy.

**Hypersensitivity.** Increased sensitivity of a plant to attack by a particular pathogen so that the host tissue dies at the point of infection and thus prevents spread of the disease. The only symptoms are minute necrotic flecks. Plants showing this type of reaction to a particular pathogen are very resistant.

**Hypertension.** Blood pressure.

**Hypertonic.** Having a higher osmotic pressure than an adjacent solution or a solution under comparison. If a hypertonic solution is placed within the confines of a permeable membrane and surrounded by a solution of lower osmotic pressure, then there is a net influx of solvent molecules, due to diffusion, until the solute concentrations become equal. Compare hypotonic.

**Hypertonic Solution.** A solution that has a higher osmotic pressure than some other solution.

**Hypertrophy.** An increase in the size of a tissue or organ due to an increase in the size of its component cells. Hypertrophy often occurs in response to an increased workload in an organ, which may result from malfunction or disease. Compare hyperplasia.

**Hypha.** A delicate filament in fungi many of which may form either a loose network (mycelium) or a tightly packed interwoven mass of pseudoparenchyma, as in the fruiting body of mushrooms. Hyphae may be branched or unbranched and may or may not possess cross walls. The cell wall consists of either fungal cellulose or a nitrogenous compound called chitin. The cell wall is lined with cytoplasm, which often contains oil globules and glycogen, and there is a central vacuole. The hyphae produce enzymes that in parasitic fungi digest the host tissue, and in saprophytic fungi digest dead organic matter.

**Hyphochytridiomycetes.** Mastigomycotina.

**Hyoid Arch.** The second of seven bony V-shaped arches that support the gills of primitive vertebrates. In advanced vertebrates, part of the hyoid arch has evolved to form the stapes (one of the ear ossicles). The rest of it forms the hyoid bone, which supports the tongue.

**Hyphomycetales.** The largest order of the Hyphomycetes, containing those mycelial imperfect fungi in which the conidiophores are not compacted into specialized structures. It contains over 6000 species and some 635 genera.

**Hyphomycetes.** A class of the Deuteromycotina containing mycelial imperfect fungi, which, if fertile, bear the conidia on hyphae. It contains over 7500 species in some 930 genera and is divided into the orders Agonomycetales, Hyphomycetales, Stilbellales, and Tuberculariales. In the latter two orders the conidiophores are compacted into specialized structures. Compare Coelomycetes.

**Hypobasal Cell.** The inner of the two cells formed by the first division of the zygote. In plants showing exoscopic embryogeny it gives rise to the foot and in plants showing endoscopic embryogeny it gives rise to the embryo. Compare epibasal cell.

**Hypocone**

1. In dinoflagellates, the portion of the body posterior to the annulus.
2. The inner, posterior (distolingual) cusp of an upper molar tooth.

**Hypoconid.** The outer, posterior (distobuccal) cusp of a lower molar tooth.

**Hypocotyl.** The region of the stem beneath the stalks of the seed leaves (cotyledons) and directly above the young root of an embryo plant. It grows rapidly in seedlings showing epigeal germination and lifts the cotyledons above the soil surface. In this region (the transition zone) the arrangement of vascular bundles in the root changes to that of the stem. Compare epicotyl.

**Hypodermic**

1. Below or underneath the skin.
2. Of or pertaining to the hypodermis.

**Hypodermis** (hypoderm). One or more layers of cells lying immediately beneath the epidermis in the leaves and other organs of many plants, differing morphologically from the underlying tissues. A true hypodermis develops from the ground meristem and therefore has an origin different from that of the epidermis as is evidenced by the noncoincidence of the anticlinal walls of the two tissues. However, the term is often used to refer to the layer or layers of cells immediately inside the outermost layer, regardless of their derivation. The hypodermis often contains large quantities of sclerenchyma to enable it to act as a strengthening tissue, as in the leaves of many conifers.

**Hypogastric.** Pertaining to the lower median region of the abdomen.

**Hypogeal**

1. Describing seed germination in which the seed leaves (cotyledons) remain below ground. Examples of hypogeal germination are seen in oak and runner bean. Compare epigeal.
2. Describing fruiting bodies that develop underground, such as truffles and peanuts.

**Hypogenous.** Growing on a lower surface, as fungi on the underside of a leaf.

**Hypoglossal Nerve.** The twelfth cranial nerve (XII) consisting principally of motor fibers innervating muscles of the tongue and present only in amniotes.

**Hypogynous.** Designating a flower in which sepals, petals, and stamens arise from the receptacle below and entirely free from the ovary, as in the lily. Compare epigynous, perigynous.

**Hypogyny.** The most commonly seen arrangement of floral parts in which the stamens, sepals, and petals are inserted below the ovary, giving a superior ovary. Compare epigyny, perigyny.

**Hypomere.** The ventral portion of a myotome.

**Hyponasty.** A nastic movement in which the plant responds by more rapid growth on the lower side of an organ, resulting in a curving upwards of that parts. Compare epinasty.

**Hyponome.** The funnel of a cephalopod.

**Hypophagous.** Feeding upon wood : Xylophagous.

**Hypopharynx.** In insects, a median process on the dorsal surface of the labium, elongated in sucking insects with main salivary channel opening on its tip.

**Hypophloeodal.** Growing beneath bark, with reference to fungi.

**Hypophyllous.** Growing beneath or on the under surface of a leaf.

**Hypophyseal.** Of or pertaining to the hypophysis.

**Hypophysis.** Pituitary gland.

**Hypoplasia.** Underdevelopment as a result of, disease or nutrient deficiency, giving dwarfed or stunted plants. In some cases particular parts of the plant may develop abnormally or not at all. Compare hyperplasia, hypertrophy.

**Hypopodium.** The basal portion of the petiole of a leaf.

**Hypopus.** The travelling stage of certain mites characterized by possession of special attachment structures, as in grain mites.

**Hypopygium.** The male clasping organ in certain insects, as dipterans.

**Hypopyle.** The posterior opening of the clasper tube of fishes. Compare apopyle.

**Hypostasis.** The situation in which the expression of one gene (the hypostatic gene) is dependent on a second gene (the epistatic gene). The genes need not be on the same chromosome.

**Hypostasis**

1. The settling of blood in a dependent part of the body.
2. *genetics.* Condition in which expression of a gene is suppressed by a nonallelic gene. The former gene is said to be.

**Hypostome**

1. In hydrozoans, a concial elevation during the mouth.
2. A median-ventral toothed structure forming part of the capitulum of ticks.

**Hypothalamus.** Part of the vertebrate brain that is derived from the forebrain and located on the ventral surface below the thalamus and the cerebrum. The hypothalamus regulates a wide variety of physiological processes, including maintenance of body temperature, water balance, sleeping, and feeding, via both the autonomic nervous system (which it controls) and the neuroendocrine system. Its endocrine functions are largely mediated by the pituitary gland. The pituitary responds to hormonelike substances released from the hypothalamus, which thereby indirectly controls hormone production in other glands.

**Hypothallus.** A thin, shiny membrane at the base of the fruiting body of slime molds.

**Hypothecium.** In an ascocarp, the layer of hyphae which supports the hymenium.

**Hypothermia.** Body temperature below normal.

**Hypotonic.** Below normal strength or tension.

**Hypotrich.** A ciliate of the order Hypotrichida, mostly creeping protozoans with fused cilia or cieri on ventral surface, as Stylonychia.

**Hypoxia.** Condition in which oxygen tension of the blood is below normal.

**Hypsodont.** Having or designating high-crowned, prism-shaped teeth, characteristic of grazing animals.

**Hyraceum.** A substance used in perfumery obtained from the dried deposits of hyrax dung.

**Hyrax.** One of a number of small, herbivorous, hoofed mammals of the order Hyracoidea of the Mediterranean region, as Procavia capensis, the rock hyrax. Also called dassie, coney, cony, rock rabbit, klipdas.

**Hyssop.** A European plant Hyssopus officinalis) of the mint family.

**Hysteranthous.** Developing leaves after the appearance of flowers, as the almond.

# I

**IAA** (indoleacetic acid). Auxin.

**Ice Age.** A period in the earth's history during which ice advanced towards the equator and a general lowering of temperatures occurred. The last major ice age, that of the Pleistocene period (sometimes known as the Ice Age), ended about 10 000 years ago. At least four major ice advances (glacials) occurred during the Pleistocene period, these were separated by interglacials during which the ice retreated and temperatures rose. At present it is not known if the earth is between ice ages or is in an interglacial. It has been established that ice ages also occurred during the Precambrian (about 500 million years ago) and during the Permo-Carboniferous (about 250 million years ago).

**Ichthyology.** The science which deals with fishes.

**ICSH.** Interstitial cell-stimulating hormone.

**Icterus.** Jaundice.

**Identical Twins** (monozygotic twins). Two individuals that develop from a single fertilized egg cell by its division into two genetically identical parts. Each part eventually gives rise to a separate individual and these twins are therefore identical in every respect. Compare fraternal twins.

**Idioblast.** Any cell markedly differing from the cells of the surrounding tissue. The brachysclereids of pear fruits are an example.

**Idiogram.** A diagrammatic representation of a set of chromosomes.

**I-gene.** Regulator gene.

**Ileum.** The portion of the mammalian small intestine that follows the jejunum and precedes the large intestine. It is a site of digestion and absorption. The internal lining of the ileum bears numerous small outgrowths (villus), which increase its absorptive surface area.

**Ilium.** The largest of the three bones that make up each half of the pelvic girdle. The ilium bears a flattened wing of bone that is attached by ligaments to the sacrum.

**Imago.** The adult, sexually mature stage of an insect.

**Imbibition.** The process by which a substance absorbs a liquid and, as a consequence, swells in volume but does not dissolve. Imbibition, which is usually reversible, is exhibited by many biological compounds, particularly by cell-wall constituents such as pectin, celluloses, and lignin. The testas of dehydrated seeds imbibe water just prior to germination and the process is also important in water uptake by roots.

**Imbricate.** Overlapping. The term may be used to describe the form of aestivation in which the sepals and petals overlap in the bud. It is also used of mature structures, *e.g.* the overlapping spikelets of foxtails (Alopecurus). Compare valvate.

**Imino Acid.** A molecule containing a carboxylic acid group and an imino (NH) group. Proline and hydroxyproline, often described as amino acids, are in fact imino acids. Other imino acids are probably formed during the degradation of amino acids.

**Immature.** Not fully developed; unripe.

**Immersed**

1. Embedded in or sunk below the surface of another part or structure.
2, *bot.* Entirely submerged or growing under water.

**Immigation.** In genetics, the movement or flow of genes into a population, caused by immigrating individuals which interbreed with the residents. This is the usual source of new variation in a population, although the fundamental sources of all variation are gene mutation and recombination.

**Immune.** Safe from disease; protected from the effects of disease or disease processes.

**Immune Response.** The reaction of the body to foreign or potentially dangerous substances (antigens), particularly disease-producing microorganisms. The response involves the production by specialized white blood cells (lymphocytes) of proteins known as antibodies, which react with the antigens to render them harmless. The antibody–antigen reaction is highly specific.

**Immunity.** Complete resistance to a particular disease. Plants do not have an immune system, as animals do, but instead rely on physical barriers to prevent entry of a pathogen, or on various physiological reactions, *e.g.* hypersensitivity or production of phytoalexins.

**Immunization.** The production of immunity in an individual by artificial means. Active immunization (vaccination) involves the introduction, either orally or by injection. (inoculation), of specially treated bacteria, viruses, or their toxins to stimulate the production of antibodies (vaccine). Passive immunization is induced by the injection of performed antibodies.

**Immuno-electrophoresis.** Technique for the differentiation of proteins in solution, based on both their electrophoretic and immunological properties. Initially the proteins are separated by gel electrophoresis : they are then reacted with specific antibodies by double diffusion through the gel. The pattern of precipitating arcs thus formed can be used to identify the proteins.

**Immunoglobulin.** One of a group of proteins (globulins) in the body that act as antibodies. They are produced by specialized white blood cells (lymphocytes) and are present in blood serum and other body fluids.

**Immunology.** The science which deals with immunity or resistance to disease.

**Imperfect Flower.** One which lacks either stamens or pistil : Diclinous.

**Imparipinnate.** Describing a pinnate leaf having a centrally placed unpaired terminal leaflet. Such leaves are seen in most milk vetches (Astragalus). Compare paripinnate.

**Imperfect Fungi.** Fungi Imperfecti.

**Impermeable.** Not permeable; incapable of being penetrated by solids or fluids.

**[1]Implant.** To fix or set in securely.

**[2]Implant**

1. A tissue graft placed within another tissue.
2. A radioactive tube or needle placed within a tissue for therapeutic purposes.

**Implantation**

1. The act of placing an implant within an organ or tissue.
2. In mammals, the process by which a blastocyst attaches to and becomes embedded within the endometrium of the uterus.

**Impotence.** Lack of strength, power, or vigor, especially the inability of the male to engage in sexual intercourse.

**Impregnate**

1. To make pregnant or cause to conceive; to fertilize; to fecundate.
2. To infuse, charge, or saturate throughout.

**Impressed.** Imprinted, bent inward, or marked as though pressure were applied.

**Imprint.** A type of fossil in which the original substance has disappeared but the outline or form has been retained as an impression, as that of a leaf or animal track.

**Imprinting.** General descriptive term for a form of learning that only occurs early in a young animal's life. In it, the attention of the young becomes locused on a particular moving object, usually the mother. The phenomenon was first described in detail by Konral Lorenz in 1937 in respect of precocial birds, in which it is most strongly developed. In this case imprinting occurs only during a brief critical period, possibly of only a few hours, very early in the life cycle. Such imprinting is irreversible that influences subsequent behaviour patterns, most importantly sexual behaviour.

**Impulse**

1. An action or an impelling force which drives an individual or an object onward.
2. A sudden mental activity which impels an individual to action, as the impulse to cry.
3. A physicochemical change propagated along a nerve fiber or other conductile tissue which initiates a physiological activity in nerve, muscle, or gland cells.

**Impulse** (nerve impulse). The signal that travels along the length of a nerve fibre and is the means by which information is transmitted through the nervous system. It is marked by the flow of ions across the membrane of the axon caused by changes in the permeability of the membrane, producing a reduction in potential difference that can be detected as the action potential. The strength of the impulse produced in any nerve fibre is constant.

**Inanimate.** Without life : Dead.

**Inarticulate**

1. Not distinct, clear, or understandable, with reference to speech.
2. *zool. a.* Not jointed or segmented. *b.* Lacking a hinge, as in brachiopods.

**Inborn Error.** Genetically-determined biochemical disorder that results in an enzyme defect : this produces a metabolic block and has pathological consequences. Two examples in humans are phenylketonuria, in which tissue degeneration results from the accumulation of a toxic intermediate in the pathway of tyrosine metabolism, and Wilson's disease, in which death results from poisoning by copper because of a blockage in the pathway of copper detoxification. In both cases a single nucleotide substitution has produced a recessive allele that interferes with a metabolic pathway and causes death of the homozygotes.

**Inbreeding.** Interbreeding of closely related individuals. In animals, such individuals might be siblings, or cousins, or a parent and its offspring; in plants, the process implies self-fertilization. The converse is outbreeding, which involves the mating of distantly related individuals. The inbreeding coefficient is the probability of homozygosity due to a zygote obtaining copies of the same gene from parents of common ancestry. Inbreeding increases homozygosity : unfavourable recessive genes are therefore more likely to be expressed in the offspring. In general, the genetic variability of an inbred population declines; this is usually disadvantageous for its long-term survival and success. Typically, vigour is reduced in inbred stock. Many organisms, including humans, have physical or social mechanisms that tend to discourage inbreeding and promote outbreeding.

**Incineration.** Cremation; combustion of organic material, leaving only ash.

**Incipient.** Beginning to exist or manifest itself.

**Incised**

1. Cut into.
2. *bot.* Having a deeply notched margin, as an incised leaf.

**Incision.** A cut or gash; a notch in a margin.

**Incisor.** A sharp flattened chisel-shaped tooth in mammals that is adapted for biting food and—in rodents—for gnawing. In humans there are normally two pairs of incisors (central and lateral) in each jaw.

**Inclusion.** A discrete mass of nonliving material within the cytoplasm of a cell, as fat droplets, nutrient, pigment, yolk, or secretory granules; called paraplasm, metaplastic substance.

**Inclusion Body.** A mass of virus particles within the cytoplasm or nucleus of a cell in an animal infected with a virus, as negri bodies in the cytoplasm of Purkinje cells in rabies-infected animals.

**Inclusive Fitness.** The true measure of the fitness of an organism is often considered to reside not merely in the individual organism's own success but also in the successs of all its kin, *i.e.* those bearing some portion of the same genotype. J.B.S. Haldane is reputed to have said once that he would lay down his life for more than two brothers or sisters, eight cousins, 32 second cousions, etc, these numbers corresponding to the proportions of his own genes shared by these relatives.

**Incompatibility** (ethol.). Term for the relationship between patterns of behaviour that cannot be performed simultaneously, because they are contradictory, because they require the simultaneous operation of reflexes that are mutually inhibitory, or because they are based on contradictory motivation.

**Incomplete**

1. Not complete; imperfect.
2. *bot.* Lacking one or more of the four floral parts, said of flowers.

**Incomplete Dominance** (partial dominance). The partial expression of both alleles in a heterozygote so that the phenotype is intermediate between those of the two homozygotes. Thus in Antirrhinum, the homozygotes ++ and ww are red and white flowered respectively, while the heterozygote +w is pink. Where one allele is expressed to a greater extent than another the former may be described as partially dominant. There are all degrees of dominance relationships between complete dominance and incomplete dominance : the dividing lines between the various categories are to some extent arbitrary.

**Incrassate.** Thickened; swollen.

**Incubation**

1. The act of sitting upon and hatching eggs by the heat of the body, as by fowls.
2. Artificially maintaining conditions of warmth and moisture favorable for the development of eggs, embryos, bacterial cultures, etc.
3. Maintenance of normal body temperature for a premature baby.

**Incumbation Period**

1. The period of an infections disease between infection and appearance of the first symptoms.
2. The period a virus must remains within a vector before it is capable of causing the disease in its host.

**Incubous.** A type of leaf insertion in which the upper portion of a leaf covers the base of the leaf directly above it. Compare succubous.

**Incumbent**

1. Resting against or lying upon.
2. Lying with its back against the radicle, said of cotyledons.

**Incus** (anvil). The middle of the three ear ossicles of the mammalian middle ear.

**Incubation Period.** The phase following initial penetration of a pathogen when there are no visible symptoms of the disease. It may last several months in which case it is termed a latent infection. When the first visible symptoms appear the disease is said, to have entered the infection stage.

**Incubous.** Describing the leaf arrangement in leafy liverworts where the front edges of the leaves lie above the back edges of the leaves in front. Compare succubous.

**Indeciduous.** Not deciduous, with reference to leaves; evergreen, with reference to trees.

**Indefinite Growth.** The ability of certain plants or plant organs to show unlimited growth. For example, trees continue to grow each year and the leaves of monocotyledons grow throughout the life of the plant. The term is also used of race-mose infloresences, in which growth of the inflorescence is not terminated by the production of an apical flower bud but continues indefinitely. Meristems may also be said to exhibit indefinite growth. Compare definite growth.

**Indefinite Infloresence.** Racemose in florecence.

**Indehiscent.** Describing a fruit or fruiting body that does not open to disperse its contents. Indehiscent fruiting bodies are thought to have developed from cup pression of the naturally occurring opening mechanisms found in dehiscent structures. The seeds or spores are released either when the surrounding wall decays or when it is eaten by an animal.

**Independent.** Not dependent; free from or not subject to control.

**Independent Assortment.** The separation of the alleles of one gene into the reproductive cells (gametes) independently of the way in which the alleles of other genes have segregated. By this process all possible combinations of alleles should occur equally frequently in the gametes. In practice this does not happen because alleles situated on the same chromosome tend to be inherited together. However, if the allele pairs Aa and Bb are on different chromosomes, the combinations AB, Ab, aB, and ab will normally be equally likely to occur in the gametes.

**Index** pl. **Indices**

1. A sign, token, or indicator.
2. A ratio or formula expressing the ratio of one measurement or dimension to another, as cephalic index.

**Index Fossil** (zone fossil). An animal fossil of a group that existed continuously during a particular span of geological time and can therefore be used to date the rock in which it is found. Index fossils are found chiefly in sedimentary rocks. They are an essential tool in stratigraphy for comparing the geological ages of sedimentary rock formations. Examples are ammonites and graptolites.

**Indian Bean Tree.** A deciduous tree, native to North America but grown in Europe as an ornament. It has pale, bell-shaped flowers and grows up to 2o metres high.

**Indian Floral Region.** Part of Good's Indo-Malaysian subkingdom within his Palaeotropical kingdom, and more a region of floral mixing than a distinct entity, notwithstanding the extent of the su continent. There are only about 150 endemic genera, and most of these are monotypic. Many varied and useful plants are through to be native to the region.

**Indicator.** A plant or animal species which is characteristic of a particular serai stage.

**Indicator Species**

1. Species that is of narrow ecological amplitude with respect to one or more environmental factors and that is, when present, therefore indicative of a particular environmental condition or set of conditions. In geobotanical surveys, species or ecotypes with high heavy-metal tolerance have been used as metallic-ore indicators.

2. In plant-community classification, the term is used more loosely to denote the most characteristic community members. In this case 'indicator species' may include species typical of and vigorous in a particular environment and is not necessarily restricted to species of narrow ecological amplitude.

**Indicator-species Analysis.** In general, a classificatory scheme in which the final groups are characterized by indicator species derived from the data in the course of group definition. More specifically, the term refers to a polythetic-divisive classificatory scheme proposed by M.O. Hill (1975). Sites are ranked by a reciprocal averaging ordination and divided into two groups at the mid-point—the 'centre of gravity'— of all the weighted data values of the ordination. Indicator species (usually five) are then identified as those species exclusively, or most nearly so, associated with one or other side of this division (positive and negative indicators). The site-indicator scores, effectively a rough secondary ordination, determine their final classification; and the process may then be repeated within the groups identified. The indicator species form a key, enabling new sites to be added easily into the classificatory framework without excessive recalculation.

**Indigen.** An indigenous animal or plant.

**Indigenous.** Describing a species that occurs naturally in a certain area, as distinct from one introduced by man; native.

**Indirect Flight Muscle.** The thoracic musculature that brings about the flight movement of the wings in most insects. It is not attached directly to the wings. The thorax is a box to which the wings are joined. Longitudinal muscles compress the thoracic box and cause the wings to move down. Dorsoventral muscles pull the tergites and sternites. of the thorax together, causing the wings to move upwards.

**Individualistic Hypothesis.** View, first proposed by H.A. Gleason (1917, 1926), that vegetation is continuously variable in response to a continuously varying environment. Thus no two vegetation communities are identical. It implies also that vegetation cannot be classified, and that recognition of particular individual communities will be difficult (the problem arising because of the difficulty of defining boundaries). This viewpoint underlies one of the two polarized approaches to the description and analysis of-

vegetaion communities that were much debated in the 1950s and 1960s. The individualistic hypothesis favours a continuum view of vegetation, for which ordination rather than classification methods are appropriate. Compare organismic.

**Indole Acetic Acid (IAA).** The principal auxin of most plants. The other indole compounds that also occur in plants probably owe their auxin-like activity to conversion to IAA at, or near to, the site of action. Thus, indole pyruvic acid, indole acetaldehyde, and other compounds may act as IAA reserves. The route of IAA synthesis is from the amino acid tryptophan. Studies in vivo have shown that IAA is transported in greater quantity and inactivated or destroyed more quickly than synthetic auxins. This suggests that an important aspect in the control of auxin activity is the relative rates of synthesis, transport, and inactivation in different tissues. IAA is decomposed by light and by the enzyme IAA oxidase. It may also combine with other compounds to form an inert complex. The rapid oxidation of IAA by the plant's enzymes has limited its commercial use as a weedkiller, and synthetic auxins, *e.g.* 2,4-D, 2,4,5-T, and MCPA, are normally used.

**Indole Alkaloids.** A group of alkaloids, the members of which contain an indole nucleus. They are derived either from tryptophan or phenylalanine. Examples are strychnine, from Strychnos nux vomica, and yohimbine from the bark of Corynanthe johimbe. Certain alkaloids containing quinoline are derived from indole compounds, an example being quinine, obtained from the bark of Cinchona species.

**Induced Enzyme** (adaptive enzyme). An enzyme that is synthesized in response to high concentrations of its substrate (induction). When the substrate is absent the genes governing the enzyme's synthesis are repressed.

**Induced-fit Theory.** Variation of the lock-and-key theory of enzymatic function. It is proposed that the substrate causes a conformational change in the enzyme such that the active site achieves the exact configuration required for a reaction to occur. The overall effect would be a tighter binding for the substrate and enzyme.

**Inducer.** A substance that promotes the activity of a gene or block of genes. Inducers of enzymes in prokaryotes fall into two groups. In negative control systems (*e.g.* the lac operon of Escherichia coli) they may be substrates of the enzymes they induce or analogues, derivatives, or precursors of the enzyme substrates. In any event, they bind with a regulator protein and so prevent the latter complexing with the operator gene to inhibit mRNA synthesis (operon). In positive control system (*e.g.* the ara operon in E. coli) the inducer is a complex formed from the regulator-protein substrate. This complex must bind with the operator in order for mRNA synthesis to occur. In eukaryotes the nature of inducers is less well understood but appears more diverse. Steroid and other membrane-soluble growth substances, such as gibberellic acid, can act as inducers when complexed to cytoplasmic receptors.

**Induction**

1. (in embryology). The ability of natural stimuli to cause unspecialized embryonic tissue to develop into specialized tissue.
2. (in obstetrics) The initiation of childbirth by artificial means; for examples, by injection of the hormone oxytocin.

**Inductive**

1. Capable of producing an internal change or response.

2. *bacteriol.* Designating enzymes which are produced only when specific substrates are present in the medium.

**Indumentum.**

1. *zool.* The plumage of a bird.
2. *bot.* Any dense, hairy covering or pubescence.

**Indusium** pl. **Indusia.** A membrane which serves as a covering, as *a. bot.* that which covers the sorus of a fern; *b. zool.* the double membrane which encloses the developing embryo of certain insects.

**Indusium.** A flap of tissue that partially or completely covers each sorus in certain ferns. It is an outgrowth of the placenta. Indusia are seen on the undersurface of the fronds of Dryopteris as lines of brown kidney-shaped outgrowths.

**Industrial Melanism.** Development of melanic forms of organisms in response to soot and dust pollution. Industrial melanism is especially associated with various moth species and was first noted early in the nineteenth century. In the 1950s, studies by H B.D. Kettlewell on the moth Biston betularia showed that melanism is a simple inherited trait favoured by natural selection in soot-polluted environments, where dark colouring gives better camouflage and so better protection from predators. In time the proportion of melanic forms increases in such polluted environments. The reverse process—selection in favour of pale forms—occurs in pollution-free environments where the paler, speckled form is better concealed on the tree lichens on which it settles. With appropriate calibration, the extent of melanism in a population may thus be used as an indicator of industrial soot pollution.

**Infauna.** Benthic animals living in bottom material.

**Infection.** The invasion of any living organism by disease-causing microorganisms (pathogen), which proceed to establish themselves, multiply, and produce various symptoms in their host. Pathogens may invade via a wound or (in animals) through the mucous membranes lining the alimentary respiratory, and reproductive tracts, and may be transmited by an infected individual a carrier, or an insect vector. Symptoms in animals appear after an initial symptomless incubation period and typically consist of localized inflammation, often with pain and fever. Infections are combatted by the body's natural defences (immune response). Treatment with drugs antibiotic; antiseptic) is effective against most bacterial, fungal, and protozoan infections but not against vital infections.

**Infections Agent.** Any virus or microorganism (bacterium, spirochaete, rickettsia, fungus, protozoan), helminth, or arthropod which is capable of causing an infection or infectious disease.

**Infertile.** Incapable of reproduction; barren, sterile.

**Inferior.** Describing a structure that is positioned below or lower than another structure in the body. For example, in flowering plants the ovary is described as inferior when it is located below the other organs of the flower.

**Inferior Ovary.** Ovary.

**Infectation.**

1. The state or condition of being infested by numbers of a disturbing or annoying organism, as lice or fleas.
2. The presence of multicellular organisms, especially helminths, which do not multiply within the body.

**Inflammation.** The defence reaction of tissue to injury, infection, or irritation by chemicals or physical agents. Cells in the effected tissue release a chemical (histamine) that causes localized dilatation of blood vessels so that fluid leaks out and blood flow is increased. This leads to swelling, redness, heat, and often pain. White blood cells, particularly phagocytes, enter the tissue and an immune response is stimulated. A gradual healing process usually follows.

**Inflorescence.** Any flowering system consisting of more than one flower. It is usually separated from the vegetative parts by an extended internode, and normally comprises individual flowers, bracts and peduncles, and pedicels. The change from vegetative to reproductive growth may be triggered by photoperiod or temperature and is thought to be hormonally controlled (florigen, phytochrome, vernalin). The arrangement of flowers into inflorescences is believed to have evolved from solitary flowers. The increase in flower number has been accompanied by a decrease in the size of the individual flowers, and specialization for different roles.

Development of inflorescences may terminate vegetative growth (determinate growth) or allow it to continue (interminate growth). The type of growth habit has considerable economic implications in such crops as the grain legumes where it directly affects total crop yield, and sequence and time of fruit ripening.

Inflorescences are classified morphologically by their branching behaviour into cymose inflorescences, where the apical meristem differentiates into a flower and new growth is from the axils, and into racemose inflorescences, where growth continues at the apices, and flowers are developed in the axils.

**Influenza Viruses.** Group (genus) of viruses within the orthomyxovirus group. Influenza viruses cause not only human influenza but also diseases such as fowl plague and swine influenza. Some influenza viruses continually undergo changes in their antigenic characteristics, and this is responsible for the sudden epidemics of influenza.

**Information Statistic.** Measure of disorder within a group, which is zero when all individuals within the group are identical. In information analysis an agglomerative, hierarchical classificatory technique, devised by W. L. T. Williams and others, 1966—a hierarchy is constructed by repeatedly joining together those individuals or groups which exhibit the smallest increase in heterogeneity (disorder), and therefore the smallest change in information.

**Infraspecific Variation.** Differences in appearance exhibited by different members of the same species or breeding population. The variation may be a result of environmental influences, such as nutrition, crowding, seasonal effects, etc. It may also be due to genetic factors, principally the effects of genetic recombination and mutation. Whatever the ultimate cause, natural selection plays a major role in governing the extent of the variation and types of individuals present. The term may be applied to characteristics only apparent by advanced laboratory techniques, as well as to those readily visible to the naked eye.

**Infundibulum.** A funnel-shaped structure, as *a.* the stalk of the pituitary gland, *b.* the lateral distended portion of the uterine tube.

**Ingest.** To take in a solid substance, as food into the body.

**Ingesta.** That which is ingested. Compare egesta.

**Ingression.** A method of gastrulation in which cells fill the blastoccel forming a stereogastrula, as in sponges and coelenterates.

**Inhabit.** To dwell in or on or to occupy as a place of habitation.

**Inherent.** Inborn, innate, natural.

**Inherit.** To receive from one's parent's as genetic factors.

**Inheritance.** All the characteristics of an individual which are dependent upon hereditary determiners or gene received from one's parents.

**Inhibition**

1. (in biochemistry) A reduction in the rate of an enzyme-catalysed reaction by substances called inhibitors. If the inhibitor molecules resemble the substrate molecules they may bind to the active site of the enzyme, so preventing normal enzymatic activity. Alternatively they may form a complex with the substrate-enzyme intermediate or irreversibly destroy the enzyme configuration and active-site properties. The toxic effects of many substances are produced in this way. Inhibition by reaction products (feedback inhibition) is important in the control of enzyme activity.

2. (in physiology) The prevention or reduction of the activity of effectors (such as muscles) by means of certain nerve impulses. Inhibitory activity often provides a balance to stimulation of a process, for example, the impulse to stimulate contraction of a voluntary muscle may be accompanied by an inhibitory impulse to prevent contraction of its antagonist.

**Inhibitor.** A substance that inhibits the activity of an enzyme. It may do this by binding at the active site of the enzyme in place of the substrate (competitive inhibition) or by binding with the enzyme-substrate complex. Alternatively the inhibitor may bind to some part of the enzyme other than the active side and in so doing change the three-dimensional configuration of the enzyme so it is not able to function normally. Certain enzymes containing an —SH group are inhibited by heavy metals in this manner.

**Initial.** bot, An initiating cell, a self perpetuating cell present in apical meristem and vascular cambium from which specialized tissues develop.

**Initiator.** Transfer ribonucleic acid (tRNA), that in eukaryotes carries methionine and in prokaryotes N-formylmethionine, that binds to the small unit of a ribosome bearing messenger ribonuceic acid (mRNA), thus forming an initiation complex. This, in the presence of three protein initiation factors and GTP which is hydrolysed, enables the larger ribosomal subunit to associate with the complex and peptide-chain synthesis to proceed.

**Inject.** To introduce or force a fluid into any of the vessels, cavities, or tissues of the body.

**Innate**

1. Applied to behaviour that is not learned (*i.e.* behaviour that is acquire genetically).
2. Applied to behaviour that may be learned but that has evolved by natural selection. In this case, parents behave in a particular way, and teach their offspring to behave likewise, and are more likely for this reason to reproduce successfully. The term is regarded by many ethologists as obsolete because it fails to allow for the modification of patterns of behaviour in response to environmental factors.

**Innate Behaviour.** An inherited pattern of behaviour that appears in a similar form in all normally reared individuals of the same sex and species.

**Inner Ear.** The structure in vertebrates, surrounded by the temporal bone of the skull, that contains the organs of balance and heating. It consists of soft hollow sensory structures (the membranous labyrinth), containing fluid (endolymph), surrounded by fluid (perilymph), and encased in a bony cavity (the bony labyrinth). It consists of two chambers, the sacculus and utriculus, that bear the cochlea and semicircular canals respectively.

**Innervation.** The distribution of nerves to a particular region or structure.

**Innocuous.** Harmless, producing no injury or ill effects,

**Innominate Artery.** A short artery that branches from the aorta to divide into the subclavian artery (the main artery to the arm) and the right carotid artery (which supplies blood to the head).

**Innominate Bone.** One of the two bones that form each half of the pelvic girdle in adult vertebrates. This bone is formed by the fusson of the ilium, ischium, and pubis.

**Inoculum**

1. The material that initiates disease in a previously un-infected plant, Under artificial conditions this may be a suspension of spores, which is sprayed onto the plant. In nature the inoculum is carried to a healthy plant from its source, *e.g.* an infected plant, by an agent, such as wind or an insect.
2. In microbiology or tissue-culture work, the cells that are introduced into a sterile medium to initiate a culture.

**Inosital.** A sugar alcohol formed by the complete hydroxylation of cyclohexane. The myo isomer is the only isomer with biological significance. Myo-inositol is synthesized in a two-stage reaction from glucose 6-phosphate. Its hexaphosphate ester, phytic acid, is an important storage product in seeds, in germinating seeds and young seedlings it is thought that the phytic acid is converted to myo-inositol. This then undergoes oxidation to form glucuronic acid, thus phytic acid acts as a source of uronic acids for synthesis of cell-wall components.

**Inquiline.** An organism that lives within the nest or abode of another, as insects that live in the nests of termites or ants.

**Insect.** A large group of arthropods whose bodies are divided into three distinct sections—head, thorax, and abdomen—and bear three pairs of legs and a pair of feelers or antennae. Most insects also have two pairs of wings. Examples include dragonflies, grasshoppers, earwigs, bees, butterflies, and beetles.

Young insects never have fully developed wings and cannot fly. They nearly all start life as eggs, but then they follow one of two main courses of development. Some spend their early lives as Nymphs, which often look like the adults and which gradually turn into adults. The other course of development begins with a Larva and then passes through the Pupa or chrysalis stage before reaching maturity. Both kinds of youngsters have to change their skins several times as they grow.

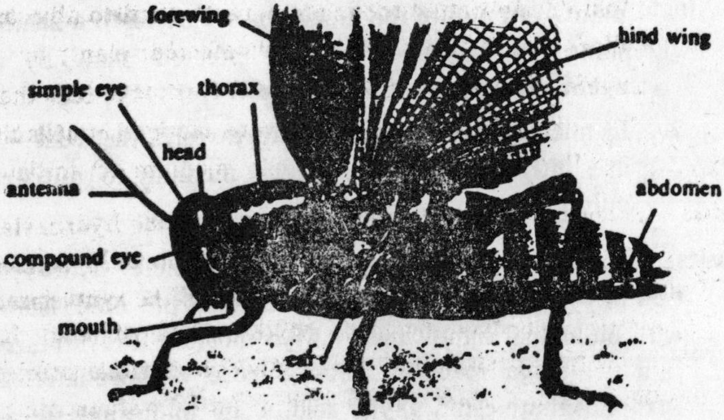


**Insecticide.** Any chemical that kills insects. Loosely the term is also applied to chemicals that kill mites, nematodes, and other invertebrate pests. The substance often affects the nervous system and may be a stomach poison (stomach insecticides). It may also act by contact or as a fumigant.

**Insectivora.** An order of small, mainly nocturnal, mammals that includes the hedgehogs, moles, and shrews. They have long snouts covered with stiff tactile hairs and their teeth are specialized for seizing and crushing insects and other small prey. The insectivores have changed very little since they evolved in the Cretaceous period, 130 million years ago.

**Insectivore**

1. Any insect-eating plant or animal.
2. Any member of the order Insectivora, small, insect-eating, placental mammals, as moles, shrews, and hedgehogs.

**Insectivorous Plant** (carnivorous plant). A plant that is adapted to obtain food by digesting small animals (particularly insects) in addition to feeding by photosynthesis. Such plants are found in regions where the soil is deficient in certain nutrients, particularly nitrates. Examples are butterworts (Pinguicula) and sundews (Drosera) growing on heathland and moorland, and tropical plants, such as the Venus' flytrap (Dionaea muscipula) and the various pitcher plants (families Nepenthaceae and Sarraceniaceae). The plants are adapted in a number of ingenious ways to attract, trap, and kill the insects, which are then digested by proteolytic enzymes secreted by the plant. Butterworts trap insects by having sticky infolded leaves. Venus' fly-traps have folding leaves with spines along the edges that spring together and trap the insect. The leaves of pitcher plants form a long narrow container shaped like a pitcher, into which the insects fall and drown if the liquid at the bottom.

**Insect Pollination.** Entomophily.

**Inseminate**

1. To impregnate, to introduce semen into the genital tract of a female.
2. To sow or distribute seed.

**Insensible**

1. Devoid of feeling or sensation, unconscious.

2. Incapable of being perceived by the senses.

**Insert**. To place, put, or set in.

**Insertion**

1. The act of inserting.
2. The mode of attachment or the place at which a structure is attached, as *a. bot.* the insertion of parts of a flower; *b. anat.* the attachment of a muscle to a relatively more movable part, in contrast to the origin.

**Inspiration**. The act of drawing air into the lungs, inhalation.

**Instar**. A stage in the larval development of an insect between two moults (ecdyses). There are usually a number of larval instars before the pupal stage and metamorphosis.

**Instinct**. An innate tendency to behave in a particular way, which does not depend critically on particular learning experiences for its development and therefore is seen in a similar form in all normally reared individuals of the same sex and species. Much instinctive behaviour takes the form of fixed action patterns. These are movements that —once started—are performed in a stereotyped way unaffected by external stimuli. For example, a frog's prey-catching tongue flick is performed in the same way whether or not anything is caught. Some complex instinctive behaviour, however, requires some learning by the animal before it is perfected. Birdsong, for example, consists of an innate component that is modified and made more complex by the influence of other birds, the habitat, etc.

**Insufflation**. The act of blowing or breathing into, especially the blowing of a gas or powder into a cavity of the body.

**Insulin**. A protein hormone, secreted by the islets of Langerhans in the pancreas, that promotes the uptake of glucose by body cells and thereby controls its concentration in the blood. Insulin was the first protein whose amino-acid sequence was fully determined (in 1955). Underproduction of insulin results in the accumulation of large amounts of glucose in the blood and its subsequent excretion in the urine. This condition, known as diabetes mellitus, can be treated successfully by insulin injections.

**Integration** (in physiology). The coordination within the brain of separate but related nervous processes. For example, sensory information from the inner ear and the eye are both necessary for the sense of balance. These stimuli must be integrated by the brain not only with each other but also with various motor nerves, which coordinate the muscles that control posture.

**Integument**. A protective structure that develops from the base of an ovule and encloses it almost entirely except for an opening, the micropyle, at the tip of the nucellus. In most angiosperms there are two integumenis, which may or may not be fused. In gymnosperms and in most dicotyledons with fused petals there is only one integument. Occasionally a third integument is formed, which becomes conspicuous as an aril following fertilization. This is seen in the spindle tree (Euonymous europaeus). The integuments have a vascular supply continuous with the parent via the funiculus.

**Interbreed**

1. To breed by mating individuals of different races, varieties, or species, to crossbreed.
2. To breed within a small, closely related population.

**Intercalated**. Inserted or interposed among.

**Intercellular** (in biology). Located or occurring between cells. Compare intracellular.

**Intercalary Meristem.** A meristem positioned (*i.e.* intercalated) more or less differentiated tissues, some distance from the apical meristem. Intercalary meristems may contain not only initials, but also relatively mature cells. This prevents it from being a structurally weak part of the organ. The primary function of an intercalary meristem is to facilitate longitudinal growth of a plant organ, independent of activity of the apical meristem. Examples are the meristems in the leaf sheaths and internodes of grasses and horsetails.

**Intercellular.** Located or taking place between cells.

**Intercostal.** Between ribs.

**Intercostal Muscles.** The muscles located between the ribs, surrounding the lungs. They play an essential role in breathing.

**Interface.** The common border or surface between two structures, phases, or systems.

**Interfascicular.** Between fascicles or bundles.

**Interfascicular Cambium.** The part of the vascular cambium that forms between the vascular bundles (fascicles) and joins up with the fascicular cambium to form a continuous meristematic ring.

**Interferon.** Proteins produced in very small quantities, by leucocytes and related cells, in response to viral infection. As a group they appear to induce the synthesis of a protein that interferes with a viral-specific function. This often confers a temporary resistance to subsequent infection by other viruses.

**Interkinesis.** The interphase of mitosis.

**Intermedin.** The melanophore-stimulating hormone (MSH) secreted by the intermediate lobe of the pituitary gland.

**Internal.** Of the inside, within, enclosed.

**Internal Environment.** The conditions that prevail within the body of an organism, particularly with respect to the composition of the intercellular fluid. Selective absorption of materials across cell membranes plays a large part in controlling the internal environment of both animals and plants. Animals in addition can regulate their body fluids by the action of hormones and the nervous system.

**International Code of Botanical Nomenclature (ICBN).** A periodically revised publication outlinning the procedures for the scientific naming of plants (*i.e.* vascular plants, bryophytes, algae, blue-green algae, fungi, and slime moulds).

The rules have been drawn up to sort out errors and ambiguities arising from past misunderstandings and misidentifications and to ensure correct naming of new taxa. Fundamental to the code are the principles that naming of families and lower ranks is by reference to nomenclatural types, that the first valid name published is maintained (for vascular plants this is the first name published on or after 1 May, 1753, the date Linnaeus' Species Plantarum was published), and that once the circumscription, position, and rank of a group have been decided it can only have one correct name. However this does not preclude a group of plants being treated in different ways (*e.g.* being given a different position) by different authors, with each auther being able to assign a different nomenclaturally correct name. For example, watercress is thought by some authors to belong to the genus Nasturtium, while others believe it is better placed in Rorippa. Following the rules of the Code, the names Nasturtium officinate and Rorippa nasturtiumaquaticum are equally acceptable. Names cannot be changed simply because they are inappropriate. However homonyms and superfluous names (names published for a taxon after that taxon already had a valid name) must be rejected. If two or more taxa are combined into one then the new taxon takes the name of the constituent that had the oldest valid name. If a taxon is split into two or more taxa, then one of the new taxa must be given the name of the old taxon.

The ICBN is only applicale to wild plants and because of the importance of many cultivated plants, a separate set of rules has been laid down in 57 Articles in the International Code of Nomenclature of Cultivated Plants or ICNCP.

**International Code of Zoological Nomenclature** (International Commission on Zoological Nomenclature, ICZN).

1. The regulations governing the scientific naming of animals.

2. The international authority that draws up those regulations and that supervises their application.

**Internode**

1. (in botany). The part of a plant stem between two nodes.

2. (in neurology). The myelinated region of a nerve fibre between two nodes of Ranvier.

**Interoceptor.** A sensory receptor located within a visceral organ.

**Interphase.** The period in the cell cycle following cytokinesis and preceding the next nuclear division.

**Interpositional Growth.** Intrusive growth.

**Interrenal Bodies.** Structures in lower vertebrates which correspond to the cortex of the adrenal gland.

**Interse.** Between or among themselves, with reference to stock breeding.

**Intersex.** Class of individuals of a species with two sexes that possesses sexual characteristics that are intermediate. It may occur through the failure of the sex-determining mechanism of the genes (*e.g.* the rate occurrence of imbalance in the number of X-chromosomes—two—and the number of autosomes—three—in Drosophila); or through hormonal or other influences during development (*e.g.* the condition in cattle called free-martin, in which the female member of a pair of oppositely sexed twins has been influenced, probably hormonally, by her twin brother, through the fusing of their placenial circulations).

**Interstice** pl. **Interstices.** A space or interval between closely placed structures.

**Interstitial.** Of or pertaining to interspaces between the cells or the structural units of an organ or structure.

**Interstital Cells**

1. Cells in the epidermis of coelenterates which give rise to sex cells.
2. In vertebrates, the cells of Leydig, located between the seminiferous tubles of the testis. They secrete the male hormone testosterone.

**Interstitial Cell-stimulating Hormone.** ICSH, produced by the anterior lobe of the pituitary.

**Interstial Fauna.** Microscopic animals which occupy interstices or spaces between mud and sand particles in lake and marine bottoms.

**Intestine**

1. The portion of the alimentary canal which extends from the stomach or crop to the cloaca or anus. In man it consists of the small intestine (duodenum, jejunum, ileum) and large intestine (cecum, colon, rectum, and anal canal).

2. The digestive cavity of certain invertebrates, as turbellarians.

**Intima.** The innermost layer of a blood vessel; the tunica intima.

**Intine.** The innermost layer of the pollen grain wall, composed mainly of cellulose. It is less resistant than the exine and hence not preserved in geological deposits.

**Intolerance.** Inability to endure or extreme sensitivity to a chemical agent or physical condition.

**Intoxication.** Poisoning, or a state of being poisoned by alcohol, drugs, serum, or an excess of any substance; a state of drunkenness; inebriation.

**Intracellular.** Taking place or situated within the cell.

**Intrafascicular Cambium.** Fascicular cambium.

**Intramembranous.** Occurring witih a membrane.

**Intramembranous Ossification.** Formation of bone within a connective tissue membrane without a preceding cartilaginous stage, as cranial bones.

**Intramural.** Within the substance of the wall of an organ or structure.

**Intraspecific Selection.** Natural selection among individuals of the same species.

**Intravital.** Within a live organism or living tissue.

**Intravital Stain.** A dye that will stain living cells without killing them, as neutral red.

**Intra Vitam.** During life or while still living.

**Intrinsic.** Enclosed within, peculiar to, or an inherent part of an organ or structure, as intrinsic muscles of the tongue.

**Introgression** (introgressive hybridization). The incorporation of genes from one species or subspecies into another related species or subspecies. It arises as a result of successful hybridization and subsequent backrossing of the hybrids with one of the parental populations. Introgression is believed to have been a major factor in the evolution of many plants, especially crop plants. For example, the present wide range of the sunflower (Helianthus annuus) over North America is thought to have been achieved fairly recently by the introgression of genes from a number of Helianthus species, each providing characteristics enabling adaptation of different environments. Introgression is the basis of some plant breeding techniques. Compare gene flow.

**Intromittent Organ.** Any male copulatory organ, as a penis or cirrus.

**Intron.** A noncoding polynucleotide sequence between two coding regions(exones) of DNA. Introns are present in eukaryotic cells, but not in bacteria. The length and number of introns in a gene varies, but in some gene introns can contain more DNA than exons. In other genes they are absent altogether. mRNA initially synthesized on intron-containing genes is called heterogeneous mRNA, or hnRNA. While in the nucleous, probably in the nucleolus, introns are removed and the ends of the mRNA are anealed to produce mature mRNA. The latter is then translated into protein. How introns can be removed with such precision, and what happens to them after their removal, is obscure. Several functions have been ascribed to them. For example, they may speed evolution by enhancing recombination between exons. It has also been suggested that they play a role in differentiation. Introns should not be confused with repeated sequences, which occur between genes.

**Introrse.** Describing anthers that release their pollen to the inside of the flower so promoting self pollination. Compare extrose.

**Introyert**

1. *a.* To turn or bend inward. *b.* To invaginate a tubular structure into another.
2. A structure that has been introverted, as the anterior portion of certain invertebrates (sipunculids or ectoprocts).

**Intrusive Growth** (interpositional growth). The type of growth exhibited by certain cells when they intrude between other cells that are either not growing or growing at the slower rate. For example, certain members of the Liliaceue have vascular trachieds that elongate at both ends to achieve a length of between 15 and 40 times that of the original. These tracheids insinuate themselves amongst the the surrounding cells, disrupting established plasmodesmata. Compare sliding growth, symplastic growth.

**Intussusception.** The insertion of cellulose into spaces within the wall of an elongating cell. Water passes into the vacuole of the cell, creating an outward pressure on the wall, which consequently stretches. The new cellulose is then incorporated, the result being an increase in wall area. The next step is usually the thickening of the walls by apposition.

**Inulin.** A storage polysaccharide composed of fructose residues linked by $\beta(2-1)$ glycosidic bonds. The inulin chain is usually headed by a glucose residue and is 30—40 residues in length. Synthesis of inulin is from sucrose precursors, hence the glucose at the beginning of the chain. Inulin is an important reserve polysaccharide in the genera Helianthus, Dahlia, Inula, and Chicorium. The tubers of Jerusalem artichoke (Helianthus tuberosus) may contain up to 58% inulin.

**Invagination.**

1. The act or process of infolding so that a pocketlike cavity is formed.

2. The ensheathing of a tubular structure : Intussusception.

3. Part invaginated.

**Invasion**. The process of entering into and spreading throughout.

**Inverse Analysis.** The grouping of attributes based on an analysis of the individuals that process or lack those attributes, *e.g.* in plant ecology the grouping of species according to their presence, absence, or relative abundances at different sample sites. The term is used particularly in numerical vegetation classification, and is sometimes referred to as a species classification. Ordination methods may similarly be described as either plot (individual) or species (attribute) ordinations. In plant ecology especially, inverse classifications are often used to complement normal analysis. Thus data will be analysed using both approaches and coincidence between the final groups examined. It is assumed that high coincidence implies the recognition of an important 'type' community or 'nodum'. In its concept, nodal analysis is a method based on these principles.

**Inversion** (chromosome inversion). A structural change in a chromosome in which a length of chromosome has detached and then rejoined the opposite way round. If the centromere is included in the inverted segment the inversion is termed pericentric. If the centromere is not in centre of the inverted segment then the relative lengths of the chromatid arms either side of the centromere will be changed, altering the karyotype. Paracentric inversions, in which the centromere is not included, are the more common. An inversion is homozygous if the same segment is inverted in both homologous chromosomes. Apart from the changed linkage arrangements of the genes and any position effects, homozygous inversions behave much as normal homologous chromosomes. Often through the inversion only occurs in one chromosome giving an inversion heterozygote. These can be detected by the characteristic looped appearance during meiosis. Inversion heterozygotes often show reduced fertility because if a crossover occurs within the loop then a dicentric chromosome (a chromosome with two centromeres) and an acentric fragment will result (diagram). Such pieces cannot move nromally on the spindle and thus only hals the gametes (those containing either of the two chromatids not involved in the crossover) will be viable. As the viable gametes will have the same linear sequence of genes as the parent, inversion heterozygotes have been termed crossover suppressors. However they do not suppress crossing over but the resultant recombinants, being inviable, are nont apparent. Viable recombinants may be obtained if two crossovers occur in the

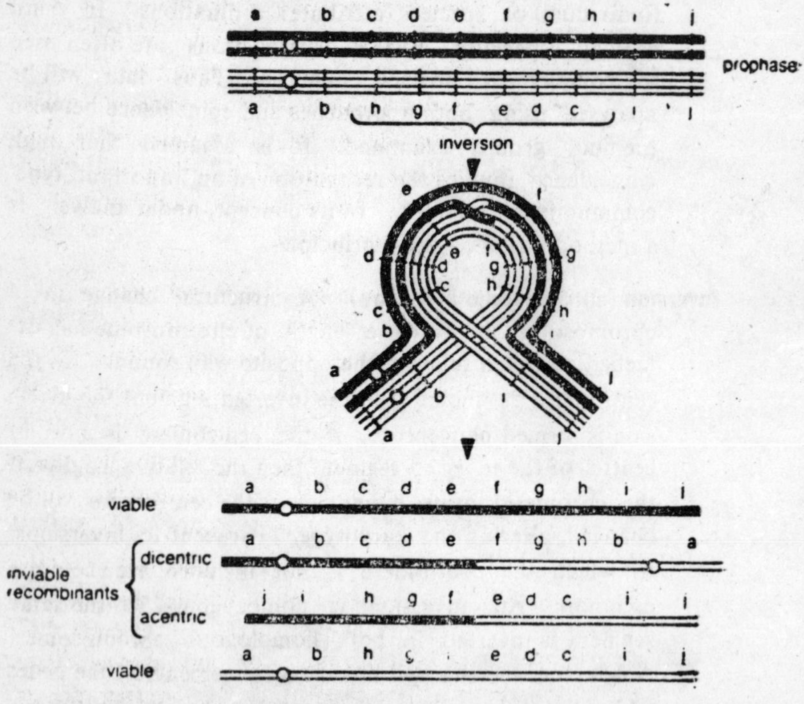


**Consequence of crossing over in an inversion heterozygote**

inversion loop. Inversion heterozygotes may have an adaptive advantage in that any useful combination of alleles in the inverted segment are likely to be held together.

**Invert**. To turn upside down or inside out.

**Invert** Sugar. Sucrose.

[1]**Invertebrate**

1. Lacking a backbone or spinal column.
2. Of or pertaining to invertebrate animals.

[2]**Invertebrate.** An invertebrate animal.

**In Vitro**. In glass, with reference to processes or reactions which take place in glass vessels, as test tubes, petri dishes.

**In Vivo**. Describing experiments investigating biological processes that are carried out in living organisms. The literal meaning is 'in life'. Compare in vitro.

**Involucel**. A small or secondary involucre.

**Involucre**

1. A whorl of bracts around or beneath a condensed inflorescence, such as a capitulum or umbel. It resembles and performs the function of the clayx of a single simple flower.
2. The sheath surrounding a group of archegonia or antheridia in certain liverworts, such [as Sphaerocarpus and its allies.
3. A tubular upgrowth of the thallus surrounding the base of the sporophyte in members of the Anthocerotae (hornworts).

**Involuntary**. Note under the control of the will ; not voluntary.

**Involuntary Muscle** (smooth muscle). Muscle whose activity is not under the control of the will ; it is supplied by the autonomic nervous system. Involuntary muscle comprises long spindle-shaped cells without striations. These cells occur singly, in groups, or as sheets in the skin, around hair follicles, and in the digestive tract, respiratory tract, urinogenital tract, and the circulatory system. The cells contract slowly in spontaneous rhythms or when stretched ; they may show sustained contraction (tonus) for long periods without fatigue. Compare voluntary muscle.

**Involute**

1. Rolled or turned in at the margins, said of leaves.
2. Curved inward or spirally.
3. Having whorls closely wound, said of shells.

**Involution**

1. The process of rolling or turning inward.
2. Retrograde evolution or development in which structures, become less complex or are lost.
3. The return of an organ to normal size following enlargement due to normal demands, as the uterus after pregnancy.
4. Retrogressive changes in an organ following peak of functional activity, as involution of the thymus after puberty or ovary after menopause.
5. bacteriol. The appearance of unusual or abnormal forms in bacterial cultures grown under unfavorable conditions.

**Iodine**. A nonmetallic halogen element occurring as bluish-black plates or scales. It is a component of the thyroid hormone and used in medicine as an antiseptic. Symbol I, at. wt. 126.91.

**Ion-beam Etching**. A method of specimen preparation for scanning electron microscopy in which the specimen is placed under high vacuum and [the surface is then eroded by a beam of ions to expose subsurface features. The specimen is then coated and examined. The technique is very successful with some materials but produces artefacts by uneven erosion of the surface of others.

**IPA** (isopentenyl adenosine) A natural cytokinin, similar in structure to zeatin. In addition to being a very active cytokinin, it has been found as a minor base in certain transfer RNA molecules. In the tRNA specific for the amino acid serine. IPA is found following the anticodon and thus may serve to mark the end of the anticodon.

**Iridium Anomaly**. The occurrence of unusually high concentrations of the relatively scarce metal iridium at the boundaries of certain geological strata. Two such layers have been discovered, one at the end of the Cretaceous, 65 million years ago, and the second at the end of the Eocene, 34 million years ago. One theory to account for these suggests that on each occasion a huge iridium-containing meteorite may have collided with the earth, producing a cloud of dust that settled out to form an iridium-rich layer. The environmental consequences of such an impact, notably in causing a general warming of the earth by the greenhouse effect, may have led to the extinction of the dinossars at the end of the Cretaceous and the extinction of many radiolarians at the end of the Eocene.

**Iris.** The pigmented ring of muscular cause, lying between the cornea and the lens, in the eyes of vertebrates and some cephalopod molluses. It has a central hole (the pupil) through which light enters the eye and it contains both circular and radial muscles. Reflex contraction of the former occurs in bright light to reduce the diameter of the pupil; contraction of the radial muscles in dim light increases the pupil diameter and therefore the amount of light entering the eye. Colour is determined by the amount of the pigment melanin in the iris. Blue eyes result from relatively little melanin; grey and brown eyes from increasingly larger amounts.

**Irish Moss.** A red alga (Chondrus crispus) of the North Atlantic, the source of carrageen, an emulsifying agent.

**Irradiation.** Exposure to any form of radiation; often exposure to ionizing radiation is implied.

**Irregular Flower.** One in which one or more members of at least one whorl is different from other members of the same whorl, as a bean or pea flower.

**Irreversibility of Evolution.** A principle which holds that an organ once lost can never be regained and that a specialized form or structure never becomes generalized.

**Irritability** (sensitivity) Response by a living organism to external stimuli. In plants, the responses often take the form of various types of movements caused by the bending of the growing region. In addition, certain aquate microorganisms and some motile gametes exhibit irritability by changing their physical position.

**Isadelphous.** Having an equal number of stamens in each group or phalanx.

**Ischium.** The most posterior of the three bones that make up each half of the pelvic girdle.

**Isidium.** An outgrowth from a lichen thallus containing both algal and fungal cells that may break off and propagate the lichen vegetatively. Isidia show a variety of forms, *e.g.* the coral-like outgrowths of Umbilicaria or the bud-like projections of Collema.

**Island Biotas.** The plants and animals of oceanic islands. Because of their isolation, the biotas normally include numerous endemic taxa. Island bions are generally fragile, unbalanced in that they lack plants and animals with poor trans-oceanic dispersal capacities, and vulnerable to disturbance by man and introduced species.

**Islets of Langerhans.** Small groups of cells in the pancreas that function as an endocrine gland to secrete the hormones insulin and glucagon. They are named after their discoverer, the German anatomist and microscopist Paul Langerhans (1847-88).

**Isobilateral.** Having leaves illuminated on both sides, their surfaces being structurally similar

**Isochromosome.** A metacentric chromosome in which the two arms are genetically identical.

**Isocyclic.** Having the same number of members in each of the whorls.

**Isodactylous.** Having digits of equal length.

**Isodiametric.** Having equal diameters.

**Isodont.** Homodont.

**Isoelectric Focusing.** Technique for the electrophoretic separation of amphoteric molecules in a gradient of pH, usually formed from a combination of buffers held on a polyacrylamide-gel support medium. The molecules will move in the gradient, under the influence of an electric field, until they reach their isoelectric pH (*i.e.* the pH at which they are electrically natural), where they form a sharp band. Separation is achieved because the various molecular species will have different isoelectric pHs.

**soelectric Point.** The pH value of a medium that results in a molecule having no net electric charge. At the isoelectric point the molecules will coalesce and precipitate, because there is no repulsion between them. A mixture of amino acids or proteins may be separated into its components by varying the pH, as different molecules have different isoelectric points.

**Isoenzyme** (isozyme). Any one of the multiple forms of a given enzyme, each with different kinetic characteristics. The different isoenzymes are usually formed by different combinations of the same two or more subunits.

**Isoetales.** An order of the Lycopsida containing two genera, Isoetes (quillworts), with about 70 species and the monotypic Stylites, both of which contain rushlike predominantly aquatic perennial plants. The stem is condensed into a fleshy rootstock from the top of which arises a bunch of long narrow ligulate leaves. Seasonal cambial activity occurs in a zone around the primary vascular tissue but is highly unusual in that it differentiates cortical rather than stelar tissue. Thus the oldest tissue occurs at the outer edge of the stem and is continually sloughed off as new material is generated from within.

The megasporangia are borne in the axils of leaves formed early in the season while the later formed leaves bear microsporangia. The antherozoids differ from those of the Selaginellales and Lycopodiales in being multiflagellate rather than biflagellate.

**Isogamous.** Having undifferentiated gametes.

**Isogamy.** Sexual reproduction involving the production and fusion of gametes that are similar in size and structure. It occurs only in some lower animals and plants, *e g.* certain protozoans an algae. Compare anisogamy.

**Isogenetric**

1. From the same genus.
2. Of the same or similar origin : Isogenous.

**Isogenic.** Genetically identical; possessing the same genes.

**Isograft.** A graft or transplant to a genetically identical individuals.

**Isokont.** Describing an organism having flagella similar in form and length, as have the motile species of algae in the Chlorophyta, hence the former name of the taxon, Isokonate. Compare heterokont.

[1]**Isolate.** To separate or set apart.

**[2]Isolate.** A group in a large population which does not interbreed with other members of the population, mating being principally between members of the group; a breeding unit.

**Isolating Mechanism.** Any of the factors that prevent interbreeding (and therefore exchange of genes) between all the members of a species. Probably the most important isolating mechanism is geographical isolation, when different populations of the same species occupy different habitats and therefore never come into contact with each other. Ultimately this may lead to the populations becoming separate species by means of adaptive radiation.

**Isolation.** The separation of a race or species from other closely related groups so that interbreeding does not occur. May result from geographic, anatomical, physiological, ecological, genetic, cultural, or other factors.

**Isolecithal.** Having yolk uniformly distributed throughout the cytoplasm, as in mammalian ova : Homolecithal.

**Isoleucine.** A nonpolar branched chain amino acid with the formula $C_2H_5CH\ (CH_3)CH(NH_2)\ COOH$ (illustration at amino acid). Isoleucine is synthesized from threonine. The pathway is similar to that for valine and leucine and many of the enzymes are common to all three. Degradation of isoleucine is also closely related to that of leucine and valine, leading to succinyl CoA. The final part of the degradation, from propionyl CoA, is common to valine, isoleucine, and methionine.

**Isomerase.** Any enzyme that catalyses the conversion of a molecule from one isomeric form to another. An example is glucose phosphate isomerase, which catalyses the conversion of glucose 6-phosphate to fructose 6-phosphate in glycolysis.

**Isomere.** One of a number of homologous structures.

**Isomerous**

1. Having an equal number of parts, as grooves, ridges
2. *bot.* Having the same number of parts in each whorl, with reference to flowers.

**Isometric Contraction.** A type of muscle contraction in which no shortening occurs.

**Isomorphic**

1. (homologous). Describing a life cycle in which the alternating generations are morphologically identical as, for example, in the brown alga Dictyota. Individuals may be identified as sporophyte or gametophyte by observation of the reproductive process. Isomorphic life cycles are seldom seen in archegoniate plants. An exception is Psilotum, in which the subterranean gametophyte resembles, in anatomy, branching pattern, and in the production of multicellular gemmae, the rhizome of the sporophyte.
2. Describing an organ or organism that exists in one form only. Compare dimorphism, polymorphism.

**Isomyarian.** Equal in size, said of the two adductor muscles of a bivalve.

**Isonome Method.** A technique used to study the distribution of plants in a particular area where there are obvious variations in species distribution. Continuous quadrats are laid out to cover the chosen area and the abundance of each species in each quadrat is recorded. The abundance values of each species are plotted on separate pieces of squared paper. Isonomes (which resemble contour lines) are then constructed by joining up roughly equal abundance values. Isonomes of certain environmental factors, such as the topography of the area, can also be constructed. By superimposing the isonomes of one species onto those of another it can be seen if there are any correlations between the distributions of the two species. Similarly, by superimposing the isonomes of a species onto the isonomes of an environmental variable it may be seen whether that particular environmental factor is correlated with the species distribution.

**Isoplanogametes.** Flagellated sex cells which are alike.

**Isopod.** Any crustacean of the order Isopoda which includes pill bugs, sow bugs, wood lice, and related forms.

**Isopteran.** An insect of the order Isoptera which includes the termites or white ants, wood-eating insects which live in colonies.

**Isorhiza.** A form of nematocyst with tube of uniform diameter and open at the tip.

**Isosmotic.** Isotonic.

**Isotonic.** Having the same osmotic pressure as the solution under comparison. If two isotonic solutions are separated by a permeable membrane there will be no net migration of ions from one to the other.

**Isotonic Contraction.** A type of muscle contraction in which a muscle shortens, resulting in movement. Compare isometric contraction.

**Isotonic Solution.** A solution in which living cells will neither gain nor lose water, as a 0.85% NaCl solution for human red blood cells.

**Isotopic Tracer.** A stable or radioactive isotope that can be used to label a metabolite and consequently follow its fate in an intact organism. Many elements found in living organisms have rare isotopes that are useful as tracers. For example, the most abundant form of carbon, carbon-12 ($^{12}C$), has six protons and six neutrons in its atomic nucleus. About 1.1% of carbon exists as the stable isotope $^{13}C$, which has one extra neutron. $^{14}C$, which has two extra neutrons, exists in minute amounts, and is radioactive, emitting beta rays. Both of the rarer isotopes are incorporated and function the same way as $^{12}C$ in an organism. The light-independent reactions of photosynthesis (Calvin cycle) were elucidated using $^{14}C$-labelled carbon dioxide and finding the order in which substances incorporated the isotope. Tritium, a radioactive isotope of hydrogen having three neutrons instead of the usual one, has been used to label precursors of DNA, *e.g.* tritiated thymidine, to examine DNA synthesis.

**Isotype.** A specimen collected at the same time and from the same plant or localized population of plants as the holotype. These duplicate specimens are often separated and deposited in several institutions.

**Isozyme.** Isoenzyme.

**Isthmus.** The narrow central portion connecting the two halves of a placoderm desmid.

**Itch Mite.** An arachnid, Sarcoptes scabiei, which burrows into the skin causing intense itching.

**Iter.** A passageway.

**Iterative Evolution.** Repeated evolution of similar or parallel structures in the development of the same main line. There are many examples of iterative evolution in the fossil record, spanning a wide range of groups. This evolutionary conservatism is probably due to the overriding morphogenetic control exerted by certain regulatory genes.

**Ivory.** A hard, white, fine-grained substance, a modified type of dentine obtained from the tusks of elephants and other large mammals.

**Ivy.** An evergreen, woody, climbing plant, commonly found clambering over trees, rocks and walls throughout Europe. It climbs by means of its aerial roots and produces clusters of pale green flowers.

# J

**Jabiru.** A large stork (Jabiru mycteria) of tropical America.

**Jacamar.** A family of small birds living in the forests of Central and South America. Most have long bills, long tails and iridescent plumage. They feed on insects and dart from their perch to catch their prey on the wing.

**Jacana.** Also called the lily trotter, the jacana is a water bird related to the curlew, although it looks more like a long-legged coot. It walks over the floating leaves, supported by its long spreading toes. Jacanas are found throughout the warmer parts of the world.

**Jacanidae** (Jacanas; order Charadriiformes). Family of rufous, greenish-brown, and black birds which have a medium-length bill, and broad wings. Their legs are long, with bare tibiae and extremely long toes and claws. They inhabit the marshy shores of lakes and streams, walk on surface vegetation, feed on insects, aquatic animals, and vegetation, and nest on floating plants. There are six genera, with eight species, found in C. and S. America, Africa, S. Asia and Australasia.

**Jacaranda.** Any of a group of trees and shrubs of tropical America. They are part of a larger group known as bignonias. They have large showy flowers and are widely cultivated in many warmer parts of the world.

**Jackal.** A fox-like member of the dog family. Two species live in Africa, and a third lives in North Africa, Asia and south-eastern Europe. Jackals range from black to dirty yellow in colour and stand about 40 cm at the shoulder. They feed on the left-overs from lion kills, but also hunt gazelles and other small animals.

**Jackass.** A male ass or donkey.

**Jackdaw.** A bird belonging to the crow family. It looks similar to the carrion crow but is slightly smaller with grey around the back of the head and blue-grey eyes. Jackdaws like to live near human habitation, where they can pick up scraps of food, nesting material and bright objects. Flocks fly in formation around their nesting sites in tree holes or cliffs, calling 'chak'.

**Jack Dempsey.** A small freshwater fish of South America. It became popular with aquarists at the time Jack Dempsey was the world heavyweight boxing champion and was named after him because of its aggressiveness.

**Jacket Cells.** Sterile cells surrounding developing spores and gametes in various plants.

**Jacksonia** (family Leguminosae, subfamily Papilionoideae). Genus of plants, most of which are shrubs with simple or palmate leaves. They are adapted to arid conditions, but a few species occur in the rain forests of central Australia. There are 46 species, all of them endemic to Australia, and mainly confined to the west.

**Jacob-monod Model** (operon model). A theory to explain how gene activity is regulated, proposed by F. Jacob and J. Monod in 1960. The theory is well substantiated for prokaryotes but there is little evidence that it is directly applicable to eukaryotic cells. The operon model shows how messenger RNA synthesis, and thus the quantity of enzymes present, may be regulated. By controlling the latter, the system as a whole provides a method of coordinating and regulating cell metabolism at the level of transcription. A parallel model, taking into account the very different organization of chromosomal DNA, has since been proposed for eukaryotes (repeated sequence).

**Jackrabbit**. One of several large American hares with long ears and long hind legs, as Lepas californicus, the black-tailed jackrabbit.

**Jacobson's Organ.** The vomeronasal organ.

**Jaeger**. A predaceous, gull-like bird of the genus Stercorarius which harasses other birds causing them to drop their prey or disgorge their food.

**Jaguar.** The largest of the American cats, the jaguar is about the same size as a leopard but more heavily built, weighing up to 150 kg. The coat is yellow with black spots arranged in rosettes of 4-5 around a central spot. It lives mainly in the dense forests of South America.

**Jaguarundi.** Although a member of the cat family, the jaguarundi is more like a large weasel in shape and habits. Its body is long, up to 1.25 metres, but with a shoulder height of only 30 cm. It has short, rusty-red or grey fur. The jaguarundi lives on the edge of forests from Mexico to Argentina.

**Japanese Beetle.** A shining leaf chafer (Popillia japonica) introduced into the United States in 1916. It is a serious pest, as adults and larvae feed on a variety of plants.

**Japweed.** Common name for the seaweed Sargassum muticum; the seaweed originated in Japan but recentlyha s become established on the coasts of Europe and N. America. It is regarded as a pest, fouling boat propellers and fishing nets and disturbing the natural balance of the indigenous marine flora and fauna.

**Jasmine.** Any of 200 species of shrubs or climbers, related to the Olive. They originated in warmer parts of the Old World. Many are grown for their starlike flowers. An oil used in perfume is extracted from common jasmine.

**Jassus Huegeli** (giant spiny lobster; order Decapoda, family Palinuridae). Species of large, edible decapod which attains a length of up to 60 cm. It occurs in southern temperate waters.

**Jatropha** (family Euphorbiaceae). Genus of shrubs, a few of which are xerophytes with swollen stems. Male and female flowers are borne in the same panicle. The fruit is a three-shouldered, leathery, indehiscent capsule. There are 175 species, occurring in the tropics and subtropics, and in N. America and S. Africa.

**Jaundice.** Icterus, a condition characterized by yellowness of skin and mucous membranes due to presence of bile pigments in the blood.

**Java Man.** Homo (Pithecanthropus) erectus, a species of fossil man, one of the earliest of human or subhuman types estimated to have lived about 700,000 years ago.

**Javelina.** The collared peccary (Tayassu angulatus).

**Jaw**

1. In vertebrates, *a.* a bony or cartilaginous structure, the mandible or maxilla, which bears teeth and is utilized in the mastication of food; *b.* in the plural, the bones and associated structures which surround the mouth and enclose the mouth cavity.
2. In invertebrates, *a.* a structure comparable to a vertebrate jaw which performs a chewing function; *b.* one of the movable parts of a forcepslike structure.

**Jawbone.** Either of the bones, maxilla or mandible, which support teeth, especially the mandible or bone of the lower jaw.

**Jay.** The most brightly coloured member of the crow family. It has a light pinkish-brown plumage with black on the wings and tail. Its most distinctive features are the bright blue patches on the wings, and the white rump which is highly conspicuous when the bird is in flight. Jays imitate the calls of other birds, and even the sounds of sheep and horses. They eat the eggs of smaller birds in spring; in autumn they eat acorns, some of which they bury for future use.

**Jejunum.** The second portion of the small intestine in mammals extending from duodenum to ileum.

**Jelly.** A soft, gelatinous, semisolid substance, as gelatin which has imbibed water.

**Jellyfish.** About 200 species of marine coelenterate with transparent umbrella-shaped bodies (medusae), ringed by long hanging tentacles. Some species grow up to 2 metres across. A jellyfish's body is 90% water, and if one becomes stranded on the shore it will quickly dry out, shrinking to nothing as it evaporates. Most jellyfishes paralyse fishes and other prey by releasing poison darts from stinging cells in their tentacles. They will also sting people swimming in the sea, and some species are quite harmful.

**Jenynsiidae** (class Osteichthyes, subclass Actinopterygii, order Atheriniformes). Small family of freshwater fish, of interest mainly because both males and females have the sex organs directed either to the left or to the right. A 'left' male can mate only with a 'right' female, and vice versa. There are about three species, none exceeding 12 cm in length, found in southern S. America.

**Jerboa.** A small, nocturnal, jumping rodent of arid regions of the Old World, as Jaculus jaculus, the Egyptian jerboa of the family Dipodidae.

**Jewfish.** One of a number of extremely large marine fishes of the family Serranidae.

**Jigger.** The chigoe or sand flea.

**Jimsonweed.** Datura stramonium, of the nightshade family Solanaceae, the source of a number of alkaloids, as hyoscine, hyoscyamine, and atropine, used medicinally. Also called Jamestown weed, thorn apple.

**Joey.** In Australia, the young of an animal, especially a young kangaroo.

**John Dory.** A marine fish whose body is flattened from side to side into a disclike shape. On each flank is a distinctive black spot edged with yellow. The John Dory lives in the Mediterranean and eastern Atlantic.

**Joint**

1. Fracture in a rock resulting from shrinkage, due to cooling or desiccation, or to the unloading of super-incumbent rocks by erosion or tectonism.
2. (columnar joint) Joint that splits a rock into long prisms or columns. It is most commonly found in tabular bodies of igneous rocks.

**Jointed.** Possessing nodes or articulations.

**Joinvillea** (family Flagellariaceae). Genus of giant grass-like herbs which have plicate leaves with a sheathing base. The flowers are bisexual, petaloid, and borne in panicles. There are three species, occurring from Malesia to the Pacific islands.

**Judas Tree.** A deciduous tree of southern Europe and western Asia. It grows to a height of 9 metres, and has clusters of bright pink flowers which usually open before the smooth heart-shaped leaves. Its name comes from the legend that it was on one of these trees that Judas Iscariot hanged himself.

**Jugal**

1. Connecting or uniting.
2. Pertaining to the zygoma or malar bone.

**Jugate**

1. Occurring in pairs.
2. Connected together.

**Juglandaceae.** Family of trees, in which the leaves are pinnate, with no stipules. The flowers are small, unisexual, and bracteate, and borne in spikes or catkins, they are wind-pollinated, and have an inferior ovary. The fruit is a drupe or nut, sometimes attached to a wing-like bract. The family yields several useful timbers (*e.g.* walnut and hickory) and fruits (*e.g.* walnut and pecan). There are six genera, with 60 species, most of which occur in northern temperate regions, but a few of which are tropical.

**Juglans** (walnut; family Juglandaceae). Genus of deciduous, nut-bearing trees, up to 30 m tall, with twisting, spreading branches. They have large, only, deeply-lobed cotyledons. The leaves are compound. Male and female catkins occur on the same tree, the male catkins dangling in the wind, the female catkins upright. They produce oval, green fruits (a drupe) with a fleshy exocarp and a bony endocarp (the shell), which splits down the midrib. The wrinkled, woody nut is eaten fresh or pickled, and used in desserts, cakes and confectionery. The most popular garden species are J. regia (Persian walnut), J. nigra (black walnut), and J. cinerea of N. America, the butternut. The wood is used for furniture. There are about 15 species, occurring mainly in northern temperate regions, but extending to the tropics and native to Asia and America.

**Jugular**

1. Of or pertaining to the neck or throat.
2. Of or pertaining to the jugular vein which drains the head region.

**Jugular Fins**. The pelvic fins of a fish when located in the throat region sometimes anterior to the pectoral fins, as in the cod.

**Jugum**

1. *bot*. *a*. A pair, as a pair of opposite leaflets. *b*. A ridge on certain fruits, especially those of the Umbelliferae.
2. *zool*. *a*. A small lobe on the posterior margin of the forewing of lepidopterous insects. *b*. A sclerite in the head of certain insects, as hemipterans and homopterans.

**Juice**

1. *bot*. The fluid contained in any part of a plant, especially that which can be expressed by squeezing, as orange juice.
2. *zool* The secretoin of a gland, as pancreatic juice.

**Julaceous**. Bearing catkins : Amentaceous.

**Jumping Bean**. The fruit of members of the spurge family, growing in Central and South America. They jump about because of the movements of caterpillars living inside them.

**Jumping Spider**. A group of small to medium-sized spiders which leap on to their prey. They have very large eyes which help them focus clearly on their victims as they jump for the kill. About 3000 species are known.

**Juncaceae**. Family of monocotyledonous herbs. They are close to Liliaceae in the structure of the trimerous flowers, but these are small and inconspicuous, with tiny, chaffy perianth-segments, and adapted to wind pollination. The leaves are long and narrow, and either grass-like or nearly cylindrical in form. They are of tittle economic value but are important ecologically, especially in poorly drained areas. There are eight genera, with some 350 species, of cosmopolitan distributions, but centred in temperate zones.

**Juncaginaceae**. Family of monocotyledonous herbs, with mostly linear, radical, sheathing leaves, and erect spikes or racemes of tiny di- or trimerous flowers without bracts. The ovary is superior, with four or six carpels, usually joined together, and a short style. Triglochin (arrow-grass) is widespread and occurs in wet places. There are three genera, with 14 species, distributed in temperate and cold, marshy habitats in the northern and southern hemispheres.

**Junco**. A finch of the genus Junco, family Fringillidae : Snow-bird.

**Junction**. A connection or point of union between two structures.

**Juncus** (rush; family Juncaceae). Genus of tufted, usually perennial herbs with entire leaves and open leaf sheaths. The inflorescence is small, with bisexual, usually brown flowers; it produces capsules and many seeds. There are well over 300 species. Distribution is cosmopolitan, but the plants are mainly restricted to cold and wet places, and are therefore rare in the tropics.

**June Bug**. A June beetle or May beetle, one of several scarabaeid beetles of the genus Phyllophaga whose larvae are the familiar white grubs of the soil.

**Jungle**. Subclimax tropical rain forest, consisting of a tangled growth of lianes, bamboo scrub, palms, etc. It forms an impenetrable barrier to travel. It is characteristic of former clearings and of riversides, where light penetration is greater than in the forest interior. By contrast, true climax rain forest has little undergrowth since light penetration is poor, and—contrary to the popular image—it is easily negotiated.

**Jungle Fowl.** A group of forest-dwelling birds belonging to the pheasant family which live in India and South-East Asia. They include the red jungle fowl from which the domestic chicken has been bred.

**Juniper.** Any of 60 species of trees or shrubs of the Cypress family. Junipers are evergreens, with reddish-brown bark and sharply pointed leaves. They produce berry-like, brown or greyish-blue cones which are used to flavour gin.

**Jurassic.** One of the three Mesozoic periods : it lasted approximately 50 million years, following the Triassic and preceding the Cretaceous. The Jurassic is subdivided into 11 stages, with clays, calcareous sandstones, and limestones being the most common rock types. Brachiopods, bivalves, and ammonites were abundant, along with many other invertebrate stocks. Reptiles flourished on land and in the sea, but mammals were relatively insignificant and mostly nocturnal. The first birds, including Archaeopteryx, appeared in the Upper Jurassic.

**Jurassic Period.** The middle period of the Mesozoic era.

**Jute**

1. A coarse fiber obtained from an Asiatic plant (Corchorus), used in the manufacture of burlap, gunny sacks, cheap twine, and coarse cloth.

2. The plant which produces the fiber, principally two species (C. capsularis and C. olitorius) cultivated for commercial production.

**Juvenal.** Juvenile.

**Juvenal Plumage.** Plumage (of a bird) that replaces down; also, in birds which lack the natal down, the first plumage.

**Juvenile**

1. Young, youthful.
2. Pertaining to a young or immature individual.
3. A young individual.

**Juvenile Hormone.** Hormone released by the corpora allata, which regulates the form of larvae after each moult. Juvenile hormone brings about the retention of juvenile characteristics in developing insects, but has other functions in adults.

**Juvenility.** The condition expressed in immature organisms, which are generally smaller in size than the adults and lack reproductive capability. The seedling represents the juvenile stage of many plants. The term is particularly used when the young plant form is very different from that of the adult. For example in gorse (Ulex), the juvenile leaves are flat and trifoliate but the adult plant has spines. In many conifers the seedlings bear needle-like juvenile leaves, and specialized leaves, such as the scalelike leaves of cypress (Cupressus) and the dwarf shoots of pine (Pinus), are formed later. The change is not always from a simple to more complex form. For example, in ivy (Hedera helix) the juvenile leaves are lobed while the mature leaves are entire (diagram). The submerged leaves of many aquatic plants are similar to the juvenile leaves of terrestrial forms of the same species. In some varieties of ornamental plants the juvenile foliage persists in the adult plant (also neoteny). Juvenile plants may also differ in various physiological ways from mature plants. For example, the immature forms of many deciduous trees, *e.g.* beech, do not shed their leaves in autumn but retain the dead leaves on the plant throughout the winter.

**Juxtapose.** To place adjacent to each other.

**Juxtaposition.** State of being placed side by side or adjacent to each other.

**Jynx** (wrynecks; family Picidae). Genus of small, cryptically coloured, brown, grey, and black birds which are zygodactylous like other woodpeckers, but which rarely cling to trees. They inhabit woodland; feed on insects, especially ants; and nest in tree cavities. There are two species, found in Europe, Asia, and Africa. J. torquilla (common wryneck) in highly migratory.